P-3

QUANTUM THEORY OF MATTER

INTERNATIONAL SERIES IN PURE AND APPLIED PHYSICS
LEONARD I. SCHIFF, CONSULTING EDITOR

The late F. K. Richtmyer was Consulting Editor of the series from its inception in 1929 to his death in 1939. Lee A. DuBridge was Consulting Editor from 1939 to 1946; and G. P. Harnwell from 1947 to 1954.

QUANTUM THEORY
OF MATTER

JOHN C. SLATER

Professor of Physics
Massachusetts Institute of Technology

New York   *Toronto*   *London*

McGRAW-HILL BOOK COMPANY, INC.

1951

QUANTUM THEORY OF MATTER

viii

58100

PREFACE

The century which is now half over has been one of the most turbulent and menacing in human history. Increasing knowledge of the powers of nature has been coupled with increasing ruthlessness and lack of morality in the use of those powers. And yet these dark years have seen the development and flourishing of one of the greatest of intellectual achievements: modern theoretical physics, and particularly the quantum theory. The history of physics has seen a series of brilliant periods: the foundation of mechanics by Galileo and Huygens, Kepler and Newton; the development of the wave theory of light, by Fresnel and Young; the discovery and formulation of electromagnetism, by Oersted and Faraday and Maxwell; the working out of the mechanical theory of heat, by Boltzmann and Gibbs. In spite of these brilliant achievements of earlier centuries, however, the work of the last half century has never been surpassed, and probably never equalled, in the history of physics. The ideas of atoms from the nineteenth century, coming on the one hand from the discoveries of the chemists, on the other from the kinetic theory of gases, began to take on definite form with the discoveries of the nature of ions and electrons in a vacuum, by Crookes and Thomson and Millikan. Rutherford, with his magnificent studies of radioactivity, opened the whole field of nuclear structure. Röntgen with his x-rays, Laue with his discovery that they could be diffracted by crystals, paved the way for the Braggs and their study of the structures of molecules and solids, and for Moseley and his x-ray spectra. Drude and Lorentz and Debye applied the idea of electrons to the nature of solids and their electromagnetic properties. Einstein, going far beyond the problem of transforming the electromagnetic equations to moving coordinates, enunciated the theory of relativity.

The direct experiments leading to the quantum theory, however, were not so much these, as those dealing with radiation. Planck, with a flash of insight, saw that the law of black body radiation could only be explained if radiant energy somehow existed in units, or quanta, and Einstein applied this same idea to two puzzling problems, photoelectric emission and the specific heat of solids at low temperatures, and showed that it explained them both. But it remained for Bohr to make the major synthesis that pulled together Rutherford's nuclear atom and

Planck's quanta, into his theory of hydrogen, which started the theory of atomic spectra, and resulted in such detailed agreement with experiment that no one could doubt the essential correctness of the concept. Bohr, Sommerfeld, and the spectroscopists unraveled much more complicated spectra, and Goudsmit, Uhlenbeck, and Pauli added essential features, but still the theory really worked in detail only for hydrogen; all other atoms were too complicated to fit into the scheme, though Bohr found a brilliant approximation for the more complicated atoms, and in doing so, explained the periodic system of the elements, the secret underlying chemistry. Still there was something missing; among other difficulties, no one could see how to apply Bohr's theory to molecules or solids.

Heisenberg and Dirac with their matrices showed one way toward the solution of these mysteries; but the real solution came from a flash of insight by de Broglie, who postulated that there were waves associated with mechanical particles, a guess which was almost immediately confirmed by the discovery of electron diffraction by Davisson and Germer. Once we knew we were dealing with waves, there was a great body of theory ready to be used, for waves had been known for a very long time; and Schrödinger was the one who had the brilliant idea of combining well-known wave theory with de Broglie's postulate. Schrödinger's equation, which resulted from this, is in many ways the foundation of quantum mechanics, though there are other ways in which it can be expressed. And with the formulation of this equation, the great episode of the discovery of quantum theory was essentially finished. It came by long and tedious steps, fitting together experimental facts, earlier partly correct but incomplete theories, and some of the most brilliant intuitive flights that have ever been made, into a final result of beautiful simplicity, and the most overwhelming generality.

It took the first quarter of the century to get that far; the next quarter century, which is just closing, has gone to the development of the methods and results of the quantum theory. It is here that we have found how inclusive is the theoretical tool. It becomes clear that we have the fundamental basis on which all the structure of matter in its ordinary forms is constructed. Molecules, solids, liquids, gases, electricity, magnetism, light, all such things follow by straightforward mathematical deduction, so that we have the theory of chemistry and metallurgy and many other things besides physics. But unfortunately the theory is enormously complicated, though mathematically beautiful. It is for this reason that, though the last twenty-five years have seen remarkable progress, we are still very far from having worked out all the problems in the structure of matter. There will be much to do for many years to come. But whenever the mathematics has been overcome, and an exact answer has been computed, it has agreed with experiment to great accuracy, so well that we have no hesitation about believing the correctness of the quantum mechanics. We shall be busy for a very long time in working out all the consequences of these beautiful theories, but all the time we are understanding more and more about nature.

We must not forget, of course, that there are still things we do not understand. The atomic nucleus appears to follow the laws of quantum mechanics; but from what we know about it, there are other features added to the theory, which we still do not know about. There is a little tendency nowadays for the nuclear theorists to be impatient on account of the slowness of discovery of the principles of nuclear structure. They should take courage. They should look back at the long and painstaking work that went into the development of wave mechanics; it could never have been formulated without all the experimental work that went before, and nuclear experimentation, though brilliant, still has far to go before it yields enough regularities and quantitative information to supply materials for another theoretical synthesis like that of the quantum theory.

We see, then, that that part of the quantum theory dealing with the structure of atoms, molecules, and solids—in other words, everything outside the nucleus—is in a sense a finished subject, in that we are quite sure that we know the theoretical framework on which it is built, just as we know that Newton's laws govern classical mechanics, and Maxwell's equations govern electromagnetism. Yet there is enormously much of interest still to be learned. It is this field, the quantum theory of matter, which is the subject of this volume. I have tried to give in the treatment something of the feeling of history, rather than presenting it as a formal set of postulates and consequences; for it is a part of history, and of history that is still developing. And I have tried to do something that is not done in most of the texts on quantum theory: to lead right through, from the fundamentals, to the applications to the properties of matter. The book is on a level where the beginner, with a fair knowledge of mathematics and mathematical methods, and of the experimental side of atomic structure, can follow it without any other study of quantum mechanics. And yet, though it does not go nearly to the highest level of mathematical difficulty, there is included a rather extensive set of appendixes with a considerable amount of material of a fair degree of advancement. The quantum theory of matter forms the basis, as we have seen, for chemistry and metallurgy and many other things besides physics, and the specialists in those fields should have a good working knowledge of it. Unfortunately, they do not usually have as much knowledge of theoretical physics as the professional physicist; and it is partly with them in mind that this present volume has been written. On the other hand, we go far enough to interest and instruct the physicist.

A word or two as to how this book came to be written may interest the reader. I first got the idea of a book combining the principles of quantum mechanics, and their applications to the structure of matter, less than five years after the development of Schrödinger's equation, and laid out a table of contents much like that which I have actually followed here. Of course, we know much more now than we did then, and if I had followed the outline then, the result would have been much less complete than it now is. But the main reason why I did not write it then was that I began to realize how important a knowledge of mechanics and electromagnetism was for the student of wave mechanics, and felt that I wished to treat all these fields together. It was with that in mind that Professor Frank and I collaborated in writing "Introduction to Theoretical Physics," of which about the last third represented a condensed version of the present volume. Next I began to realize how intimately statistical mechanics and thermodynamics are tied up with the structure of matter and with the quantum theory, and this led me to write "Introduction to Chemical Physics." After the war, a revision of "Introduction to Theoretical Physics" became desirable, and Professor Frank and I decided to do this in several volumes, for convenience both in teaching and in writing. Two volumes of that revision have come out, "Mechanics" and "Electromagnetism." The present volume, which I have written without collaboration (as the section on quantum mechanics in "Introduction to Theoretical Physics" was written almost entirely without collaboration), completes that task. I have carried the development, however, far beyond that of the earlier volume. In writing it, I have had in mind the thought that the four books, "Mechanics," "Electromagnetism," "Quantum Theory of Matter," and "Introduction to Chemical Physics," formed together a fairly complete treatment, on the intermediate level of difficulty, of most of theoretical physics with the exception of nuclear theory. Of these, the present volume and "Introduction to Chemical Physics" are complementary, and form together an introduction to the structure of matter. Though these four books can well be used together, each has been made independent of the others, so that it can be used by itself.

My aim in the present volume has been of the same sort that it was in writing the earlier texts: to encourage the reader to think for himself, to regard what he is learning as a tool for further development, rather than a set of facts to be remembered. This is the only spirit in which the real physicist can grow. I have included many problems. Most of them represent the sort of thing which I like to work through myself, to be sure that I understand the principles of the subject. I have not given large bibliographies or many references, but this is only on account of the intermediate level of the text; as soon as the reader gets a little further along, one of his major efforts should be to study the original literature. The quantum theory of matter is a living, growing subject; and unless the student learns to follow this growth, he does not really understand its nature.

Though Professor Frank did not collaborate with me in writing the present volume, his advice and encouragement have been very valuable, and I wish to acknowledge them with thanks.

JOHN C. SLATER

CAMBRIDGE, MASS.
August, 1951

CONTENTS

CHAPTER 11

MECHANICAL, CHEMICAL, AND THERMAL PROPERTIES OF
MATTER.. 296

CHAPTER 12

ELECTRICAL CONDUCTIVITY................................. 333

CHAPTER 13

THE NATURE OF DIELECTRICS............................. 377

CHAPTER 14

MAGNETISM.. 399

xiv CONTENTS

APPENDIXES

CHAPTER 1

DE BROGLIE WAVES AND WAVE MECHANICS

The last half century has seen the development of completely new foundations both for optics and for mechanics. In 1900, the wave theory of light, founded on the electromagnetic theory of Maxwell, was unchallenged, and the mechanics of particles, based on Newton's laws of motion, had been accepted for hundreds of years. Two developments of the early 1900's, however, upset the certainty of these theories. The photoelectric effect, together with Einstein's theoretical explanation of its behavior, showed that light had some properties in which it acted as if it were composed of particles, or corpuscles. On the other hand, Bohr's explanation of the hydrogen spectrum showed that the mechanics of electrons definitely differed from Newtonian mechanics, and de Broglie's hypothesis of wave mechanics, supplemented by Schrödinger's mathematical formulation of that hypothesis, showed that the difference was that mechanics had definite wave aspects. The two types of phenomena thus proved to have a far-reaching parallelism which had not been suspected earlier. Our main purpose in this volume is to discuss the mechanics which has resulted from this synthesis, called quantum mechanics or wave mechanics. We shall start our discussion, however, with the similar problem of optics, both because for historical reasons it forms a suitable introduction to wave mechanics, and because we must understand it to study the interaction of atomic systems and radiation, a very important aspect of the structure of matter.

1.1. The Quantum Hypothesis in Optics. The beautiful success of the wave theory of optics in explaining diffraction patterns has always been the best proof of the correctness of this theory. But the proof has not always gone unchallenged. Ever since the time of Newton, at least, there has been a rival theory, the corpuscular theory. Newton imagined light to consist of a stream of particles. These particles, or corpuscles, traveled in straight lines in empty space and were reflected by mirrors, as billiard balls would be by walls, making equal angles of incidence and reflection. Refraction was explained by supposing that different media had different attractions for the corpuscles. Thus glass would attract them more than air, the potential energy of a corpuscle being constant within any one medium, but being lower in glass than in air, so that the corpuscles would have a normal component of acceleration toward the glass, without corresponding tangential acceleration, and would be bent toward the normal on entering the glass. By working out this idea, the law of refraction easily follows. Newton was aware of the wave theory; Huygens was advocating it at the time. Newton's objection was that light travels in straight lines, whereas the waves he was familiar with, waves of sound or water waves, certainly are bent out in all directions on passing through apertures. Newton considered this to be a fatal objection to the wave theory.

The answer to this objection, of course, came later with the quantitative investigation of diffraction. A plane wave of light, falling on a small aperture of dimension a, does not form a perfectly parallel ray on emerging from the hole. On the contrary, it spreads out, first by forming fringes on the edges of the ray (Fresnel diffraction), then, at greater distance, by developing a conical form, with definitely diverging rays (Fraunhofer diffraction). The angle of this cone is of the order of magnitude of λ/a, where λ is the wave length. Newton was tacitly assuming that the wave length, as with sound, was large, that λ/a would be large for a small slit, and that there would be large spreading out and a completely undefined ray. But it was found early in the nineteenth century that the wave length was really so small that, with apertures of ordinary size, we can neglect diffraction and obtain an almost perfectly sharp ray, a band of light separated from the darkness by sharp, straight edges.

More recently, in the present century, a more serious argument for a corpuscular theory has appeared. This is the hypothesis of quanta, originated by Planck in discussing the radiation from a heated black body. The most graphic application of this hypothesis was made by Einstein to the theory of the photoelectric effect. It is known that light of frequency ν, falling on a metal surface, is absorbed and sometimes ejects electrons, as for example in the photocell. Now the law of emission is remarkable: the energy of each emitted electron, independent of the intensity of the light, is a definite amount $h\nu$, proportional to the frequency, where h is Planck's constant, introduced by Planck in his first discussion, equal to 6.61×10^{-27} erg-sec, or 6.61×10^{-34} joule-sec. This is as if the energy in the light wave were concentrated in quanta, or photons, of this energy $h\nu$, an intense light source emitting many photons per second, a weak one relatively few photons, but all photons of a given frequency having a given energy. The energy of the emitted electron is really decreased by the amount of energy it loses in penetrating the surface, so that $h\nu$ will act as a maximum energy rather than the energy of each electron. Of course, the total emission is proportional to the intensity of the light, but increasing the intensity increases the number of electrons, not their energies. According to Einstein's hypothesis of photons, it is obvious that if no photon falls on a spot of the metal, no electron will be ejected; but a photon which happens to fall on a given place will transfer all its energy to an electron, being absorbed, and ceasing to exist as light. The intensity of light is measured by the number of photons crossing an arbitrary surface per second, times the energy carried by each photon.

All these phenomena suggesting photons, and a corpuscular structure for light, must not cause one to forget that light still shows interference, and that the arguments for the wave theory are as strong as ever. The apparent contrast between waves and particles formed for many years a great stumbling block in the way of interpreting the quantum theory. Various attempts were made to set up laws of motion for the photons, which would lead to the correct laws of interference and diffraction (Newton had already done it for refraction), but without success. We can easily see why this should be so. Consider very weak light, so weak that we have only a photon every minute, for example, going through a diffraction grating. Such weak light, we know experimentally, is diffracted just like stronger light. But the resolving power of a grating depends on the cooperation of the whole grating; if half of it were shut off, its resolving power would be decreased, and the intensity distribution changed. Even the single photon shows evidence of the full resolving power in that, if we make a long enough exposure to have many photons, so that we can develop the photograph and measure the blackening, which surely measures the number of photons which have struck the plate, we find the full resolving power of the grating in the final photograph. But it is difficult to imagine any law of motion of a photon which will depend on rulings over the whole face of a grating, if the photons went through only one point of it.

After such difficulties, people gradually became reconciled to accepting the dualism of having two different pictures of radiation, a wave theory and a corpuscular theory, and of using a sort of statistical relation between them. It is assumed that atoms emit wave fields as in the electromagnetic theory, emitted by certain oscillators connected with the atom, and vibrating with the emitted frequencies. These waves do not carry energy, but the energy flows in photons, and the intensity of the wave gives the average rate of flow of the photon energy. The rate of emission of waves by the oscillators determines the probability of emission of photons by the source. The Poynting's vector at any point of the radiation field determines the probability that a photon will cross unit cross section normal to the radiation, per second. If the oscillator is damped with time, the probability of emission of a photon decreases with time;

that is, the probability that the atom is in an excited state decreases with time. One can carry such a probability connection through in detail.

Probably the most graphic picture of the probability relation between photons and waves is obtained if we imagine very weak light, in which photons come along one in several seconds, forming a diffraction pattern. The diffraction pattern is assumed to be on a screen which is capable of registering the individual photons as they come along. This screen might be a photographic plate, in which a single photon is enough to make a grain developable, or it might be a screen having slits opening into Geiger counters or other devices for registering individual photons. First, one photon would strike the screen in one spot, then another photon in another spot, and so on. So long as there were only a few photons, the arrangement might seem to be haphazard. But as more and more photons were present, we could find where they were densely distributed and where there were only a few. It would then prove to be the case that the places where photons were dense were just those places where the wave theory predicted a large intensity, and the places where there were no photons were those where the wave theory indicated darkness.

This statistical connection between a continuous function describing the energy flow and the actual discrete flow of particles is really nothing new in physics. If we had a gas composed of atoms, the amount of material flowing across a unit area per second would actually consist of a discrete number of atoms, each of finite size; but we could set up a continuous function representing the average flow, such that the actual flow in unit time would fluctuate, depending on the exact number of atoms happening to cross, but would average to a constant value. In accordance with the usual laws of statistical fluctuations, the deviations from the average would be greater the smaller the number of atoms crossing the area in the time considered. It is a general law of statistics that if an average number of events is N_0 (say, the average number of atoms crossing a given area in a given time), then if we measure the actual number N of events in a particular case, form the quantity $N - N_0$, or deviation from the average, and find the mean square $\overline{(N - N_0)^2}$ of the deviation, this mean square will be equal to N_0, provided the events come at random. Stated otherwise, the fractional root-mean-square deviation $[\overline{(N/N_0 - 1)^2}]^{1/2}$, a sort of probable error of an individual reading, equals $1/\sqrt{N_0}$, decreasing as N_0 increases; it is for this reason that increasing the number of observations of a randomly fluctuating quantity increases the accuracy of the average of the observations. Hence we see that our average flow of atoms agrees closely with the observed flow, provided we use a large enough area and long enough time of observation, so that many atoms have crossed the surface, but the actual number crossing will deviate widely from the average if this number itself is a small integer.

The analogy of this situation of a continuous function representing the average flow of atoms, the actual flow fluctuating more and more from this average the fewer the atoms, to our situation of the continuous Poynting vector and the flow of discrete photons, is obvious. If we observe a diffraction pattern with a photographic plate, taking a long exposure, we observe a uniform blackening in the interference fringes, the amount given by the classical theory, the spacing of light and dark fringes being also as in classical theory. But if we had observed with a photocell and electron multiplier, to count individual photons, we should have found the radiation coming along in pulses, and should have a very graphic picture of its fluctuations; for this device measures essentially the amount of radiation falling on it in a very small time interval, so small that there is seldom more than one photon received in the interval.

1.2. Bohr's Quantum Theory; Sommerfeld's Quantum Condition. One of the first supports for Einstein's hypothesis of photons came from the structure of atoms. Atoms emit monochromatic spectrum lines, falling often into regular series. Bohr was able to explain this, at least in hydrogen, the simplest atom, by assuming that the atom was capable of existing only in certain definite stationary states, each of a definite energy. He supposed that radiation was not emitted continuously, as the electromagnetic field from a rotating or vibrating particle would be, but that the atom stayed in one energy level until it suddenly made a jump to a second, lower, level, with emission of a photon. If the higher energy is E_2, the lower E_1, the energy of the photon would be $E_2 - E_1$, so that its frequency would be $(E_2 - E_1)/h$. This formula has proved to be justified by great amounts of experimental material. First, it states that the frequencies emitted by atoms should be the difference of "terms" E/h, each referring to an energy level of the atom. This is found to be true in spectroscopy and has been the most fruitful idea in the development of that science. Even tremendously complicated spectra can be analyzed to give a set of terms, and the number of terms is much less than the number of lines, since any pair of terms, subject to certain restrictions, gives a line.

But also, Bohr was able to set up a system of mechanics to govern the hydrogen atom, very simple in its fundamentals, though different from classical mechanics, which gives a very simple formula for the energy levels, agreeing perfectly with the extremely accurate experimental values. We shall outline this type of mechanics, as applied to a few simple problems, in a moment. Before doing this, however, we note that Bohr's idea of stationary states was tested by experiments on electron bombardment, as well as by spectroscopy. It was found that an atom in state of energy E_1 could be bombarded by an electron. If the electron's energy, as determined from the electrical difference of potential through which it had fallen, was less than $E_2 - E_1$, where E_2 is the energy of the upper state (we consider only one), it would bounce off elastically, without loss of energy. But if its energy was $E_2 - E_1$ or greater, it would often raise the atom to the upper state, which could be proved by subsequent radiation by the atom, and would lose this amount of energy itself. This definitely verified the existence of sharp energy levels in the atom. At the same time, it furnishes an example of a very interesting phenomenon. An electron bombards an atom, loses energy $E_2 - E_1$. This energy is emitted as a photon $h\nu$. The photon falls on a metal, is absorbed, ejects a photoelectron of energy $E_2 - E_1$ (minus a little, for the work of coming through the surface). The photoelectron bombards an atom, loses its energy, which goes off as a photon. Energy, in other words, passes back and forth from electrons to photons indiscriminately. If electrons are particles, surely photons are too.

We now understand Bohr's hypothesis as to the relation between energy levels and the emission of radiation. The remaining part of Bohr's theory consisted of the formulation of laws for finding the stationary states. He assumed that electrons and other atomic particles obeyed classical mechanics, but that there were additional conditions, called quantum conditions, imposed on them, which limited the allowed classical motions to a discrete set, the stationary states. The simplest method of formulating these quantum conditions was suggested by Sommerfeld, and the quantum conditions are often known by Sommerfeld's name. The Sommerfeld quantum condition is stated most simply for a particle moving in one-dimensional motion. Thus let the particle have a coordinate x, a mass m, velocity v, and momentum $p = mv$. Let it oscillate back and forth along x periodically under the action of some type of force capable of producing such an oscillation classically (it is only for such periodic motions that the quantum condition can be applied). Then let us calculate what is called the phase integral $\oint p\, dx$. Here we are to find the momentum p at every point of the path, and integrate p with respect to x from a particular starting point around the complete path of the particle, first to its extreme displacement in one direction, then back to its extreme displacement in the other direction (when the particle is going back, both p and dx will be negative, so that the contribution to the integral here will be positive, as it is when the particle travels forward), and finally back to the starting point. The integral sign $\oint$ indicates that the integral is to be taken around a complete cycle. Then Sommerfeld's quantum condition is that the phase integral must be an integral multiple of Planck's constant h:

$$\oint p\, dx = nh. \tag{1.2.1}$$

This condition, superposed on classical mechanics, leads to the stationary states of Bohr's theory.

Let us examine the consequences of the quantum conditions in a few simple cases. First let us take the hydrogen atom, for which Bohr had his most striking success. This consists of an electron of mass

$$m = 9.1 \times 10^{-31} \text{ kg,}$$

charge $-e = -1.61 \times 10^{-19}$ coulomb, moving about a proton of charge e, and of mass so large that it can be considered infinite in a first approximation, under the action of the inverse-square electrostatic attraction between the opposite charges. The general orbit of the electron is an ellipse, as in planetary motion; for simplicity we shall treat only the special case where it is a circle, taking up the more general elliptical case in Appendix 1. In this case, if the electron moves with linear velocity v in a circle of radius r, the centripetal acceleration is v^2/r, by elementary mechanics. There must then be a force mv^2/r pulling it to the center, and this must be the electrostatic attraction, which in the rationalized mks system of units is $e^2/(4\pi\epsilon_0 r^2)$, where ϵ_0 is the permittivity of free space, or in the nonrationalized cgs units it is e^2/r^2. (These two sets of units, both of which will be employed in this volume, are discussed in Appendix 2.) We then have

$$\frac{mv^2}{r} = \frac{e^2}{4\pi\epsilon_0 r^2},$$

for mks units; the corresponding formula in cgs units is obtained by omitting the factor $4\pi\epsilon_0$. Let us compute various mechanical quantities which we shall want for our discussion. We have

$$\text{Kinetic energy} = \frac{1}{2}mv^2 = \frac{1}{2}\frac{e^2}{4\pi\epsilon_0 r} \tag{1.2.2}$$

$$\text{Potential energy} = -\frac{e^2}{4\pi\epsilon_0 r} = -2 \times \text{kinetic energy} \tag{1.2.3}$$

$$\text{Total energy} = -\frac{1}{2}\frac{e^2}{4\pi\epsilon_0 r} = -\text{kinetic energy} \tag{1.2.4}$$

$$\text{Angular momentum} = mvr = \sqrt{\frac{e^2 mr}{4\pi\epsilon_0}} \tag{1.2.5}$$

$$\text{Phase integral} = \oint mv\, ds = 2\pi mvr = 2\pi\sqrt{\frac{e^2 mr}{4\pi\epsilon_0}} \tag{1.2.6}$$

$$= 2\pi \times \text{angular momentum.}$$

These are all obvious, except perhaps the last; in finding the phase integral we integrate the momentum with respect to the distance ds around the circumference of the circle; that is, we multiply the constant momentum mv by the circumference $2\pi r$.

From these mechanical results we can now proceed to the quantum condition, which is, from (1.2.1), that the phase integral (1.2.6) equals nh. This then, in combination with the results (1.2.2) to (1.2.6), leads to a number of important conclusions:

$$\text{Energy} = -\frac{2\pi^2 m e^4}{(4\pi\epsilon_0)^2 h^2}\frac{1}{n^2}, \tag{1.2.7}$$

$$\text{Radius} = n^2\frac{h^2(4\pi\epsilon_0)}{4\pi^2 m e^2}, \tag{1.2.8}$$

$$\text{Angular momentum} = \frac{nh}{2\pi}. \tag{1.2.9}$$

In all these formulas we omit the expression $4\pi\epsilon_0$ wherever it occurs to get the formulas in cgs units; formulas as stated are in mks units. The energy levels as given by (1.2.7), for all integral values of n, were those which proved to give the observed levels of the hydrogen atom to a high degree of accuracy, and thus verified Bohr's calculations. Furthermore, Bohr was able to extend his discussion to give results of very considerable accuracy for the energy levels of other atoms, including both optical and x-ray levels, basing his work largely on the structure of hydrogen, as we have developed it. Thus he was able to add greatly to the confidence which physicists felt in his form of quantum theory. The results (1.2.7) and (1.2.8) were so important that abbreviations are generally used for the combinations of constants which occur in them. The energy $2\pi^2 m e^4/(4\pi\epsilon_0)^2 h^2$, occurring in (1.2.7), is the so-called Rydberg unit of energy. To get its value in electron volts, for instance, we set it equal to eV and solve for V. This is most easily done in mks units, and gives at once that the Rydberg energy is 13.54 volts. A corresponding frequency is defined by letting the Rydberg energy equal $h\nu$, and a corresponding wave number (reciprocal of wave length) by the equation $\nu/c = 1/\lambda$, where c is the velocity of light. This wave number is called the Rydberg number, denoted by R, and is equal to 109,737 cm^{-1}. Thus the Rydberg energy is Rhc. The energy levels are then given by

$$E = -Rhc/n^2.$$

The fundamental length $h^2(4\pi\epsilon_0)/4\pi^2 m e^2$, from (1.2.8), is usually denoted by a_0. When we insert numerical values, we find that it is 0.53 A (where 1 angstrom unit, denoted by A, is 10^{-8} cm $= 10^{-10}$ m). Thus the radius of the nth orbit is $n^2 a_0$.

We have treated only the circular orbits, but, as shown in Appendix 1, the formula for energy is not altered if we include the elliptical orbits as well.   To treat them, we must extend the quantum condition (1.2.1) so that it can handle problems with more than one degree of freedom.   This can be done so long as we can do what is called separating the variables, a process described more in detail in Appendix 1.   When this can be done, we can set up separate phase integrals, and separate quantum conditions, for each variable.   If we have a generalized coordinate q and its related momentum p, we have a quantum condition

$$\oint p \, dq = nh \qquad (1.2.10)$$

for each variable, each having an appropriate quantum number n (we ordinarily use a different letter to denote the different quantum numbers).   The situation proves to be the following.   There is a quantum number, called the principal quantum number n, in terms of which the energy even of the elliptical orbits is given by the formula (1.2.7).   This quantum number also determines the major axis of the elliptical orbit, this major axis being the same as the diameter of the circular orbit, equal to twice the radius given in (1.2.8).   There is another quantum number, called k, which determines the angular momentum: the angular momentum is $kh/2\pi$, rather than $nh/2\pi$ as in the circular orbit.   The integer k can take on the integral values from the maximum value n down to unity; thus the state for $n = 1$ has only $k = 1$, that for $n = 2$ has $k = 2$ or 1, and so on.   The integer k, called the azimuthal quantum number, also determines the eccentricity, or minor axis, of the elliptical orbit: the ratio of minor to major axis is k/n.   At the same time k determines the area of the orbit, which is $\pi/4$ times the product of major and minor axes and hence is proportional to k; this is necessary on account of Kepler's second law, which relates the angular momentum of an orbit to its area. We often denote all the energy levels, or term values, associated with a given k value as a series; the reason for this will become clearer later when we take up nonhydrogenic atoms.   Thus the terms with $k = 1$ are called the s levels (s being an abbreviation for "sharp," these levels being concerned in the so-called "sharp series" of lines); terms with $k = 2$ are the p levels (p being an abbreviation for "principal," coming from the "principal series"); terms with $k = 3$ the d levels (d for "diffuse"); and terms with $k = 4$ the f levels (f for "fundamental").   It is generally agreed now that these names for the series are not very well chosen, but the notation s, p, d, f is in very common use.

A third quantum number is generally called m, a magnetic quantum number (on account of its importance in the theory of the Zeeman effect, the effect of a magnetic field on the spectral lines).   This is connected with a phenomenon called space quantization. The numbers n, k, refer to shape and size of the orbit in a plane; but so far the plane of the orbit is not determined. It now proves to be the case that if there is a preferred direction in space, such as the direction of an applied magnetic field, only certain orientations of the plane of the orbit with respect to this direction are allowed. In particular, we remember that k measures the angular momentum in units $h/2\pi$. We consider this to be a vector, at right angles to the plane of the orbit. The quantum condition relating to the magnetic quantum number then states that the component of this angular momentum along the preferred direction must be an integral multiple of $h/2\pi$. This component is given as $mh/2\pi$. Thus m can take on all integral values from k to $-k$. The orientations thus allowed in space, with their discrete values, are referred to as space quantization. The relation to the magnetic problem is simple. It can be shown by electromagnetic theory (see Appendix 1) that associated with an orbit of a given angular momentum is a given magnetic moment. This arises because the electron rotating in its orbit has the characteristics of a current circulating in a loop, or a solenoid. This magnetic moment, furthermore, is proportional to the angular momentum, equal to $e/2m$ times the angular momentum in the mks system of units, or $e/2mc$ times the angular momentum in the Gaussian system, where e is the electronic charge, m its mass (not to be confused with the quantum number m), and c the velocity of light. There is then a natural unit of magnetic moment, $eh/4\pi m$ or $eh/4\pi mc$ in mks and Gaussian units respectively, called the Bohr magneton, and often denoted as μ_B. We then see that m, the magnetic quantum number, measures the component of magnetic moment along the axis in units of Bohr magnetons. In a magnetic field B along the axis, the energy of the magnetic moment will be $-m\mu_B B$, the product of magnetic field and the component of moment along the field, the energy being a minimum when the magnetic moment points along the field. Thus there will be a modification of the energy levels, produced by the magnetic field, and proportional to it; this effect on the spectrum is called the Zeeman effect.

There are many further interesting points connected with the hydrogen spectrum, and with other atomic spectra, which could be attacked by Bohr's theory; we have given enough, however, to indicate the sort of results which it obtained. It will be well to state here that many, but not all, of its results were correct and are taken over into wave mechanics. The principal modifications relate to space quantization, the Zeeman effect, and related subjects. There the general idea is correct; but in details there have to be modifications. In particular, complications arise between use of the integer k, and of another integer l, one unit smaller; and there are further complications on account of the existence of an intrinsic angular momentum and magnetic moment of the electron itself, generally called the electron spin, the angular momentum having the magnitude $\frac{1}{2}(h/2\pi)$, and the magnetic moment one Bohr magneton. We mention these matters now, though they will not become clear until later, only to put the reader on his guard, and to indicate that there were enough difficulties with the Bohr theory, before the advent of wave mechanics, to show that it needed modification.

To show the versatility of the Bohr theory, we shall apply it to two other cases, both much simpler than the hydrogen atom. One is the rotator, a simple model of a rotating diatomic molecule. Suppose we have two mass points (the atoms), separated by a fixed distance, like a dumbbell, and capable of rotating about their center of mass, where the dumbbell is supposed to be pivoted. Let the moment of inertia about this point be I, the angular velocity ω, so that the angular momentum is $I\omega$. We can then use the angle of rotation as the variable in the quantum condition (1.2.10), in which case the angular momentum is the appropriate momentum. Since $I\omega$ stays constant during the motion, the quantum condition becomes $I\omega \oint d\theta = nh$. But $\oint d\theta = 2\pi$; hence we find that the angular momentum, $I\omega$, must equal $nh/2\pi$. We notice that this is the same condition which we found in (1.2.9) for the hydrogen atom; that problem is essentially the same mathematically as the one we are now considering. The kinetic energy of our rotator is $\frac{1}{2}I\omega^2$, and there is no potential energy. Hence, for the rotator, we have

$$\text{Energy} = \frac{n^2 h^2}{8\pi^2 I}. \qquad (1.2.11)$$

In this problem, as in the hydrogen atom, we find that there is space quantization. The angular momentum vector $nh/2\pi$ can be oriented in only a discrete set of ways in an external field, such that its component along the axis is an integral multiple of $h/2\pi$.

As a final example, let us take a linear oscillator, a particle held to a position of equilibrium by a force proportional to the displacement. An example of this is a vibrating atom in a molecule or solid. This, in contrast to the rotator, is a case in which the momentum depends on the position, so that we must really carry out the integration in the quantum condition (1.2.10). To find how the momentum depends on q, the displacement from the position of equilibrium, we can most conveniently use the total energy and potential energy. If the force acting on the particle is $-kq$, where k is a constant, q the displacement, then the potential energy is the negative of the integral of the force with respect to the displacement, $V = -\int F \, dq$, where F is the force, or

$$V = k \int q \, dq = \frac{kq^2}{2}.$$

If the total energy is E, we can express the law of conservation of energy in the form $E = mv^2/2 + kq^2/2 = p^2/2m + kq^2/2$. This expresses a relation between p and q, which we may write

$$\frac{p^2}{2mE} + \frac{kq^2}{2E} = 1. \qquad (1.2.12)$$

We can solve this equation directly for p, substitute in (1.2.10), and carry out the integration directly; we leave this direct approach for a problem, and show that we can get the quantum condition in an alternative way, using a coordinate space in which q is plotted as abscissa, p as ordinate.

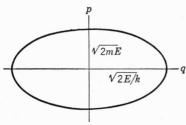

FIG. 1.2.1.   Phase space for linear oscillator, with line of constant energy E.

Such a space, in which momentum is plotted against coordinate, is called a phase space, and is of great use in statistical mechanics. In this phase space, (1.2.12) is the equation of an ellipse, of semiaxis $\sqrt{2E/k}$ along the abscissa, $\sqrt{2mE}$ along the ordinate, as shown in Fig. 1.2.1. To find the momentum corresponding to any coordinate, we need only look up the value of p on this curve corresponding to the given q; the two possible values (positive and negative) correspond to the two cases in which the particle is moving in the direction of increasing q, or in the opposite direction. The amplitude of oscillation is $\sqrt{2E/k}$; for this value of q, the momentum, and hence the velocity, reduces to zero, and the particle reverses its motion. We can now carry out the calculation of the integral $\oint p \, dq$ by elementary methods. If we travel around our ellipse in the clockwise direction, which is the direction in which the particle would traverse it, the whole integral $\oint p \, dq$ is seen to be simply the area of the ellipse. But the area of an ellipse is π times the product of the two semiaxes; thus our quantum condition becomes $2\pi E \sqrt{m/k} = nh$. This can be rewritten in another form by use of the fact that the period of oscillation, in classical mechanics, would be $2\pi \sqrt{m/k}$, or the frequency, which we shall call ν_0, would be the reciprocal of this. Thus we find that the condition is

$$E = nh\nu_0. \qquad (1.2.13)$$

This formula, stating that the energy of a linear oscillator is an integral multiple of the amount $h\nu_0$, is a very important result in quantum mechanics. It reminds us closely of the result, mentioned in Sec. 1.1, that the energy of a photon is $h\nu$; as a matter of fact, more careful study of quantum electrodynamics shows that the energy of photons is determined by a study of certain linear oscillators, the modes of electromagnetic vibration of a resonant electromagnetic cavity, so that this relationship proves to be fundamental, not just an accident. Here, as in the case of hydrogen, the Bohr theory, though near the truth, proves not to agree exactly with the results of wave mechanics; we shall find later that (1.2.13) has to be modified to the form $E = (n + \frac{1}{2})h\nu_0$ when we take up wave mechanics.

1.3. The Wave Hypothesis of de Broglie. The theory of Bohr, which we have been reviewing in the preceding section, had many successes, but it also had many shortcomings. We have mentioned a few points, relating to ambiguity of various quantum numbers by half or whole integers, the existence of the electron spin, and other similar effects which might be regarded as minor details, but which all combined in the early 1920's to indicate that the theory certainly needed modification. There were more serious ways in which it was inadequate, however. The quantum conditions could be stated only for problems in which a separation of variables could be carried out. Yet this could be done only for those problems called multiply periodic, a very special type of mechanical problem. When the many-electron problem was attacked, it was, very clear that this was not of the simple multiply periodic type. Bohr's theory was able to get valuable qualitative results about the heavy atom with many electrons, but no one even knew how to formulate it to try to get an exact solution of these problems. Another shortcoming was the lack of a clear understanding of the way to set up the oscillators responsible for producing the electromagnetic field, if we used the statistical relation between electromagnetic field and photons. An important part of Bohr's theory, which we have not so far taken up, was the correspondence principle. This, as we shall discuss later, related the amplitudes of these electromagnetic oscillators to the Fourier coefficients in the Fourier analysis of the classical multiply periodic motion of the particles. Many important results were obtained from this principle. Most important were certain selection principles. It was found that in many cases certain Fourier coefficients were zero. It was inferred that the corresponding radiation would not be emitted in the quantum theory, and hence that the corresponding quantum transitions could not occur. For instance, it was found in this way that the azimuthal quantum number k, in the hydrogen problem, could change only by ± 1 unit, and the magnetic quantum number m only by ± 1 or 0. Such selection principles proved to be satisfied in practice, and they greatly simplified the observed spectrum. But in cases where the correspondence principle predicted an intensity different from zero for a spectrum line, it could give no clear-cut value for the intensity; it only indicated an analogy, not an equality, between this quantity and a corresponding classical Fourier coefficient.

All these facts, and more too, combined to convince the physicists of the middle of the 1920's that Bohr's theory was inadequate, and that a new formulation of quantum mechanics must come along, embracing those results of Bohr's theory which were right, but extending far beyond that theory. The key to this new formulation was furnished by the bold hypothesis of de Broglie. He postulated that just as there is a wave, the electromagnetic wave, associated with the photons, so there must be a wave, the de Broglie wave, associated with any material particle. The intensity of this wave would determine the probability of finding the particle at a given point, just as in the optical case, so that if the fundamental rules of physics were those determining the behavior of the wave, and if there were only a statistical relation between waves and particles, the behavior of the particles would be determined only on the average, not in detail. Let us consider the general type of behavior which this wave would have to have, and see what de Broglie was able to accomplish by postulating it.

First, the wave must be such that it predicts properly the results of classical mechanics. Suppose we have a particle and its associated de Broglie wave; how do we pass to the limit of classical, or Newtonian, mechanics? The characteristic of Newtonian mechanics is that we can define precisely the position of the particle at all values of the time. The associated de Broglie wave must then be one whose intensity is zero except where the particle is known to be, very large at that point. Such a wave is called a wave packet. We could set up a wave packet in the case of electromagnetic theory, and it helps us in understanding the de Broglie case if we consider this electromagnetic wave packet. The first step in setting up such a wave packet is to set up a ray of light: we let a parallel wave fall on a pinhole, and what comes through is a narrow bundle of radiation, or a ray, following practically a straight line. Next we equip the pinhole with a shutter and allow this to open only for an exceedingly small length of time, so short that the light comes through in a sort of puff, traveling along the ray like a particle. The result is a wave packet. It will go in a straight line as long as the ray is straight, and its velocity will be the velocity of light. But the situation is different if the index of refraction changes from point to point, as it does in heated air in the well-known phenomenon of the mirage. There the ray is curved, the velocity of the wave changes from point to point, and the result is a packet traveling with variable velocity along a curved path.

This electromagnetic wave packet in a region of varying index of refraction forms a very close analogy to the de Broglie wave packet representing the limiting case of classical mechanics.   Definite assumptions, which we shall take up shortly, were made by de Broglie as to the way in which the wave length of his wave varied with position.   These were such that the velocity, or index of refraction, changes from point to point in an easily predictable way.   The theory is set up so that, if we investigate the motion of a wave packet, we find that it moves precisely according to the laws of Newtonian mechanics.   This then forms the basis for saying that wave mechanics reduces to classical mechanics in the limit.   To the extent that it reduces to Newtonian mechanics, de Broglie's hypothesis results in nothing new.   It is a remarkable historical fact that over 100 years earlier, Hamilton, in setting up the equations of motion which are known by his name, was guided by an optical analogy of just this sort.   Hamilton realized that it was mathematically possible to set up a wave motion such that the rays associated with this wave were the trajectories of particles, according to Newtonian mechanics.   The whole mathematica background of Hamiltonian mechanics is based on an analogy with geometrical optics in a medium of variable index of refraction.   Hamilton thus, in a very real sense, anticipated de Broglie by 100 years, for Hamilton's waves and de Broglie's were in many ways equivalent.   But the great difference was that in the intervening time new, nonclassical aspects of mechanics had been discovered, which we have been reviewing in the preceding sections, and which de Broglie showed fitted in with his wave hypothesis, though not with classical mechanics.   Let us now look at these aspects of de Broglie's waves which lead to new results, not predictable from classical mechanics.   Classical mechanics is related to de Broglie's theory as geometrical optics is to electromagnetic theory. What we now seek is the analogue to physical optics, the phenomena which depend on the finite size of the wave length.

Perhaps the most striking experimental fact verifying de Broglie's hypothesis is one which we have not so far mentioned: it is the existence of electron diffraction, which was discovered by Davisson and Germer, G. P. Thomson, and others, at about the same time as de Broglie's work. The hypothesis made by de Broglie about the wave length of the waves proved to be just right to explain the observations of electron diffraction; the waves prove, in this case, to have wave lengths of the order of magnitude of atomic dimensions, so that diffraction by the atomic lattice of a crystal is possible.   More far-reaching than this, however, was the fact that de Broglie's hypothesis was able to explain the significance of the Bohr-Sommerfeld quantum condition, and hence to bring the whole Bohr theory, with its great successes in describing atomic processes, within its scope. The suggestion of de Broglie was that in wave mechanics we can have standing waves, and that the stationary states of atoms and molecules correspond to the various overtones of a standing wave system. Thus the waves associated with particles not only can have progressive form, connected with particles traveling along, but can also exist as standing waves. Further than this, it has proved to be the case that these standing waves have close connection to the oscillators which we have already postulated, in discussing the statistical relation of waves and photons, as being responsible for the emission of electromagnetic waves. By an extension of de Broglie's work, the detailed theory of these oscillators was shown to follow from wave mechanics, so that wave mechanics can discuss the probability of transition between stationary states, as well as the existence of stationary states themselves.

Standing waves are familiar in any type of wave motion. They exist only when, by reflection or refraction, it is possible for a wave to double back on itself, so that it can traverse the same path many times. Thus in a string held at the two ends, the wave can be successively reflected from each end, so that after such a round trip it has come back to where it was. In such a case, reinforcement of the amplitude, and a steady state of oscillation, can occur only if the number of wave lengths in this round trip is an integer; for then the returning wave will be in phase with the original wave, and all successive multiply reflected waves will also reinforce each other, whereas with any other relation between wave length and dimensions the waves would interfere destructively, and no stable oscillation is possible. The result of any standing wave phenomenon is, then, that the wave length is limited to certain discrete values: integral submultiples of the dimension of the round trip. Since the wave length determines the frequency, this quantity is also limited to certain discrete values, as for instance in musical instruments, where the strings or organ pipes can oscillate only with certain definite pitches. And the mathematical condition determining these allowed wave lengths or frequencies is always the same: the number of wave lengths in a round trip must be an integer. To see how this general concept applies to wave mechanics, we must then know the wave length and frequency of the de Broglie wave. In the next section we go on to give the detailed assumptions of de Broglie regarding wave length and frequency, and to show how these assumptions lead to a wave motion which reduces to classical mechanics in the limiting case of very short wave length, analogous to geometrical optics; how we are led to diffraction effects when the size of the wave length becomes comparable with the dimensions of the apparatus; and how the standing waves lead to the Bohr-Sommerfeld quantum conditions.

1.4. Frequency and Wave Length in Wave Mechanics. It was assumed by de Broglie that the frequency and wave length of the de Broglie wave were related to the energy (kinetic plus potential) and momentum which a classical particle would have at the same point of space by the relations

$$E = h\nu, \qquad p = \frac{h}{\lambda}, \qquad (1.4.1)$$

where E is the energy, p the momentum, ν the frequency, λ the wave length, and h Planck's constant. Let us first observe that these are the same relations which are assumed to hold for the case of electromagnetic waves and photons, as taken up in Sec. 1.1. The relation between E and ν is obvious, but we have not so far considered that between p and λ. The argument for this relation between momentum and wave length, in the electromagnetic case, is based on the momentum associated with a given amount of energy in electromagnetic theory. This relation can be most easily shown by means of the theory of relativity. According to this theory, a particle which has a mass m_0 when it is standing still (its so-called "rest mass") has a mass $m = m_0/(1 - v^2/c^2)^{1/2}$ when traveling with a velocity v, so that the mass approaches infinity as the velocity approaches c. Then the momentum is shown to be mv, and the kinetic energy is $mc^2 - m_0c^2$, a quantity which approaches the classical value $\frac{1}{2}mv^2$ at low velocities. As we approach the velocity of light, where m becomes infinite in comparison to m_0, the momentum approaches mc and the kinetic energy mc^2, so that the momentum equals the energy divided by c. This relation holds for a photon, or for electromagnetic radiation, as if it were a particle with zero rest mass. Hence if we have a photon of energy $h\nu$, its momentum must be $h\nu/c$, which equals h/λ, since ν/c equals $1/\lambda$. Thus we verify that the relation (1.4.1) is the correct one for the optical problem.

Before we start applying the relations (1.4.1) to the mechanical case, let us consider the magnitudes of the frequency and wave length predicted by them in actual cases. We are interested in knowing how important are the phenomena of interference and diffraction, and of standing waves, which occur with any type of wave motion if the wave lengths are comparable in size with the systems we are considering. We find that classical mechanics forms a correct treatment of a problem in which the wave lengths of the particles are very small compared with any significant dimension of the problem, while quantum theory must be used if the wave lengths are comparable with other dimensions. If a significant dimension is called q, and the momentum p, so that the wave length is

h/p, we then find that the number of wave lengths in this dimension is pq/h. As a first illustration, let us consider problems on a large scale, such as we meet in everyday life. If masses are of the order of a gram, velocities of the order of centimeters per second, dimensions of the order of centimeters, pq will be of the order of magnitude of erg-seconds, enormously large compared to h, which is 6.61×10^{-27} erg-sec. Thus in such problems classical mechanics is completely adequate, and this holds even more in such problems as astronomical motions, where the masses, velocities, and dimensions are much greater. It is clear that to get situations where we must use quantum mechanics, we must reduce greatly the momentum, the coordinate, or both. We know that in atomic and molecular processes we ordinarily meet rather large velocities; thus it is in the reduction of the masses and dimensions that we look for an approach to the region of applicability of quantum mechanics.

Before we ask about the application to problems on an atomic scale, it is a little more convenient to rephrase our quantity pq/h in another form. We often deal with atomic problems by computing not the momentum and the dimensions, but the energy and the frequency or the period of oscillation. The energy of a harmonically oscillating system is twice the kinetic energy, that is, $E = mv^2$, where m is the mass, v the velocity. The period τ is of the order of magnitude of a dimension divided by a velocity, that is, q/v. Thus the product $E\tau$ of energy and period is of the same order of magnitude as pq, so that the number of wave lengths in the dimension q will be of the order of $E\tau/h$. We can use either this quantity or pq/h interchangeably for calculations of order of magnitude; if either one is large compared with unity, the motion can be handled classically, while quantum theory must be used if the quantity is small. If the energy is computed in electron volts, and the frequency $1/\tau$ in cycles per second, we have $E = eV$, where e is the electronic charge, and V is the energy in electron volts. Thus we have

$$pq/h = eV/h\nu = (1.6 \times 10^{-19}/6.61 \times 10^{-34})(V/\nu) = 2.4 \times 10^{14}(V/\nu).$$

Let us now put in some numbers and find the order of magnitude of this quantity for certain atomic problems. First we consider an electron in an atom. The energies of the outer electrons are of the order of magnitude of 5 ev (electron volts); the frequencies are of the order of 10^{15} cycles/sec. Thus from the formula $eV/h\nu = 2.4 \times 10^{14}(V/\nu)$, putting in $V = 5$, $\nu = 10^{15}$, we see that our quantity is of the order of magnitude of unity, so that the electrons in the atom must be handled by quantum mechanics. This is of course no accident; it is, in fact, precisely the way in which the magnitude of atomic dimensions is fixed. These same numbers correspond to dimensions of the order of 10^{-8} cm and velocities of the order of 10^9 cm/sec for electrons.   It is such magnitudes as these that we find for the electronic motions in atoms.

For the vibrations of atoms as a whole, in molecules and crystals, the vibration frequencies are of the order of magnitude of 10^{13} cycles/sec. We then have $eV/h\nu = 1$ for V equal to about 0.04 ev.   For energies less than this amount quantum theory must be used, while for larger energies the classical theory is appropriate.   In this case, we can more conveniently measure the energy, not in volts, but in terms of an equivalent temperature.   From statistical mechanics we know that the mean energy of a classical oscillator, at temperature T, is kT, where k is Boltzmann's constant $(1.38 \times 10^{-16}$ erg/deg $= 1.38 \times 10^{-23}$ joule/deg).   Thus to each voltage V we can associate a temperature by the equation $eV = kT$. A convenient way to remember the numerical values of the constants is the fact that the voltage corresponding to $T = 300°K$, roughly room temperature, is 0.025 ev $= \frac{1}{40}$ ev.   We then see that, referring to our example of a vibrator of frequency 10^{13} cycles/sec, $eV/h\nu = 1$ for a temperature of about $500°K$, somewhat above room temperature, so that we find that the vibrations of atoms can be handled by classical mechanics at high temperatures but must be treated by quantum theory at low temperatures.   For different frequencies of oscillation the dividing point comes at different temperatures.   A heavy atom tends to vibrate with lower frequency than a light one, since the restoring forces do not vary greatly with the mass of the atom, and the frequency of a classical vibrator varies as the square root of the elastic constant divided by the mass. Thus for a heavy atom the transition temperature comes at low temperatures compared with room temperature.   In a solid this temperature is closely related to the Debye temperature, which occurs in the theory of specific heats.   Above the Debye temperature, the specific heat of a solid is given with good accuracy by classical mechanics and statistics; below the Debye temperature, characteristic quantum effects come into play.   And as a general rule, Debye temperatures tend to be well below room temperature for solids composed of heavy atoms, whereas for very light atoms these temperatures can be comparable with room temperature or even higher.

1.5. Geometrical Optics and Classical Mechanics.   Now that we understand the range of magnitudes of variables in which classical mechanics holds, we can ask how wave mechanics reduces to classical mechanics in this limit.   We have already seen that this involves investigating the motion of a wave packet.   Such a wave packet moves along the direction of a ray, and moves with a velocity called the group velocity. We shall then look into the direction which a ray would take in wave mechanics and find the group velocity of a packet along such a ray.   We notice first that since de Broglie assumed that the frequency of the wave was given by the relation $h\nu$ = energy, the law of conservation of energy results in a constant frequency. On the other hand, the wave length, given by h/p, changes from point to point. For conservative motion, in which $p^2/2m + V = E$, $\lambda = h/p = h/\sqrt{2m(E - V)}$, a function of position on account of V, with E staying constant. The variable λ corresponds to a variable index of refraction. There are only a few optical cases where we have this situation. Generally the index changes sharply from one medium to another, and the ray of light consists of segments of straight lines. In refraction by the atmosphere, however, as in astronomy, or in the refraction by heated air over the surface of the earth, as in mirages, the path of the light rays is curved instead of sharply bent, and this corresponds to the usual mechanical case, where the paths or orbits are curved. To proceed further with the connection between wave mechanics and Newtonian mechanics, we must first investigate the shape of a ray in a case where the index changes with position. The general principle governing this is called Fermat's principle.

Assume that we have an optical system with a ray traveling from P_1 to P_2. We may start the ray by letting parallel light fall on a pinhole, so that really the light travels in a narrow beam, eventually reaching P_2. We assume that the dimensions are so large in comparison to the wave length that diffraction can be neglected. Then suppose we compute the time taken for light to pass from the point P_1 to P_2 along the actual ray. This time will be $\int_{P_1}^{P_2} \dfrac{ds}{v}$, where the integral is a line integral, computed along the ray from P_1 to P_2, ds is the element of length along the ray, and v is the phase velocity, a function of position if the index of refraction changes from point to point. Next, suppose that we compute the same integral for other paths which join P_1 and P_2 but differ between these points. Since in general the integral is not independent of path, we shall get different answers. In general, if we go from one path to another, the difference of the integral between the paths will be of the same order of small quantities as the displacement of the path. But Fermat's principle says that if one path is the correct ray, and the other is slightly displaced from it, the difference in the integral is of a higher order of small quantities. This is a sort of condition met in the calculus of variations. In that subject we have what is called the variation of an integral: $\delta \int_{P_1}^{P_2} \dfrac{ds}{v}$ is the variation of the integral, and it means the difference between the integral over one path and over another infinitely near to it. Fermat's principle says that the variation of the integral is zero for the actual path; meaning that the actual variation is infinitesimal of a higher order than the variation of path, so that it vanishes in the limit of small variation of path. The idea of the variation of an integral is closely analogous to that of the differential of a function in ordinary calculus. Thus, if the variation of an integral is zero for a given path, it means that the integral itself is a maximum or minimum with respect to variations of path, or more generally, that it is stationary, not changing with small variations of path. Setting the variation equal to zero corresponds to setting the derivative of a function equal to zero in calculus.

Let us verify Fermat's principle in two simple cases. First, we assume that v is everywhere constant, so that there are no mirrors or lenses. Then we can take v outside the integral, multiplying through by it, and having $\delta \int_{P_1}^{P_2} ds = 0$. That is, the true path of light between P_1 and P_2 is that line which has minimum (or maximum) length and joins P_1 and P_2. Obviously, the minimum is desired in this case; and the shortest line between P_1 and P_2 is a straight line, which then is the ray. Let us compute the variation of path to check the variation principle. In Fig. 1.5.1 we show in (a) the straight line joining P_1 and P_2 and also a varied path P_1BP_2. The length of this second path is

$$2\sqrt{(P_1A)^2 + (AB)^2} = 2(P_1A)[1 + \tfrac{1}{2}(AB)^2/(P_1A)^2 + \cdots]$$
$$= (P_1P_2) + 2(AB)^2/(P_1P_2),$$

differing from the direct path P_1P_2 by an infinitesimal of the second order if (AB), the deviation of the path P_1BP_2 from P_1AP_2, is regarded as small of

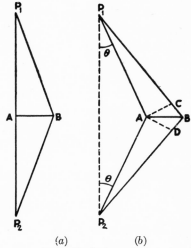

(a)   (b)

Fig. 1.5.1. Variation of length of path. (a) The straight line P_1AP_2 differs in length from the varied path P_1BP_2 by a small quantity of the order of the square of AB. (b) The broken line P_1AP_2 differs from P_1BP_2 by a quantity of the order of AB itself. Hence the straight line of (a), rather than the broken one of (b), is the one for which the variation of length is zero.

the first order. In other words, the path P_1AP_2 satisfies the condition that the variation of its length is zero (that is, small of the second order). On the other hand, if we started with a crooked path, as P_1AP_2 in (b), then the path P_1BP_2 differs from it approximately by the amount (BC) + (BD), or approximately $2(AB) \sin \theta$, an infinitesimal of the same order as (AB), so that in this case the variation is not zero, and the crooked path is not the correct one.

As a second example, we take the case of reflection. In Fig. 1.5.2 consider the path P_1AP_2, connecting P_1 and P_2, satisfying the law of reflection on the mirror AB. This path evidently equals $P_1'AP_2$ in length, where P_1' is the image of P_1. Similarly a slightly different path P_1BP_2 equals $P_1'BP_2$, which is therefore longer, since $P_1'AP_2$ is the straight line connecting P_1' and P_2. In other words, P_1AP_2 makes the integral a minimum and is the correct path. In this case we could again easily show that the integral along P_1BP_2 differed from that along P_1AP_2 by

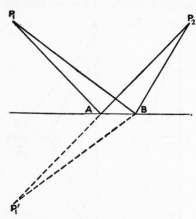

quantities in the square of (AB), verifying our statement that if the path is displaced by small quantities of the first order (AB), the integral is changed only in the second order $(AB)^2$. A similar proof can be carried through for the case of refraction, showing that the law of refraction is given by Fermat's principle.

FIG. 1.5.2. Fermat's principle for reflection. The path P_1AP_2, equal to $P_1'AP_2$, differs in length from its neighbor P_1BP_2 by a small quantity of the order of the square of AB.

A fundamental proof of Fermat's principle can be given directly from the determination of the ray from diffraction theory. The condition that a point P_2 lie in the ray, if we discuss diffraction through an aperture in a screen between P_1 and P_2 by Huygens' principle, is that the various paths leading from P_1 to P_2, by going to various points of the aperture and then being scattered in Huygens' wavelets from there to P_2, should be approximately the same, so that light can interfere constructively at P_2. This means that such paths, as measured in wave lengths, are all approximately the same length. In other words, for constructive interference, $\int_{P_1}^{P_2} \frac{ds}{\lambda}$, the number of wave lengths between P_1 and P_2, must be independent of slight variations of path, or $\delta \int_{P_1}^{P_2} \frac{ds}{\lambda} = 0$. This clearly is the condition whether λ is independent of position or not, for even if the waves change in length from point to point, we must still have the waves interfere to get the ray, and this still demands the same number of wave lengths along neighboring paths. Now $\lambda = v/\nu$, and since ν, the frequency, is a constant throughout the path of the light, we may then write the variation as $\nu\delta \int_{P_1}^{P_2} \frac{ds}{v} = 0$, from which, dividing by ν, we have

Fermat's principle. This interpretation in terms of the interference of the waves along the ray is the fundamental meaning of Fermat's principle.

We shall now show that if we use the analogue to Fermat's principle in mechanics, it leads to the correct motion of the particle according to Newtonian mechanics. As we have seen, the wave problem representing the motion of a single particle whose variables we know is a ray. And the path of this ray is given by Fermat's principle, which we may write in the form $\delta \int ds/\lambda = 0$. But now in wave mechanics $h/\lambda = p$, the momentum, so that, canceling out the constant factor h, this becomes $\delta \int p \, ds = 0$. But this is a well-known equation of ordinary mechanics: the integral $\int p \, ds$, or $\int p \, dq$, if q is the coordinate in a one-dimensional motion, is called the action, and the principle $\delta \int p \, dq = 0$, showing that the action is a maximum, or more often a minimum, is called the principle of least action. By the calculus of variations we can show that the principle of least action leads to Lagrange's equations, or to Newton's equations of motion, as the equations giving the motion of a particle which obeys the principle. (See Appendix 3 for discussion of this method.) This principle, or a closely related one called Hamilton's principle, also stated in terms of the calculus of variations, is often considered a fundamental formulation of the whole of mechanics, more fundamental than Newton's laws of motion, since these, in the form of Lagrange's equations, follow from it. As a matter of fact, the derivation of Lagrange's equations from the variation principle is the simplest way of deriving them, for one familiar with the calculus of variations, and leads to the equations directly in any arbitrary coordinate system. But here we have gone even further: we have sketched the derivation of the principle of least action from wave mechanics, as the law giving the shape of a ray, determined from interference of the waves. As we see from this, wave mechanics is the fundamental branch of mechanics, and ordinary Newtonian mechanics, the mechanics of particles, is derived from it.

To complete our demonstration of the relation between wave mechanics and Newtonian mechanics, we should show that the wave packet moves along the ray with the correct velocity. It is a familiar fact of wave motion that a wave packet does not move with the phase velocity $\lambda \nu$ but with the group velocity $v_g = d\nu/d(1/\lambda)$. (See Appendix 4 for a discussion.) If we have propagation in three-dimensional space, the quantity $1/\lambda$ becomes a vector function of position, its direction being the direction of the wave normal, its magnitude the magnitude of $1/\lambda$. In that case, if we call the three components $\beta_x, \beta_y, \beta_z$, we have the vector relation of which the x component is $(v_g)_x = \partial\nu/\partial\beta_x$, with similar expressions for the other components. Now in our case we have $\nu = E/h$, $1/\lambda = p/h$; the vector quantity related to $1/\lambda$ is obviously a vector of magnitude p/h, pointing along the direction of the momentum. The energy E is to be expressed as a function of coordinates and of either the wave length or p. But the energy, as expressed in terms of the coordinates and components of momentum, is known as the Hamiltonian function, denoted by H. Thus our expression for group velocity leads to the result

$$(v_g)_x = \frac{\partial H}{\partial p_x}, \qquad (v_g)_y = \frac{\partial H}{\partial p_y}, \qquad (v_g)_z = \frac{\partial H}{\partial p_z}. \qquad (1.5.1)$$

The reader familiar with Hamilton's equations will recognize these as three of Hamilton's equations for this particular problem, stating that v_g is in fact the velocity of the particle. To understand this, we need only take the explicit formula for H, $H = (p_x^2 + p_y^2 + p_z^2)/2m + V$, where V is the potential energy. Then we have $\partial H/\partial p_x = p_x/m$, which certainly should be v_x according to classical mechanics.

As a result of this derivation, we must be on our guard to distinguish properly between the group velocity, given by (1.5.1), which is the velocity of the classical particle or of the wave packet, and the phase velocity, given by $\lambda \nu = E/p$. This phase velocity has no direct interpretation in classical mechanics. It is, however, the quantity which is implied in our discussion of Fermat's principle and its mechanical analogue, the principle of least action.

The derivation we have given in the present section shows that wave mechanics reduces properly to classical mechanics in the limit where we can neglect the size of the wave length. In a later chapter we shall be able to give an even simpler derivation, proving straightforwardly that the center of gravity of a wave packet moves precisely according to the Hamiltonian equations of motion, or in accordance with Newton's laws. We are thus justified in using classical mechanics in any problem in which a wave packet can be set up which does not spread appreciably. Next we shall consider the limitation on classical mechanics imposed by diffraction.

1.6. Wave Packets and the Uncertainty Principle. If we try to pass an electromagnetic wave through a pinhole, and make the pinhole smaller and smaller, we reach a point where the resultant beam of light, instead of getting narrower and narrower and more and more like a geometrical ray, actually starts to spread out again. This is the phenomenon of diffraction. Similarly, if we try to let our shutter be open a shorter and shorter length of time, at first the packet will get shorter and shorter, but finally (at least in a dispersive medium) we reach a point when we shall find that the packet spreads out again. In both these cases, putting things very crudely, we find that we cannot make the packet smaller than a wave length, either transversely or longitudinally. That means that we cannot specify the position of our particle more precisely than to a wave length. This is a very crude statement of the principle of uncertainty; we shall give a more precise statement presently.   We may then well say that classical mechanics is applicable to a problem in which the de Broglie wave length is negligible compared with the other significant dimensions of the problem, while it is not applicable if the de Broglie wave length is comparable to other dimensions.   Let us look into the statement of the principle of uncertainty more closely.

If we let a plane wave of light fall on a slit of width a, the light passing through will be in the form of a beam, spreading by diffraction, but still, in the region of Fresnel diffraction, of width approximately a.   Thus if x is the coordinate along the wave normal, y the coordinate at right angles, the photon will surely be in a beam whose length along the x axis is infinite, but whose width is only about a along the y axis, as in Fig. 1.6.1.   That is, the uncertainty Δy in the y coordinate is $\Delta y = a$.   At the same time, however, a compensating uncertainty in the momentum appears. The wave is spreading, the wave normals making angles up to about λ/a

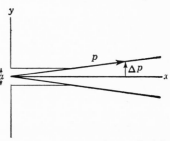

Fig. 1.6.1.   Uncertainty principle in diffraction through slit.

$$\Delta p/p = \lambda/\Delta q, \quad \Delta p \Delta q = \lambda p = h.$$

with the x axis, as we know from the elementary theory of Fraunhofer diffraction.   Thus if the whole momentum remains h/λ, this will have a component along y equal to p times the sine of the angle between the momentum and the x axis, or approximately $p\lambda/a = h/a$.   But we do not know which angle, up to the maximum, the actual deviation will make, for all we know is that the photon is somewhere in the diffraction pattern.   Hence the uncertainty in y momentum is of the order of magnitude of h/a.   If we call it Δp_y, we have the relation

$$\Delta y \, \Delta p_y = \frac{ah}{a} = h. \tag{1.6.1}$$

This is an example of the uncertainty principle, concerning the amount of uncertainty inherent in the description of the motion of photons by the probability relations with wave theory.   Further examination indicates that this law is very general: where a beam is limited to acquire more accurate information about the coordinates of the photon, we incur a corresponding loss in our knowledge as to its momentum, and vice versa.

A similar relation holds between energy and time.   Suppose we have a shutter over our hole and open it and close it very rapidly, so as to allow light to pass through for only a very short interval of time Δt. Then the wave on the far side is an interrupted sinusoidal train of waves, and if we analyze this train by Fourier analysis, we find that the frequency is no longer a definitely determined value but is spread out through a frequency band of breadth $\Delta\nu$, given by

$$\Delta\nu/\nu = 1/(\text{number of waves in train}).$$

(See Appendix 5 for discussion.) Now the number of waves in the train is $c\,\Delta t$, the length of the train, divided by λ. Hence $\Delta\nu/\nu = \lambda/(c\,\Delta t)$, $\Delta\nu\,\Delta t = 1$. Using $E = h\nu$, we have

$$\Delta E\,\Delta t = h, \tag{1.6.2}$$

an uncertainty relation between E and t, showing that energy and time are roughly equivalent to momentum and coordinate: if we try to measure exactly when the photons go through the hole, their energy becomes slightly indeterminate. Further, here we know that the x coordinate is now determined, at any instant of time, with an accuracy $c\,\Delta t$: the photon must be in the little puff of light, or wave packet, sent through the pinhole while the shutter was open. Thus $\Delta x = c\,\Delta t$. But now the x component of momentum, which to the first order is the momentum itself, is uncertain. For $p_x = p = h\nu/c$, $\Delta p_x = (h/c)\Delta\nu = h/(c\,\Delta t) = h/\Delta x$, so that

$$\Delta x\,\Delta p_x = h, \tag{1.6.3}$$

again the uncertainty relation. We can, in other words, make our wave packet smaller and smaller, until it seems almost like a particle itself, and its path is the path of the photon. The wave packet will be reflected and refracted, just as large waves would be, giving the laws of motion of photons in refracting media. But if we try to go too far, making the wave packet too small, we defeat our purpose, and make it spread out by diffraction. We cannot, that is, get exactly accurate knowledge about the laws of the photon's motion from the probability relation between intensity of the wave and the position of the photon. In some cases, this is even more obvious than here. Thus if a wave packet is sent through a diffraction grating, it will spread out, much as a plane wave would, into the various orders of the diffraction pattern. We cannot, then, make any prediction at all, except a statistical one, as to which order of the pattern a given photon will go to. We completely lose track of the paths of individual photons in a diffraction pattern.

The arguments in the present section now apply to particles and to the diffraction of de Broglie waves, just as well as to photons and electromagnetic waves; for they depend only on de Broglie's assumptions $E = h\nu$, $p = h/\lambda$, which are common to both theories. Thus we see that the general uncertainty relations apply here: the uncertainty in any coordinate, multiplied by the uncertainty in the corresponding momentum, equals h. That is to say, we cannot set up a de Broglie wave which determines these quantities more accurately than is prescribed by this principle. This sets the limit to the applicability of classical mechanics.

It shows that even if we let the momentum be so poorly defined that we allow a variation Δp comparable with the momentum p itself, we still have a variation Δq in the corresponding coordinate at least as great as h/p or as the wave length; this is the origin of our earlier crude statement that the wave packet could not be made smaller than a wave length. But now we see that if we insist on prescribing the momentum with a greater accuracy, we lose in the accuracy of describing the coordinate: the wave packet grows larger than a wave length, in a compensating way. These limitations are of no importance in the case of classical mechanics; but in the problems which must be treated by quantum theory, they are of the greatest importance and must be constantly kept in mind.

1.7. Standing Waves and the Sommerfeld Quantum Condition. We are now ready to understand how de Broglie's hypothesis of wave mechanics leads in a very simple way to Sommerfeld's quantum condition. We see at once that $\int p \, dq/h$ measures the number of waves along the path of integration. Thus when we carry the integration around the path of a particle moving with periodic motion, to get the phase integral $\oint p \, dq$, we have h times the number of waves around the orbit. If we demand that we have standing waves, this number of waves must be an integer n. Thus we have precisely the Sommerfeld quantum condition $\oint p \, dq = nh$.

As we go further, we shall understand in more detail just how we must imagine the waves which set up the standing waves determined by Sommerfeld's quantum condition to circulate; de Broglie's original hypothesis did not carry us much further than we have already stated, but it is obvious that we must be concerned with the precise nature of the waves, for instance, in a circular orbit in hydrogen. The answer to all such questions comes from the next step in the mathematical formulation of quantum mechanics, the wave equation of Schrödinger. In all types of wave motion, the proper mathematical method of formulating the problem is to set up a wave equation, a partial differential equation determining the wave function as a function of position and time. In the next chapter we shall proceed to the formulation of this wave equation for wave mechanics.

Before we finish our present qualitative discussion, however, it is worth while to point out one fact. In Sec. 1.4 we discussed the condition which would have to be satisfied in order to have classical mechanics give an adequate approximation in any given problem. We stated this condition in the form that pq/h should be large compared to unity, where p/h was $1/\lambda$, and q was a significant dimension of the problem; in other words, there must be many wave lengths in the dimensions we are concerned with. If p depends on position, of course, this can be rewritten in the form $\int p \, dq/h \gg 1$. But now we see that this has an intimate relation to Sommerfeld's quantum condition. If we are dealing with a periodic motion, $\int p \, dq/h$ is just the quantum number n, which is in fact the number of wave lengths in the path of the particle. Our condition for the applicability of classical mechanics is then simply that the system must be in a very high quantum state, with very large value of n.

PROBLEMS

1. A point source of radiation emits energy at the rate of 10 watts, the intensity being uniform in all directions. The radiation falls on a counter at a distance r from the source, capable of counting individual photons if they fall on it at intervals greater than the resolving time, which is 10^{-6} sec. The counter has a sensitive area of 1 sq cm. Find the minimum distance from the source at which the counter must be located to resolve the individual photons, if the wave length of the radiation is (a) 60 cm; (b) 6,000 A; (c) 0.6 A.

2. A certain photographic material requires an exposure of 0.1 erg/sq cm for light of wave length 5,000 A to produce appreciable blackening. If the sensitive grains of the emulsion are assumed to be squares 1 micron on a side, how many photons must fall on each grain to produce this effect?

3. A certain ferromagnetic material has a saturation magnetization M corresponding to $B = 10,000$ gauss $= 1$ weber/sq m. (*Note:* In the mks system $B = \mu_0 M$, where $\mu_0 = 4\pi \times 10^{-7}$.) Assume that the magnetization is produced by atoms arranged on a simple cubic lattice, each having a magnetic moment of two Bohr magnetons. Find the distance between atoms.

4. Apply the quantum condition to a linear oscillator, solving (1.2.12) for p, and computing $\oint p \, dq$. Arrive at the energy levels of the problem in this way.

5. If d is the spacing between parallel sets of crystal planes, Bragg's law states that the glancing angle of incidence θ for x-ray or electron diffraction in the first order is given by $\lambda = 2d \sin \theta$. Show that, if V is the voltage through which electrons have fallen to acquire their velocity, the Bragg equation for electron diffraction may be written $\sin \theta = \text{constant}/\sqrt{V}$. Find the value of the constant, if V is given in volts; let $d = 3$ A.

6. In relativistic mechanics the kinetic energy H of a particle of rest mass m_0, traveling with velocity v, is given by $H = m_0 c^2/\sqrt{1 - v^2/c^2}$, and its momentum p is $m_0 v/\sqrt{1 - v^2/c^2}$. Prove that $H = \sqrt{m_0^2 c^4 + p^2 c^2}$. From this find the group velocity of the de Broglie wave, with x component $\partial H/\partial p_x$, and show that this equals the velocity of the particle. Find the phase velocity of the de Broglie wave, and show that this is greater than the velocity of light, and that, in fact, the velocity of light is the geometric mean of the group and phase velocities.

7. A beam of particles of mass m, traveling with velocity v ($v \ll c$), falls on a slit of width d. After traveling a distance D ($D \gg d$), the diffraction pattern is observed. For what value of d will this diffraction pattern have minimum width? (Use the uncertainty principle rather than working out the details of the diffraction pattern.)

8. A microscope cannot resolve objects much smaller than a wave length. What energy of electrons (in electron volts) would be required to give a theoretical resolving power of 1 A in an electron microscope? (*Note:* Real electron microscopes so far are still rather far from attaining theoretical resolving power.)

9. A helium atom moves with the kinetic energy characteristic of a temperature of 1°K (the kinetic energy is given by $\frac{3}{2}kT$). Find the de Broglie wave length associated with its motion. Would you expect these atoms to show diffraction effects if they could be scattered from a crystal lattice?

10. Show that if a beam of particles has a cross section with a diameter less than a wave length, it must diverge enough so that within a distance comparable to a wave length it will have spread to a diameter greater than a wave length; in other words, to keep an approximately constant cross section for a length several times the diameter, the diameter must be greater than a wave length.

11. Show that the difference of radii of successive Bohr circular orbits for hydrogen is of the same order of magnitude as the de Broglie wave length in one of the orbits. Since the uncertainty principle does not allow under any circumstances that a beam of particles can be of cross section much less than a wave length, this means that according to the uncertainty principle the electrons cannot be localized sharply enough to tell which of two adjacent orbits they are occupying.

12. An electron moves in a circular path around the lines of force of a magnetic field. Apply the quantum condition to the rotation. Find the radius of the orbit corresponding to a quantum number of unity in a magnetic field of 10^5 gauss, and find the kinetic energy (in electron volts) of the electron in this orbit.

13. An electron beam passes through a small circular aperture adjusted so as to give the beam a minimum diameter after traveling a distance D. There is a magnetic field B along the direction of the beam, so that the electrons which acquire any component of velocity in the plane normal to B, on account of the uncertainty principle, will have a circular motion in the plane normal to B superposed on their motion along the direction of the field. Show that this circular motion will approximate that in the ground state of the rotator, as discussed in Prob. 12, at the distance D from the aperture.

14. A projectile shot horizontally with velocity v in the earth's gravitational field moves in a parabola, but at the top of the path this parabola can be approximated by a circle. Show that the radius of the circle is given by $r = v^2/g$. If the trajectory of the particle is approximately a circle, the wave fronts of the de Broglie waves are the radii of the circle. Since these radii get farther apart as we rise above the surface of the earth, the de Broglie wave length must increase with height. Show that the increase of wave length is just consistent with the decrease of momentum with height given by classical mechanics. This is a simple case where we can find the shape of the trajectory of a particle as predicted from the de Broglie waves by elementary means.

15. Assume that in the accompanying figure POP' is the path of the optically correct ray passing from one medium into another of different refractive index. Prove Fermat's principle for this case, showing that the time for the ray to pass along a slightly different path, as PAP', differs from that along POP' by a small quantity of higher order than the distance AO. The figure is drawn so that AB, CO are arcs of circles with centers at P and P' respectively, and it is to be noted that for small AO, the figures AOB, AOC are almost exactly right triangles.

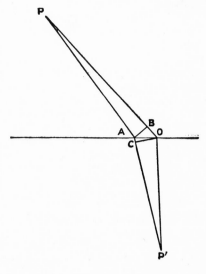

16. An electron of charge $e = 1.61 \times 10^{-19}$ coulomb falls through a difference of potential of V volts and bombards a target, converting all its energy into radiation which travels out as one photon. Using the relations that the energy of the photon $= h\nu$, $\nu = c/\lambda$, where c, the velocity of light, is 3×10^8 m/sec, find the wave length of the resulting radiation. Find the number of volts necessary to produce visible light of wave length 5,000 A; x-rays of length 1 A; gamma rays of length 0.001 A.

17. Assume that light falls on a metal and ejects photoelectrons, the energy required to pull an electron through the surface being at least 2 volts. Find the photoelectric threshold frequency, the longest wave length which can eject electrons, remembering that the long wave lengths have small photons which have not enough energy. Discuss the effect of the work function (the energy required to pull the electron out) on the photoelectric threshold.

18. Consider the accuracy of Newtonian mechanics for a hydrogen atom in a hydrogen molecule. The hydrogen atom weighs about 1,800 times as much as an electron. Assume the speed of the atom to be such that its energy is the mean kinetic energy of a one-dimensional oscillator at temperature 300°K, or $\frac{1}{2}kT$. Compare the wave length with the amplitude of oscillation of the atom. To find this, assume that it oscillates with simple harmonic motion, and that its frequency of oscillation is 3,000 cm^{-1}. (The unit of frequency, cm^{-1}, is the frequency associated with a wave length of 1 cm.) Knowing the energy and mass, it is then possible to find the amplitude.

19. Consider, as in Prob. 18, the same hydrogen molecule at 10°K; an atom of atomic weight 100, in a diatomic molecule of two like atoms, similar to the hydrogen molecule, with the same restoring force acting between the atoms (therefore with a much slower speed of vibration, on account of the larger mass), at 300°K; at 10°K.

20. Conjugate foci in optics are points connected by an infinite number of possible correct paths. Thus by Fermat's principle the optical path, or length of time taken to traverse the ray, is stationary for each of these paths, meaning that the optical path is the same for each. Discuss this, showing that for the conjugate foci of a simple lens the optical path is the same for each ray, carrying out the actual calculation of time.

21. Using the properties of conjugate foci mentioned in Prob. 20, prove that if a hollow ellipsoid of revolution is silvered to form a mirror, the foci of the ellipsoid are optical conjugate foci. Prove that a paraboloidal mirror forms a perfect image of a parallel plane wave coming along its axis.

CHAPTER 2

SCHRÖDINGER'S EQUATION

Schrödinger, it is said, was asked to report on de Broglie's theories in the colloquium at Zurich, where he was a professor at the time. De Broglie's arguments had been largely qualitative, of the sort outlined in the preceding chapter, though buttressed by more use of relativistic mechanics than we employed. Schrödinger, however, was a mathematical physicist well acquainted with the mathematics of vibrating media, and he was in the habit of expressing such problems by means of wave equations. With this background he was led quite unambiguously and simply to the equation which bears his name; and when he started to solve it, he found that the results of Bohr's theory of the hydrogen atom, the theory of the linear oscillator, and the other problems of quantum mechanics to which he applied it, came out as simple and elegant results. His equation has been similarly tested by problems of successively greater and greater difficulty, and it has emerged successfully from each such test. Its only limitations seem to come in connection with problems of quantum electrodynamics and relativity, and there the difficult features seem to come from the electrodynamics and relativity rather than from the mechanics. We seem to be justified in concluding that Schrödinger's formulation of wave mechanics in terms of a wave equation forms a fundamental law of nature, applying with great generality to quantum mechanics (and by a passage to the limit, to classical mechanics) in the same sort of general way in which Newton's laws of motion form the fundamental laws for classical mechanics, or Maxwell's equations those for electromagnetism. Most of the rest of our study, in fact, will consist of the application of Schrödinger's method to special problems.

2.1. The Nature of Wave Equations. The simplest wave equation which we meet in physics arises from the problem of the vibrating string. Let the transverse displacement of a string from its undisplaced position be ψ, a function of x (the distance along the string) and t (the time). Then we consider an element of length of the string dx, and apply Newton's equation $f = ma$ to this element, where f is the force, m the mass, a the acceleration. The force arises on account of the fact that the tension T in the string will be acting in different directions on the two ends of the element dx. Thus the transverse component of the tension force

31

is approximately $T \, \partial\psi/\partial x$, as shown in Fig. 2.1.1.   At the point $x + dx$, this component is $T \, \partial\psi/\partial x$ as computed at the point $x + dx$; but at the point x there is a force of the opposite sign, $-T \, \partial\psi/\partial x$, where the derivative is now to be computed at the point x.   The sum of these two gives a total transverse force, and it can be written approximately $T(\partial^2\psi/\partial x^2)dx$. This force must be equal to the mass times the acceleration.   If μ is the

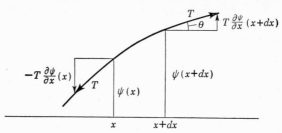

Fig. 2.1.1.   Tensions on an element of string.   Vertical component at $x + dx$ is T sin θ. If we approximate sin θ by tan θ, this is $T \, \partial\psi/\partial x$, computed at $x + dx$. Similarly, at x the vertical component is $-T \, \partial\psi/\partial x$, computed at x.

mass per unit length, the mass of element dx is $\mu \, dx$.   The acceleration is $\partial^2\psi/\partial t^2$.   Thus we have the equation

$$T\frac{\partial^2\psi}{\partial x^2} = \mu \frac{\partial^2\psi}{\partial t^2}. \tag{2.1.1}$$

This is the wave equation for the vibrating string.

Ordinarily we are interested in solutions of (2.1.1) which vary sinusoidally with the time, so that ψ depends on time through a factor sin ωt, where ω is an angular frequency; thus let $\psi = u(x)$ sin ωt, where u gives the dependence on x.   In this case $\partial^2\psi/\partial t^2$ equals $-\omega^2\psi$, and (2.1.1) may be rewritten, canceling out the time dependence, in the form

$$\frac{d^2u}{dx^2} + \omega^2 \frac{\mu}{T} u = 0. \tag{2.1.2}$$

Equation (2.1.2) is now the equation for a sinusoidal oscillation:

$$u = \sin 2\pi x/\lambda,$$

where λ is the wave length, given by

$$\frac{2\pi}{\lambda} = \omega \sqrt{\frac{\mu}{T}}. \tag{2.1.3}$$

Thus we may rewrite (2.1.2) in the form

$$\frac{d^2u}{dx^2} + \left(\frac{2\pi}{\lambda}\right)^2 u = 0. \tag{2.1.4}$$

This is a standard form of the wave equation with the time eliminated. Similar equations hold in many other branches of physics: in problems of wave propagation in electrical lines, in acoustics, and in the vibrations of membranes, solids, electromagnetic cavities, and so on. In cases where the medium extends through two or three dimensions, as a membrane or a solid, u is a function of x and y, or of x, y, and z, and the second derivative d^2u/dx^2 has to be replaced by the sum of the two or three partial derivatives of u with respect to x, y, and z, symbolized by the expression $\nabla^2 u$, called the Laplacian of u.

The wave equation (2.1.4) is the simple case holding when the properties of the string, or more generally, of the medium, do not vary from point to point. The more general case is that in which the properties, and hence the wave length, depend on position. It is clearly this case which we must use to set up a wave equation for the de Broglie waves. We find a hint as to how to proceed from the form (2.1.2) of the wave equation. Suppose the density μ of the string varied from point to point. Then the wave length as defined by (2.1.3) would vary with position. But we see that (2.1.4) will still preserve the same form, provided only we define λ to be a suitable function of x, by Eq. (2.1.3). This same equation, then, is the appropriate one for a wave length varying with position; but then, since λ can be any arbitrary function of x, it becomes a differential equation of much greater mathematical difficulty, an equation which can be solved analytically only in certain specially simple cases. It is this general form, however, which we encounter in setting up Schrödinger's equation.

2.2. The Formulation of Schrödinger's Equation. We now have enough mathematical background to be able to retrace the path, really a very simple one, by which Schrödinger was led to his wave equation. Suppose we have a particle of mass m, moving along the x axis subject to a force whose potential energy is $V(x)$. We can then proceed, just as we did in the discussion of the linear oscillator in Sec. 1.2, to find the momentum, and hence the wave length, at every point of the path, by use of the energy equation. The conservation of energy states that E, the total energy, equals $mv^2/2 + V$, or $p^2/2m + V$. Thus we have

$$p = \sqrt{2m(E - V)}. \tag{2.2.1}$$

But de Broglie's hypothesis states that $p = h/\lambda$, and we thus have the wave length which must be substituted in (2.1.4) to get the wave equation. Substituting (2.2.1) in (2.1.4), we have at once

$$\frac{d^2u}{dx^2} + \frac{8\pi^2 m}{h^2}(E - V)u = 0. \tag{2.2.2}$$

Equation (2.2.2), where V is an appropriate function of x (different of course for each problem), is Schrödinger's equation. In case the particle is capable of moving in three dimensions rather than one, as of course is usually the case, (2.2.2) is to be replaced by

$$\nabla^2 u + \frac{8\pi^2 m}{h^2}(E - V)u = 0, \tag{2.2.3}$$

where the Laplacian $\nabla^2 u$ is as defined above, and where now V is a function of x, y, and z. Such an equation, with an arbitrary V, is a partial differential equation of a type which is very hard indeed to solve, though some general properties of it can be stated. In the rest of this chapter we shall state some qualitative and quantitative results about the solutions of Schrödinger's equation, and about their relations to problems in atomic and molecular structure.

2.3. The WKB Type of Solution and the Quantum Condition. There are a few special but important cases in which Schrödinger's equation (2.2.2) or (2.2.3) can be solved exactly, some of which we shall take up in detail later. Examples are the linear oscillator, the hydrogen atom, the particle in one dimension in a potential field where the potential energy has one constant value for certain ranges of x, another value for another range of x, and so on, and the particle in three dimensions in a potential well, such that the potential energy has one value through a spherical volume, another value outside this volume. We can go part way toward an analytic solution of the general central field problem, in which the potential energy is an arbitrary function of the distance r from an attracting center. But beyond these simple cases, there are hardly any important soluble cases. We can get much more insight into the solutions of general cases, and even of these analytically soluble problems, by an approximate solution called the WKB method (abbreviation for the names of Wentzel, Kramers, and Brillouin, who separately suggested it, as in fact several other people also did). This method is very closely related to the quantum condition, which we have discussed in the preceding chapter. It is readily applied only to the one-dimensional case of Eq. (2.2.2).

The idea behind the WKB method, which is a method applicable to any problem of wave propagation in a medium where the wave length depends on position, is that if the wave length varies only slowly with position, the wave function u in a restricted range of coordinates will be very similar to what would be found if the wave length were constant and equal to the average value through the range considered. We already know from Sec. 2.1 that such a solution is a sinusoidal oscillation, similar to $\sin 2\pi x/\lambda$, where λ is the local value of wave length. Such a solution really has three parameters determining its character: the wave length, the amplitude (which we have not included in the sine function above), and the phase (which we should have included above if we had combined a sine and a cosine function). The WKB method assumes that the wave function can be written approximately in a form of a sinusoidal function with the amplitude, as well as the wave length, varying appropriately with position. It operates by substituting such a function in Schrödinger's equation (2.2.2), and finding the differential equations obeyed by the amplitude and wave length. Such differential equations are set up in Appendix 6. It then proves to be possible to state very simple rules telling how these quantities must vary with x, provided the relative change of wave length is small in a distance of one wave length.

The result of the WKB method is that u, the solution of (2.2.2), can be written approximately in the form

$$u = \frac{A}{\sqrt{p}} \sin\left(\frac{2\pi}{h} \int p\,dx + \alpha\right), \qquad (2.3.1)$$

where p is to be determined from (2.2.1) as a function of x, and where A, α are arbitrary constants; there must be two arbitrary constants, in order to get the general solution of the second-order differential equation (2.2.2). Let us now examine the interpretation of this solution and see why it is reasonable. First, the quantity $(2\pi/h)\int p\,dx + \alpha$ increases in a distance dx by the amount $(2\pi/\lambda)dx$, the correct increment for a sine function of wave length λ; thus (2.3.1) correctly is associated with the wave length varying with position which we have already assumed. As for the amplitude, proportional to $1/\sqrt{p}$, the interpretation is simple. We shall find that, as usual with wave motions, the intensity is proportional to the square of the amplitude or to $1/p$, or inversely proportional to the velocity of the classical particle. But from the statistical interpretation of the preceding chapter we expect the intensity of the de Broglie wave to be proportional to the probability of finding the particle at the point in question. If we had a classical particle traveling along the x axis subject to certain forces, the length of time it would be found in a distance dx would be simply dx/v, where v was its velocity, and we should assume that, with a statistical collection of particles, the probability of finding a particle in a given range dx would be proportional to the length of time which any one particle would spend in this range. Thus we see that the inverse proportionality between the intensity of the de Broglie wave and the velocity correctly leads to this classical relationship.

We may now examine the relationship between (2.3.1) and the quantum condition. The general form of relation is clear. If the variable x measured distance along a closed path, such as a circle, it would be clear that the sine function would have to come back to the same value after a complete rotation that it had before the rotation.   Thus the increase in phase $(2\pi/h)\int p\,dx + \alpha$ in a complete rotation would have to be an integral multiple of 2π.   This would lead just to the condition $\oint p\,dx = nh$, already met as the quantum condition in Eq. (1.2.1), and this as a matter of fact is the simple case considered in the derivation of that equation. However, usually we do not have this simple case.   A much more typical example is the linear oscillator, where the classical particle would vibrate back and forth, being reflected by the repulsive force at each end of its

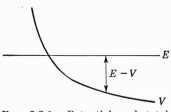

FIG. 2.3.1. Potential and total energy for reflection.

path.   It is not clear in this case just what is the range of x over which the integration should be performed, or just what is the quantum-mechanical mechanism corresponding to the classical reflection at the end of the path.   We shall now examine this question a little more in detail and shall find that it results in a small modification of the quantum condition as previously stated.

Let us suppose that we have a potential energy varying as in Fig. 2.3.1, and a motion with a total energy E as shown.   Classically, the particle with energy E in this field would travel to the left with negative momentum, slowing up gradually as the difference $E - V$ decreased, until finally when $E = V$ it would come to rest, since the kinetic energy would be zero.   It would then reverse, start back to the right, and travel off indefinitely to the right.   This is a classical picture of a reflection.   Now let us see how we get a picture of the same thing according to wave mechanics, using the approximation (2.3.1).   We observe that in the motion where the kinetic energy is positive, and where the classical motion occurs, p is real; but it decreases, and consequently the wave length increases, as does the amplitude, as we approach the turning point of the classical motion.   On the other hand, in the region where V is larger than E, and the kinetic energy as computed classically would be negative, so that the classical motion does not occur, p becomes imaginary.   This still leaves us with a perfectly valid solution, using the approximation (2.3.1). For we remember that $\sin iw$, where $i = \sqrt{-1}$, is equal to $(i/2)(e^w - e^{-w})$, and $\cos iw$ equals $(\frac{1}{2})(e^w + e^{-w})$.   Thus the sine function of (2.3.1) goes into a combination of the exponentials $\exp \pm[(2\pi/h)\int \sqrt{2m(V - E)}\,dx]$, which are real exponentials, increasing or decreasing with increasing x. Similarly the amplitude, proportional to $1/\sqrt{p}$, can be rewritten to be proportional to $(V - E)^{-\frac{1}{4}}$ by using a complex value for the constant A of (2.3.1), so that this is likewise real.   The net result, then, is that in the region where no classical motion occurs, to the left of the turning point of the classical motion in Fig. 2.3.1, we have these two exponential solutions; to the right of the turning point we have a sinusoidal function with arbitrary phase and amplitude. Each of these combinations of functions has two arbitrary constants, and somehow we must fit together the solutions in the two regions and determine the arbitrary constants.

As far as the fitting together is concerned, it is a rather complicated problem in complex function theory to describe how to do it analytically. The solution (2.3.1) becomes indeterminate just at the point where the E and V curves cross; for at that point p becomes zero, and we have zeros both in the numerator and denominator of (2.3.1). Thus we cannot use the solution (2.3.1), of either the sinusoidal or the exponential type, quite up to the joining point. On the other hand, going back to the differential equation (2.2.2), we see that when $E = V$ this becomes simply $d^2u/dx^2 = 0$, showing that the curve of u against x becomes a straight line, so that all we have to do is to join our two curves by a straight-line interpolation. The more elaborate theory which we have mentioned tells us just how to make this interpolation, and in particular it tells us just what will be the phase and amplitude of the sinusoidal function to join onto any arbitrary combination of increasing and decreasing exponentials, or vice versa. When we have carried out this joining properly and drawn smooth curves to connect the two types of functions, so that we have really good approximations to solutions of Schrödinger's equation, the resulting family of solutions will resemble those shown in Fig. 2.3.2. Here we have drawn a family of curves corresponding to different values of the phase of the oscillatory part of the solution, each curve joining properly onto an exponential portion. We have not shown the variation produced by the second arbitrary constant; this simply changes the vertical scale of each curve by an arbitrary amount.

When we look at this family of curves, we observe the interesting feature that almost all of them increase without limit as we move into the region to the left, where the classical motion would not penetrate. The reason is that the solutions have some of the exponential increasing to the left, as well as the exponential decreasing to the left. Now when we remember the interpretation of the de Broglie wave, we realize that it is only the function decreasing exponentially to the left which is appropriate for our use; all other functions would correspond to the assumption that the particle was infinitely likely to be found at infinite distance to the left, where the amplitude of the wave is infinite. Thus we see that when we have a repulsive barrier like the one we are considering, we are automatically limited to a single function (apart from the vertical scale, which is unimportant), which has a quite definite phase in the region where the

classical motion occurs.   This particular curve is the center one in Fig.
2.3.2.   We observe that the sine curve occurring to the right of the classical turning point is not headed precisely to zero at this turning point,
since it joins onto the decreasing exponential.   As a matter of fact, the
more exact theory which we have mentioned earlier shows that, to a good

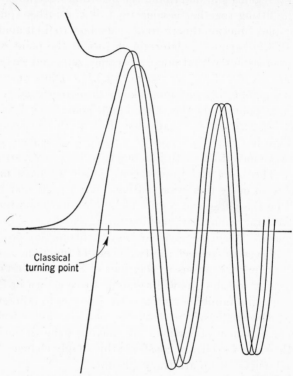

Classical
turning point

FIG. 2.3.2.   Joining of exponential and sinusoidal functions at classical turning point
of orbit, with different phases.

approximation, it is as if one used up one-eighth of a wave length to the
left of the classical turning point.

We can now consider a problem in which the classical motion would
have two turning points, as with the linear oscillator.   There will be a
boundary condition of the type we have considered at each turning point:
the phase of the oscillation, in the region where the classical motion would
occur, will be set by the condition that the wave function must go to zero
at infinity in each direction.   In general, however, these two conditions
will be inconsistent with each other.   They will be consistent only if a
single oscillatory solution satisfies the two conditions simultaneously,

having an eighth of a wave length extending outside of the classical region of motion on each end.   If x_1 and x_2 are the two turning points, the number of wave lengths between these two points is $\int_{x_1}^{x_2} (p/h)dx$, and the number of half wave lengths is twice as great.   Our condition is then that the number of half wave lengths between x_1 and x_2, plus a quarter wave length to account for the two ends (or half of a half wave length), must be an integer.   That is,

$$2 \int_{x_1}^{x_2} \frac{p}{h}\, dx + \frac{1}{2} = \text{integer,}$$

$$2 \int_{x_1}^{x_2} p\, dx = (n + \tfrac{1}{2})h, \qquad n = 0, 1, 2, \ldots \tag{2.3.2}$$

This is like the quantum condition (1.2.1), only using half integers instead of integers; for twice the integral of $p\, dx$ from x_1 to x_2 is the integral around the complete cycle, as in Chap. 1.

It is now an interesting fact that our quantum condition (2.3.2), though it is derived from the WKB method, which is only approximately correct, nevertheless gives exactly correct values for energy levels for several important problems, in particular for the linear oscillator and the hydrogen atom.   The wave functions determined by the WKB method, however, are only approximate, as is clear from the fact that that analytical formula breaks down at the turning point of the classical orbit. Nevertheless it is still capable of giving rather good approximations in actual cases, and it is often very useful.

2.4. The Linear Oscillator.   We shall now discuss several examples of the solution of Schrödinger's equation, chosen to give us a qualitative understanding of different types of results actually met in problems of the structure of matter.   The first example which we shall take is the linear oscillator, already taken up by elementary methods in Sec. 1.2. Here we have a turning point at each end of the path, and the arguments of the preceding section hold for it, so that the quantum condition is as in (2.3.2).   The phase integral $\oint p\, dx$ has been computed in Sec. 1.2; thus, using the half quantum numbers from (2.3.2), and comparing with (1.2.13), we see that the correct energy levels are given by

$$E = (n + \tfrac{1}{2})h\nu_0, \tag{2.4.1}$$

where ν_0 is the frequency of mechanical oscillation.   As we have stated in the preceding paragraph, this is a case where the WKB method gives exactly the correct energy levels, as determined by the complete analytical solution.   The exact solution is not hard to set up, however, and on account of its value in showing the general nature of analytical solutions of Schrödinger's equation and the importance of the problem of the linear oscillator in later applications, such as the mechanical vibrations of atoms in molecules and solids, we shall show how this exact solution is obtained.

The potential energy of a particle moving with simple harmonic motion with natural frequency ν_0, in classical mechanics, is $V = 2\pi^2\nu_0^2mx^2$. Schrödinger's equation then is

$$\frac{d^2u}{dx^2} + \frac{8\pi^2m}{h^2}(E - 2\pi^2\nu_0^2mx^2)u = 0. \tag{2.4.2}$$

We can remove the various dimensional quantities by making a change of scale, letting $y = 2\pi\sqrt{m\nu_0/h}\ x$. Then (2.4.2) becomes

$$\frac{d^2u}{dy^2} + \left(\frac{2E}{h\nu_0} - y^2\right)u = 0. \tag{2.4.3}$$

The term in y^2 can be eliminated by letting $u = e^{-y^2/2}v$, where v is a function of y. If we make this substitution in (2.4.3), expressing the derivative of u in terms of the derivatives of v, we find that

$$\frac{d^2v}{dy^2} - 2y\frac{dv}{dy} + \left(\frac{2E}{h\nu_0} - 1\right)v = 0. \tag{2.4.4}$$

Equation (2.4.4) has one very simple solution: if $2E/h\nu_0 = 1$, or

$$E = (\tfrac{1}{2})h\nu_0,$$

we can set v equal to a constant and (2.4.4) is satisfied. This is, as a matter of fact, the solution for the ground state of the linear oscillator. The energy is the value given by setting $n = 0$ in (2.4.1), and the wave function is simply $e^{-y^2/2}$. For the higher levels, however, we must look for solutions of (2.4.4) corresponding to different values of the energy E.

We can get the general solution of (2.4.4) by expanding v as a power series in y and determining the coefficients of this expansion, a standard method of attack on such differential equations. If we assume

$$v = A_0 + A_1y + A_2y^2 + \cdots,$$

we can differentiate the series to obtain the derivatives needed in (2.4.4), substitute in that equation, and combine terms in the same power of y. The resulting equation can be written in the form

$$\sum_{n=0}^{\infty}\left[(n+2)(n+1)A_{n+2} + \left(\frac{2E}{h\nu_0} - 1 - 2n\right)A_n\right]y^n = 0. \tag{2.4.5}$$

This is a power series in y which must be equal to zero for every value of

y if (2.4.4) is to be satisfied. But no power series can equal zero for all values of the argument unless all its coefficients are zero. Hence each of the expressions in brackets in (2.4.5) must be separately zero. This gives us an equation for A_{n+2} in terms of A_n. If we assume values for A_0 and A_1 [the two arbitrary constants which we must have in the general solution of a second order differential equation like (2.4.4)], we can then determine all the other A's from these, and we have the complete solution of (2.4.4) in power-series form.

The resulting function is not of elementary form; if it had been, we should have been able to solve (2.4.4) directly, without resorting to power-series expansion. However, we can investigate behavior for very large values of y, and this is important to our problem, because this is the region of negative kinetic energy, where we hope that the solution will be decreasing exponentially. We can, in fact, find by application of the WKB method just how we expect the function to behave for large values of x or of y. For large x, where the potential energy is much greater than E, we can neglect E compared with it, and we then find $p = i \sqrt{4\pi^2 m^2 \nu_0^2 x^2} = 2\pi i m \nu_0 x$. Then the exponential term arising from the WKB approximation (2.3.1) is $\exp \pm (2\pi/h)(\pi m \nu_0 x^2) = \exp \pm y^2/2$. The decreasing exponential has just the form which we have already assumed when we set $u = e^{-y^2/2}v$; one way of seeing that that is a sensible change of variables is by consideration of the limiting form of the function for large y by means of the WKB method, just as we have done here. But we must expect that most solutions, for most energy values, will behave like the increasing exponential, for we know that it is only for the stationary states, satisfying the quantum conditions, that we have only the decreasing exponential. Thus we must infer that v generally will behave like e^{y^2} for large y values, so as to make u behave like $e^{y^2/2}$. Let us see if this is in fact the case.

If we express the function e^{y^2} in power series, we may write it

$$e^{y^2} = \sum_{n=0,2,4,\ldots} \frac{1}{(n/2)!} y^n, \qquad (2.4.6)$$

where we have expressed it as a series over even integers n. If we let the coefficient $1/(n/2)!$ of the term in y^n be B_n, we see that

$$B_{n+2} = \frac{B_n}{(n+2)/2}, \quad \text{or} \quad (n+2)B_{n+2} - 2B_n = 0. \quad (2.4.7)$$

But this recursion formula for the B_n's is just the same that we should get for the A_n's from (2.4.5), if we had such a large value of n that $2E/h\nu_0$ could be neglected in comparison with n; for then we could approximately write the condition (2.4.5) in the form

$$(n + 2)(n + 1)A_{n+2} - 2(n + 1)A_n = 0,$$

which is equivalent to (2.4.7). As far as the terms of high power of n are concerned then, the function v is equivalent to e^{y^2}. But at very large y values it is these terms that are important. Hence in the limit of large y, we see that our function v does in fact approach e^{y^2}, if it is expressed in power series, and the function u approaches $e^{y^2/2}$.

We must now ask how this situation can be avoided, so that u will in fact behave like $e^{-y^2/2}$ at infinity, rather than like $e^{y^2/2}$. There is only one possible answer: the power series for v must not have any terms corresponding to large n values. This can be accomplished only if the series breaks off somewhere and is only a polynomial, instead of an infinite series. We have already seen one example of this in the solution for the ground state, for which v is a constant. If it were a polynomial whose highest term was in y^n, with n a definite integer, the behavior of u for very large values of y would be like the function $y^n e^{-y^2/2}$, and the exponential makes the function decrease so strongly for large y's that even this function goes to zero as y approaches infinity, in spite of the factor y^n. But we can now see easily from (2.4.5) how to make the series for v break off after the nth term. If we set $2E/h\nu_0 - 1 - 2n = 0$, or

$$E = (n + \tfrac{1}{2})h\nu_0, \qquad (2.4.8)$$

then we see from (2.4.5) that $A_{n+2} = 0$, and from that $A_{n+4} = 0$, $A_{n+6} = 0$, and so on. In other words, if n is even, all the even terms beyond that in y^n will be zero, or if n is odd, all the odd terms beyond that in y^n will be zero. Let us then choose $A_1 = 0$ (if n is even) or $A_0 = 0$ (if n is odd), so that v will have only even or only odd terms respectively, and we shall find a polynomial for v, so that the function u will go exponentially to zero as y becomes infinite. These are the wave functions of the problem; from (2.4.5) we can get the recursion formula to set up the coefficients of the polynomial in terms of A_0 or A_1; and the energy levels, as given by (2.4.8), are those already found from the quantum condition as given by the WKB method.

We have given the solution in this much detail, so as to make clear the analytical method by which the boundary conditions at large values of x, or in the region of negative kinetic energy, are taken care of in an exact analytic solution of Schrödinger's equation. Other soluble cases show very similar behavior. We now have found how to get the analytic solution, and in Fig. 2.4.1 we give wave functions corresponding to several values of n. We see the way in which the wave function for a given value of n has essentially $n - 1$ half wave lengths in the whole range of the variable or has n nodes (points where $u = 0$). Furthermore, for the case of large n value which we have included, we see how the amplitude of the oscillation and the wave length both increase as we approach the turning point of the classical motion, in agreement with

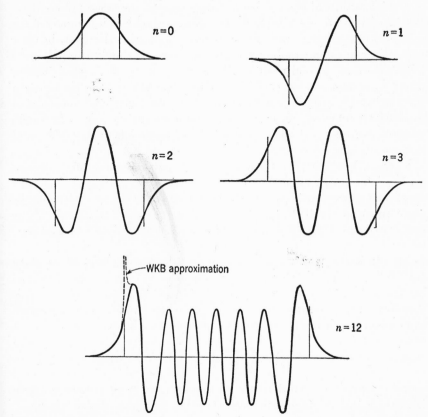

Fig. 2.4.1.   Wave functions for the linear oscillator.   Vertical lines show classical turning points.

the requirements of the WKB approximation (2.3.1). For comparison, we show in this case the behavior of the WKB approximate solution. We see that it agrees well with the exact solution, except in the neighborhood of the classical turning point, where it diverges as we approach this point from either side.

2.5. Problems with Potential Discontinuities.   The case of the linear oscillator, which we have just discussed, is a good example of a problem in which there is a classical turning point of the motion, outside which the kinetic energy gradually becomes more and more negative.   Another class of problems of great importance, and easily soluble, is the class in which the potential energy has a discontinuity at certain points, so that it can well be that the kinetic energy is positive on one side of such a discontinuity, negative on the other side.   In such cases, the momentum, or wave length, will change discontinuously, and the assumptions of the WKB method are not applicable, for that method is suitable only if the change of wave length in one wave length is small.   However, in these cases, we can adopt another method of solution, simple to apply, and leading to many useful results.   We solve Schrödinger's equation separately in the regions on each side of the discontinuity; for instance, if the potential is constant on each side, we shall simply have sinusoidal or exponential functions on each side.   Then we satisfy boundary conditions of continuity at the discontinuity of potential.   Let us see what these conditions are.

In the first place, it is obvious that we wish the wave function u to join continuously across the discontinuity of potential.   The second condition, which is not quite so obvious, is that the first derivative of the wave function must be continuous.   Let us see why this must be the case.   We can see this by approaching the discontinuous potential by a limiting process, first letting the potential change very rapidly but at a finite rate from one value to the other in a small but finite distance along x, then letting this distance decrease to zero so that the jump of potential becomes discontinuous.   When the change is in a distance Δx, let us assume that we can set up the exact solution of Schrödinger's equation by some means.   We then know that within the range Δx, we have

$$\frac{d^2u}{dx^2} = \left(\frac{8\pi^2 m}{h^2}\right)(V - E)u,$$

a finite quantity, which does not go to infinity as Δx is reduced to zero. Let us integrate this expression over the range Δx; we have then

$$\left(\frac{du}{dx}\right)_{x+\Delta x} - \left(\frac{du}{dx}\right)_x = \frac{8\pi^2 m}{h^2} \int_x^{x+\Delta x} (V - E)u \, dx. \qquad (2.5.1)$$

As Δx goes to zero, the integrand on the right stays finite, and the range of integration goes to zero; thus the right side of (2.5.1) goes to zero.   But we see that this is simply the change in first derivative of the function as we go across the discontinuity of potential; hence in the limit there is no change in first derivative, or the first derivative is continuous.

If then we know the solution of Schrödinger's equation on one side of a discontinuity of potential, we use its value and the value of its first derivative to determine the values of these quantities in the solution on the other side of the discontinuity.   Since two arbitrary constants are enough to determine a solution of a second order differential equation uniquely, we see how to join solutions across such a discontinuity.   We also see that, since a solution of Schrödinger's equation in a region of constant potential is a sinusoidal or exponential function, we have the means of getting analytical solutions for any problem in which the potential is made up of a number of constant regions, separated by discontinuities.   It is fortunately possible to approximate almost any type of potential function in this simple way, and as a result, we can get analytic solutions, approximating to a fair degree of accuracy, to many more complicated problems.   We shall now take up some of these special cases which are important in pointing out interesting characteristics of problems of physical importance.

An easily soluble problem of great practical importance is that of a free particle in a box with infinitely rigid walls.   That is, we let the potential V be zero within the box, infinitely great outside it, so that there would be no forces acting on a particle within the box, but an infinitely great repulsion opposing the particle if it tried to escape.   First we shall take the one-dimensional case, where the box extends along the x axis from $x = 0$ to $x = a$, so that the potential is zero in this range, infinite outside it; then we shall extend to the three-dimensional case.   Outside the box, since V is infinite, the solution is made up of an increasing and a decreasing exponential, the decreasing exponential falling infinitely rapidly to zero.   That is, the wave function u must be zero everywhere outside the box and hence must vanish on the boundary.   Hence the boundary condition on the solution within the box is simply that it vanish at the end of the box.   The wave function within the box is simply a sine function, and the quantum condition is simply the statement that a, the dimension of the box, must be an integral number of half wave lengths, so that the boundary condition of the vanishing of the wave function can be set up at each boundary.   The quantum condition is then $n = 2a/\lambda$, which, when we remember that the energy in this case is wholly kinetic, leads at once to

$$ E = \frac{n^2h^2}{8ma^2}, \tag{2.5.2} $$

where m is the mass of the particle.   If we have the three-dimensional problem, a particle in a box whose dimensions along the x, y, z axes are a, b, c, then we must have a standing wave of the form $\sin 2\pi x/\lambda_x$ $\sin 2\pi y/\lambda_y \sin 2\pi z/\lambda_z$, where λ_x, λ_y, λ_z have separate quantization, with quantum numbers n_x, n_y, n_z. If we substitute this wave function into Schrödinger's equation (2.2.3), we find at once that the energy is

$$E = \frac{h^2}{8m}\left(\frac{n_x^2}{a^2} + \frac{n_y^2}{b^2} + \frac{n_z^2}{c^2}\right),\tag{2.5.3}$$

where n_x, n_y, n_z are integers. This result will be very useful later in connection with the problem of electrons in a metal. It is a fairly good approximation to this problem to treat the electrons as being free so long as they are within the metal, but with a barrier at the surface preventing them from leaving, so that we have essentially the problem of the present paragraph.

A problem with applications to various more complicated cases, and

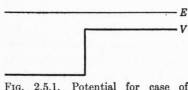

FIG. 2.5.1. Potential for case of reflection.

with a close optical analogy, is that of a particle in a potential having one constant value to the left of a transition and another value to the right, as in Fig. 2.5.1. This corresponds to the optical case where a wave falls from a medium with one index of refraction on a medium with another index. We know in the optical case that in general part of the incident wave will be reflected, part refracted. The same thing happens in the present problem. If the incident wave approaches from the left, then we can build up a solution of Schrödinger's equation by superposing the following waves: a wave approaching from the left, one traveling away to the right in the right-hand region, and a reflected wave traveling to the left in the left-hand region. The wave lengths of these are determined by Schrödinger's equation, once the energy is assumed. Thus the incident and reflected waves are in a region where the potential energy is zero, so that they are given by $\frac{\sin}{\cos}(2\pi/h)(\sqrt{2mE}\,x)$. In order to express the fact that we are dealing with a progressive, rather than a standing, wave, we must in fact use exponential rather than sinusoidal forms for the functions above, as we shall describe more in detail in the next chapter. Thus if the time part of the wave function is the exponential $e^{i\omega t}$, a wave traveling to the right will be expressed in the form

$$\psi = e^{i\omega t}e^{-2\pi i x/\lambda} = e^{i(\omega t - 2\pi x/\lambda)} = e^{i\omega t}e^{-(2\pi i/h)\sqrt{2mE}x},\tag{2.5.4}$$

where ψ is the wave function including the time. The reason for this exponential form is well known from all types of wave motion, in which we can write the function representing a wave traveling to the right with velocity v as $e^{i\omega(t-x/v)}$, a function which obviously remains constant if

$x = vt +$ constant, or if we travel along with the velocity v of the wave. Thus from (2.5.4) our wave function u for the wave traveling to the right is of the form $\exp(-2\pi i/h)(\sqrt{2mE}\,x)$, which is of course a linear combination of the sine and cosine functions which we have previously employed. In the same way a wave traveling to the left has a positive sign in the exponential.

We can then build up the superposition of direct and reflected wave in the left-hand medium (for $x < 0$) in the form

$$u = e^{-(2\pi i/h)(\sqrt{2mE}x)} + Re^{(2\pi i/h)(\sqrt{2mE}x)}, \qquad (2.5.5)$$

where we have assumed that the first term, the direct wave, has unit amplitude, and the second term, the reflected wave, has amplitude R, to be determined, R being then a reflection coefficient. Similarly, for the right-hand medium, where we have only a transmitted wave, we have

$$u = Te^{(-2\pi i/h)[\sqrt{2m(E-W)}x]}, \qquad (2.5.6)$$

where T is the amplitude of the transmitted wave, and W is the value of the potential energy for positive values of x. Our conditions that u and its first derivative must be continuous at $x = 0$ then are

$$1 + R = T$$

$$1 - R = \sqrt{\frac{E-W}{E}}\,T. \qquad (2.5.7)$$

When we solve for R and T, we then find

$$R = \frac{1 - \sqrt{(E-W)/E}}{1 + \sqrt{(E-W)/E}}, \qquad T = \frac{2}{1 + \sqrt{(E-W)/E}}. \qquad (2.5.8)$$

Thus we see that the magnitude of the reflection coefficient becomes greater, the greater W is in proportion to E. This is just similar to the case of optical reflection, where the reflection coefficient at a boundary between air and a refracting medium with index of refraction n has the value $(1-n)/(1+n)$, becoming greater the more n departs from unity.

The solution we have set up is for the case where E is greater than W, so that there is real propagation for positive values of x. The situation is different if the energy is so low that the particle in the right-hand region would have a negative kinetic energy. Then we have the exponential, rather than the sinusoidal, solution in this region, and by the same arguments used previously we must use only the decreasing exponential, rather than the sinusoidal, solution in this region. This situation is similar to that of total internal reflection in optics, and we find here, as there, that the amplitude of the reflected wave in the left-hand medium equals the amplitude of the incident wave, though there is a change of phase, the magnitude of the reflection coefficient being unity. To see this, we need only modify u in the right-hand medium to take on the value $T \exp(-2\pi/h)[\sqrt{2m(W-E)}\,x]$ in place of (2.5.6). The solution goes through just as before, leading to

$$R = \left[1 - i\sqrt{\frac{(W-E)}{E}}\right] \Big/ \left[1 + i\sqrt{\frac{(W-E)}{E}}\right]$$

in place of (2.5.8). But this value of R is the ratio of a complex number to its complex conjugate (that is, to the value obtained by changing the sign of i wherever it appears), and such a ratio is always a complex number whose magnitude is unity, though it has a phase different from zero, verifying our statement about the reflection in this case.

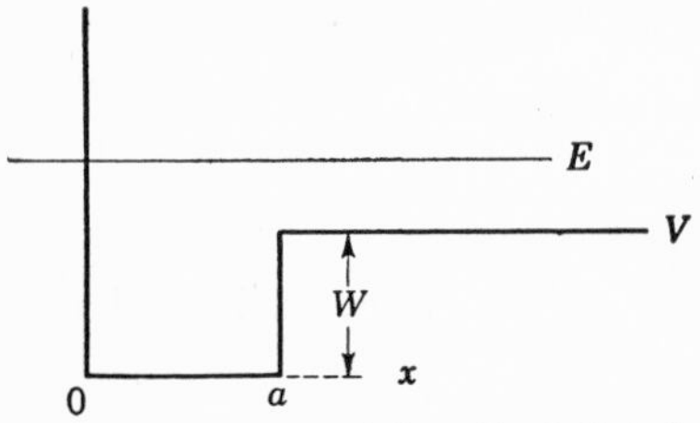

A case combining the one just discussed with the particle in a box is that shown in Fig. 2.5.2. In this case, the wave function must go to zero at the left boundary of the box, so that it must start out as a sine curve. At the right boundary, however, we have a situation similar to that of the reflection case above. To get a solution, we assume a sinusoidal function to the right, with arbitrary amplitude and phase, and determine this amplitude and phase by the condition that the function and its derivative must be continuous at $x = a$. We now find very different situations, depending on whether E is greater than W (so that the kinetic energy is real, and the wave function sinusoidal, to the right of $x = a$), or less than W (so that the wave function is exponentially decreasing to the right of $x = a$). In the first case we have a solution for any value of the energy E. We have what is called a continuous spectrum. Motion is possible, then, in which the particle approaches from the right with any arbitrary energy and is reflected, returning to the right again. In this case it is obvious that the amplitude of the reflected wave, for $x > a$, must equal that of the incident wave, for there is nothing for the particle to do except to be reflected. Thus the solution for $x > a$ is a sum of complex exponentials representing waves traveling to left and to right with equal amplitudes, and such a sum can always be written as a sinusoidal function, unlike the case of the reflection problem of Fig. 2.5.1.

On the other hand, if the energy E is less than W, we have stationary states and discrete energy levels; for it is only for discrete energies that

FIG. 2.5.2. Potential well, infinitely high wall on left, finite potential on right.

the wave length in the region between $x = 0$ and $x = a$ will be right to allow the wave function to be zero at $x = 0$ and to join onto the exponential at $x = a$. We could, if we chose, set up a quantum condition, though on account of the discontinuous break in the potential at $x = a$ we could not use the WKB method. We can, however, set up the problem analytically and get an explicit solution. The lower wave functions and energy levels will not be far from those given in (2.5.2) for a constant potential region with infinitely high boundary walls. This problem is particularly interesting, in that it combines a continuous spectrum for higher energies with a discrete spectrum at lower energies. We shall see in subsequent chapters a number of very important practical examples of problems of this sort, in which the potential function differs from the one we have just drawn only in having the sharp corners of the curve rounded off, a change which does not affect the qualitative nature of the solution. Two of the applications are to the energy levels of an electron in an atom, in which the radial part of the motion has a potential curve of this sort, and in which we have both a line spectrum and a continuous

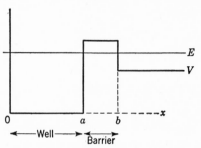

Fig. 2.5.3. Potential well, infinitely high wall on left, finite potential on right, with barrier between.

spectrum; and to the vibrations of a diatomic molecule, where the curve of potential energy as a function of distance of separation has this form, and where stable vibrations are possible for energies less than a certain critical value, while for higher energies the two particles fly apart and dissociate. It is only for the stable vibrations that the energy is quantized.

A still more complicated case, still capable of analytic solution by piecing sine curves together and demanding that the function and its first derivative be continuous, is shown in Fig. 2.5.3, with a high barrier between the potential well and the region of free motion. In such a case, the interesting problem comes for energies such as that shown, in which classically the motion could not extend over the barrier from one region to the other. In constructing the solution of Schrödinger's equation, we start at the left boundary, $x = 0$, with a sine function. When we reach the barrier, between $x = a$ and $x = b$, we must use both a decreasing and an increasing exponential to satisfy the boundary conditions at $x = a$. This combination of functions must then be joined, at $x = b$, to a sine function of the appropriate wave length, with amplitude and phase chosen to satisfy the boundary conditions. Such a solution can be set up in every case, and it will correspond to the case of a particle coming from the right, being reflected by the barrier, and returning to the right; or also a particle confined to the well, being reflected back and forth there. There will be certain energies for which a particle in the potential well would have stationary states, if the barrier were infinitely high, and others for which it would not. It proves to be true that in the first case the amplitude of the wave function within the well is much greater than outside the barrier, while in the second case it is much less. In any case, the amplitude is not zero within the barrier itself, so that there is some chance of finding the particle within the barrier.

This problem becomes much more interesting if, instead of dealing only with stationary states, we build up wave packets. When one examines Schrödinger's equation involving the time, which we have not yet done, one finds that the following procedure is allowed: to take each wave function corresponding to a given energy E, multiply it by a sinusoidal function of the time, with frequency ν given by de Broglie's relation $E = h\nu$, and add any number of such solutions, with appropriate phases and amplitudes. This process of addition is analogous to that which is carried out with vibrating strings, in which the general solution of the motion of a vibrating string is a superposition of all its possible overtone vibrations, each with its own frequency, and with arbitrary phases and amplitudes. Such a superposition is always necessary to produce a wave packet, or in fact any disturbance except one which is only a sinusoidal function of the time. We can now build up wave packets corresponding to certain initial conditions; examine the behavior of these packets as time goes on; and, as the different wave functions associated with different stationary states get out of step with each other on account of their different frequencies, deduce the way in which systems change with time.

In the present case, one possible circumstance which we might want to describe is that in which, at the initial time $t = 0$, the particle is known to be located within the potential well, with an energy which would correspond to a stationary state if the walls of the well were infinitely high. We can set up such a wave packet, by suitable superposition of wave functions of different energies. It will have large amplitude within the well, no amplitude outside it. But each of the wave functions of which it is composed has some amplitude outside the well, as well as within the barrier; the packet has no amplitude outside the well only because we arrange to have complete destructive interference of those parts of the wave functions to the right of the barrier. This interference becomes inoperative after a sufficiently long time, because the waves have different frequencies, and their phase relationships are eventually lost. The result is that, after a certain lapse of time, intensity begins to appear to the right of the barrier, and correspondingly the intensity within the well decreases. We interpret this as saying that particles can penetrate the barrier, even though classical mechanics says that it would be impenetrable. Calculation shows that the rate of penetration gets rapidly slower as the barrier becomes either wider or higher. This process of penetrating barriers is called the tunnel effect, and is an important nonclassical effect of quantum mechanics. It is encountered, among other places, in the theory of radioactive decay, where the potential energy of a nuclear particle is in some cases similar to the one we have just been considering. It is worth noting that the penetration of barriers works in the other

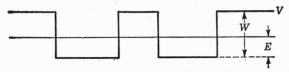

FIG. 2.5.4. Two equal potential wells, with barrier between.

direction, too: we can build up a wave packet corresponding to a particle approaching the barrier from the right, with no intensity within the well, and after a lapse of time intensity will be found within the well, corresponding to penetration of the barrier by the incoming particle. Furthermore, we find that if the energy corresponds to the approximately quantized energies within the well, the probability of penetrating is much greater than it is in other cases.

A final case, again involving penetration of barriers, is the case of a particle in two identical potential wells, separated by a barrier, as shown in Fig. 2.5.4. Here, since the particle is confined to a limited region of space, there will be real stationary states, and they will be close to the stationary states of a particle in a single potential well. An interesting fact now appears. Corresponding to each stationary state of a single well, there will be two for the problem of two wells, separated from each other by an energy difference which is smaller, the higher or wider the barrier between them, so that their energy levels finally coincide in the limit as the barrier gets infinitely high. The wave functions corresponding to these two energy levels are particularly interesting. They look as in Fig. 2.5.5: one is symmetrical, the other antisymmetrical, in the mid-point of the barrier. The antisymmetrical wave function corresponds to the higher energy (for it proves to be a general rule that, the more nodes or zeros a wave function has, the higher is its energy). This splitting of each energy level into two, with symmetrical and antisymmetrical wave functions, when the number of potential minima is doubled, is a general characteristic of all such problems of two potential minima, not confined to the particular potential function which we have in this case.   It is found, for instance, in the problem of the diatomic molecule composed of two identical atoms, in which the potential energy of an electron has minima at each atom, and in which there are both symmetric and antisymmetric wave functions, with slightly different energies.

Here, as in the preceding case of a single potential barrier, we have interesting results if we set up wave packets.   Let us superpose the symmetric and antisymmetric wave functions at a certain instant of time, with equal amplitudes.   Then the amplitude of the resultant wave function will be large in one of the potential wells, where the two functions have the same sign, and will be zero in the other well, where they are opposite to each other.   After a lapse of time, however, the two waves will have got opposite in phase, and the wave functions will reinforce on the other side of the barrier, so that we shall say that the particle has penetrated the barrier.   After another lapse of time it will have gone back to the original side and, in general, will oscillate between one side and the other. The frequency of this oscillation is the difference between the frequencies of the two waves, just as in the phenomenon of beats in acoustics.   Thus the closer the energies of the two states (that is, as we have seen, the higher or wider the barrier), the less frequent will be the oscillation of the particle from one side of the barrier to the other.   This example shows particularly simply the mathematical mechanisms behind the penetration of barriers by particles and the process of oscillation of a particle between different equivalent potential minima.   This process is often called resonating, since it occurs when the particle in either well would have the same natural, or resonant, frequency, and it furnishes the first example which we have seen of a process which proves to be of great importance in the theory of valence bonds and in many other cases.   We shall see later that a corresponding situation exists in the case of many identical potential minima, a situation which occurs in a crystalline solid; there, instead of having just two wave functions corresponding to almost identical energies, we have as many wave functions as there are identical potential minima.

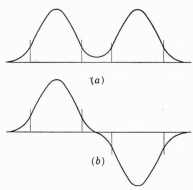

(a)

(b)

Fig. 2.5.5.   Symmetric and antisymmetric wave functions for problem of two equal potential wells.   Classical turning points shown by vertical lines.

PROBLEMS

1. Bessel's equation is

$$\frac{d^2y}{dx^2} + \frac{1}{x}\frac{dy}{dx} + \left(1 - \frac{m^2}{x^2}\right)y = 0.$$

Show that by making the change of variables $u = y\sqrt{x}$ the differential equation for u has the form of Schrödinger's equation (2.2.2). Use the WKB method to get an approximate solution for $J_m(x)$, the solution for Bessel's equation above.

2. Using the approximation of Prob. 1, compute approximate values of the functions J_0 and J_1 for a number of values of x, and show by a table of values how well these agree with the correct functions. Choose the arbitrary amplitude and phase factors to make the functions agree with the values of J_0 and J_1 in the tables, for example, making the zeros agree by adjusting the phase, and the maxima by adjusting the amplitude, taking such values as to get the best agreement possible for large x's.

3. Note that in Bessel's equation, when $m > 0$, there is a region near the origin where the WKB approximate solution is exponential rather than sinusoidal. Discuss the solution qualitatively for $x < m$, where m is fairly large, showing how this solution joins onto the sinusoidal one found in Prob. 1.

4. Compute and plot wave functions of the linear oscillator corresponding to $n = 0, 1, 2, 3, 4$. From the graphs find the region in which the solution is oscillatory (that is, the region between the points of inflection). Draw the potential curve and the values of E corresponding to these five stationary states, and show that the motion is oscillatory in the region where the kinetic energy is positive.

5. Set up the approximate solution for the linear-oscillator problem by the WKB method, getting expressions for the functions in both the sinusoidal and exponential ranges. Investigate to see how well these functions join on at the point of inflection.

6. Compute and plot the approximation of Prob. 5 corresponding to $n = 4$, and compare with the exact solution.

7. The potential energy in a Schrödinger problem equals zero for $-d < x < d$ and equals W for x outside this range. Set up the exact solution of Schrödinger's equation for $E < W$, and find the equation determining the stationary states. Devise a graphical method of solution for this transcendental equation, and use it to discuss the total number of stationary states for a given W and the limiting value of the energy of the lower states as W becomes large.

8. In the case of Prob. 7, show that there is always at least one stationary state, or quantized energy level, no matter how small W may be. What happens to the wave function and energy level of this lowest state in the limit as W goes to zero?

9. Find how many energy levels there are between energy E and $E + dE$ for the problem of electrons in a box of dimensions a, b, c. *Hint:* If the quantum numbers n_x, n_y, n_z are used as variables, there will be one state per unit volume in the space in which they are plotted. Hence the number of energy levels of energy less than E will equal the volume inside an energy surface corresponding to this value E. Find how many energy levels there are in a box 1 cm on a side, corresponding to energy less than 1 ev.

10. Find the stationary states of the problem of Fig. 2.5.2, for the case $E < W$, and see how they compare with the stationary states of a particle in a box with infinitely high potential barriers at both ends.

11. A particle moves in a potential, as shown in the accompanying figure, with an energy E so much less than W that $(2\pi/h)\sqrt{2m(W - E)}\,(x_2 - x_1)$ is large compared to unity. Show that the amplitude of the wave function in the region $0 < x < x_1$ is

small compared with that in the region $x_2 < x$, except in the special case where the energy is almost exactly equal to one of the energy levels of a particle confined by infinitely high barriers at $x = 0$ and $x = x_1$.

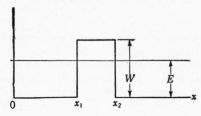

12. The potential energy in a Schrödinger problem is as shown in Fig. 2.5.4. Set up the exact solution of Schrödinger's equation for $E < W$, finding the equation determining the stationary states. For $E \ll W$, show that you can get approximate analytic solutions for the energies of the symmetric and antisymmetric wave functions. Show how the separation between the energies of symmetric and antisymmetric states decreases to zero as the barrier gets larger, either W or b becoming infinite.

13. In the case $E \ll W$ in Prob. 12, set up a solution which at $t = 0$ corresponds as closely as possible to the particle being in the left-hand potential well, with no probability that it is in the right-hand well. Investigate the beat phenomenon, finding after how long a time the particle will be found in the right-hand well. How does this time depend on the height and breadth of the barrier?

CHAPTER 3

AVERAGE VALUES AND MATRICES

In the preceding chapter we have seen how Schrödinger's equation is to be set up, and how it results in solutions which, in the case of motion which would be periodic according to classical mechanics, can be set up only for certain discrete values of the energy, which we interpret as the energy levels of the problem. We are now ready to look at Schrödinger's equation and its solutions in a rather broader manner. We recall that in Chap. 1 we have seen that the de Broglie wave had a statistical connection with the motion of particles. [Its intensity measured the probability of finding the particle at a given point.] We saw that we could set up waves which were in the form of wave packets, whose motion approximated the motion of classical particles. These packets, however, could not be too sharply localized in space; we were limited by the uncertainty principle. The stationary states and discrete energy levels were a result of standing de Broglie waves; but these formed only a part of the whole problem of interpreting wave mechanics. In the present chapter we consider the general question of the statistical relations between the wave function and the motion of particles, and related questions of average values of physical quantities. We look more closely into the nature of wave packets and their behavior, and the whole problem of the physical interpretation of wave functions. In connection with this, we encounter an interesting mathematical aspect of the problem, the relation of certain quantities to the matrices met in the study of algebra. The first step in our discussion will be to set up Schrödinger's equation in the form involving the time; for it is only this form of Schrödinger's equation which is general enough to form a foundation for the statistical theory.

3.1. Schrödinger's Equation Involving the Time. The ordinary wave equation of mathematical physics, like (2.1.1), involves a second time derivative; it is only when we assume that the function varies sinusoidally with the time that we can eliminate the time and get an equation like (2.1.2), or like our Schrödinger equation (2.2.2) or (2.2.3), which does not involve the time. We wish now to retrace this step, and try to find the appropriate Schrödinger equation involving the time. What we find, however, is that our equation is not analogous to (2.1.1) as far as its time dependence is concerned; further examination shows that we must set

55

up quite a different form of equation, involving a first rather than a second time derivative.   In this respect wave mechanics is a quite unique branch of mathematical physics.   Let us examine the reasons for this situation.

First we shall point out a remarkable relation between our Schrödinger equation (2.2.3), and the classical mechanics, which we have not so far mentioned.   One form of statement of the equations of motion of classical mechanics makes use of the Hamiltonian function, and this proves to be particularly closely related to quantum mechanics.   As we have already mentioned, the Hamiltonian function is simply the energy, expressed as a function of the coordinates and momenta of the problem.   Thus in rectangular coordinates the Hamiltonian function for a particle of mass m, moving in a potential field of potential energy V, a function of x, y, and z, is

$$H = \frac{1}{2m} (p_x^2 + p_y^2 + p_z^2) + V(x,y,z). \tag{3.1.1}$$

The expression of the law of conservation of energy is simply the equation $H = E$, where E, a constant, is the total energy; we have already used this equation to determine the momentum as a function of position and hence to find the de Broglie wave length as a function of position.

Now it was observed by Schrödinger that the wave equation can be formulated in the following fashion.   First, we replace p_x, p_y, p_z by differential operators, according to the following rule:

$$p_x \rightarrow \frac{h}{2\pi i} \frac{\partial}{\partial x}, \qquad p_y \rightarrow \frac{h}{2\pi i} \frac{\partial}{\partial y}, \qquad p_z \rightarrow \frac{h}{2\pi i} \frac{\partial}{\partial z}. \tag{3.1.2}$$

If we make this substitution in (3.1.1), H is changed into a quantity called the Hamiltonian operator:

$$H \rightarrow -\frac{h^2}{8\pi^2 m} \nabla^2 + V, \tag{3.1.3}$$

where ∇^2 is the Laplacian operator already introduced in Sec. 2.1.   We now take the equation $H = E$ and regard it as an operator equation, operating on the wave function u, which of course is a function of x, y, and z.   The resulting equation, which may be symbolized $Hu = Eu$, is

$$-\frac{h^2}{8\pi^2 m} \nabla^2 u + Vu = Eu. \tag{3.1.4}$$

We see at once that this is identical with the Schrödinger equation (2.2.3) which we have earlier derived in an intuitive manner.   There is every indication, from further development of wave mechanics, that the form of derivation of this equation which we have given in the present para-

graph is very fundamental.   Thus, in cases where the Hamiltonian function H has a more complicated form than the simple one given in (3.1.1),
as for instance in cases of many-body problems, or cases involving magnetic fields, the procedure of making H into an operator by use of the
assumptions (3.1.2), and of setting up Schrödinger's equation by the condition $Hu = Eu$, still proves to give results which agree with experiment.

Once we have made our substitutions (3.1.2), another similar substitution will occur to us.   In the theory of relativity it is shown that there is a
far-reaching parallelism between the three coordinates x, y, z of space, and
the time t.   These quantities are often considered to be the four components of a four-dimensional vector.   When this type of formalism is
used, most of our ordinary three-dimensional vectors prove to have an
associated scalar quantity which appears as their fourth component.
Thus in particular the fourth quantity associated with the three components p_x, p_y, p_z of the momentum proves to be the negative of the
energy E.   (Alternatively, we may take x, y, z, $-t$ to be four components
of a vector, in which case p_x, p_y, p_z, E form the four components of another
vector.)   We have already seen an indication of this parallelism in our
discussion of the uncertainty principle in Sec. 1.6, where we had uncertainty relations of just the same sort between p_x and x and between E and
t.   These analogies would then suggest that we might appropriately
make a substitution

$$E \rightarrow -\frac{h}{2\pi i}\frac{\partial}{\partial t}. \tag{3.1.5}$$

Let us consider the effect of making this substitution in our energy equation $H = E$.

If we make this substitution (3.1.5), and again regard $H\psi = E\psi$ as a
differential equation, writing ψ for a wave function which now depends on
time as well as on x, y, and z, the resulting Schrödinger equation is

$$-\frac{h^2}{8\pi^2 m}\nabla^2\psi + V\psi = -\frac{h}{2\pi i}\frac{\partial\psi}{\partial t}. \tag{3.1.6}$$

In (3.1.6) we have the form of Schrödinger's equation involving the time.
As we mentioned earlier, it involves a first time derivative.   We can
readily set up a solution of this equation in such a form as to eliminate
the time, and show that it reduces to the same type of equation which we
have considered earlier.   Thus, using a very common device in mathematical physics, let us look for a solution of (3.1.6) in the form

$$\psi = u(x,y,z)T(t), \tag{3.1.7}$$

where u is a function of x, y, and z, and T is a function of the time.   If we substitute (3.1.7) in (3.1.6), we find, dividing through by ψ, that

$$\frac{1}{u}\left(-\frac{h^2}{8\pi^2 m}\nabla^2 u + Vu\right) = \frac{1}{T}\left(-\frac{h}{2\pi i}\frac{dT}{dt}\right). \tag{3.1.8}$$

Equation (3.1.8) is of a peculiar form: the left side, by hypothesis, is a function of x, y, and z only, whereas the right side is a function of t only. It is impossible that this equation should be satisfied for all values of x, y, z, and t, unless each side of (3.1.8) is in fact a constant. Let us call this constant E. Then we have two equations, which may be written

$$-\frac{h^2}{8\pi^2 m}\nabla^2 u + Vu = Eu, \qquad \frac{dT}{dt} = -\frac{2\pi i}{h}ET. \tag{3.1.9}$$

The process which we have used is the familiar one of separating variables in a partial differential equation.

We now observe that the equation for u, in (3.1.9), is simply the Schrödinger equation not involving the time, (3.1.4), if we interpret E as the energy. The second equation is one which can be at once solved: its solution is

$$T = \text{constant} \times e^{-(2\pi i/h)Et}. \tag{3.1.10}$$

That is, we are led to a sinusoidal time dependence of our wave function, with a frequency ν given by $\nu = E/h$, $E = h\nu$, which is just the assumption made by de Broglie about the frequency of the de Broglie wave. We thus see that our equation (3.1.6) is consistent with everything which we have done so far about the wave function. It does, however, carry us farther. It shows us that the correct time variation of the wave function is a complex exponential, as given in (3.1.10), and that in particular it has a negative sign in the exponent. This is a very different situation from that found in any other branch of mathematical physics. It is very common in all sorts of problems in vibrations to assume solutions varying exponentially with time, in the form $e^{\pm i\omega t}$. This is always done, however, as a device to simplify the solution. In the ordinary wave equation, with a second time derivative, we find that either the plus or minus sign in the exponential leads to an acceptable solution; and when we want physical results, we take the real part of the resulting function, which we can prove is also a solution, and use this real function. Our present situation is fundamentally different. It is only the solution varying as the complex exponential of (3.1.10) which is an acceptable solution of Eq. (3.1.6). We are not allowed to take its real part; this would not be a solution of Schrödinger's equation. Our wave function ψ is inherently a complex quantity. And yet, of course, all measurable quantities must be real. It is clear that we have a problem of interpretation, to find how to get real observable quantities out of this complex wave function. We shall shortly find the answer to this question.

3.2. The General Solution of Schrödinger's Equation Involving the Time.

By the separation of variables which we have just carried out, we have found a particular solution of Schrödinger's equation involving the time, but it is far from a general solution. In the first place, we verify at once that we may multiply it by an arbitrary constant, in general complex, which will give the oscillation an arbitrary amplitude and phase. Beyond this, however, the constant E is so far undetermined. If Schrödinger's equation not involving the time, (3.1.4), is one for which there are acceptable solutions only for certain energy levels E associated with stationary states, we may of course use only these E's; but otherwise E is at our disposal. We may, then, set up as many solutions as there are stationary states or energy levels. If we denote the ith allowed energy by E_i, and its related wave function by u_i, such a solution is

$$\psi_i = c_i e^{-(2\pi i E_i/h)t} u_i(x,y,z). \tag{3.2.1}$$

Here c_i is an arbitrary complex constant, the real and imaginary parts of c_i furnishing essentially two arbitrary constants. We have such solutions for at least a denumerable infinity of values of i, if we have discrete stationary states, and for an infinity of higher order, if we have a continuous spectrum of allowed energies.

We now observe that (3.1.6) is an equation of the type known as a homogeneous linear differential equation (linear because it does not contain ψ or its derivatives in powers higher than the first, homogeneous because it does not contain any terms independent of ψ). Any such differential equation has the property that a sum of two solutions is itself a solution, as we can at once verify by substituting the sum of two solutions ψ_1 and ψ_2 into (3.1.6). Thus we may make up a solution of (3.1.6) by adding all our functions ψ_i of (3.2.1); and this, in fact, is the general solution of the differential equation:

$$\psi = \sum_i c_i e^{-(2\pi i E_i/h)t} u_i(x,y,z). \tag{3.2.2}$$

This function, like any general solution of a partial differential equation, contains an infinite number of arbitrary constants, the c_i's. The summation is over all energy values E_i for which allowable solutions of (3.1.4) exist; that is, solutions which do not become infinite within the range of the variables, or otherwise misbehave themselves. If some of our energy spectrum is continuous rather than discrete, part of the summation in (3.2.2) might have to be replaced by an integration. We shall generally, however, transform any problem having a continuous spectrum of energies into one with a discrete spectrum by putting it in a box large compared with the dimensions of the system, so that the problem of an integration will not arise. This makes no essential physical change in the problem, and it simplifies the mathematical formulation.

Our general solution (3.2.2) is of a form familiar from all problems in wave motion: it is a superposition of all possible vibrations, each with its appropriate amplitude and phase. With a vibrating string, for instance, we know that we have particular solutions in the form of vibrations with one or another of the possible harmonics of the string, the vibration having a pure sinusoidal wave form, and each point of the string moving with simple harmonic motion. This is a very special situation, however; the general situation is a superposition of all these waves, each with an arbitrary amplitude and phase. And here, as there, the method of finding the arbitrary constants, the amplitudes and phases, is simple: we are given certain initial conditions at some instant of time, as $t = 0$. We find that the constants must be chosen in a particular way to satisfy those initial conditions. They determine the solution uniquely. Once we have set up these constants, the c_i's of (3.2.2), we can then use the form of that solution to predict the future behavior of ψ. Let us now consider the problem of determining the c_i's, once the initial value of ψ is known.

3.3. Orthogonality of Wave Functions and Determination of c's. There is a standard way of determining the arbitrary phases and amplitudes in any problem of wave motion, depending on what is called the orthogonality of the wave functions, and this method holds in the case of Schrödinger's equation as well. Let us first state the method and show how it is used in the present case, and then go back and prove the necessary theorems. The theorems which we shall prove are the following: First, two wave functions u_i and u_j, associated with different energy values E_i and E_j, are orthogonal to each other in the sense that

$$\int u_i^*(x,y,z)u_j(x,y,z)dx\, dy\, dz = 0 \qquad \text{if } i \neq j, \qquad (3.3.1)$$

where u_i^* indicates the complex conjugate of u_i, and where the integration is over all space, or over the whole region in which the wave functions are different from zero. We shall shortly prove this theorem directly from Schrödinger's equation. Next, we assume that each of the wave functions u_i is normalized in the sense that

$$\int u_i^*(x,y,z)u_i(x,y,z)dx\, dy\, dz = 1. \qquad (3.3.2)$$

This can always be achieved, provided the region over which the wave function is different from zero is finite, by properly choosing the constant of proportionality which is arbitrary in the definition of u_i. In any case where the wave function cannot be normalized in this way, for instance because it remains finite over the whole of infinite space, as with a plane wave, we can adopt other alternative methods of normalization, such as making the integral of (3.3.2) over unit volume equal to unity; but such complications will not trouble us for the moment. We often combine the statements (3.3.1) and (3.3.2) in a single equation,

$$\int u_i^*(x,y,z)u_j(x,y,z)dx\ dy\ dz = \delta_{ij}, \tag{3.3.3}$$

where δ_{ij}, sometimes called the Kronecker symbol, is defined as being unity when $i = j$, zero when $i \neq j$.

Before proving the orthogonality relation (3.3.1), let us see how it is used in determining the c_i's of Eq. (3.2.2). Let us assume that the initial condition is that at $t = 0$, ψ must be a definite function $\psi_0(x,y,z)$. Then we have

$$\psi_0(x,y,z) = \sum_j c_j u_j(x,y,z). \tag{3.3.4}$$

Let us multiply (3.3.4) by $u_i^*(x,y,z)$, where i is a particular value, and integrate both sides of the equation over $dx\ dy\ dz$. We have

$$\int u_i^*(x,y,z)\psi_0(x,y,z)dx\ dy\ dz = \sum_j c_j \int u_i^*(x,y,z)u_j(x,y,z)dx\ dy\ dz$$

$$= \sum_j c_j\delta_{ij} = c_i. \tag{3.3.5}$$

Thus we see that there is a simple procedure for finding the coefficients c_i in terms of definite integrals, as a result of the orthogonality and normalization of the wave functions.

Now that we have seen the usefulness of the fact of orthogonality in determining the c's, let us prove that (3.3.1) is in fact true. From (3.1.4) we have

$$-\frac{h^2}{8\pi^2 m}\nabla^2 u_j + V u_j = E_j u_j,$$
$$-\frac{h^2}{8\pi^2 m}\nabla^2 u_i^* + V u_i^* = E_i u_i^*, \tag{3.3.6}$$

where the second equation of (3.3.6) is obtained by writing the Schrödinger equation for u_i and taking the conjugate of the resulting equation, remembering that V and E are real quantities. We now multiply the first equation of (3.3.6) by u_i^*, the second by u_j, subtract the second from the first, and integrate with respect to $dx\ dy\ dz$. We have

$$-\frac{h^2}{8\pi^2 m} \int (u_i^* \nabla^2 u_j - u_j \nabla^2 u_i^*)dx\ dy\ dz$$

$$= (E_j - E_i) \int u_i^* u_j\ dx\ dy\ dz. \quad (3.3.7)$$

In this equation we may use Green's theorem on the left side, converting into a surface integral over the surface bounding the volume of integration. We have

$$-\frac{h^2}{8\pi^2 m} \int \left(u_i^* \frac{\partial u_j}{\partial n} - u_j \frac{\partial u_i^*}{\partial n} \right) da = (E_j - E_i) \int u_i^* u_j\ dx\ dy\ dz. \quad (3.3.8)$$

Under any circumstances which cause the surface integral on the left to vanish, the right side will be zero. In case $E_j \neq E_i$, this will then demand that $\int u_i^* u_j\ dx\ dy\ dz = 0$, which is what we wished to prove. Let us then examine the conditions under which this will occur.

In the first place, the surface integral in (3.3.8) will be zero if the wave functions vanish over the surface of the volume of integration. This will be the case if we are dealing with the problem of particles in a box with walls consisting of infinitely high potential barriers, as we were considering in Sec. 2.5. It will also be the case if, as with the linear oscillator, the integration is over all space, and the wave function falls to zero at infinity. It is, of course, necessary that the function go to zero rapidly enough so that, even though the area of the surface of integration becomes infinite, the integral nevertheless vanishes; this is the case with the exponential type of decrease which the wave function has. The cases we have mentioned are the most important ones in which the surface integral vanishes; there are, however, other cases, such as one which we shall presently meet, called periodic boundary conditions, in which it also vanishes, and in all such cases we have orthogonality.

As for E_j being different from E_i, we certainly expect in general that if we are dealing with two different wave functions, as we shall be if $i \neq j$, we shall have $E_i \neq E_j$, since normally different stationary states have different energy levels. In any such case, then, our proof of orthogonality holds. It is possible, however, to have two wave functions which are quite distinct and yet have the same energy. This occasionally happens in one-dimensional problems; for instance, in the problem with two potential wells, as shown in Figs. 2.5.4 and 2.5.5, the energies of the symmetric and antisymmetric functions become equal if the potential barrier between the two wells becomes infinitely high. The situation frequently occurs in problems in two and three dimensions; for instance, if the potential has spherical symmetry, so that rotation in space does not change the potential energy, it is obvious that any solution of Schrödinger's equation can be rotated in space without changing its energy, and yet this may result in quite a different wave function. Such a case is called degeneracy; it is clear that our proof does not hold in cases of degeneracy, since if $E_j - E_i = 0$ in (3.3.8), we cannot draw any conclusions about the vanishing of the integral $\int u_i^* u_j \, dx \, dy \, dz$. Thus in such a case we cannot prove that the wave functions must be orthogonal. However, in a case of degeneracy we can see at once that any linear combination of degenerate wave functions is itself a solution of Schrödinger's equation for the same energy, and hence an equally good wave function. It can be proved that we can always set up wave functions in this way which are orthogonal, though these do not form a unique set of wave functions. We shall assume that this has been done, so that even in cases of degeneracy we are justified in assuming orthogonality as well as normalization of the wave functions. This question is discussed further in Appendix 7.

3.4. The Probability Density. We have now seen the way to set up the general solution ψ of Schrödinger's equation. Let us next remember what it means physically. Our argument from the beginning has shown that it represented the amplitude of a wave whose intensity gave the probability of finding the particle at the point in question. We shall now investigate this statement more in detail. The intensity of an ordinary wave, as of sound or light, is the square of its amplitude. In the present case, in which the amplitude ψ is necessarily a complex function of time, we cannot make this simple assumption, for the resulting square would not be real, and yet the probability of finding the particle must be a real quantity. The assumption of wave mechanics is the only one which could reasonably be made under the circumstances: it is that the probability of finding the particle is determined by the square of the absolute magnitude of ψ, or, what is the same thing, by the product of ψ and its conjugate. To be precise, we assume that the probability of finding the particle in the volume element $dx \, dy \, dz$ is $\psi^*(x,y,z)\psi(x,y,z)dx \, dy \, dz$. This leads at once to one result. The probability of finding the particle somewhere must certainly be unity. This is the integral of the probability of finding it in element $dx \, dy \, dz$ over all values of $dx \, dy \, dz$. In other words, we must have

$$\int \psi^* \psi \, dx \, dy \, dz = 1, \tag{3.4.1}$$

or the wave function ψ must be normalized, just as the functions u_i were.

This normalization of the wave function shows a real difference between wave mechanics and the case of optics, which we used as an analogy in Chap. 1. In optics, of course, the amplitude of the electromagnetic wave is not in any sense normalized to unity. Rather, the more intense the light, the greater is the amplitude. The difference is that the electromagnetic wave determines the motion of any number of photons. Our Schrödinger wave, however, determines the motion of only one particle. We have not so far stressed the fact, but our discussion of the present chapter, and in fact most of our discussion to this point, has been limited to the case of the motion of a single particle in a potential field. When we come to taking up the motion of many particles, we shall treat it, not by assuming that our function ψ determines the behavior of all the particles, but in quite a different way: by introducing a ψ which is a function of the coordinates of all the particles, not just of one particle, so that if there are N particles, ψ is a function of $3N$ dimensions, or forms in a sense a wave in a $3N$-dimensional space. This is a quite different concept from the three-dimensional wave of optics, and it shows us that while the optical analogy was useful in leading to the idea of wave mechanics, it is not a very profound or far-reaching analogy. The fundamental difference between photons and charged particles, which leads to the different treatment, is that the charged particles act on each other, whereas photons do not.

We can now return to our hypothesis that $\psi^*\psi \, dx \, dy \, dz$ measures the probability of finding the particle in $dx \, dy \, dz$ and draw some conclusions from it. We may well call $\psi^*\psi$ the probability density. Let us now take our solution (3.2.2) for ψ and write down the expression for $\psi^*\psi$ to see how it varies with x, y, z, and t. We have at once

$$\psi^*\psi = \sum_i \sum_j c_i^* c_j e^{-(2\pi i/h)(E_j - E_i)t} u_i^* u_j. \tag{3.4.2}$$

This is a very important result, with many implications regarding quantum mechanics.

We notice first that (3.4.2) contains terms of two kinds: those for which $i = j$, and those for which $i \neq j$. A typical term for $i = j$ is $c_i^* c_i u_i^* u_i$. Being the product of a quantity $c_i u_i$ with its conjugate, it is real. Furthermore, it is independent of time. These terms give the time average dependence of $\psi^*\psi$; for all other terms average to zero, varying sinusoidally with time. As for these terms varying with time, we note that they come in pairs; if i equals a particular number, say 1, and j equals another number, say 2, then we naturally group with this term the other one in which i equals 2, j equals 1. That is, we may in (3.4.2) sum over each pair of different indices i, j only once, but take the two terms explicitly, in the form

$$c_i^* c_j e^{-(2\pi i/h)(E_j - E_i)t} u_i^* u_j + \text{conjugate}, \tag{3.4.3}$$

since the term with i and j interchanged is the conjugate of the one written explicitly in (3.4.3). Thus we again have a real quantity. Now the important thing to notice about this quantity is that it is oscillating sinusoidally with a frequency $(E_j - E_i)/h$. In other words, these oscillations obey Bohr's frequency condition, according to which the frequencies of emitted oscillations of light equal the differences of two term values E_i/h. It is in this way that Bohr's condition enters into wave mechanics. We shall find later that the oscillations of probability density given by terms like (3.4.3) give rise to real oscillations of charge, and to emission or absorption of electromagnetic radiation, with frequencies given by Bohr's condition. And now, having seen this result, we begin to understand the rather arbitrary way in which our complex quantities have been manipulated in setting up the theory. It is only because we took ψ to be a complex quantity and multiplied by its conjugate in (3.4.2), that all the sinusoidal oscillations came out with frequencies given by Bohr's condition. If instead we had first taken the real part of ψ, then squared, we should have found terms not only in the differences, but also in the sums, of energies, which is clearly contrary to our physical assumptions regarding the meaning of the wave function.

3.5. Mean Value of a Function of Coordinates. In the preceding section we have found that $\psi^*\psi \, dx \, dy \, dz$ is the probability of finding the coordinates of the particle in the volume element $dx \, dy \, dz$. This then allows us to find the average value of any function of the coordinates. To find the average of any quantity, given a distribution function like this, we multiply the quantity by the fraction of systems in the volume element concerned and integrate over the whole volume. This is simply the process of finding a weighted mean: we weight each value of x, y, z according to the number or fraction of all systems which will be found with that value of x, y, z. Thus if we have a function $F(x,y,z)$ of the coordinates and wish its mean value, we have

$$\bar{F} = \int F\psi^*\psi \, dx \, dy \, dz = \int \psi^*F\psi \, dx \, dy \, dz, \tag{3.5.1}$$

where the bar over the F indicates the average value, and where we prefer the latter method of writing because it fits in with formulas which we shall have later. It is now very interesting to substitute our expansion (3.4.2) of $\psi^*\psi$ in this expression (3.5.1) for a mean value. It gives

$$\bar{F} = \sum_i \sum_j c_i^* c_j e^{-(2\pi i/h)(E_j - E_i)t} \int u_i^* F u_j \, dx \, dy \, dz$$

$$= \sum_i \sum_j c_i^* c_j e^{-(2\pi i/h)(E_j - E_i)t} F_{ij}, \tag{3.5.2}$$

where by definition $F_{ij} = \int u_i^* F u_j \, dx \, dy \, dz$. The quantities F_{ij} form a two-dimensional array of numbers, of the sort known in mathematics as a matrix, and the individual F_{ij}'s are called matrix components.

When we examine the average value in (3.5.2), we observe the same thing which we saw in the preceding section in discussing the probability density. We observe that there are terms of two sorts in the summation: those for which $i = j$, which are independent of time, and which therefore express the time average of F; and those for which $i \neq j$, which oscillate sinusoidally with time with the frequencies given by Bohr's frequency condition, and which average to zero. If we make a scheme of matrix components like

$$
\begin{array}{cccc}
F_{11} & F_{12} & F_{13} & \cdots \\
F_{21} & F_{22} & F_{23} & \cdots \\
F_{31} & F_{32} & F_{33} & \cdots \\
\multicolumn{4}{c}{\cdots \cdots \cdots \cdots}
\end{array}
$$

we see that the components F_{11}, F_{22}, F_{33}, etc., along the principal diagonal, are those for which $i = j$, and which are therefore associated with the time averages; they are called the diagonal components of the matrix. The other terms, for which $i \neq j$, called the nondiagonal terms, are associated with the sinusoidal oscillations. We notice one fact about these nondiagonal terms. Ordinarily we shall be finding the averages of real functions of x, y, z, since it is only such functions that have physical significance. Then we note that

$$
F_{ji} = \int u_j^* F u_i \, dx \, dy \, dz = \int u_i F u_j^* \, dx \, dy \, dz = F_{ij}^*, \tag{3.5.3}
$$

showing that interchanging the order of the subscripts in a nondiagonal matrix component changes the component to its complex conjugate. A matrix which has this property is called Hermitian.

We shall have occasion later to use matrix components of various quantities; particularly interesting in many ways is the matrix component of the displacement of the electron or other particle from a fixed position. For example, we may consider the x coordinate of the particle. The diagonal components x_{ii} will refer to the time average of x, and the non-diagonal components x_{ij} to its sinusoidal displacement from this average position. We observe, then, that on the average a particle will be found oscillating about its position of equilibrium with a superposition of sinusoidal oscillations, corresponding to the various frequencies which would be emitted according to Bohr's frequency condition. Now in the electromagnetic theory we find that an oscillating charge emits electromagnetic radiation, whose frequency is equal to that of the oscillation, and whose intensity is proportional to the square of the amplitude of oscillation of the charge. This suggests that we shall be able to get a relation between the values of the matrix components of the displacement of a charged particle, and the intensity of electromagnetic radiation emitted by the system.   Such a relation does in fact occur, and we shall take it up in a later chapter: we can to a considerable extent identify the oscillating charge described by our matrix components with the linear oscillators responsible for emitting radiation in the classical electromagnetic theory of light.   The relation is not simple, however, and we cannot do anything as elementary as assuming that we have an oscillating density of charge, given for instance by (3.4.2), which emits radiation according to classical electrodynamics.   This would, it is true, give the correct frequencies; but we shall see later that it would not give the correct intensities.

A simple picture like this does, however, allow us to make correctly one prediction about radiation: if one of the matrix components x_{ij} of displacement is zero, so that the corresponding term in (3.5.2) would be absent, then we should suspect that no radiation of the frequency $(E_j - E_i)/h$ would be emitted, since it certainly would not be emitted by the classical oscillator.   If in turn no such radiation was emitted, then using Bohr's picture of the relation between emitted radiation and transitions between energy levels, we should say that the transition between states i and j would never occur by emission of radiation.   Such a statement, to the effect that certain transitions do not occur or are forbidden, is called a selection principle, and when we investigate properly the relations between our theory and the emission of radiation, we see that our conclusion is really right: if a matrix component of x_{ij} is in fact zero, then the corresponding transition is forbidden.

We shall meet many examples of such selection principles in our later work.   A very simple one may be mentioned here.   In the linear oscillator, taken up in the preceding chapter, we have energy levels $(n + \frac{1}{2})h\nu_0$.   A transition from the state with a given n, to a state whose n is less by the amount k, would then lead to an energy difference $kh\nu_0$, so that the emitted radiation would have a frequency $k\nu_0$, by Bohr's rule.   However, when we take the wave functions of the linear oscillator and compute the matrix components x_{ij}, we find that they are in fact zero, unless the states i and j correspond to values of n differing by ± 1.   Thus the only allowed transitions are those in which n changes by one unit, so that k must be unity, and the emitted radiation has a frequency ν_0, agreeing exactly with the classical frequency.   This is a simple example of what is called Bohr's correspondence principle.   Bohr was able to show that if the motion of a given system according to classical mechanics is periodic (or, more generally, what is called multiply periodic), and if we then analyze its displacement into a Fourier series in the time, it is possible to make a correlation or correspondence between the amplitudes of the various Fourier components and the magnitudes of the matrix components x_{ij}. This leads to a certain relation between the type of radiation that would be emitted by such a system in classical and in quantum theory; the simplest example of the correlation is the case we have just taken up, the linear oscillator, in which the radiation is the same in both theories. Before the development of Schrödinger's theory this correspondence principle of Bohr was the only available method for estimating probabilities of transition, or intensities of spectral lines, and for that reason it was historically important. It retains considerable importance, since it throws a good deal of light on the relations between classical and quantum mechanics. It is discussed in Appendix 8.

In the expression (3.5.2), we have taken up the meaning of the matrix components F_{ij}; we have not yet considered, however, the significance of the constants c_i. It is hard to interpret physically the meanings of these constants in the nondiagonal terms; this difficulty is tied up with the complicated relations between quantum mechanics and electromagnetic theory, which we mentioned above and shall take up in a later chapter. As far as the diagonal terms are concerned, however, the meaning is simple. Thus for the time average of $\bar{F}$ we have

$$\text{time average of } \bar{F} = \sum_i c_i^* c_i F_{ii}. \tag{3.5.4}$$

Now if we know that a system is in a given stationary state, we set up a solution of Schrödinger's equation which, instead of being of the general form (3.2.2), has all the c_i's equal to zero, except the one relating to that particular stationary state. That is, the solution is of the form (3.2.1). Since both ψ and the u's are normalized, this tells us that $c_i^* c_i$ must be equal to unity. The average of $\bar{F}$ is in that case simply F_{ii}, which then represents the average value of F for this particular stationary state.

The expression (3.5.4), then, for the more general case, has the appearance of a weighted mean: it is as if the system had a probability $c_i^* c_i$ of being found in the ith state, and as if we used this as a weighting factor in connection with the average value F_{ii} of F for the ith state, in order to get a weighted mean. This interpretation is in fact correct. When we build up a superposition of sinusoidal oscillations, like (3.2.2), as our general solution of Schrödinger's equation, it does not correspond to the situation where the particle is known to be in a given stationary state. Rather, it has a certain chance of being found in each possible stationary state, and the probability that it be found in the ith state is $c_i^* c_i$. We should expect, then, that the sum of all the $c_i^* c_i$'s would be unity, for the probability that the particle be in some state is certainly unity. This is the case, as we can easily prove. Thus let us integrate the expression (3.4.2) over $dx\, dy\, dz$. On the left, we have unity, by the normalization condition (3.4.1). On the right, we use the orthogonality and normalization relation (3.3.3), and this leads at once to the statement $\Sigma c_i^* c_i = 1$. This then gives us the interpretation of the c's. As to why we should wish to set up a wave function which does not correspond to a stationary state, we recall that we may have to do this to satisfy initial conditions, as we saw from Eq. (3.3.5) for determining the c's. In fact, if we set up a wave packet, for example, we always have to do precisely this, superposing wave functions corresponding to all energy levels to build up the desired wave function. We shall investigate later how this is done.

3.6. Mean Values of Functions of Momenta. The method of finding mean values of functions of the coordinates is perfectly straightforward, but the treatment of the momenta is peculiar and is one of the characteristic features of wave mechanics. The momentum shows itself in the wave function through the wave length of the wave, and in order to get information about wave length, it turns out that the proper procedure is to differentiate the wave function. We can find the correct formulas from a very simple case; and since we are setting up a theory which is not derived from any other, we can do nothing but postulate the general formulas, which prove to be the same ones that we find in this special case. Thus suppose we have a free particle in empty space, traveling with a momentum p, energy E. Its wave function, if it travels along the x axis, will be $e^{(2\pi i/h)(px-Et)}$, corresponding to the wave length $1/\lambda = p/h$. More generally, if its components of momentum along the three axes are p_x, p_y, p_z, its wave function will be

$$e^{(2\pi i/h)(p_x x + p_y y + p_z - Et)}, \tag{3.6.1}$$

a plane wave. If we wanted to find the mean x momentum of this particle, we should multiply p_x by the probability, and integrate; we should get p_x, of course, since the mean value of a constant is the same constant. But the question is, how is this to be generalized so that it can be used in more complicated cases, where the momentum does not appear explicitly, and is not constant?

The answer proves to be the following. If our function is called ψ, we observe that $\dfrac{h}{2\pi i}\dfrac{\partial\psi}{\partial x}$ equals $p_x\psi$. Thus if we form the expression $\psi^* \dfrac{h}{2\pi i}\dfrac{\partial\psi}{\partial x}$ and integrate, the answer will be the same as integrating $\psi^* p_x \psi$, which gives p_x. Similarly, we see that integrating $\psi^* \left(\dfrac{h}{2\pi i}\dfrac{\partial}{\partial x}\right)^2 \psi$ would give p_x^2, and so on. In other words, the operator $\dfrac{h}{2\pi i}\dfrac{\partial}{\partial x}$, operating on ψ, and averaged, can be taken to stand for the x component of momentum.

It is now assumed that this process can be applied in general. Thus with any wave function ψ, the mean value of the x component of momentum is $\int \psi^* \frac{h}{2\pi i} \frac{\partial}{\partial x} \psi \, dv$, where dv stands for $dx \, dy \, dz$. Or more generally, if we have any function of momenta and coordinates, say $F(x,y,z,p_x,p_y,p_z)$, we have for the mean value

$$\bar{F} = \int \psi^* F\left(x,y,z, \frac{h}{2\pi i} \frac{\partial}{\partial x}, \frac{h}{2\pi i} \frac{\partial}{\partial y}, \frac{h}{2\pi i} \frac{\partial}{\partial z}\right) \psi \, dv. \tag{3.6.2}$$

This is the general rule, reducing to our former one (3.5.1) when F involves only coordinates. If we assume that ψ is given by the general form (3.2.2), then we find at once that (3.6.2) takes on the form (3.5.2), where now

$$F_{ij} = \int u_i^* F\left(x,y,z, \frac{h}{2\pi i} \frac{\partial}{\partial x}, \frac{h}{2\pi i} \frac{\partial}{\partial y}, \frac{h}{2\pi i} \frac{\partial}{\partial z}\right) u_j \, dv. \tag{3.6.3}$$

This is the general definition of the matrix component of any function F of coordinates and momenta; F expressed in terms of the differential operators in place of the p's is spoken of as the operator F.

It is now obvious that the method we have been setting up is very closely analogous to the procedure described in Sec. 3.1 for setting up Schrödinger's equation involving the time. In fact, the rule (3.1.2) for replacing the momentum components by differential operators is just the one used in (3.6.3). Thus Schrödinger's equation (3.1.4), with the time eliminated, may be written simply $Hu = Eu$, where H is the operator corresponding to the Hamiltonian function. Let us now compute the matrix components H_{ij} of the energy. These are $H_{ij} = \int u_i^* H u_j \, dv$. But by Schrödinger's equation $Hu_j = E_j u_j$. Thus we have

$$H_{ij} = \int u_i^* H u_j \, dv = E_j \int u_i^* u_j \, dv = E_j \delta_{ij}, \tag{3.6.4}$$

where we have used the orthogonality relation (3.3.3). In other words, the matrix H_{ij} of the energy is what is called a diagonal matrix: only its diagonal terms are different from zero. This means that if we set up the average value of H, as in (3.5.2), we have only terms independent of time. Thus we have the translation into quantum-mechanical language of the familiar conservation of energy in classical mechanics.

If any other operator, say F, had a diagonal matrix, it would likewise be independent of time; and this is the method used to prove other conservation theorems. For instance, if we find the matrix of the angular momentum in a problem in which there is no torque, we find that it is a diagonal matrix, thus proving the conservation of angular momentum (though it is best to say that this situation, in a three-dimensional problem, is really somewhat more complicated, in that certain components of angular momentum are constant, not because they have no nondiagonal terms, but because the frequencies associated with certain nonvanishing nondiagonal terms are zero). With any operator, whether it has a diagonal matrix or not, we can write an equation somewhat similar to Schrödinger's equation. With an operator F, we have

$$Fu_j = \sum_i F_{ij}u_i, \tag{3.6.5}$$

expressing Fu_j as a sum of the vectors u_i, each multiplied by the corresponding matrix component. To prove this, we need only multiply by u_i^* and integrate, where the right side, on account of orthogonality, leaves only F_{ij}. Such an expansion as (3.6.5) has interesting connections with the general theory of expansion in orthogonal functions, as taken up in Appendix 7.

It is to be noted that a matrix depends on two things: first, the operator, and second, the set of orthogonal functions with respect to which it is computed. Thus a given operator, as energy or angular momentum or x coordinate, can have its matrix computed with respect to any set of orthogonal functions. The problem of solving Schrödinger's equation with a given energy operator may be considered as that of finding the particular set of orthogonal functions which makes the matrix derived from that operator diagonal. In a similar way, we can find a set of orthogonal functions which would make any other desired operator have a diagonal matrix. Sometimes we can find a set of functions in which two operators, as the energy and angular momentum, simultaneously have diagonal matrices, or are constant; we shall inquire in a moment regarding the necessary condition for this to be possible. An interesting application of matrix operation is the perturbation theory, which we shall take up in the next chapter. This is used in case we have been able to solve a problem similar to the one we are interested in, but differing slightly from it. That is, we have been able to set up some wave functions, called unperturbed wave functions, with respect to which the energy matrix is almost diagonal or has very small nondiagonal terms. Then it is not hard to proceed by a power-series development in those small nondiagonal terms to set up an expression for the correct wave functions and energies.

3.7. Some Theorems Regarding Matrices. We can compute the matrix components of an arbitrary operator by the rule (3.6.3); but sometimes it is a help to be able to find the matrix of a complicated function from the components of simpler functions, by processes analogous to ordinary algebra. To solve such problems, we set up a set of rules, called matrix algebra, which we shall now consider. As a preliminary step, we must note that there is one difficulty which has not previously been pointed out in connection with our rule (3.6.3). It turns out that if there are any terms in F involving products of coordinates and momenta, the answer will depend on the order in which they occur. The best example is the case of the product $p_x x$. We have

$$\overline{p_x x} = \int \psi^* \left[\frac{h}{2\pi i} \frac{\partial}{\partial x} (x\psi) \right] dv$$

$$= \int \psi^* \left(\frac{h}{2\pi i} \psi + x \frac{h}{2\pi i} \frac{\partial \psi}{\partial x} \right) dv$$

$$= \frac{h}{2\pi i} + \int \psi^* \left(x \frac{h}{2\pi i} \frac{\partial}{\partial x} \right) \psi \, dv$$

$$= \frac{h}{2\pi i} + \overline{x p_x},$$

$$\overline{p_x x} - \overline{x p_x} = \frac{h}{2\pi i}. \tag{3.7.1}$$

This is the so-called commutation rule; it states that interchange, or commutation, of the order of a coordinate and momentum operator changes the values, since the difference is not zero. In most actual cases that we meet, we shall not be troubled by this difficulty of noncommutability of coordinates and momenta, but it is something against which we must be on our guard.

Let us now approach our problem of building up the matrix of a complicated function from the matrices of simpler functions. We can do this if we know how to find the matrix of the sum of two functions F and G from the matrices of F and G separately, and how to find the matrix of the product. As far as the sum is concerned, the result is trivial; we can prove at once that $(F + G)_{ij} = F_{ij} + G_{ij}$. The multiplication rule is more involved. We assume that we know F_{ij} and G_{ij} and wish to find $(FG)_{ij}$. We have

$$G u_j = \sum_i G_{ij} u_i$$

from (3.6.5). Then

$$F G u_j = \sum_i G_{ij} F u_i = \sum_{i,k} G_{ij} F_{ki} u_k = \sum_k \left(\sum_i F_{ki} G_{ij} \right) u_k.$$

But also

$$(FG) u_j = \sum_k (FG)_{kj} u_k,$$

by (3.6.5). Hence

$$(FG)_{kj} = \sum_i F_{ki} G_{ij}, \tag{3.7.2}$$

the formula for multiplying matrices. This is the same rule used in the algebra of matrices and hence justifies our using the same name for them here as in algebra.

In addition to the operations of multiplication and addition, we sometimes want to find the matrix of the time derivative of a quantity. We can do this at once by differentiating (3.5.2) with respect to time. If we do this, we have

$$\frac{\partial \bar{F}}{\partial t} = \sum_i \sum_j c_i^* c_j e^{-(2\pi i/h)(E_j - E_i)t} \left(-\frac{2\pi i}{h} \right) (E_j - E_i) F_{ij}.$$

Thus we have

$$\left(\frac{\partial F}{\partial t} \right)_{ij} = -\frac{2\pi i}{h} (E_j - E_i) F_{ij}.$$

But we can rewrite this in the form

$$\left(\frac{\partial F}{\partial t} \right)_{ij} = \frac{2\pi i}{h} (HF - FH)_{ij}, \tag{3.7.3}$$

where this last step comes by using the multiplication rule (3.7.2) for the matrix components of HF and FH, and by remembering that H has a diagonal matrix with components $E_j \delta_{ij}$.

Suppose now we have a matrix F which commutes with H, that is, for which $HF = FH$, whether expressed in the language of operators or matrices. In other words, $HF\psi = FH\psi$, where ψ is any wave function, or $\overline{HF} = \overline{FH}$, where we are referring to average values, or $(HF)_{ij} = (FH)_{ij}$. Then by (3.7.3) the time rate of change of F is zero. We could infer from this that F would have a diagonal matrix, since we know that an operator whose average value is independent of time has a diagonal matrix. This is in fact the case, as we can prove directly. For if we have $(HF - FH)_{ij} = 0$, and if we remember that H has a diagonal matrix on account of Schrödinger's equation $Hu_i = E_i \delta_{ij} u_j$, we have

$$(HF - FH)_{ij} = \sum_k (H_{ik} F_{kj} - F_{ik} H_{kj}) = 0$$

$$= (E_i - E_j) F_{ij}. \tag{3.7.4}$$

Thus either $E_i = E_j$, which will be true if $i = j$, or in the case of degeneracy (which can be handled as in discussing orthogonality, and which does not really form an exception to our statements), or $F_{ij} = 0$, so that we conclude that $F_{ij} = 0$ if $i \neq j$, or F has a diagonal matrix. Conversely, if F as well as H has a diagonal matrix, we verify at once that $(FH - HF)_{ij} = 0$. We see, then, that for two operators, as F and H, simultaneously to have average values independent of time, or for both to have diagonal matrices, they must commute with each other. This is the condition which we stated in Sec. 3.6 could be proved to be necessary in order to have two operators simultaneously constant, such as energy and angular momentum.

It is a rather remarkable fact that the method of operating with matrices was discovered before the wave mechanics. The multiplication rule and method of differentiating with respect to time, as well as the commutation rule, were developed, as well as various more elaborate procedures. They were used for a number of complicated calculations, without use of wave functions, for example for finding the energy levels of the linear oscillator, its intensities of radiation, and even the energy levels of the hydrogen atom. For most of these problems the method of matrices is more complicated than that of wave functions, but this is by no means always the case.

3.8. Average Values and the Motion of Wave Packets. In earlier chapters we have made statements about the way in which wave packets move according to wave mechanics; now we can investigate their motion by simple and straightforward methods. We shall investigate the motion of the center of gravity of a wave packet, the point whose coordinates are $\bar{x}$, $\bar{y}$, and $\bar{z}$, and shall show that in fact it moves precisely according to Newton's equations of motion. This is then, in a sense, the fundamental theorem of classical mechanics, or the proof of Newton's laws from wave mechanics. Fortunately we can give a perfectly general proof, without having to assume any particular form for the wave packet.

As a first step, we can prove that the average momentum, whose x component, for instance, is $\overline{p_x}$, is the mass times the x component of the velocity, or equal to $m \, d\bar{x}/dt$. This is a straightforward result. The proof merely involves writing the expression for $\bar{x}$ as in (3.5.1), then differentiating the whole integral with respect to time. This involves derivatives of ψ and ψ^* with respect to time; the x which appears inside the integral sign in (3.5.1) is not directly a function of time, but merely a variable of integration, and hence does not have to be differentiated. We then insert the time derivative of ψ from Schrödinger's equation (3.1.6), the time derivative of ψ^* from its conjugate, use Green's theorem, and assume the same boundary conditions which we needed to prove orthogonality, namely, usually, that ψ is zero around the surface of integration. When these steps are carried out, the result follows directly and can be written in the form

$$\frac{d}{dt}(\bar{x}) = \frac{1}{m} \int \psi^* \left(\frac{h}{2\pi i} \frac{\partial}{\partial x} \right) \psi \, dv. \qquad (3.8.1)$$

We could, as a matter of fact, have used this same argument, in a reverse direction, to justify our rule for calculating the mean value of the momentum.

The remaining part of the proof of Newton's laws comes by differentiating (3.8.1) again with respect to time, to get the acceleration of the center of mass. We should like, in fact, to prove that the mass times the acceleration of the center of mass, which is the same thing as the time rate of change of the average momentum, equals the average over the wave packet of the force. Now the x component of force acting on a particle is $-\partial V/\partial x$, if V is the potential energy, a function of x, y, and z. Thus we wish to prove that

$$\frac{d(\overline{p_x})}{dt} = -\frac{\overline{\partial V}}{\partial x}. \tag{3.8.2}$$

To do this, we multiply (3.8.1) by m and differentiate with respect to time. We have

$$\frac{d(\overline{p_x})}{dt} = \frac{h}{2\pi i} \int \left(\psi^* \frac{\partial}{\partial t} \frac{\partial}{\partial x} \psi + \frac{\partial \psi^*}{\partial t} \frac{\partial \psi}{\partial x} \right) dv$$

$$= \frac{h}{2\pi i} \int \left(\psi^* \frac{\partial}{\partial x} \frac{\partial \psi}{\partial t} + \frac{\partial \psi^*}{\partial t} \frac{\partial \psi}{\partial x} \right) dv. \tag{3.8.3}$$

We now substitute for $\partial\psi/\partial t$ and $\partial\psi^*/\partial t$ from (3.1.6) and its conjugate and find

$$\frac{d(\overline{p_x})}{dt} = \int \left[\psi^* \frac{\partial}{\partial x} \left(\frac{h^2}{8\pi^2 m} \nabla^2 \psi - V\psi \right) + \frac{\partial \psi}{\partial x} \left(-\frac{h^2}{8\pi^2 m} \nabla^2 \psi^* + V\psi^* \right) \right] dv$$

$$= \int \left[\frac{h^2}{8\pi^2 m} \left(\psi^* \nabla^2 \frac{\partial \psi}{\partial x} - \frac{\partial \psi}{\partial x} \nabla^2 \psi^* \right) - \psi^* \frac{\partial V}{\partial x} \psi \right] dv. \tag{3.8.4}$$

The first terms in (3.8.4), involving the Laplacians, can be transformed by Green's theorem to the form

$$\frac{h^2}{8\pi^2 m} \int \left[\psi^* \frac{\partial}{\partial n} \left(\frac{\partial \psi}{\partial x} \right) - \frac{\partial \psi}{\partial x} \frac{\partial \psi^*}{\partial n} \right] da, \tag{3.8.5}$$

a surface integral over the surface enclosing the volume of integration, and it will vanish if ψ and its derivatives vanish sufficiently strongly on the boundary, which will be the case where the wave function falls off exponentially as we go to infinite distance. It will not necessarily be true if the particle is confined in a box, where ψ goes to zero on the surface but where its normal derivative does not. In this case our theorem, as we stated it in (3.8.2) and shall prove in a moment, is not in fact true, and we should not expect it to be; for the wall of the box exerts a pressure on the particle inside it, as the wall of a vessel exerts a force on a gas inside it, and this force must be considered in Newton's law but does not come into our formulation of the wave equation.

Let us then, for simplicity, disregard this case of the particle in the box, and take only the simple case of a system without external stresses. Then the surface integral in (3.8.5) vanishes, and we are left with

$$\frac{d(\overline{p_x})}{dt} = - \int \psi^* \frac{\partial V}{\partial x} \psi \, dv = - \overline{\frac{\partial V}{\partial x}},$$

which is identical with (3.8.2), and which we wished to prove. Thus we have justified the use of Newton's equations of motion for wave packets.

3.9. The Equation of Continuity for the Probability Density. We have seen that the quantity $\psi^*\psi$ plays the part of a probability density, in the sense that $\psi^*\psi \, dx \, dy \, dz$ gives the probability of finding the particle in the volume element $dx \, dy \, dz$. We have a sort of conservation law for this probability density: its integral over all space is unity, as shown in (3.4.1). In this respect it resembles the other familiar cases of conservation laws, such as those for mass and charge. In all such cases we can also set up a vector quantity representing the flux of the quantity which is conserved, such that the component of flux normal to any given surface gives the amount of material crossing unit area of the surface per second. If the density is ρ, the flux density f, then we always have the so-called equation of continuity,

$$\frac{\partial \rho}{\partial t} + \operatorname{div} f = 0. \tag{3.9.1}$$

This has the following significance: $\partial \rho / \partial t$ represents the increase in the amount of material per unit volume in unit time. By the divergence theorem, the integral of $\operatorname{div} f$ over unit volume can be converted into the surface integral of the outward flux of f over the surface of the unit volume. Thus (3.9.1) states that the amount of increase of material in unit time is the negative of the outward flux, or is the inward flux of material. In other words, the material is conserved: the amount within the unit volume increases in unit time by just the amount which has flowed in over the surface of the volume, and no material is created inside.

We must now expect that our probability density $\psi^*\psi$ will have a flux density associated with it, such that the two together will satisfy the equation of continuity (3.9.1). This is in fact the case, and the corresponding flux density is easily seen to be

$$f = \frac{h}{4\pi m i} (\psi^* \operatorname{grad} \psi - \psi \operatorname{grad} \psi^*). \tag{3.9.2}$$

To prove this, we need only take the divergence of f as given in (3.9.2), use Schrödinger's equation for the resulting Laplacians of ψ and ψ^*, and we find that div $f = -\partial(\psi^*\psi)/\partial t$, giving just the equation of continuity which we wished to prove. The flux f, given in (3.9.2), has an important place in quantum mechanics, as we see by analogy with electromagnetic theory. In that theory, we remember that there are quantities analogous to the density and flux; they are the energy density in the electromagnetic field, and Poynting's vector, measuring the flux of energy across a surface. When we set up the connection between classical electromagnetism and the quantum theory, as we did in Chap. 1, we assume that the energy density measures the probability of finding a photon in a given volume, and that Poynting's vector measures the probability that a photon will cross a given surface. In a similar way here $\psi^*\psi$ measures the probability of finding a particle in a given volume, and f measures the probability that it will cross a given surface. In other words, it has an analogy to Poynting's vector, and is used in the same sort of way that Poynting's vector is, in computing the flow of particles. We shall find it particularly useful, for instance, in studying electrical conduction, where we wish to get the flow of electrons constituting a current.

A flux f is often written in an alternative way as ρv, where ρ is the density, v the velocity, of the material, for the amount of material crossing unit area per second is always the density, times the component of velocity perpendicular to the surface. Thus there must be a relation between our flux (3.9.2) and the velocity, as found for instance in (3.8.1). We should in fact have $f = \psi^*\psi v$, since $\psi^*\psi$ stands for ρ in this case. If we wish the average velocity, we should integrate $\psi^*\psi v$ over all space, according to our general methods of getting averages. Thus we should have $\bar{v} = \int f\,dv$. The x component would be

$$\bar{v}_x = \frac{h}{4\pi mi} \int \left(\psi^* \frac{\partial \psi}{\partial x} - \psi \frac{\partial \psi^*}{\partial x}\right) dv. \tag{3.9.3}$$

This looks very much like the expression (3.8.1), but it is not exactly the same. To prove their identity, we consider the quantity

$$\int \int \int \frac{\partial}{\partial x}(\psi^*\psi) dx\,dy\,dz = \int \int \int \left(\psi^* \frac{\partial \psi}{\partial x} + \psi \frac{\partial \psi^*}{\partial x}\right) dx\,dy\,dz. \tag{3.9.4}$$

Here we have indicated the integrations separately with respect to x, y, and z. Let us carry out the integration first with respect to x in the expression on the left of (3.9.4). Since we are integrating a derivative, the result is the difference of the expressions $\psi^*\psi$ at the two limits of integration. If we have our usual case where we carry the integrations to infinity and ψ vanishes there, the left side of (3.9.4) is seen to vanish, showing that

$$\int \psi^* \frac{\partial \psi}{\partial x} \, dv = - \int \psi \frac{\partial \psi^*}{\partial x} \, dv.$$

When this result is substituted in (3.9.3), it leads to exactly the expression on the right side of (3.8.1), showing that our expression for f may in fact be considered as being equal to $\psi^*\psi v$, and that the average of this v is the same as the average velocity we have considered before, or the time rate of change of the average of x.

When we see the simplicity of the expression (3.8.1), containing only one term, we might well be tempted to ask why in (3.9.2) we have to have two terms, and why it is that f is not given by the simpler expression $(h/2\pi mi)\psi^*$ grad ψ. This is just what we should get if we took our operator p and let f be $\psi^*(p/m)\psi$, which would seem a very obvious way to set up the quantity. Yet our equation of continuity comes out right using (3.9.2), and we can easily prove to ourselves, by trying it out, that it does not come out right with the simpler alternative expression. The point is that f, as given in (3.9.2), is a real quantity, and the alternative form is complex, so that it cannot represent a physical flux. To see that (3.9.2) is real, we note that it is a complex quantity ψ^* grad ψ, minus the conjugate of this quantity, divided by i. Now any complex quantity minus its conjugate is pure imaginary, as we can see if we write the complex quantity as $a + bi$, its conjugate as $a - bi$. Thus when we divide it by i to get f, we have a real flux.

PROBLEMS

1. Prove that a coordinate commutes with another coordinate; a momentum commutes with another momentum; and a coordinate commutes with a momentum conjugate to another coordinate.

2. Write down the operators for the three components of angular momentum in rectangular coordinates.

3. Show that for the linear oscillator the assumptions

$$E_n = (n + \tfrac{1}{2})h\nu$$
$$x_{nn} = 0$$
$$x_{n+1,n} = x_{n,n+1} = \sqrt{\frac{h(n+1)}{8\pi^2 m\nu}}$$
$$x_{nm} = 0 \quad \text{if } m \neq n \pm 1$$

satisfy the quantum mechanics. To do this, compute the matrix components of $\dot{x}_{nm}$ and find the matrix of the energy expression $(m/2)(\dot{x}^2 + 4\pi^2\nu^2 x^2)$, computing the matrices of $\dot{x}^2$ and x^2 by the multiplication rule. Show that this matrix is diagonal, its diagonal components being the energy values given above.

4. By comparing with the wave functions of the linear oscillator given in Sec. 2.4, and in Prob. 4, Chap. 2, verify that the values of matrix components in Prob. 3 are

correct. If you cannot give a general proof, take the actual wave functions you have worked out in Prob. 4, Chap. 2, using them for $n = 0, 1, 2$, normalizing, and calculating the matrix components by direct integration.

5. Show that a linear oscillator radiating from the nth stationary state cannot jump except to the $(n - 1)$st state, so that there is a selection principle for its radiation. Compute the rate of radiation of the oscillator in the nth state, on the assumption that it is the same as that of a classical oscillator whose charge is e, displacement is $x_{n,n-1}e^{(2\pi i/h)(E_n - E_{n-1})t} + x_{n-1,n}e^{(2\pi i/h)(E_{n-1} - E_n)t}$. Compare this displacement with the displacement of a classical oscillator of energy E_n, showing that in the limit of large quantum numbers both amplitude and frequency of the classical oscillator agree with the quantum values. This is an example of the correspondence principle.

6. Solve Schrödinger's equation for a rotator, whose kinetic energy is $\frac{1}{2}I\dot{\theta}^2$, in the absence of an external force. Find wave functions, showing that the angular momentum is an integral multiple of $h/2\pi$. Compute the matrix of $R \cos \theta$, one component of displacement of a point attached to the rotator at a distance R from the axis. Show that all matrix components are zero except those in which the angular momentum changes by $\pm$ unity.

7. Find what $p^2q - qp^2$ is equal to, using the commutation rule for $pq - qp$.

8. Show that $e^{(2\pi i/h)p\alpha}u(x)$, where p is the x component of momentum, α is a constant, is equal to $u(x + \alpha)$. Use Taylor's expansion of the exponential operator.

9. Write down Schrödinger's equation in spherical polar coordinates, by using the Laplacian in these coordinates, assuming a potential $V(r)$. Discuss the method of deriving the equation from the Hamiltonian by replacing the momenta by differentiations, showing that the former method is consistent with the latter, but that the latter method does not lead to unique results.

10. A particle moves in a region of constant potential, bounded by infinitely high potential barriers at $x = 0$ and $x = L$. Find the normalized wave functions. From these find the matrix components of the momentum operator.

11. For the same system as in the previous problem, find the matrix components of the coordinate (measured from the center of the interval). From this find the matrix component of the velocity by differentiating with respect to time. Prove by direct comparison with the result of the preceding problem that the matrix of the velocity is $1/m$ times that of the momentum, where m is the mass of the particle.

12. A wave packet can be represented at time $t = 0$ by a function $e^{ikx}e^{-a(x-x_0)^2}$, or a sinusoidal wave with propagation constant k, modulated by a Gauss error curve which has its amplitude fall off as we go away from $x = x_0$. Assume that the wave packet is set up at $t = 0$, for the Schrödinger problem of motion of a free particle in a region between $x = 0$ and $x = L$, bounded at each limit by an infinitely high repulsive barrier. Find the coefficients c_i for the expansion of this wave packet in terms of the wave functions of the problem.

13. In the preceding problem it might be supposed that the wave packet would move, as time went on, with the group velocity (or velocity of the particle) along the x axis. Set up an expression for such a moving wave packet, and investigate how nearly this represents the appropriate solution of Schrödinger's equation.

14. The nonrelativistic Hamiltonian function for a charged particle of charge e, mass m, moving in an electric field $E = -\text{grad } \varphi$, and a magnetic field $B = \text{curl } A$, both independent of time, where φ, A are scalar and vector potentials, and where $\text{div } A = 0$, can be written $H = (p - eA)^2/2m + e\varphi$. Prove that Hamilton's equations $dx/dt = \partial H/\partial p_x$, $dp_x/dt = -\partial H/\partial x$ etc., lead to the correct equations of motion of the particle, $m\ddot{x} = e[E + (v \times B)]_x$, etc. *Hint:* In computing dA_x/dt, etc., you

must remember that A_x is to be computed at the position where the particle is. Thus

$$\frac{dA_x}{dt} = \frac{\partial A_x}{\partial x}\frac{dx}{dt} + \frac{\partial A_x}{\partial y}\frac{dy}{dt} + \frac{\partial A_x}{\partial z}\frac{dz}{dt}, \text{ etc.}$$

15. Using the Hamiltonian of the preceding problem, set up Schrödinger's equation for a particle moving in an electric and magnetic field.

16. Using the results of Probs. 9 and 15, set up Schrödinger's equation in spherical polar coordinates for a particle acted on by a spherically symmetrical potential $V(r)$ and a constant magnetic field along the z axis.

CHAPTER 4

PERTURBATIONS AND THE ACTION OF RADIATION

There are many problems in wave mechanics which, though they cannot be solved exactly, are approximated by soluble problems. Thus we may be able to solve the problem of an atom in free space, but when we put it in an external magnetic or electric field, the solution may become more difficult. The perturbation theory is a method for starting with the known approximate solution, and expanding in power series in the perturbation. In addition to external fields, there are many cases where the perturbation theory is applied. For example, in the study of atomic structure, it proves to be possible to set up a rather good approximation to the wave function of an atom by assuming that each electron moves in an electric field of spherical symmetry which approximately represents the forces exerted in the electron by the other electrons. This central field approximation is used as the starting point of a perturbation calculation, in which the real interactions of the electrons are taken into account. Again, in studying molecules, we can get a first approximation to the wave function by assuming that the electrons move as they would in the isolated atoms; the interaction of the electron of one atom with the other atoms forms the perturbation. These are only a few cases of the use of the method, which finds further application in almost all parts of wave mechanics.

The uses of perturbation theory which we have mentioned so far apply the method to the calculation of the stationary states and energy levels of a system too complicated for exact analysis. There is another type of application which is also of great importance, and this is to the interaction of radiation with atomic systems. We have already seen, in our discussion of Bohr's theory, the general principles governing the absorption and emission of radiation by atoms. However, we have noted that Bohr's theory did not allow one to make an exact calculation of the probability of transition from one state to another, or the intensity of radiation. We find that we can consider an external radiation field as a perturbation, and that instead of merely changing the wave functions and energy levels, as is the case with perturbations independent of the time, the effect is quite different: the radiation leads to transitions between stationary states, just as Bohr's theory would suggest. It is possible to give a fairly satisfactory treatment, by elementary application of perturbation theory, for the problem of absorption. The problem of emission, however, is more complicated, and leads us far into quantum electrodynamics to handle it properly. In this chapter we shall take up some of the more elementary aspects of the problem, going far enough, however, so that we can state the quantitative predictions regarding transition probabilities, and pointing out the rather important ways in which this elementary theory is incomplete.

4.1. Expansion in Unperturbed Wave Functions. Suppose that we wish to solve Schrödinger's equation $Hu_i = E_i u_i$, where H is the given Hamiltonian operator. Let us assume that we have a set of orthogonal functions u_i^0, called the unperturbed functions, which we know are not very far from the correct solutions u_i. We may know that the u_i^0's satisfy Schrödinger's equation $H^0 u_i^0 = E_i^0 u_i^0$, where H^0, the unperturbed Hamiltonian, is not far from the real Hamiltonian H. On the other hand, we may have set up the u_i^0's in some other way. It makes no difference in our calculation; but we shall generally assume that the u_i's will not differ far from the u_i^0's. Now let us expand the correct wave functions u_i in series in the u_i^0's. It is a general characteristic of sets of orthogonal functions that if the sets are what is called complete, we can expand any arbitrary function (with certain limitations regarding continuity) in series of the functions. Fourier's theorem forms an elementary example of this situation; the sines and cosines in terms of which we set up a Fourier's series form a complete orthogonal set of the type we are considering. In all such cases, it is a very difficult mathematical problem to prove that such an expansion can be made, and that it converges; but it is a very simple problem to find the coefficients of the expansion, for this can be done directly from the orthogonality relation, just as we determined the coefficients c_i in the expansion of the function ψ_0 in Eqs. (3.3.4) and (3.3.5).

We assume, then, that we can expand the u_i's as series in the u_i^0's. Let the series be written in the form

$$u_i = \sum_j S_{ji} u_j^0, \qquad (4.1.1)$$

where the S_{ji}'s are expansion coefficients. Then the problem may be regarded as that of finding these expansion coefficients. To do this, let us substitute the expression (4.1.1) into Schrödinger's equation $Hu_i = E_i u_i$. It becomes $\sum_j S_{ji}(H - E_i)u_j^0 = 0$. Let us multiply this by u_k^0* and integrate.   We then have, recalling that the u^0's are orthogonal,

$$\sum_j S_{ji}(\int u_k^0{}^*Hu_j^0 \, dv - E_i\delta_{kj}) = 0. \qquad (4.1.2)$$

Now the expression $\int u_k^0{}^*Hu_j^0 \, dv$ is the matrix component H_{kj} of H with respect to the unperturbed wave functions u^0. This, of course, is quite different from the matrix of H with respect to the correct wave functions u. This latter matrix, when we find it, will be diagonal, with the diagonal elements given by the E_i's. Our whole problem is to find these energy values, and the S_{ji}'s from which we can find the wave functions. However, we can calculate the matrix components $\int u_k^0{}^*Hu_j^0 \, dv$ at once, provided we know H and the u^0's, which we assume that we do (and provided also, of course, that the integration is not too hard to perform). We shall denote these components by H_{kj}, remembering that they are computed with respect to the unperturbed wave functions. We can then rewrite (4.1.2) in the form

$$\sum_j (H_{kj} - E_i\delta_{kj})S_{ji} = 0. \qquad (4.1.3)$$

The expression (4.1.3) reminds us in a symbolic way of Schrödinger's equation. We can rewrite it in a simpler way:

$$\sum_j H_{kj}S_{ji} = E_iS_{ki}, \qquad (4.1.4)$$

or

$$(HS)_{ki} = E_iS_{ki}, \qquad (4.1.5)$$

in which we have treated S_{ji} as if it formed a matrix itself and have used the law of matrix multiplication, (3.7.2), to find the matrix components of HS. In a symbolic way S takes the place of the wave function, and (4.1.4) or (4.1.5) resembles the ordinary Schrödinger equation $Hu_i = E_iu_i$. These symbolic matters are interesting, and when they are well understood they are suggestive in leading to new ways of handling problems. For the moment, however, let us look at our problem in a simple and straightforward way, and note that (4.1.4) forms in reality an infinite set of equations for the infinite set of S_{ki}'s.   Let us write them for a particular stationary state, say the ith.   Then we have

$$(H_{11} - E_i)S_{1i} + H_{12}S_{2i} + H_{13}S_{3i} + \cdots = 0 \qquad (k = 1)$$
$$H_{21}S_{1i} + (H_{22} - E_i)S_{2i} + H_{23}S_{3i} + \cdots = 0 \qquad (k = 2) \qquad (4.1.6)$$
$$\cdot \, \cdot$$

These equations, an infinite number of simultaneous homogeneous linear algebraic equations, must be solved for the S's and the quantity E_i. There is no straightforward way to solve such an infinite number of equations. The only way we can proceed is to start with a finite number and generalize as the number becomes infinite. Let us therefore ask what would happen if we cut the system off somewhere mathematically, keeping only n terms in each equation, and only n equations; later we ask what happens when n becomes infinite. We shall start with the simplest non-trivial case, $n = 2$, where we can very easily get the complete solution. We shall later see that this simple case has many very interesting applications itself; and at the same time, it points the way to the results in the general case.

4.2. Perturbations with Two Stationary States.   With only two terms to consider, (4.1.6) reduces to two simultaneous equations,

$$(H_{11} - E)S_1 + H_{12}S_2 = 0,$$
$$H_{21}S_1 + (H_{22} - E)S_2 = 0, \qquad (4.2.1)$$

where we have dropped the second subscript i. We now notice that we can divide each equation by S_1, so that there is only one quantity S_2/S_1 which is unknown, in addition to E. With two equations we can solve for these two quantities; but obviously we cannot find S_1 and S_2 separately, but only their ratio. This is natural; Schrödinger's equation cannot determine the function u_i uniquely, but only to an arbitrary factor, which must be determined by normalization. The easiest way to solve the simultaneous equations (4.2.1) is to set up the ratio S_2/S_1 from each, and equate them. That is, we have

$$\frac{S_2}{S_1} = -\frac{H_{11} - E}{H_{12}} = -\frac{H_{21}}{H_{22} - E}. \qquad (4.2.2)$$

Using the last two, we have

$$(H_{11} - E)(H_{22} - E) - H_{12}H_{21} = 0. \qquad (4.2.3)$$

This is a quadratic for E, if we multiply it out. If we solve it by formula, we find at once

$$E = \frac{H_{11} + H_{22}}{2} \pm \sqrt{\left(\frac{H_{11} - H_{22}}{2}\right)^2 + H_{12}H_{21}}. \qquad (4.2.4)$$

In (4.2.4) we have an expression for the two values of E, arising from the two signs of the square root. We should now denote one of these E_1, the other E_2; in other words, the index i, which we have discarded, is to take on different values for the different stationary states and energy levels of the exact problem. We may well ask which subscript should go with each sign in (4.2.4). The answer is simple. We are assuming that the unperturbed functions u^0 are not far from the correct wave functions u. But we know that in the correct system of wave functions, H has a diagonal matrix. We may therefore expect that the nondiagonal component H_{12} will be small with respect to the u^0's. Thus the term $H_{12}H_{21}$ in the radical in (4.2.4) is small. If it were zero, obviously the value of E arising from the positive sign in (4.2.4) would be H_{11}, and that arising from the negative sign would be H_{22}. These of course would be the energies E_1 and E_2 in this case. Since the correct E's will not depart greatly from these values, we use the same notation in the general case. Thus we write in general

$$E_1 = \frac{H_{11} + H_{22}}{2} + \sqrt{\left(\frac{H_{11} - H_{22}}{2}\right)^2 + H_{12}H_{21}}$$

$$E_2 = \frac{H_{11} + H_{22}}{2} - \sqrt{\left(\frac{H_{11} - H_{22}}{2}\right)^2 + H_{12}H_{21}}. \tag{4.2.5}$$

Knowing E_1 and E_2, we can now use either of the remaining equations (4.2.2) to find the ratio S_2/S_1. If we substitute E_1 in these equations we get S_{21}/S_{11}, and if we substitute E_2 we have S_{22}/S_{12}.

The solution in the form (4.2.5) is exact; but in more complicated cases we cannot get it in this explicit form, since the exact solution depends on having a quadratic, which we have only in our simple case $n = 2$. We can, however, get certain power series expansions in the general case, in powers of H_{12}, regarded as a small quantity. As a guide in setting up such expansions, let us expand the square root in (4.2.5) in power series, using the binomial expansion. We obtain without trouble

$$E_1 = H_{11} + \frac{H_{12}H_{21}}{H_{11} - H_{22}} + \cdots$$

$$E_2 = H_{22} + \frac{H_{12}H_{21}}{H_{22} - H_{11}} + \cdots . \tag{4.2.6}$$

This result is very interesting, in that it shows in a simple way the effect of the perturbation on the energy levels. In the first place, the numerator $H_{12}H_{21}$ of the perturbation term is necessarily positive. The reason is that the matrix H_{12} is Hermitian, so that $H_{21} = H_{12}^*$, and $H_{12}H_{21}$, being the product of H_{12} and its conjugate, equals the square of the absolute magnitude of H_{12}. The proof that H_{12} is Hermitian is a little more complicated than that given in (3.5.3), which applies to functions of the coordinates only; we discuss the Hermitian nature of matrices involving the momenta as well as coordinates in Appendix 9. If then the numerator of the perturbation term in (4.2.6) is positive, we see that if we assume H_{11} is greater than H_{22} (purely a matter of nomenclature), then E_1 is greater than H_{11}, and E_2 is less than H_{22}. In other words, the effect of the perturbation is to push the two unperturbed energy levels farther apart. This is a universal effect in perturbation theory, and will prove to have results of great importance in atomic and molecular structure. It is, for instance, the effect leading to the phenomenon of the covalent bond in molecular structure, responsible for holding atoms together to form molecules in large classes of materials.

There is one thing obvious about (4.2.6): the series of which we have written the first two terms will not converge if $H_{11} - H_{22}$ is small compared with $H_{12}H_{21}$. The binomial expansion used in setting up (4.2.6) converges only when $H_{12}H_{21}$ is smaller than $[(H_{11} - H_{22})/2]^2$, and converges rapidly only when it is a good deal smaller. Thus in a degenerate problem we cannot use this method. By a degenerate problem, in this connection, we mean one in which the energy levels H_{11} and H_{22} of the unperturbed problem coincide; and the difficulty remains if the difference $H_{11} - H_{22}$ is small compared with the magnitude of H_{12}. Expression (4.2.5) is of course usable even in this case. Thus if $H_{11} = H_{22}$, we have

$$E_1 = H_{11} + |H_{12}|, \qquad E_2 = H_{11} - |H_{12}|, \tag{4.2.7}$$

where we use the expression $|H_{12}|$ for the magnitude of H_{12}, which equals $\sqrt{H_{12}H_{21}}$. Here again the effect of the perturbation is to push the two energy levels apart; but the amount of the separation in this case goes as the first power of the nondiagonal matrix component H_{12}, rather than as the second power as in (4.2.6). This perturbation problem applied to the degenerate case proves in fact to be of even more practical importance than the nondegenerate case given in (4.2.6).

We can get considerable information about our perturbation problem by rewriting the expression (4.2.2) for the ratio S_2/S_1, using either of the approximate formulas (4.2.6) or (4.2.7) for the energy. For the nondegenerate case (4.2.6) we find

$$\frac{S_{21}}{S_{11}} = \frac{H_{21}}{H_{11} - H_{22}} + \cdots, \qquad \frac{S_{12}}{S_{22}} = \frac{H_{12}}{H_{22} - H_{11}} + \cdots. \tag{4.2.8}$$

That is, we have

$$u_1 = u_1^0 + \frac{H_{21}u_2^0}{H_{11} - H_{22}} + \cdots,$$

$$u_2 = u_2^0 + \frac{H_{12}u_1^0}{H_{22} - H_{11}} + \cdots. \tag{4.2.9}$$

In setting up the expressions (4.2.9), we have tacitly assumed that S_{11} and S_{22} were unity. We really are supposed to determine the absolute magnitudes of the S's, as we have mentioned earlier, by the condition that the u's, as well as the u^0's, must be normalized. If we apply this condition in the general case (4.1.1), multiplying u_i by u_i^* and integrating over the volume, taking advantage of the assumed normalization and orthogonality of the u^0's, the resulting condition is

$$\sum_j S_{ji}^* S_{ji} = 1, \qquad (4.2.10)$$

or the sum of the squares of the magnitudes of the S's equals unity. In our case, this leads to conditions like $|S_{11}|^2 + |S_{21}|^2 = 1$. This can be rewritten as $|S_{11}|^2(1 + |S_{21}|^2/|S_{11}|^2) = 1$. But we see from (4.2.8) that $|S_{21}|^2/|S_{11}|^2$ is of the order of magnitude of $|H_{12}|^2$, which is a smaller order of magnitude than we are keeping in our discussion of the S's, and therefore is to be discarded [though we have retained terms of this order in finding the energy in (4.2.6)]. Hence, to the order to which we are working, we have $|S_{11}|^2 = 1$, and we may take S_{11} to be real, as it will be in the limiting case where $H_{12} = 0$, and set it equal to unity. Thus the formulas (4.2.9) are justified.

The effect of the perturbation, then, in the nondegenerate case, is to modify each unperturbed wave function by adding to it a small amount of the unperturbed wave function associated with the other stationary state. The coefficient of this other function is proportional to the nondiagonal matrix component of energy between the two states, and inversely proportional to the energy difference between them. Thus the closer the two unperturbed energy levels, and the larger the nondiagonal matrix component between them, the greater will be the perturbation. A perturbation, then, in a sense mixes up the unperturbed wave functions. We shall find this same situation to hold in the general case, and it gives us a valuable physical insight into the effect of perturbations and the way in which a real stationary state can be, in a sense, a mixture of several unperturbed states.

The degenerate case, with energy as given in (4.2.7), is even simpler. In that case we have

$$\frac{S_{21}}{S_{11}} = \sqrt{\frac{H_{21}}{H_{12}}}, \qquad \frac{S_{22}}{S_{12}} = -\sqrt{\frac{H_{21}}{H_{12}}}. \qquad (4.2.11)$$

In the usual case where H_{12} is real, so that $H_{12} = H_{21}$, these lead to

$$\frac{S_{21}}{S_{11}} = 1, \qquad \frac{S_{22}}{S_{12}} = -1, \qquad (4.2.12)$$

and

$$u_1 = \frac{1}{\sqrt{2}}(u_1^0 + u_2^0), \qquad u_2 = \frac{1}{\sqrt{2}}(u_1^0 - u_2^0). \qquad (4.2.13)$$

In (4.2.13) we have determined the factors multiplying the wave functions in accordance with the normalization condition (4.2.10); here, since the coefficients multiplying the two unperturbed wave functions are of equal magnitude rather than one being small compared with the other, we cannot disregard the normalization factor $1/\sqrt{2}$ even for a first-order approximation.

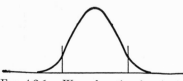

Fig. 4.2.1.   Wave function for single potential well.

This result, according to which the correct wave functions in a case of degeneracy are the sum and difference of the unperturbed functions, has many applications.   Let us mention one which we have already met, although we did not realize it at the time.   In Sec. 2.5 we took up the problem of a particle in two identical potential wells, separated by a barrier, as shown in Fig. 2.5.4.   This problem is simple enough so that we could quote the exact solution, shown in Fig. 2.5.5, in which we had two solutions, one symmetrical, the other antisymmetrical, in the midpoint of the barrier.   If it had happened to be too hard to solve exactly,

however, as it might in a corresponding three-dimensional case of an electron in a diatomic molecule, we could still have used a perturbation method to attack it. Suppose we could solve the problem of a single potential well, as in Fig. 4.2.1. The wave function, if it happened to be that of the lowest state, might look as in the figure. We could then use as two unperturbed wave functions u_1^0 and u_2^0 the functions as shown, appropriate to the two potential wells. Since the wells are identical, these two functions would

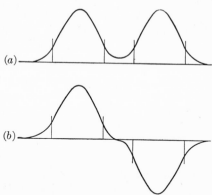

Fig. 4.2.2.   (a) Symmetric and (b) anti-symmetric wave functions for problem of two equal potential wells.

correspond to the same unperturbed energies, or the problem would be degenerate.   Then our result (4.2.13) tells us that the correct wave functions arising from the perturbation will be proportional to the sum and difference of these two functions.   The sum will resemble that shown in Fig. 4.2.2(a), and the difference in (b), symmetrical and antisymmetrical respectively.   Thus we can arrive at these ideas of symmetry and antisymmetry of wave functions in problems too complicated to solve completely.   We shall find such results to be of great importance in the study of molecular and solid-state structure.

4.3. Perturbations in the General Case.   We shall now try to generalize the results which we have obtained in the preceding section, for $n = 2$, to the general case, where we consider n unperturbed wave functions and n perturbed wave functions and energy levels arising from them.   In this case equations (4.1.6), again omitting the subscript i, become

$$(H_{11} - E)S_1 + H_{12}S_2 + \cdots + H_{1n}S_n = 0$$
$$H_{21}S_1 + (H_{22} - E)S_2 + \cdots + H_{2n}S_n = 0$$
$$\cdots \cdots \cdots \cdots \cdots \cdots \cdots \cdots \cdots \cdots \cdots \quad (4.3.1)$$
$$H_{n1}S_1 + H_{n2}S_2 + \cdots + (H_{nn} - E)S_n = 0.$$

Here again we can divide each equation through by one of the S's, say S_n, so that the unknowns are E, and the $n - 1$ ratios of the S's to S_n. With our n equations, we can determine these n quantities.   We cannot do it, however, by the elementary method of direct solution used in Sec. 4.2 and must use a little more powerful algebraic methods to handle the solution of the simultaneous equations.   In order to do this, we remind the reader of a few facts about the solution of simultaneous linear equations in algebra.

Suppose we have n simultaneous linear equations for n unknowns $S_1, \ldots, S_n$, of the form

$$a_{11}S_1 + a_{12}S_2 + \cdots + a_{1n}S_n = b_1$$
$$a_{21}S_1 + a_{22}S_2 + \cdots + a_{2n}S_n = b_2$$
$$\cdots \cdots \cdots \cdots \cdots \cdots \cdots \cdots \cdots \cdots \quad (4.3.2)$$
$$a_{n1}S_1 + a_{n2}S_2 + \cdots + a_{nn}S_n = b_n.$$

These form the general case of simultaneous linear equations.   In (4.3.1) the a's are obviously given by the equations $a_{ii} = H_{ii} - E$, $a_{ij} = H_{ij}$ if $i \neq j$, or more generally $a_{ij} = H_{ij} - E\delta_{ij}$.   Our case (4.3.1) is the special one where the b's are zero; in this case equations (4.3.2) are called homogeneous linear equations.   Now the general solution of (4.3.2) for the S's is well known from algebra and can be written in terms of determinants.   For S_1, for instance, we have

$$S_1 = \frac{\begin{vmatrix} b_1 & a_{12} & \cdots & a_{1n} \\ b_2 & a_{22} & \cdots & a_{2n} \\ \cdot & \cdot & \cdots & \cdot \\ b_n & a_{n2} & \cdots & a_{nn} \end{vmatrix}}{\begin{vmatrix} a_{11} & a_{12} & \cdots & a_{1n} \\ a_{21} & a_{22} & \cdots & a_{2n} \\ \cdot & \cdot & \cdots & \cdot \\ a_{n1} & a_{n2} & \cdots & a_{nn} \end{vmatrix}}. \quad (4.3.3)$$

The similar equation for any of the other S's is obtained by replacing the appropriate column of a's in the determinant in the numerator by the b's.

The general solution (4.3.3) is unfortunately not applicable in our case of the homogeneous equations. The reason is seen at once by considering the determinant in the numerator of (4.3.3) in case all the b's are zero, as they are if the equations are homogeneous. In this case the determinant in the numerator is zero, for it can be written as a sum of terms, each being one of the b's multiplied by its cofactor, and all the b's are zero. Thus we should conclude that all the S's were zero, except in one special case: that in which the determinant in the denominator was also zero. In that case the S's would be indeterminate, each equal to the ratio of $0/0$, and they could well be different from zero. In other words, our homogeneous case has no nonvanishing solutions unless the determinant of coefficients is zero. The reason why we should need some condition like this, in order to have solutions, is quite obvious. If the b's are zero in (4.3.2), we can divide each equation by S_n, and we then have n equations for the $(n - 1)$ ratios of the S's. Obviously we cannot satisfy these n equations for $(n - 1)$ unknowns, unless the coefficients satisfy special conditions, so that if $(n - 1)$ of the equations are satisfied, the nth also will be. This condition, obtained by setting the determinant of coefficients a_{ij} equal to zero, is necessary to make the equations compatible with each other and is often called the condition of compatibility.

In our problem this leads to the condition that the determinant of the quantities $H_{ij} - E\delta_{ij}$ must be zero; that is,

$$\begin{vmatrix} H_{11} - E & H_{12} & H_{13} & \ldots & H_{1n} \\ H_{21} & H_{22} - E & H_{23} & \ldots & H_{2n} \\ \cdots & \cdots & \cdots & \cdots & \cdots \\ H_{n1} & H_{n2} & H_{n3} & \ldots & H_{nn} - E \end{vmatrix} = 0. \qquad (4.3.4)$$

This is an equation for E and will have solutions for certain values of E which are then the energy levels E_i of the perturbed problem. For these particular energies, the equations (4.3.1) will be compatible and can be used to determine the ratios of the S's. This equation (4.3.4) is often called the secular equation. The reason comes from a problem in celestial mechanics. It is common to solve the problems of the perturbations of the planetary orbits by other planets by a perturbation method, applied to classical mechanics of oscillating systems, which has considerable mathematical analogy to our present methods. In place of E, the equation similar to (4.3.4) gives the perturbed frequencies of oscillation. Sometimes these perturbations lead to frequencies which, instead of being real, are pure imaginary; that is, the oscillations, instead of being given by an oscillatory term like $e^{i\omega t}$, are given by a real exponential e^{at}, increasing exponentially with the time. Such an exponential increase, denoting an unstable situation, is called a secular perturbation, and the equation analogous to (4.3.4) tells us which perturbations are secular. It is from this use that the term "secular equation" arose. Equations similar to (4.3.4) are met in many branches of mathematical physics.

We now notice that the secular equation (4.3.4) is an algebraic equation of the nth degree for E. The term of highest degree in E will come by multiplying together all the E's which appear in the diagonal terms of the determinant, and there are n of them. We have seen an example in our case of $n = 2$, where the secular equation can be written

$$\begin{vmatrix} H_{11} - E & H_{12} \\ H_{21} & H_{22} - E \end{vmatrix} = 0. \tag{4.3.5}$$

When we expand this determinant, we see that this equation is identical with the quadratic (4.2.3) which we obtained by elementary means in our case of $n = 2$. By a fundamental theorem of algebra, we know that any algebraic equation of the nth degree has n roots. Thus there will be n different values of E, which we may label E_1, E_2, . . . , E_n. As with the case for $n = 2$, we can decide how to label them by observing that they will approach H_{11}, H_{22}, . . . , H_{nn} as the nondiagonal matrix components of H approach zero, and we label each root E_i according to the diagonal matrix component H_{ii} which it approaches in that case. We can then take these n values of E_i, insert them in the equations (4.3.1), and in principle compute the ratios of the S's.

These steps, of course, cannot be carried out exactly in practice. A quadratic equation is easy to solve by formula; an equation of the third or fourth degree can be solved by formula, though it is rather complicated; while an equation of degree higher than four cannot be solved in elementary form. Thus for large values of n, with which we are concerned in our case, since we wish the limit as n becomes infinite, we are forced to use series methods. It is not hard, by considering the secular equation (4.3.4) and Eqs. (4.3.1), to arrange the terms formally in order of descending orders of magnitude, treating the nondiagonal matrix components H_{ij} as being small quantities. Then we can discard terms smaller than a given order, and the resulting equations prove to be easy to solve. We take up the details of this process, which is straightforward, in Appendix 10 and give only the results here. These results are very simple generalizations of those found earlier for the case $n = 2$. We find for the energy levels

$$E_i = H_{ii} + \sum_{j \neq i} \frac{H_{ij}H_{ji}}{H_{ii} - H_{jj}} + \cdots, \tag{4.3.6}$$

a direct generalization of (4.2.6). This shows us that the first approximation to the energy E_i is the diagonal matrix component H_{ii} of energy with respect to the unperturbed wave functions, or the average of the energy over this unperturbed function. This is correct not only to the zero-order approximation, but also to first-order terms: there is no term in the series (4.3.6) linear, or of the first order, in the H_{ij}'s. The next correction is the so-called second-order term in the energy, depending on the $H_{ij}H_{ji}$'s. Here we see, as for $n = 2$, that each other state exerts a perturbing effect on the ith state, that this effect is to push the ith state away from the jth in energy, and that the effect is proportional to the square of the nondiagonal matrix component of energy between the two states and inversely proportional to the energy difference between them. The total effect on the ith state, of course, is made up of a resultant of all these effects from other states; they all tend to push each other apart, and the net effect may displace any particular level either upward or downward, depending on whether more other levels push it one way or the other.

Proceeding in a similar way, we find approximate solutions for the perturbed wave functions, generalizations of Eqs. (4.2.9) which held for $n = 2$. We find

$$u_i = u_i^0 + \sum_{j \neq i} \frac{H_{ji} u_j^0}{H_{ii} - H_{jj}} + \cdots \qquad (4.3.7)$$

As in the case $n = 2$, we see that all unperturbed wave functions are mixed up in the correct functions, the contribution of any unperturbed function being greater, the greater the nondiagonal matrix component of energy between the states, or the less the unperturbed energy differences.

4.4. Perturbation Theory for Degenerate Systems. We shall often meet cases in which the unperturbed problem is degenerate; that is, where the diagonal energies H_{nn} of several states are almost exactly equal to each other. In this case the power-series method evidently does not work; the differences of energy which appear in the denominator of the terms in Eq. (4.3.6) or (4.3.7) become zero, or very small, and the series diverge and even have infinite terms. If there were only two levels, as in the special case taken up in Sec. 4.2, we could solve the problem explicitly, not using the power series at all; thus in (4.2.7) we found that the energy levels in such a case were $H_{11} \pm H_{12}$. With a finite number of degenerate levels, we have a secular equation of finite degree, and while we cannot solve it as conveniently as the quadratic, we can still approximate its solutions, even for the degenerate case where the differences of diagonal energies are smaller than the nondiagonal energy terms.

Now it fortunately happens that in many problems in which degeneracy enters, as in atomic spectra, the levels fall into groups, the energies of all the levels in a group being about the same, but the different groups being well separated in energy. Such groups of levels are the multiplets in atomic spectra. In these cases we first solve the problem of the levels within a group, finding an exact solution for the finite secular equation. This solution gives us not only energy levels, but also coefficients of linear combinations transforming the original wave functions of the group into a new set which has the property that it makes the matrix components of the energy diagonal with respect to the states of this group. We then use these transformed functions as the starting point of a new perturbation calculation, in which perturbations between adjacent groups are considered. In terms of these transformed functions, the energy will have no nondiagonal components between levels which lie close to each other in the groups, but only between levels in different groups, at a considerable energy distance apart. Thus we may use the series method of Eqs. (4.3.6) and (4.3.7), and the second-order terms will be small, since the only terms of the summation for which the denominator is small will have numerators equal to zero. It is to be particularly noted in this discussion that the difficulty in applying the power-series method to degenerate systems arises not on account of any unusual size of the nondiagonal energy components, but on account of the unusually small energy differences between diagonal terms. The method converges only if the nondiagonal component between any two levels is small compared with the difference of diagonal energies of the two terms. This demands that, before applying the power-series method, the nondiagonal terms between degenerate levels be removed, but it imposes no such requirement on the terms between levels of quite different energy.

When we handle a set of approximately degenerate, unperturbed levels by carrying out an exact solution of the secular equation, such as (4.3.4), there is an algebraic result, called the diagonal sum rule, which sometimes is very useful. This is a theorem, which we can easily prove, which states in words that the sum of all the perturbed energy levels E_i equals the sum of all the unperturbed diagonal energy components H_{ii}; in other words, those levels which are pushed upward by the perturbation just balance those which are pushed downward. Let us first prove this result, then show how it can be used. To prove it, we first expand the determinant (4.3.4) in descending powers of E. The terms in E^n and E^{n-1} both come entirely from the product of terms along the principal diagonal. We see by inspection, multiplying these terms together, that these terms are

$$E^n - (H_{11} + H_{22} + \cdots + H_{nn})E^{n-1} + \cdots = 0. \quad (4.4.1)$$

On the other hand, let us suppose that the roots of the secular equation (4.4.1) are E_1, E_2, . . . E_n. Then the fundamental theorem of algebra states that the equation can be written in the form

$$(E - E_1)(E - E_2) \cdots (E - E_n) = 0.$$

If we expand the equation in this form it is

$$E^n - (E_1 + E_2 + \cdots + E_n)E^{n-1} + \cdots = 0. \quad (4.4.2)$$

Comparison of (4.4.1) and (4.4.2), which must be alternative ways of writing the same equation, proves at once our theorem that

$$\sum_i H_{ii} = \sum_i E_i. \quad (4.4.3)$$

Now let us inquire how this sum rule can be used. We always know the sum of the H_{ii}'s. Then if, for instance, we have some way of finding all but one of the E_i's, (4.4.3) immediately gives an equation for finding the other one. More generally, if we have an independent way of finding several of the E's, say E_1, E_2, . . . , E_s, then we know the sum of the remaining ones, and this can often be very useful information. We shall find a case, in dealing with atomic multiplets, where this can lead to a solution of very complicated problems. We shall find a number of different groups of levels, containing a certain number of common energy values. Some of these values can be found from some of the groups, and we shall find that this information, plus the sum rule, allows us to get all the energy levels in many cases without solving any secular equations at all. There is another closely related way in which knowledge of some of the energy levels simplifies the secular equation. Since it can be written in the form $(E - E_1)(E - E_2)(E - E_3) \cdots (E - E_n) = 0$, we can divide it through by factors $(E - E_1)$, etc., in case we know E_1, etc. The equation will automatically be divisible by this factor, and each time we carry out such a division, we reduce the degree of the secular equation by one. Thus, for instance, if we have a problem with $n = 3$, leading to a cubic secular equation, but through some independent means know one of the energy levels, we can immediately reduce the problem to a quadratic equation, which can be solved at once.

4.5. The Method of Variation of Constants. A slightly different point of view in perturbations from that which we have so far used is obtained by considering the time variation of ψ. Let us expand ψ, the correct wave function depending on time, in series in the unperturbed functions u^0: $\psi = \sum_m C_m(t)u_m^0(x)$, where the C's, functions of time, would be pure exponentials, $c_m e^{-(2\pi i/h)E_m t}$, if the u^0's were the correct solutions of the problem. Whether correct or not, we can always make the expansion above, for at any instant ψ can be expressed in series in the orthogonal functions u^0, the coefficients being functions of time. Now let us try to satisfy the equation $H\psi = -\dfrac{h}{2\pi i}\dfrac{\partial\psi}{\partial t}$. We have

$$\sum_m \left(C_m H u_m^0 + \frac{h}{2\pi i}\frac{dC_m}{dt}\, u_m^0 \right) = 0.$$

We multiply by u_k^{0*} and integrate, and find

$$\frac{dC_k}{dt} = -\frac{2\pi i}{h}\sum_m H_{km} C_m. \tag{4.5.1}$$

These equations for the time derivatives of the C's in terms of their instantaneous values are enough to determine the complete solution of the problem.

To make connection with the ordinary method, we need only assume $C_m = S_{mn} e^{-(2\pi i/h)E_n t}$, an exponential solution. Then immediately we have, canceling the exponential and the factor $-2\pi i/h$,

$$E_n S_{kn} = \sum_m H_{km} S_{mn}, \tag{4.5.2}$$

or exactly the equation we have previously used. In more general cases, however, it is not always possible to make this assumption. An example is that in which the perturbative force depends on the time.

The method of variation of constants allows us to take up certain problems which throw a great deal of light on the question of transitions from one stationary state to another. As a first, very simple example, let us consider a particle in two identical potential wells, as illustrated in Fig. 2.5.4. Let us approach this problem by the perturbation method, as in the discussion of Fig. 4.2.1. The two unperturbed wave functions which we use are the same u_1^0 and u_2^0 considered in Sec. 4.2, corresponding to the particle being in a single well, with infinitely high barrier between. From our study of the corresponding perturbation problem in Sec. 4.2, we know that the energy levels are given by (4.2.7) and the S's by (4.2.12). Then we can set up the C's; and when we do this, adopting constants such that the final result will be normalized, we find

$$C_1 = \tfrac{1}{2}[e^{-(2\pi i/h)(H_{11}+H_{12})t} + e^{-(2\pi i/h)(H_{11}-H_{12})t}]$$

$$= e^{-(2\pi i/h)H_{11}t}\cos\frac{2\pi}{h}H_{12}t,$$

$$C_2 = i e^{-(2\pi i/h)H_{11}t}\sin\frac{2\pi}{h}H_{12}t, \tag{4.5.3}$$

where we assume that H_{12} is real, so that we do not need absolute value signs, as in (4.2.7). Now from our fundamental equation for ψ, we know that $C_1^* C_1$ will be the probability of finding the particle in state 1 (that is, in the first potential well), and $C_2^* C_2$ the probability of finding it in state 2 (in the second potential well). From (4.5.3) we have

$$C_1^* C_1 = \cos^2 \frac{2\pi}{h} H_{12} t, \qquad C_2^* C_2 = \sin^2 \frac{2\pi}{h} H_{12} t. \tag{4.5.4}$$

That is, we have a pulsation of the particle from one potential well to the other, as we described qualitatively in Sec. 4.2, but as we can see much more clearly from this expression. Obviously we have

$$C_1^* C_1 + C_2^* C_2 = 1,$$

from (4.5.4), as we must expect.

The interpretation of this result is very significant. The unperturbed states 1 and 2 are not really stationary states of the perturbed system; and (4.5.4) can be interpreted as saying that if we try to regard them as stationary states, the perturbation, whose matrix component is H_{12}, induces transitions from one to the other, so that if the probability is unity of finding the particle in state 1 (or potential well 1) at $t = 0$, as the constants of (4.5.4) give, then after a time $h/4H_{12}$ the probability of finding the particle in the first well will have gone to zero, and that of finding it in the second well will be unity. After an equal time it will be back in the first well, and so on, pulsating from one well to the other in a phenomenon of beats. This pulsation is a result of our treating the unperturbed states as being stationary states when they really are not; if we used the linear combinations of them, which really are stationary states, we could set up a situation independent of time, in which the particle was in either the symmetric or the antisymmetric state. Our present solution, resulting in pulsations, is effectively a way of setting up wave packets.

We can now set up more complicated problems of the same general sort. For example, we can have a problem with n identical potential wells, where n is greater than 2. Then the solutions for $C_1, \ldots, C_n$, similar to (4.5.3), will be superpositions of terms with n frequencies, so that the C^*C's, like (4.5.4), will have many beat frequencies. Here we shall have a situation different in one essential respect from the case of $n = 2$ which we have just taken up. The superposition of many oscillations, with many beat frequencies, will not result in a periodic solution, but rather in one of the type called multiply periodic. If we start at $t = 0$ with a particular solution, say corresponding to $C_1 = 1$, all other C's $= 0$, this solution will never recur, for this would demand that all the sinusoidal terms should come back to their original values. Instead, the probability will remain distributed over the various potential wells, and the larger n is, the less likely will it be to become concentrated in any one potential well at any future time.   In other words, a probability function, or wave function, which at one instant is concentrated in one potential well, will then become dissipated irreversibly over all the wells.   This irreversibility is of a thermodynamic type and is a direct consequence of the largeness of n.   Such phenomena are common in mechanics.   Thus consider a system of n particles elastically coupled by springs.   If we set one of these into oscillation, the energy will be transmitted to its neighbors through the mechanism of the springs.   If n is very small, say equal to 2, the energy will pulsate back and forth between the two particles.   But if n is very large, it will be dissipated permanently and irreversibly.   This is a simple mechanical model for heat conduction in a solid: the atoms of the solid are like the particles, the elastic forces like the springs, and if we have one atom excited initially, with large kinetic energy, the others remaining fixed, the energy of this excited atom resembles thermal excitation to a high temperature, which will gradually be dissipated through the whole solid by conduction.

Similar irreversible results of the application of the method of variation of constants are seen when we study collision problems.   Suppose that an electron collides with an atom, being scattered either without change of energy, or with decrease or increase of energy corresponding to raising or lowering the energy of the atom.   We can start with a number of unperturbed, not quite stationary states: first, the electron approaching the atom, with the atom in its original state; second, an electron being scattered, say in a definite direction, or better, with some function of angle represented by a spherical harmonic, with its initial energy, the atom being unchanged; third, an electron scattered with a decrease of energy corresponding to a transition of the atom, with the atom in the correspondingly excited state; fourth, an electron scattered with increase of energy, the atom being in a lower state, after what is called a collision of the second kind.   All these states have approximately the same energy, so that the perturbation problem between them, resulting from the fact that they are not solutions of the problem in the region where the electron is in the atom, is one of transition between systems of approximately the same energy.   Here, as before, it is often convenient to proceed by the method of variation of constants, and from this we get the probabilities of the various elastic and inelastic impacts.   One thing is worth noting in all these problems: in the method of variation of constants, the quantity determining the probability of transition is the nondiagonal matrix component of the perturbing energy between the different approximately stationary states. Thus the calculation resolves itself into a computation of these matrix components, and transitions are likely for which the matrix components are large.

We see from these examples the way in which perturbations can be regarded as causing transitions between unperturbed stationary states: if we try to describe a system by states which would be stationary in the absence of a perturbation, but which are not correct stationary states in the presence of the perturbation, the method of variation of constants shows us that the effect of the perturbation may be described as producing transitions between these unperturbed states. Probably the most familiar agency for causing transitions between stationary states is radiation; and in the next section we show that the absorption and emission of radiation by atomic systems can be handled by the method of variation of constants, in a way quite analogous to what we have been taking up already, and that in that problem, as in the ones we have considered, the probability of transition depends on nondiagonal matrix components of perturbative energy between the stationary states in question.

4.6. The Action of Radiation on Atomic Systems. The general nature of the action of radiation on atoms and molecules was explained by Bohr, and particularly by Einstein, before wave mechanics was developed. We shall first look into this general explanation, to gain background for the wave-mechanical treatment. Bohr assumed that an atom in an excited state had a certain probability per unit time of radiating to any lower energy level, the emitted quantum having a frequency given by the frequency condition. Also he assumed that under action of an external radiation field of the appropriate frequency, there was a certain probability, proportional to the intensity of the radiation, that energy would be absorbed and the atom raised to a higher state. Einstein formulated the probabilities in mathematical language and, furthermore, investigated the thermodynamic relations of the radiation, and the requirements of thermal equilibrium under the action of black-body radiation. From these requirements he was able to deduce relationships between the probabilities of emission and absorption.

Einstein assumed that an atom in the mth state has a probability A_{mn} of radiating spontaneously to any state n of lower energy, with emission of the corresponding photon of frequency ν_{mn}, given by $E_m - E_n = h\nu_{mn}$. That is, if there are N_m atoms in the mth state, the number of these radiating per second to the nth state is $N_m A_{mn}$. Secondly, if there is an external radiation field, with energy density ρ_{mn} at the frequency concerned, he assumed a probability $B_{mn}\rho_{mn}$ of absorbing a photon of frequency ν_{mn} from the radiation field, where now the state n has a higher energy than m, and jumping up to the state n. Furthermore, he found that to get thermal equilibrium, he also had to postulate a similar probability $B_{mn}\rho_{mn}$ of emitting radiation accompanied by a transition from the mth state to a state n, which now has lower energy than m, under action of the external radiation field; this is called induced or forced emission.

He then considered the interaction of a system of atoms in thermal equilibrium at a temperature T, with black-body radiation at this same temperature. The black-body radiation is known to satisfy Planck's distribution law, which states that the energy density ρ_ν at frequency ν is given by

$$\rho_\nu = \frac{8\pi h\nu^3}{c^3}\frac{1}{e^{h\nu/kT}-1}, \tag{4.6.1}$$

where c is the velocity of light. Furthermore, the atoms will satisfy the Maxwell-Boltzmann distribution law, according to which the number of atoms in a state of energy E is proportional to $e^{-E/kT}$. Then let us consider a particular set of atoms, having a lower state 1, an upper state 2, with energies E_1 and E_2 respectively. Let there be N_1 atoms in state 1, N_2 in state 2; the Maxwell-Boltzmann law states that

$$\frac{N_2}{N_1} = e^{-(E_2-E_1)/kT} = e^{-h\nu/kT},$$

where ν is the frequency emitted or absorbed in the transition between states 1 and 2. But now we should be able to deduce N_1 and N_2 from our probabilities of transition, combined with the density (4.6.1) of black-body radiation: we know that atoms can be maintained in thermal equilibrium by interaction with black-body radiation, so that if we find the probabilities of transition from state 1 to state 2, and state 2 to state 1, under the action of radiation of density (4.6.1) and write the condition that the number of atoms in each state shall be independent of time, as in equilibrium, these resulting numbers must satisfy the Maxwell-Boltzmann relation. Let us carry out this calculation.

If there are N_1 atoms in state 1, the number having transitions per second to state 2 will be $N_1B_{12}\rho_\nu$; while if there are N_2 in state 2, the number having transitions per second to state 1 will be $N_2(A_{21}+B_{21}\rho_\nu)$. For thermal equilibrium, these numbers must be equal; otherwise the difference would represent the rate at which the excess of atoms in one state or the other was building up. Thus we have

$$N_1B_{12}\rho_\nu = N_2(A_{21}+B_{21}\rho_\nu).$$

But now let us use the Maxwell-Boltzmann relation between the N's. We then have

$$B_{12}\rho_\nu = e^{-h\nu/kT}(A_{21}+B_{21}\rho_\nu). \tag{4.6.2}$$

First let us consider the case of a very high temperature, where ρ_ν is very great.   If it is great enough, we can neglect the term A_{21} in comparison with B_{21} and can set $e^{-h\nu/kT} = 1$.   Thus from this limit we see that we must have $B_{12} = B_{21}$: the probabilities of absorption and of forced emission are equal.   It is from this argument that Einstein deduced the necessity for the existence of forced emission.   We can now solve (4.6.2) for ρ_ν, and obtain

$$\rho_\nu = \frac{A_{21}}{B_{21}} \frac{1}{e^{h\nu/kT} - 1}.$$

Comparison with Planck's law (4.6.1) shows at once that we must have

$$\frac{A_{21}}{B_{21}} = \frac{8\pi h\nu^3}{c^3} \tag{4.6.3}$$

in order that Planck's law should lead to thermal equilibrium.   Einstein postulated (4.6.3), and used this as a derivation of Planck's law; but we can equally well use it to prove (4.6.3) from thermodynamics, and hence to allow us to get all the probability coefficients for interaction with radiation, provided one of them, say B_{21}, is known.

The rules we have just stated take on a particularly interesting form if we look a little more deeply into the derivation of Planck's law.   This is commonly carried out in the following way:[†] First, we assume a perfectly reflecting enclosure and consider the standing waves of light or electromagnetic radiation in it.   The boundary conditions on these waves are very simple if the enclosure is rectangular: we must have a whole number of half wave lengths contained in each dimension, just as in our problem of the standing Schrödinger waves in a box, in Sec. 2.5.   We find the frequency of each such wave, count the number of waves whose frequencies lie in the interval $d\nu$, and find that this number is $8\pi\nu^2/c^3 \, d\nu$.   Next we consider that a standing wave really does not have an arbitrary, continuously variable energy, but that its energy must be quantized and equal to an integer times $h\nu$.   Then (as shown, for instance, in the reference above) the mean energy, in the form of photons, which will be found in connection with this standing wave, at temperature T, is

$$\text{Energy} = \frac{h\nu}{e^{h\nu/kT} - 1}. \tag{4.6.4}$$

If we combine the number of such waves in the interval $d\nu$, with the mean energy per wave given in (4.6.4), we are led at once to Planck's law (4.6.1).

† See, for instance, J. C. Slater, "Introduction to Chemical Physics," McGraw-Hill Book Company, Inc., New York, 1939, Chap. XIX.

It is clear that the number of waves in the interval $d\nu$, which we have seen to be $8\pi\nu^2/c^3\,d\nu$, has a close relationship to the ratio A_{21}/B_{21} of (4.6.3). Let us see just what this relationship is. We can see it by writing out probabilities of emission and absorption not in terms of the density ρ_ν, but in terms of the average number N_ν of photons in the electromagnetic wave of frequency ν. The energy in a frequency range $d\nu$ can be written, on the one hand, as $\rho_\nu\,d\nu$; but it can be written alternatively as $N_\nu h\nu(8\pi\nu^2/c^3\,d\nu)$; that is, the product of the number of photons per wave, the energy of a photon, and the number of waves in $d\nu$. If we use this relation, the number of atoms in state 2 emitting photons per second will be

$$N_2(A_{21} + B_{21}\rho_\nu) = N_2 B_{21}\left(\frac{8\pi h\nu^3}{c^3} + N_\nu\,\frac{8\pi h\nu^3}{c^3}\right)$$

$$= N_2 B_{21}\frac{8\pi h\nu^3}{c^3}\,(N_\nu + 1). \tag{4.6.5}$$

Similarly the number of atoms in state 1 absorbing photons per second will be $N_1 B_{21}(8\pi h\nu^3/c^3)N_\nu$. When we write the probabilities in this form, it is clear that the term representing spontaneous emission resembles a correction term of unity to the number N_ν measuring the density of radiation.

4.7. Dirac's Theory of the Radiation Field. We have now secured enough background so that we can understand the general ideas of the theory of interaction of radiation and matter suggested by Dirac, though we shall not give the details. (They are taken up in Appendix 11.) The essential point is that the radiation field is treated, not by the classical Maxwell's equations, but by wave mechanics. According to Maxwell's equations, the energy in a reflecting cavity can be treated as the sum of the energies in the various standing waves, and each of these standing waves can be characterized by an amplitude oscillating sinusoidally with the time, as if it were the amplitude of a linear oscillator, vibrating in classical mechanics. Dirac assumed that instead of treating these amplitudes by classical mechanics, they had to be treated by quantum theory. We could, for instance, assume that there was a Schrödinger equation applying to each of the amplitudes. There would be a wave function describing each and giving the probability that this amplitude should lie within given limits. In other words, we assume that in quantum electrodynamics it is just as impossible to determine the value of an electric field precisely, as it is impossible to determine an ordinary coordinate precisely in ordinary quantum mechanics. When we quantize the amplitudes of the separate electromagnetic oscillations in this way, we find, just as for any linear oscillator, that the energy can have only the values $(n + \frac{1}{2})h\nu$, where n is an integer, ν the frequency of the standing wave.

In other words, we find that the energy associated with a given standing wave can take on only quantized values, differing by the amount $h\nu$. This is the interpretation, according to quantum electrodynamics, of the existence of photons: the number of photons associated with a given electromagnetic wave is another way of describing the quantum number of the quantum-theoretical problem of finding the wave function governing the amplitude of that electromagnetic wave. The $\frac{1}{2}h\nu$ of energy associated with $n = 0$ is generally considered to have no physical significance: it would imply, literally, that there was an infinite amount of energy always present in the radiation field, since there are an infinite number of standing waves, but since this is a constant correction and does not change in any physical process, it does not have to be considered. (This is one, though by no means the worst, of the various points in which the present theory of quantum electrodynamics is still imperfect on account of infinite additive terms which are very difficult to remove.)

We can follow further this interpretation of the quantum number n as the number of photons associated with a standing electromagnetic wave. If the amplitude of such a wave is governed by quantum theory, it is clear that fluctuations in the electric field, or electromagnetic energy, must be allowed. If we try to define an electromagnetic field precisely, we form a sort of wave packet, not of the elementary type we have previously considered, but one in which the coordinates are the amplitudes of the various electromagnetic waves. We can ask what are the limiting conditions which must hold so that this wave packet moves according to classical mechanics, that is, so that the resulting average field, averaged over the wave packet, will satisfy Maxwell's equations, with negligible fluctuation. We find that this limiting case is that in which all the n's are very large; that is, there are many photons associated with each standing wave. If we consider ordinary electromagnetic or radiation problems, we find that this is always the case in the part of the energy spectrum which we commonly treat by electromagnetic means: say at electromagnetic wave lengths from a millimeter up. On the other hand, in the visible and ultraviolet part of the spectrum it is almost never the case. In other words, we are justified in treating electromagnetic problems by classical electromagnetic theory, as we habitually do, but radiation in the optical region must be handled by the quantum theory. We can ask what is the nature of the fluctuations which occur when the n's are small; and we can show that they are precisely the sort which we should expect if the radiation in fact consisted of small particles of energy $h\nu$, and if the number of these per unit volume were fluctuating according to the same rules as the molecules of a gas.   It is from such arguments as these (which are taken up in more detail in Appendix 11), that the particle nature of the photon follows from the general theory of quantum electrodynamics.

The number N_ν which we introduced earlier, in Eq. (4.6.5), is the same as the average value of n.   We have just seen that classical electromagnetic theory can be expected to hold only when the N_ν's are all large. From (4.6.5) we see that in this case unity is negligible compared to N_ν, or that the spontaneous emission is negligible compared to the induced emission or absorption.   On the other hand, in the ordinary optical case, N_ν has an average value very small compared with unity.   Of course, this means that a few of the waves have $n = 1$, still fewer have n greater than 1, but the great majority have $n = 0$, since n must be an integer. We can see why this is the case from Planck's law (4.6.1).   This can be written, in our present language, as

$$N_\nu = \frac{1}{e^{h\nu/kT} - 1}.$$

If $h\nu$ is large compared with kT, as it will be if ν is a frequency in the visible range, T is anything of reasonable magnitude, then clearly N_ν will be small compared with unity.   Then we may expect that the treatment of spontaneous emission, which depends on the term unity in comparison with N_ν, will be handled completely nonclassically, as far as the electromagnetic theory is concerned.   This proves in fact to be the case.

Let us now consider how Dirac treated the interaction of matter and radiation.   He started with an unperturbed state in which the atom he was considering was in its mth state, and each of the electromagnetic oscillations had an amplitude determined by a given quantum number n_ν.   These would be correct stationary states if there were no interaction between the atom and the radiation.   Next he introduced the interaction as a perturbation.   This interaction energy can be written as the electric dipole moment of the atom, times the component of electric field in the direction of the dipole moment; alternatively, it can be written in terms of the vector potential of the electromagnetic field, and the current density or velocity in the atom.   This can be phrased to be written in terms of the coordinates of the particles of the atom and the coordinate which gives the amplitude of the electromagnetic wave.   There will be such a term for the interaction with each electromagnetic wave.   Dirac then applied the method of variation of constants to the problem.   This introduces transitions, in the manner which we have considered in Sec. 4.5, to a great many other possible states of the combined system. These other states are those in which the atom has had a transition to some other state, say the nth, with either greater or less energy than the original mth state; and in which, simultaneously, one of the electromagnetic wave coordinates has had its quantum number make a compensating transition, such that the final energy of the composite state is approximately equal to the initial, the radiation component gaining or losing approximately enough energy to compensate for the energy change of the atom. There are many such states, for each possible transition of the atom, for many different electromagnetic waves have about the right energy to compensate for the energy change in the transition. Dirac, in his original calculation, did not set up a complete solution of the differential equations concerned in the method of variation of constants, analogous to (4.5.1); but he carried it far enough to show that $C_m^* C_m$, which started with the value unity, decreased for a short time linearly with time, the rate of decrease being in exact agreement with Einstein's postulates: that is, it was as if there were transitions to all other possible atomic states, transitions to higher states occurring at a rate proportional to the density of external radiation, those to lower states having in addition a spontaneous transition probability of the suitable type. At the same time that the $C_m^* C_m$ for the original stationary state decreased, compensating probabilities built up for states in which the atom appeared in another stationary state, and appropriate electromagnetic waves had a different quantum number, or number of photons. In this way Einstein's hypothesis was fully confirmed.

At the same time that this general confirmation of the laws of transition between stationary states was derived, it was naturally possible to get an explicit formula for the A_{mn}'s or B_{mn}'s associated with the transitions, for these come from the matrix component of perturbative energy between the stationary states in question. We have already stated that the energy can be written as the product of the atomic dipole moment and the electric field. The terms in the time rate of change of $C_m^* C_m$ coming from the first power of this matrix component vanish on the time average, as we should expect from the random phase which the electromagnetic field has, and it is products or squares of matrix components which are concerned in the A's and B's. We expect, then, that the probability of transition will depend on the square of the field (that is, on the intensity or energy density of the radiation), as it should, and furthermore, on the square of the matrix component of the electric dipole moment of the atom. This is in fact correct, and the formula proves to be

$$A_{21} = \frac{64\pi^4 (ex)_{12}^2 \nu^3}{(4\pi\epsilon_0) 3 c^3 h}. \tag{4.7.1}$$

Here $(ex)_{12}$ is the matrix component of x component of electric moment of the atom between states 1 and 2, that is, the charge on the electron times the matrix component of the displacement of the electron.   The quantity ν is the frequency absorbed or emitted in the transition.   The formula is given in the rationalized mks system of electromagnetic units; ϵ_0 is the fundamental constant occurring in those units.   To get the corresponding formula in the non-rationalized Gaussian system we omit the factor $4\pi\epsilon_0$.

This formula (4.7.1) has an interesting semiclassical interpretation, which was used to derive it before the quantum electrodynamics was fully developed.   If we have an electric dipole whose dipole moment is $M \cos 2\pi\nu t$, it radiates according to classical electromagnetic theory at a rate†

$$\frac{16\pi^4 M^2 \nu^4}{(4\pi\epsilon_0)3c^3}.$$

This is obviously similar to (4.7.1).   Corresponding to our transition, we have matrix components, according to the quantum theory, which are

$$(ex)_{12}e^{-(2\pi i/h)(E_2-E_1)t} + (ex)_{21}e^{-(2\pi i/h)(E_1-E_2)t} = 2(ex)_{12} \cos 2\pi\nu t,$$

where $h\nu = E_2 - E_1$.   Thus the M above is $2(ex)_{12}$, and the rate of radiation above is

$$\frac{64\pi^4(ex)_{12}^2\nu^4}{(4\pi\epsilon_0)3c^3}.$$

The number of photons radiated per second by such an oscillator would be just that given by (4.7.1).   This analogy between classical radiation from a dipole and our values of the A's from quantum theory, though suggestive, cannot be carried far enough to give a completely classical treatment of the radiation and absorption.

Formula (4.7.1) is obviously of great importance when we wish to find the intensity of spectral lines.   It is also the origin of the selection principles, which have been mentioned earlier.   If a matrix component $(ex)_{12}$ is zero, we now see that the probability of a transition between the two states concerned, with emission or absorption of radiation, is zero, and we say that the transition is forbidden.

We have discussed the application of Dirac's method to the evaluation of the probabilities of emission and absorption; these matters are discussed in more detail in Appendix 11.   The same method can, however, be carried much further, to discuss all the optical properties of the atoms and the radiation.   Thus we can investigate the angular dependence of the emitted intensity (our formulas given above are for the assumption that it is emitted isotropically), and its polarization.   We can look into the spectral distribution of the radiation.   We have pointed out that the

† See, for instance, Slater and Frank, "Electromagnetism," McGraw-Hill Book Company, Inc., New York, 1947, p. 159.

modes of electromagnetic radiation which are excited must have photons corresponding approximately to the energy difference in the atom; but this correspondence does not have to be exact. The effect of energy difference is like that always found in perturbation problems, the states corresponding to almost the same energy being most important. We do not, then, have a perfectly monochromatic emitted wave, and by looking into the distribution of energy, we can investigate the spectrum of the emitted light. We find, as in classical optics, that the more slowly the atom radiates, or the longer it stays in its stationary state before its transition, the narrower is the resulting spectral line. In fact, we find that the breadth $\Delta \nu$ of the line is related to the lifetime τ of the atom by the relation $\tau \, \Delta \nu = 1$, or $\tau \, \Delta(h\nu) = \tau \, \Delta E = h$, a form of the uncertainty principle, showing that the product of the uncertainty in the time when the atom radiates (that is, the lifetime in the excited state), multiplied by the uncertainty in its energy, which we should need to account for the breadth of the spectrum line, equals h. This simple formula is, as a matter of fact, too simplified in one respect: if both the initial and the final state corresponding to a transition have finite lifetimes, we must ascribe an uncertainty in energy to each, according to the formula above; the uncertainty in energy difference, or the frequency breadth, then is the sum of the uncertainties arising from both initial and final states.

We shall not go further into the many problems of the optical behavior of matter which can be treated by these methods. There is one problem, however, to which we shall return later: that of the polarizability of atoms or molecules, as related to the refractive index and dielectric constant. We find that at each absorption frequency of an atomic system, there is also an anomaly in the refractive index, just as in the classical theory of refractivity, and its amount is determined by the same quantities A_{12} and B_{12} which we have derived. These quantities will then prove to be important in the theory of dielectrics. This is natural, since dielectric behavior is determined by the existence of electric dipoles in the atoms or molecules concerned.

PROBLEMS

1. Prove that if both unperturbed and perturbed functions u_n^0 and u_n are orthogonal and normalized, the transformation coefficients S_{mn} satisfy the orthogonality and normalization conditions.

2. Show that if we expand the correct wave functions in a series of functions which are not exactly orthogonal or normalized, the equations for the transformation coefficients S_{mn} are

$$\sum_m (H_{km} - E_n d_{km}) S_{mn} = 0,$$

where $d_{km} = \int u_k^{0*} u_m^0 \, dv$, which now is not diagonal and is not equal to δ_{km}.

3. Consider a degenerate system in which there are two unperturbed wave functions, having equal diagonal energies $H_{11} = H_{22}$, which are normalized but not orthogonal to each other, so that $\int u_1^0{}^* u_2^0 \, dv = d_{12} \neq 0$. Show that the two energy levels are $\dfrac{H_{11} + H_{21}}{1 + d_{12}}, \dfrac{H_{11} - H_{21}}{1 - d_{12}}$.

4. Show that the two correct wave functions in Prob. 3 are $\dfrac{u_1^0 + u_2^0}{\sqrt{2(1 + d_{12})}}$, $\dfrac{u_1^0 - u_2^0}{\sqrt{2(1 - d_{12})}}$, respectively. Prove them to be normalized and orthogonal.

5. Prove from Schrödinger's equation that the sum $\displaystyle\sum_n c_n^* c_n$ always remains constant.

6. Start with the solution of the problem of a single potential well, as in Fig. 4.2.1. Use the solutions of this problem as a starting point in discussing the problem of two potential wells, as in Fig. 2.5.4. First show that the correct linear combinations of the unperturbed functions are the symmetric and antisymmetric combinations, as mentioned in the text. Find the energies of these states by first-order perturbation theory.

7. Solve the problem of a particle in three identical and equally spaced potential wells, as in the accompanying figure, by perturbation theory, starting with the solution for a single potential well as the unperturbed problem. If you proceed directly,

you will encounter a cubic secular equation. To avoid having to solve this, note that all solutions may be expected to be either symmetric or antisymmetric in the mid-point of the system of wells. Set up symmetric and antisymmetric combinations of the solutions of the separate wells and use these as the unperturbed solutions. You will find that there are no matrix components of energy between a symmetric and an antisymmetric function, and this will simplify the problem enough so that you can solve the problem of degeneracy. Draw the form of the correct wave functions found from perturbation theory, discuss their qualitative nature, and find the energy levels.

8. Find whether a rotator's energy is affected, to the first or higher orders of approximation, by a constant external field in the plane of the rotator.

9. Prove by perturbation theory that the energy levels of a linear oscillator are not affected by a constant external field, except in absolute value, all being shifted up or down together. Why should this be expected physically?

10. A linear oscillator is perturbed by having a small perturbative potential ax^3, where x is the displacement from equilibrium. Find the matrix components of the perturbative energy. (*Hint:* You can do this easily by matrix algebra from the matrix components for x found in Prob. 3, Chap. 3.) Will this perturbation make any first-order change in the energy levels?

11. The perturbation discussed in the preceding problem will appear to cause transitions between stationary states if we describe the oscillator by its unperturbed wave functions. What selection rule will govern these transitions, and what will be the matrix components determining the rate of transition?

12. A linear oscillator is in its nth stationary state. Find the rate of spontaneous radiation of energy to the $(n - 1)$st state according to the quantum theory of radia-

tion, using the values of the matrix components of electric moment found from Prob. 3, Chap. 3. Compare the rate of radiation with the corresponding classical rate of radiation of an oscillator of the same energy.

13. Carry out a discussion of the absorption of radiation by a one-electron atom, treating the radiation field as an electric field $\sum_{\nu} \mathbf{E}_{\nu} \cos 2\pi(\nu t - \alpha_{\nu})$, where $\mathbf{E}_{\nu}$ and α_{ν} are constants, $\mathbf{E}_{\nu}$ being a vector, and the summation is over many components of different frequencies. Treat the corresponding energy $-e\mathbf{r} \cdot \sum_{\nu} \mathbf{E}_{\nu} \cos 2\pi(\nu t - \alpha_{\nu})$ of the electron of charge $-e$, at a vector distance $\mathbf{r}$ from the nucleus, as a perturbation energy depending on the time. Such a treatment gives a correct account of the absorption, but not of spontaneous emission. Use the method of variation of constants, showing that the field produces transitions between different stationary states. Assume that at $t = 0$ the systems are all in the ground state, so that the constant c_0, corresponding to the ground state in the expression

$$\psi = \sum_{n} c_n(t) e^{-(2\pi i/h) H_{nn} t} u_n^0(x)$$

is unity, all the other c_n^0's being zero. For a short time all other c's will be small, so that in the equation of the method of variation of constants they can be neglected in comparison with unity. Proceeding in this way, integrate the differential equations of the method of variation of constants to get c_n as a function of time. Find $c_n^* c_n$ as a function of time, showing that it has a form resembling that of Eq. (24), Appendix 11.

14. Convert this summation into an integration by using the relation that the energy density in the frequency interval $d\nu$ between successive ν's in the summation can be written either as $\rho_{\nu} d\nu$ or as $\epsilon_0 E_{\nu}^2/2$, so that we can replace E_{ν}^2 by $(2/\epsilon_0)\rho_{\nu} d\nu$ and integrate instead of summing. An additional factor $\frac{1}{3}$ must be included, as in Appendix 11, to take account of the fact that the average of the square of the cosine of the angle between the electric field and the dipole moment of the atom is $\frac{1}{3}$. Proceeding in this way, show that the final result is $c_n^* c_n = B\rho_{\nu} t$, where B is as given in Appendix 11.

CHAPTER 5

THE HYDROGEN ATOM

In the preceding chapters we have been studying the general principles of wave mechanics. We have seen that these principles lead to Newtonian mechanics in the limiting case where we are dealing with heavy particles, low frequencies, or, more generally, with high quantum numbers. On the other hand, we have seen that for problems of electronic motion in atoms and molecules we must always use wave mechanics, and that in dealing with atomic and molecular vibrations and rotations we generally must use it. We are now ready to start our main task, the investigation of the structure of matter, studying particularly those aspects in which the quantum theory is essential. It is obvious that our study of matter must start with atoms; and in this chapter we take up the simplest of the atoms, hydrogen, which is not only important in itself, but which furnishes a model for all the others. We have seen in the first chapter that Bohr's success in explaining the structure of hydrogen according to the older quantum theory was the greatest triumph of that theory, but that, nevertheless, there were minor features in which it needed correction. When Schrödinger set up his equation, hydrogen was the first problem on which it was tested, and here again the success formed a convincing proof of the correctness of the theory. We now proceed to the discussion of the structure of the hydrogen atom on the basis of wave mechanics.

5.1. Schrödinger's Equation for Hydrogen. In the hydrogen atom, we have an electron moving in the field of force of the proton, its nucleus. The proton attracts the electron according to the inverse-square law, or Coulomb's law of attraction, met in electrostatics; but most of our results are more general than this law and hold for any central force, that is, any radial force directed toward a center of attraction and depending only on the distance, not on the angle. This is important, for we shall find that we can approximate the general atomic problem by a central field, which however differs from an inverse-square field, so that the results of the present chapter can be used later. The feature of the present problem which allows us to generalize it is the fact that a central field can exert no torque, or moment of force, on the particle; thus, by Newton's second law, the angular momentum of the particle is constant, in classical mechanics, and this result has a simple analogue in wave mechanics. This results in simple and important consequences in the quantization of the angular momentum.

For generality, we shall treat not merely hydrogen, but the problem of a single electron moving about a nucleus of charge Ze, where Z is an integer, e the magnitude of the electronic charge. This will allow us to discuss ions of heavier atoms with atomic number Z; it will also prove to give valuable information about the inner electrons of other atoms. The first thing that we notice about our problem is that the nucleus is very heavy compared with an electron. Now if we have a single electron and a single nucleus, exerting forces on each other, we find, in wave mechanics as in classical mechanics, that the center of gravity of the system remains fixed, each particle moving about the common center of gravity. But the center of gravity is very close to the nucleus. Since the mass of the proton is 1,846 times that of the electron, the center of gravity divides the vector joining nucleus and electron in the ratio of 1 to 1,846. Thus the nucleus executes only very slight motions, and practically we can treat it as being fixed, and the electron as moving about a fixed center of attraction. We shall find that this is a very general method in discussing the structure of matter: we first assume all nuclei to be fixed, and discuss the motion of the electrons about them. Only later do we have to take the motions of the nuclei into account. We discuss this more in detail in a later chapter.

We have, then, an electron of charge $-e$, mass m, moving in a central field of force. The attractive force of the nucleus has a potential energy $-Ze^2/4\pi\epsilon_0 r$, in mks units, where we remember that here, and in other cases, we can get the result in nonrationalized Gaussian units by substituting $1/4\pi$ for ϵ_0, or eliminating the factor $4\pi\epsilon_0$. Thus Schrödinger's equation, with the time eliminated, is

$$Hu = \left(-\frac{h^2}{8\pi^2 m}\nabla^2 - \frac{Ze^2}{4\pi\epsilon_0 r}\right)u = Eu. \tag{5.1.1}$$

We shall find it convenient in all our atomic problems to introduce at the outset the atomic units of distance and energy which were defined in Chap. 1. The unit of distance is $a_0 = h^2(4\pi\epsilon_0)/4\pi^2 me^2$, and the unit of energy is $Rhc = 2\pi^2 me^4/(4\pi\epsilon_0)^2 h^2$. In terms of our atomic units, Schrödinger's equation for hydrogen can be rewritten, eliminating all the dimensional constants. Thus if our new distances are the old ones divided by a_0, the new energy the old divided by Rhc, we easily find that

$$\left(-\nabla^2 - \frac{2Z}{r}\right)u = Eu, \tag{5.1.2}$$

where the derivatives are to be taken with respect to the new x, y, z. The coefficient 2 in the potential energy appears in the process of changing variables, the potential energy of two electronic charges being $2/r$ in these units.

The next step in solving Schrödinger's equation (5.1.2) is to introduce spherical coordinates, and carry out the process known as separation of variables. This is a familiar process in mathematical physics, and we give the details in Appendix 12. The result is that we can write u as a product of functions R, Θ, Φ, which are functions, respectively, of r, θ, φ, the three spherical coordinates. We can find separate differential equations for these three functions; and these differential equations prove to be

$$\frac{1}{r^2}\frac{d}{dr}\left(r^2\frac{dR}{dr}\right) + \left[E + \frac{2Z}{r} - \frac{l(l+1)}{r^2}\right]R = 0$$

$$\frac{1}{\sin\theta}\frac{d}{d\theta}\left(\sin\theta\frac{d\Theta}{d\theta}\right) + \left[l(l+1) - \frac{m^2}{\sin^2\theta}\right]\Theta = 0$$

$$\frac{d^2\Phi}{d\varphi^2} + m^2\Phi = 0. \qquad (5.1.3)$$

Here l, m are constants which are introduced in connection with the separation of variables, and which have to be determined from further conditions. The solution of the last equation is obvious: we must have $\Phi = e^{\pm im\varphi}$ or $\cos m\varphi$ or $\sin m\varphi$. In order to have Φ a single-valued function of φ, m must be an integer. The other equations are more complicated.

The equation for Θ in (5.1.3) is well known in mathematical physics; it is a form of Legendre's equation, and its solutions are the associated spherical harmonics, denoted by $P_l^m(\cos\theta)$. We solve it by a method which reminds us somewhat of the solution of the problem of the linear oscillator in Sec. 2.4. We make a transformation to the form

$$\Theta = \sin^m\theta(A_0 + A_1\cos\theta + A_2\cos^2\theta + \cdots), \qquad (5.1.4)$$

where the A's are to be determined. When we substitute this series into the differential equation, we get a recursion formula for the A's. This is derived by the same sort of argument used in deriving (2.4.5), and is

$$A_k = A_{k-2}\frac{(k+|m|-1)(k+|m|-2)-l(l+1)}{k(k-1)}. \qquad (5.1.5)$$

For integral l's, this series breaks off, the last nonvanishing term being for $k = l - |m|$. For even $l - |m|$ the expansion is in even powers, and for odd $l - |m|$ it is in odd powers. If the series does not break off, the series (5.1.4) proves to diverge in the limit where $\cos\theta = 1$, the function going infinite, in much the same way that we found divergence in the problem of the linear oscillator if we allowed the series to continue. Since we cannot allow our solution to be infinite when $\cos \theta = 1$, this means that we must choose l to be an integer.   In order for the series to break off, we see from (5.1.5) that l must be greater than or equal to $|m|$. We shall look into the meaning of these numbers later; they prove to be the same azimuthal and magnetic quantum numbers which we have already mentioned in Sec. 2.4.

The differential equation for R, in (5.1.3), is solved in a similar manner. We let

$$R = e^{-r\sqrt{-E}} r^l (A_0 + A_1 r + A_2 r^2 + \cdots) \tag{5.1.6}$$

and find the recursion formula

$$A_k = -2A_{k-1} \frac{Z - (l + k) \sqrt{-E}}{(l + k)(l + k + 1) - l(l + 1)}. \tag{5.1.7}$$

Here again we can use arguments similar to those of Sec. 2.5 and find that the series in (5.1.6) represents a function going infinite as r becomes infinite, provided it does not break off.   In fact, we can show that the series becomes infinite like $e^{2r\sqrt{-E}}$, so that R goes infinite like $e^{r\sqrt{-E}}$, under these circumstances.   In other words, it represents the exponentially increasing, rather than the exponentially decreasing, function in this region of large r.   To get a usable function, which decreases exponentially to zero for large r, we must have the series break off, and this demands that there be some integer k for which the numerator of (5.1.7) shall vanish.   This will come about if $E = -Z^2/n^2$, where n is an integer; and in this statement we recognize the result (1.2.7) for the energy levels of hydrogen (now extended to a one-electron atom with atomic number Z) which, as we have already seen, forms the prediction of the Bohr theory.   The number n is the principal quantum number already introduced in Sec. 1.2.   In terms of it, we can rewrite (5.1.6) and (5.1.7) in the form

$$R = e^{-rZ/n} (rZ)^l [A_0 + A_1(rZ) + A_2(rZ)^2 + \cdots] \tag{5.1.8}$$

$$A_k = -\frac{2}{n} \frac{n - l - k}{(l + k)(l + k + 1) - l(l + 1)} A_{k-1}. \tag{5.1.9}$$

From this recursion formula, we see that l cannot be greater than $n - 1$, in order to have any terms to the series.

5.2. Discussion of the Function of r for Hydrogen.   In (5.1.8) and (5.1.9) we have obtained a complete solution for the function R; but it will pay us to look at the problem in a qualitative way, so as to get a more physical feeling for the meaning of the solution. The kinetic energy of a particle can be written in terms of two components of momentum: p_r along the radius, and p_l at right angles to the radius. The radial part of the kinetic energy is $p_r^2/2m$, whereas the angular part is $p_l^2/2m$. We can rewrite this latter in the form $(p_l r)^2/2mr^2$, where the quantity $p_l r$ is the angular momentum. Then we can write the equation of conservation of energy in the form

$$\frac{p_r^2}{2m} + \frac{(p_l r)^2}{2mr^2} - \frac{Ze^2}{4\pi\epsilon_0 r} = E. \tag{5.2.1}$$

But by the law of conservation of angular momentum, the quantity $p_l r$ remains constant, provided there is no torque acting on the particle. Thus (5.2.1) is like the law of conservation of energy for a particle in one-dimensional motion along r, subject to a potential energy which consists not merely of $-Ze^2/4\pi\epsilon_0 r$, the Coulomb energy, but also the term $(p_l r)^2/2mr^2$, which may be interpreted as the potential energy associated with the fictitious centrifugal force which we must insert if we wish to treat the problem as a one-dimensional one. We can then solve (5.2.1) for p_r as a function of r, and treat the problem by the Sommerfeld quantum condition, or the WKB method, as if it were a one-dimensional problem. We can also set up a Schrödinger equation for it in a one-dimensional form. Thus if we let the wave function be $y(r)$, we should expect that

$$\frac{-h^2}{8\pi^2 m}\frac{d^2 y}{dr^2} + \left[\frac{(p_l r)^2}{2mr^2} - \frac{Ze^2}{4\pi\epsilon_0 r} - E\right]y = 0. \tag{5.2.2}$$

It now appears that we can throw this equation and the equation for the function R in (5.1.3) into identical form, as follows: First, we must introduce atomic units. Next, we must assume that the angular momentum is given by the relation

$$(p_l r)^2 = l(l+1)\frac{h}{2\pi}. \tag{5.2.3}$$

Finally, we must assume that $y = rR$. This last change of variables results in transforming the equation for R in (5.1.3) to the form

$$\frac{d^2 y}{dr^2} + \left[E + \frac{2Z}{r} - \frac{l(l+1)}{r^2}\right]y = 0. \tag{5.2.4}$$

This is equivalent to (5.2.2), expressed in atomic units.

We see, then, that our radial problem is like a one-dimensional problem with the potential energy $-2Z/r + l(l+1)/r^2$. In Fig. 5.2.1 we draw this potential energy, for the case $Z = 1$, as a function of r, for various values of l. We also draw lines at constant energy, corresponding to the actual energy levels of the system. We see that in the case of each value of l, horizontal lines corresponding to those energy levels for which n is equal to or greater than $l + 1$ will cross the potential-energy curve twice. Between two limiting values of r, the points where the curves cross, the classical kinetic energy is positive, and the wave function behaves in a more or less sinusoidal fashion. Outside this range the classical kinetic

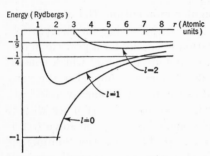

FIG. 5.2.1. Effective potential energy $-2/r + l(l+1)/r^2$ for the hydrogen problem.

energy is negative, and the wave function decreases rapidly to zero. We have seen in (5.1.8) that for small r's the function behaves as r^l; that is, the greater l is, the more rapidly the function approaches zero as r approaches zero. This is natural from Fig. 5.2.1, for we see that the larger l is, the greater is the effective potential energy near the origin, and hence the greater the negative kinetic energy. This corresponds to the classical situation. In Chap. 1, and Appendix 1, we saw that classical orbits of large angular momentum (there denoted by $kh/2\pi$) did not penetrate close to the nucleus, while those of small angular momentum penetrated very close. We shall see that k is equal to $l + 1$, so that these results are consistent with our present observations that the wave functions are large near the nucleus for small l value, small for large l value.

For large values of r, the limit to the classical motion is set mostly by the total energy, or by n, the principal quantum number. The greater n is, the larger the classical orbit. Corresponding to this, the Schrödinger wave function has large values further out, for large n values. It is easy to find approximately how large the orbit is. For large values of r, the most important term in the function R is that in the highest power of r. From (5.1.9) we see that this term has an exponent $n - 1$, or the highest power of r in the expansion of $y = rR$ is n. In other words, for large r this function y approaches $e^{-Zr/n}r^n$, using atomic units. We can now find the value of r at which this quantity has its maximum; this will give us a certain measure of the size of the orbit. We find at once that the radius is n^2/Z, measured in atomic units. This is the same as the radius of the corresponding circular orbit in Bohr's theory.

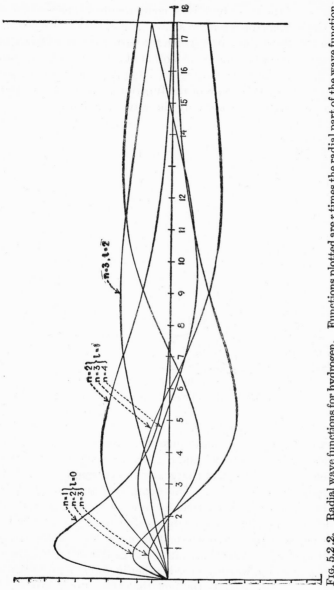

FIG. 5.2.2.   Radial wave functions for hydrogen.   Functions plotted are r times the radial part of the wave function.

After this qualitative discussion, we are prepared to understand the actual values of the wave functions, computed from the exact solution of the problem.   Some of these are shown in Fig. 5.2.2.   We note particularly from this figure the way in which the various functions corresponding to the same value of l resemble each other at small values of r, while those of the same n resemble each other at large r.   We notice in each case that the outermost maximum of the function is the largest in amplitude.

It is interesting to plot not only the wave function itself, but also the

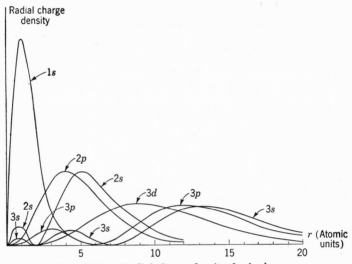

FIG. 5.2.3.   Radial charge density for hydrogen.

quantity y^2, which is equal to r^2R^2.   The reason is that this is proportional to the density of charge per unit range of r.   If we wish to find the amount of charge contained between r and $r + dr$, we must multiply R^2, which is proportional to the density of charge, by the volume of the shell between r and $r + dr$, which is $4\pi r^2\, dr$.   This quantity y^2 is often called the radial charge density, and it is plotted for several stationary states in Fig. 5.2.3.   Plots of this sort are valuable in discussing the structure of other atoms besides hydrogen, and we shall have occasion later to make use of them.   It is clear that the maximum charge density coincides with the maximum value of y, which we used earlier in deriving an effective radius for an orbit.   In these plots the fact that the outer maximum is more important than the inner ones is exaggerated as compared with the plots of the wave function itself.

As the energy goes through smaller and smaller negative values to zero, the principal quantum number n becoming larger and larger, the orbits get larger and larger, and for positive energies they extend to infinity. At the same time, the motion ceases to be quantized, and we have a con-- tinuous spectrum. This is similar to the case taken up in Sec. 2.5 and illustrated in Fig. 2.5.2, where we showed a potential function leading to quantized energy levels for low energies and a continuous spectrum for high energy. The continuous spectrum is observed in experiments on the hydrogen atom. An electron can absorb energy sufficient to raise it from a low energy level, such as the ground state (the state with $n = 1$, the lowest energy level), to the continuous band of energies, and as a result, it can absorb any frequency greater than that corresponding to the series limit (that is, to the energy sufficient to raise it to the state $E = 0$, or $n = \infty$). At the same time, the electron becomes free, or ionized; the potential corresponding to the energy necessary to raise the electron to the series limit is the ionization potential.

5.3. The Angular Momentum; Dependence of the Wave Function on Angles. We have already mentioned that the classical kinetic energy can be written $p_r^2/2m + (p_l r)^2/2mr^2$. The corresponding operator in wave mechanics, as we find it in Appendix 12, is

$$\frac{1}{2mr^2} \frac{h}{2\pi i} \frac{\partial}{\partial r} \left(r^2 \frac{h}{2\pi i} \frac{\partial}{\partial r} \right)$$
$$+ \frac{1}{2mr^2} \left[\frac{1}{\sin \theta} \frac{h}{2\pi i} \frac{\partial}{\partial \theta} \left(\sin \theta \frac{h}{2\pi i} \frac{\partial}{\partial \theta} \right) + \frac{1}{\sin^2 \theta} \left(\frac{h}{2\pi i} \right)^2 \frac{\partial^2}{\partial \varphi^2} \right].$$

By comparison, it is plain that the operator for $(p_l r)^2$ is

$$(p_l r)^2 = \left(\frac{h}{2\pi i} \right)^2 \left[\frac{1}{\sin \theta} \frac{\partial}{\partial \theta} \left(\sin \theta \frac{\partial}{\partial \theta} \right) + \frac{1}{\sin^2 \theta} \frac{\partial^2}{\partial \varphi^2} \right].$$

But now from the differential equations (5.1.3) for Θ and Φ, we easily have, using this operator,

$$(p_l r)^2 u = l(l + 1) \left(\frac{h}{2\pi} \right)^2 u. \tag{5.3.1}$$

That is, $(p_l r)^2$ has a diagonal matrix [since $(p_l r)^2 u$ is a constant times u, without any terms in other characteristic functions], and the diagonal value is $l(l + 1)(h/2\pi)^2$, so that the total angular momentum is constant, as it must be in the absence of torques. We can also easily find the component of angular momentum along the z axis. The angular momentum along this axis is the momentum conjugate to the angle φ of rotation about this axis, so that its operator is $\dfrac{h}{2\pi i} \dfrac{\partial}{\partial \varphi}$. Now take the solutions where φ

enters into the wave function as the exponential $e^{\pm im\varphi}$. Then

$$\frac{h}{2\pi i}\frac{\partial u}{\partial \varphi} = \frac{mh}{2\pi}\,u.$$

This again is diagonal, showing that the component of angular momentum along the axis remains constant. Further, if we use the wave function $e^{im\varphi}$, the component equals $mh/2\pi$.

We thus see that our quantum number l takes the place of the number k of Bohr's theory, discussed in Sec. 1.2. It is called the azimuthal

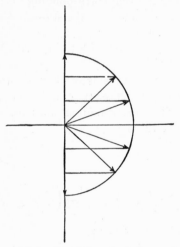

quantum number, and it measures the total angular momentum of the orbit, in units $h/2\pi$. The number l is one unit less than k; that is, its smallest value is zero, corresponding to the s levels; $l = 1$ corresponds to the p levels, 2 to the d levels, 3 to the f levels, which were described in Sec. 1.2. And while it measures the total angular momentum, in units of $h/2\pi$, we see from the result (5.3.1) that we have a complication, in that the square of its magnitude is represented, not by l^2, but by the slightly different value $l(l + 1)$, which can be rewritten as $(l + \frac{1}{2})^2 - \frac{1}{4}$.

FIG. 5.3.1. Possible orientations of angular momentum, for $l = 3$.

In other words, it is a little as if we were using half quantum numbers rather than whole quantum numbers. We also see that m takes the place of the magnetic quantum number of Sec. 1.2, measuring the component of angular momentum along the axis. This leads to space quantization, or orientation of the orbits in space, as we discussed earlier. In considering this, we can draw a figure like Fig. 5.3.1, showing the possible orientations in space of the angular momentum vector, such that the component of the vector $lh/2\pi$ along the axis is $mh/2\pi$.

A diagram like Fig. 5.3.1 is of course only suggestive. The real orbit, on account of the principle of uncertainty, does not move in a plane; and the ambiguity of the interpretation of l, by which it is not clear whether the length of the vector should be $lh/2\pi$ or $\sqrt{l(l + 1)}\, h/2\pi$, would not allow us to draw the figure uniquely anyway. We can get a more useful picture of the distribution of the wave functions in angle by showing polar diagrams of the spherical harmonics, plotting the square of the spherical harmonic, which gives the density, as a function of angle. This is done in Fig. 5.3.2, for $l = 1$, $m = 1$ and 0, and $l = 2$, $m = 2$, 1, ∪ ($l = 0$ does not depend on angle). If we imagine these figures rotated about the axes, we see that for $m = l$ the figure indicates that most of the density is in the plane normal to the axis, but a considerable part is out of the plane. For $l = 2$, $m = 1$, for instance, the density lies near a cone, as if the plane of the orbit took up all directions whose normal made the proper angle with the axis.

It is interesting to consider a little more in detail the s and p wave functions, which are very important in molecular binding. For s levels, $l = 0$, the function is independent of angle, as we have mentioned. For

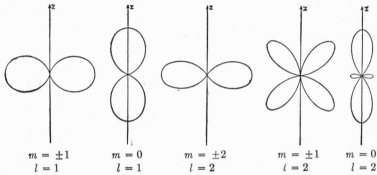

| $m = \pm 1$ | $m = 0$ | $m = \pm 2$ | $m = \pm 1$ | $m = 0$ |
| $l = 1$ | $l = 1$ | $l = 2$ | $l = 2$ | $l = 2$ |

Fig. 5.3.2.   Dependence of wave functions on angle. Θ^2 plotted in polar diagram.

p states, $l = 1$, there are three functions, for $m = \pm 1$, 0. The function for $m = 0$ is independent of the angle φ, the angle of rotation about the z axis; the spherical harmonic, as a matter of fact, takes the simple form z/r. For $m = \pm 1$, the spherical harmonic depends on φ through the complex exponential forms $e^{\pm i\varphi}$, whose magnitude is unity, so that each of these distributions of intensity is independent of φ. However, in some cases we find that we wish to use different functions of φ, representing standing rather than traveling waves. These functions are $\sin \varphi$ and $\cos \varphi$, and when we combine these with the appropriate function of θ, it proves to be the case that the whole spherical harmonics can be written in the form x/r, y/r, showing a symmetry with the value z/r mentioned above. In this case, there is one of the wave functions in which the largest intensity is along the x axis, one large along y, and one along z. For d levels, $l = 2$, there are five wave functions, depending in a more complicated way on direction than for the p states.

In all cases, we can prove an interesting theorem about the spherical harmonics: if we add the intensities for all the functions corresponding to a given l value, the result is independent of orientation. Thus, for instance, with p states the three amplitudes are proportional to x/r, y/r, and z/r; the sum of the squares of these quantities, proportional to the intensities, is $(x^2 + y^2 + z^2)/r^2 = 1$, independent of angle. Similar results hold for the other l values. The importance of this result will be seen in the next chapter, where we talk about the structure of more complicated atoms. In such cases, the wave functions of the various electrons still depend on angle, as in the case of hydrogen; but we have many electrons, and in particular we often have what is called a closed shell of electrons, a situation in which we have one electron in each of the states connected with a given l value. The average charge density from such a closed shell is then proportional to the sum of the squares of the wave functions of the various electrons; and from the theorem we have just mentioned, we see that this charge density for a closed shell is spherically symmetrical, or independent of angle.

5.4. Series and Selection Principles.   All the states for a given value of l and n, but different m, have the same function of r and the same energy. We shall find that this is still true with an arbitrary central field, so that even in that problem the solution is degenerate. Physically, so long as the angular momentum is determined, it cannot make any difference, as far as the energy is concerned, which way the orbit is orientated, on account of the spherical symmetry. Thus we often group together the various substates with the same l and n but different m, regarding them as constituting a single degenerate state with a $(2l + 1)$-fold degeneracy. For hydrogen, as a matter of fact, the energy depends only on n, so that all states of the same n but different l values are degenerate, but this is not true in general for a central field. It is convenient, rather, to group all the states of the same l value but different n together to form a series, since they are closely connected physically, having the same functions of angle, while those of the same n merely happen to have the same energy, but without important physical resemblances. The series of different l values, as we have already mentioned, are denoted by the letters s, p, d, f, etc., derived from spectroscopy.

The classification into series becomes important when we consider the transition probabilities from one level to another. We recall that these are given by the matrix components of the electric moment between the states in question. When these components are computed, it is found that there are certain selection rules:

1. The component is zero unless the l's of the two states differ by ± 1 unit.

2. The component is zero unless the m's differ by 0 or ± 1 unit.

The latter rule is easily proved. For, suppose we compute the matrix components of $x + iy$, $x - iy$, z, which are simple combinations of x, y, z, the three components of displacement. If we find the matrix components of all three of these to be zero for a given transition, the transition will be forbidden.   Now these three quantities, in polar coordinates, are $r \sin \theta$ $e^{i\varphi}$, $r \sin \theta \, e^{-i\varphi}$, $r \cos \theta$, respectively.   If u is $R\Theta e^{im\varphi}$, we have

$$(x + iy)u = rR \sin \theta \Theta e^{i(m+1)\varphi},$$

showing that this quantity has a matrix component only to states having the quantum number $m + 1$, since the quantity on the right could be

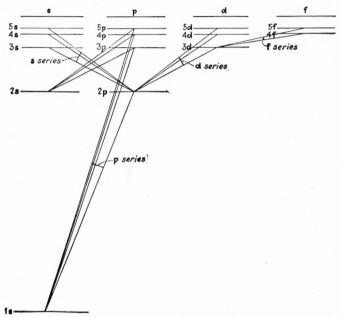

FIG. 5.4.1.   Energy levels and allowed transitions and series in hydrogen.

expanded in series of functions with many values of n and l, but only the one value $m + 1$. Similarly $(x - iy)u = rR \sin \theta \, \Theta e^{i(m-1)\varphi}$, allowing transitions only from m to $m - 1$, and $zu = rR \cos \theta \, \Theta e^{im\varphi}$, allowing transitions in which m does not change. The proof of the selection principle for l is slightly more difficult, involving the theorem that $\sin \theta \, P_l^m(\cos \theta)$ or $\cos \theta P_l^m(\cos \theta)$ can be expanded in spherical harmonics whose lower index is $l + 1$ or $l - 1$ only.

The selection rules have the following results: if we arrange the series in order, $s, p, d, f, \ldots$, a level of one series can only have transitions to the immediately adjacent series. This gives us the transitions indicated in Fig. 5.4.1 (all of the transitions between upper states are not indicated; merely some of the more important ones down to lower states). The series of lines arising from transitions of the p states to $1s$ is called the principal series; from the s terms to $2p$, the sharp series; from the d terms to $2p$, the diffuse series; from the f terms to $3d$, the fundamental series. When the matrix components are worked out, the strongest lines are those in which l decreases by one unit (principal, diffuse, and fundamental series), and those for which l increases (as the sharp series) are weaker. Of course, on account of the degeneracy in l in hydrogen, the different series are not separated, but they are in other atoms, and it is for those that the classification is important. To see this, we must study the energy levels in the general central field, which we shall do in the next chapter.

When we look into the theory of the hydrogen spectrum with more care than we have done so far, we find several types of corrections, which have the effect of slightly displacing the energy levels, so that the degeneracy is removed, and levels with the same n value, but different l's, no longer exactly coincide. The resulting splitting of the energy levels and lines is referred to as fine structure. It is on such a small scale that it is hard to observe, but still measurable, and capable of shedding light on the further refinements of the theory. One of the perturbations, the one which has been understood longest, is the relativistic correction. The electrons in hydrogen travel rather slowly compared with the velocity of light, but still they approach close enough to it so that corrections to their motion on account of the theory of relativity are barely detectable. Sommerfeld many years ago worked out a relativistic theory of the fine structure which, remarkably enough, agreed very closely with the experiments. This was remarkable, because several other perturbing effects have been discovered since then, each of which modified the theory, but in just such a way as to leave the net result very close to the original prediction of Sommerfeld. The most important of these effects is the electron spin. It was discovered by Goudsmit and Uhlenbeck, guided by the theory of more complicated spectra than that of hydrogen, that the electron itself possesses a magnetic moment and an angular momentum, quite aside from its rotation in an orbit. This intrinsic spin must be considered in the theory of atomic spectra, and we shall meet it many times in our future work. As far as its effect on the hydrogen spectrum is concerned, it produces perturbations of the same order of magnitude as the relativity correction. In the first place, there proves to be a space quantization of the electronic spin with respect to the orbital angular momentum, resulting in most cases in a doubling of the number of energy levels. These energy levels are split apart by the magnetic energy associated with the magnetic interaction between the magnetic moments of orbital motion and of spin. By extraordinary coincidence, as we have mentioned, the net result of this splitting and displacement of levels is to have new levels, with a different interpretation from the old ones, nevertheless lying at just the same energies that Sommerfeld predicted. We shall not go further into this effect here, since it is relatively unimportant in hydrogen, whereas we shall later find it to be of great importance in discussing the heavier atoms.

There is a final type of perturbation, very recently discovered, called the Lamb-Retherford shift, resulting from a higher-order interaction term in the energy, involving interaction between electrostatic energy and radiation energy. This involves the complicated quantum electrodynamics, in forms which we hardly touched on in the last chapter, and while it is of considerable theoretical interest, it is of small practical importance.

In addition to these small perturbative effects in the hydrogen spectrum, which occur in the absence of external field, there are, of course, perturbations produced by external magnetic or electric fields. We have already mentioned in Chap. 1 the Zeeman effect, the effect of an external magnetic field, producing displacement of the levels by an amount proportional to the field strength and to the magnetic quantum number m. This effect is greatly complicated by the electron spin, and we postpone its discussion until a later chapter, where we shall take up the general theory of multiplet structure and the Zeeman effect. Similarly an external electric field produces a perturbation, the Stark effect, which is interesting in some connections, but which we shall not discuss further.

PROBLEMS

1. Carry out the solution of the radial wave function for hydrogen, deriving Eq. (5.1.7), following the method outlined in the text, and verifying that if the series does not break off, it represents a function which becomes infinite as r approaches infinity.

2. Assume that the solution of Schrödinger's equation for hydrogen, (5.2.4), can be expressed in the form $y = r^n e^{-ar}(1 + A_1/r + A_2/r^2 + \cdots)$. Find the recursion formula for the A's, and the value of a. Find the condition that the series break off. Show that the resulting function is the same as that found in ascending powers of r in the text.

3. The solution of the preceding problem can be used to discuss the outer part of the wave function of a nonhydrogenic problem in which the potential energy is $2Z/r$ in the outer part of the orbit but deviates further in. In such a case the energy levels will be different from the hydrogen values. Consider the nature of the solution for an arbitrary energy value. Show that as $r \to 0$, the series diverges. This does not interfere with this use of the solution, in which the potential departs from the hydrogenic value for small r, so that we do not use the solution in this region.

4. Set up the solution of the radial Schrödinger equation for hydrogen by the WKB method. Carry the solution as far as you can and compare with the exact solution.

5. Work out the spherical harmonics for $l = 3$, and draw diagrams for them similar to Fig. 5.3.2.

6. Prove from the differential equation that the associated spherical harmonics are orthogonal. Verify this for the cases of $l = 1$ and 2.

7. Draw an energy-level diagram in which the substates of different m's are shown, drawing them as if slightly separated, including states 1s, 2s, 3s, 2p, 3p, 3d. Indicate all transitions allowed by the selection principles for l and m, as in Fig. 5.4.1.

8. Set up the angular part Θ of the wave function corresponding to $l = 0$, $m = 0$; $l = 1$, $m = 0$; $l = 2$, $m = 0$; $l = 3$, $m = 0$. Then investigate the selection principle for l by showing that $\cos \theta \, \Theta_l$ can be expanded in terms of Θ_{l-1} and Θ_{l+1}, so that there are only transitions for which $l \rightarrow l \pm 1$. Carry out for $l = 1, 2$.

9. Set up normalized hydrogen wave functions corresponding to $n = 2$, $l = 1$, $m = 1, 0, -1$; and $n = 1$, $l = 0$. Find the matrix components of electric moment for the transitions from the $n = 2$ levels to the ground state $n = 1$. Compute Einstein's A and B coefficients for these transitions.

10. Use Schrödinger's equation in spherical polar coordinates, for the case of a central field and a constant magnetic field along the z axis, as set up in Prob. 16, Chap. 3, to discuss the Zeeman effect in hydrogen. Disregard the electron spin and proceed by perturbation theory. Use the ordinary hydrogen wave functions as set up in this chapter as unperturbed wave functions, and find the average value of the perturbed Hamiltonian, including magnetic terms, over these unperturbed wave functions. Show that there are two sorts of terms: terms proportional to the magnetic field, and to the magnetic quantum number; and terms proportional to the square of the magnetic field, and to the mean value of the quantity $x^2 + y^2$ over the orbit. The terms of the first sort are those concerned in the ordinary Zeeman effect, and we shall later find that those of the second sort explain the phenomenon of diamagnetism.

CHAPTER 6

THE CENTRAL FIELD MODEL FOR ATOMIC STRUCTURE

An atom of atomic number Z consists of a heavy nucleus of charge Ze, where e is the magnitude of the electronic charge, surrounded in its uncharged state by Z electrons. The nucleus is heavy enough so that, as in discussing the hydrogen atom, we can consider it to be fixed, with the Z electrons moving around it. Thus the problem becomes a problem of Z bodies, attracted to the nucleus by Coulomb forces, repelling each other with similar forces. The hydrogen atom is a simple mathematical problem; but all other atoms are so much more complicated, as far as their theory is concerned, that we cannot solve them without making drastic approximations. The situation is not very different from that in classical mechanics, where the two-body problem (one particle revolving around another) is a simple, soluble one, whereas the problem of three bodies presents extreme mathematical difficulties, and can be handled only by approximate methods.

In the next atom beyond hydrogen, helium, numerical methods have been used to get approximate wave functions for the atom, and these calculations have been carried far enough so that very accurate numerical checks have been found between observed energy levels and the calculation, good enough so that we have no doubt as to the correctness of the wave-mechanical approach to many-electron atoms. But even these numerical calculations get so complicated that they have not been attempted for any atoms with more electrons than helium. It is fortunate under these circumstances that approximation methods of a lower degree of accuracy, but still having great qualitative significance as well as a certain degree of quantitative accuracy, have been developed for all the atoms, and that these methods lead to the main features of atomic structure, the nature of the periodic table of the elements, the size and general properties of atoms, and a fairly accurate prediction of their spectra. In the present chapter we shall start the discussion of this model of the atom, continuing in the next chapter. In the present chapter we treat the cruder part of the theory, based on the approximation that the various electrons of an atom move approximately as if each were acted on by a central field produced by the average motion of all the other electrons of the atom. In the next chapter we treat the multiplet structure, which arises on account of interactions between the electrons which cannot be described by means of central fields.

6.1. The Schrödinger Equation for the Many-body Problem. We cannot hope to proceed in a logical manner toward the solution of the many-body problem in wave mechanics, unless we know exactly what is the starting point. This must be a Schrödinger equation, and the only way we can proceed in a new problem such as this one is to start by postulating the equation, regarding it as a fundamental law of nature, then deducing consequences of it, and seeing if these consequences agree with experiment. The equation which we shall set up is justified in this way by the results to which it leads in atomic and molecular structure, in particular by its prediction of correct results in such problems as the structure of helium, and of the other more complex atoms, which we have mentioned in the preceding paragraph.

We naturally wish our Schrödinger equation for the many-body problem to be a logical extension of Eq. (3.1.6) for the one-body problem, which we can write in the form $H\psi = E\psi$, where H is the energy or Hamiltonian operator, the energy written in terms of the coordinates and momenta, with each momentum component replaced by a differential operator as in (3.1.2), and where E is to be interpreted as a time differentiation $-(h/2\pi i)\partial/\partial t$, as in (3.1.5). The wave function ψ, in the one-body problem, is a function of the coordinates x, y, z of the particle, and of the time t. We may now extend this equation in a very natural way to a problem of N particles, each moving in three-dimensional space. If we do this, the Hamiltonian function H will be a function of the $3N$ coordinates and $3N$ momenta of the problem, so that the corresponding operator will involve differentiation with respect to the $3N$ coordinates. Our wave function ψ, then, must be a function of the $3N$ coordinates, in order to permit differentiation with respect to all these coordinates. If our Schrödinger equation, set up in this way, represents a wave propagation, this propagation must then be in a space of $3N$ dimensions, not our ordinary 3-dimensional space; and this shows us that wave mechanics is really a more complicated theory than we have so far expected, and that its analogy to electromagnetic waves, which exist in three-dimensional space, is far from complete.

Even though our wave phenomenon is complicated, still the statistical interpretation of the wave function follows in the many-body problem from the same principles which we have already learned in the simple case of one body. The statistical interpretation in that case was the following: the probability that the particle be found in the element of volume $dx\,dy\,dz$ equals $\psi^*\psi\,dx\,dy\,dz$, where ψ is the wave function. Similarly in the $3N$-dimensional problem, with coordinates $x_1, \ldots, z_N$, we assume that the probability that particle 1 be in the volume $dx_1\,dy_1\,dz_1$, that simultaneously particle 2 be in $dx_2\,dy_2\,dz_2$, and so on down to particle N, which is to be in $dx_N\,dy_N\,dz_N$, is $\psi^*\psi\,dx_1 \cdots dz_N$. From this interpretation it is clear that ψ must in general depend on the coordinates of all particles, in order to uphold our statistical interpretation.

There is a special case which sometimes occurs, and which has great importance: there is the possibility that the motions of two particles may be statistically independent of each other. In such a case, the probability that simultaneously particle 1 be in the volume $dx_1\,dy_1\,dz_1$, and that particle 2 be in $dx_2\,dy_2\,dz_2$, is simply the product of the probability that particle 1 be in $dx_1\,dy_1\,dz_1$, and that particle 2 be in $dx_2\,dy_2\,dz_2$. Thus in this case the wave function ψ, which is a function of all six variables x_1 to z_2, can be factored into two factors, one depending on the coordinates of the first particle, the other on the coordinates of the second. In all cases, with many particles as well as one, we can separate the time variable from the others. Thus in this problem of statistical independence of the two particles, we can write ψ in the form

$$u_1(x_1y_1z_1)u_2(x_2y_2z_2)e^{-(2\pi i/h)Et},$$

where E is the energy. Such a process is called separation of variables; and we can show at once that it occurs when the potential energy is a sum of two terms, V_1 depending only on the coordinates of the first particle, V_2 depending only on the coordinates of the second. Let us demonstrate the possibility of separation in such a case.

If the masses of the two particles are m_1, m_2, the Schrödinger equation with the time eliminated becomes

$$-\frac{h^2}{8\pi^2m_1}\,\nabla_1^2(u_1u_2) - \frac{h^2}{8\pi^2m_2}\,\nabla_2^2(u_1u_2) + (V_1 + V_2)(u_1u_2) = Eu_1u_2, \quad (6.1.1)$$

where ∇_1^2, ∇_2^2 symbolize differentiation with respect to the coordinates of the first and second particles, respectively. We recall that u_1 and V_1 depend on $x_1y_1z_1$ only, and u_2 and V_2 on $x_2y_2z_2$ only. If we divide (6.1.1) by u_1u_2, it can then be written in the form

$$\frac{1}{u_1}\left(-\frac{h^2}{8\pi^2m_1}\,\nabla_1^2u_1 + V_1u_1\right) = -\frac{1}{u_2}\left(-\frac{h^2}{8\pi^2m_2}\,\nabla_2^2u_2 + V_2u_2\right) + E. \quad (6.1.2)$$

We notice that the left side of (6.1.2) is a function of $x_1y_1z_1$ only, the right side a function of $x_2y_2z_2$ only. Since they are equal for all values of the coordinates, we conclude by a familiar argument that each must be a constant. Let us define this constant as E_1, and let us also define another constant E_2 by the relation

$$E = E_1 + E_2.$$

Then Eq. (6.1.2) turns into two equations, which may be written

$$- \frac{h^2}{8\pi^2 m_1} \nabla_1^2 u_1 + V_1 u_1 = E_1 u_1,$$

$$- \frac{h^2}{8\pi^2 m_2} \nabla_2^2 u_2 + V_2 u_2 = E_2 u_2. \tag{6.1.3}$$

These are Schrödinger equations for one-particle problems with the potential energies V_1 and V_2, respectively. We thus see that if we solve these problems and find energy levels E_1 and E_2, respectively, the product of the wave functions satisfies the two-particle Schrödinger equation (6.1.1), and the energy levels of that problem are the sums of the energy levels of the one-particle problem. In other words, we see that the condition for statistical independence of two particles is that the potential energy must not involve any terms depending simultaneously on the coordinates of both particles, since in that case the separation (6.1.3) could not be carried out. This means, in other words, that we get statistical independence if the two particles do not exert forces on each other. This relation, though we have proved it only for two particles, can of course be generalized to any number of particles.

In case the particles exert forces on each other, there is no longer statistical independence in their motions. We may reasonably expect, for example, that if two particles repel each other, as two electrons do, the probability of finding one of the particles at a given region of space will be smaller if the other particle happens to be near that region than it will be otherwise. Such correlations between the motions of electrons cannot be described by wave functions which are products of functions of the various electrons; and they certainly must exist, since electrons really do repel each other. In fact, the potential energy V of a set of electrically charged particles, like electrons and nuclei, is a sum of terms, each of the nature of $e_i e_j / 4\pi\epsilon_0 r_{ij}$, where e_i, e_j are the charges of the particles, r_{ij} is the distance between them. Each such term depends on the coordinates of two particles and expresses the repulsive or attractive force between them, so that it is clear that a problem of electrons in an atom cannot lead to a statistical independence of the particles, or a separation of variables. Nevertheless, the central field approximation which we are discussing in the present chapter is based on an assumption of just such statistical independence. In the next section we shall see how this can be a valid approximation, even though it is certainly not exact.

6.2. The Self-consistent Field Approximation. The problem of the interaction of many electrons, or other charged particles, is not peculiar to atomic and molecular structure; it is also found in the theory of vacuum tubes in the discussion of space charge. The method of handling it there is simple and straightforward and furnishes us with a valid guide for an equivalent approximation in discussing the structure of atoms, molecules, and solids. This is called the method of the self-consistent field, and its principal applications to atomic problems have been made by Hartree. Let us see how we are led to its fundamental ideas by considering space-charge problems.

Suppose we have a space charge in a vacuum tube, produced, for instance, by electrons emitted thermionically from a hot filament. The electrons are, it is true, discrete particles, but we can approximately set up a continuous volume density of electric charge resulting from them, and from this charge density we can calculate an electrostatic potential as a function of position. We can then assume that each electron moves in this resulting potential field. We can solve Newton's equations of motion for an electron in such a field (Newton's equations are appropriate in the vacuum-tube case, for we readily find that the de Broglie wave lengths of the electrons are very small compared with any of the significant dimensions of the problem, so that wave mechanics reduces to classical mechanics with great accuracy in this case). Once we know how the electrons move, we can find what charge density they lead to, just as we can find the density of a fluid or gas in a problem of hydrodynamics or aerodynamics if we know the motion of the material. Thus we start our calculation by assuming a volume density of electric charge, and we finish by finding the volume density, as resulting from electrons which move in the potential field set up by the original volume density. Now it is clear that this volume density with which we finish our calculations must be the same one with which we started, if our problem is correctly formulated. This does not follow automatically from our mathematics, however; if we start with any arbitrary initial volume density, we shall be able to follow the motion of electrons in the resulting potential field and come out with a final density which, in general, will not agree with the initial one.

The requirement that the field be self-consistent is simply that the final density equal the initial one, so that we can say that the field is set up by those electrons which move according to the laws of mechanics in the field itself. If we impose this condition, it determines the charge density, potential field, and motion of the electrons uniquely (provided we specify certain auxiliary quantities, such as the voltages imposed on the tube, dimensions, etc.). In the simplest cases of vacuum tubes, the condition can be imposed analytically without trouble, and it leads to a simple and straightforward solution of the space-charge problem. The well-known Child-Langmuir equation, stating that the emission from a space-charge-limited filament is proportional to the three-halves power of the applied voltage, is derived in this way.   In more complicated cases, however, this straightforward method proves to be too complicated to apply, and we are forced to use a method of successive approximations, in the following way.   We may make a good initial guess as to the charge density; compute potential, electron motion, and resultant charge density from this initial charge density; and then use the resultant charge density as the starting point for still another calculation of the same type, and so on, proceeding by successive approximations.   It is clearly conceivable that this process should converge, successive steps of approximation approaching each other, and hence approaching the correct answer (since if the final stage of an approximation agrees exactly with the initial step, we have by hypothesis found the correct solution); or that it should diverge, successive steps getting further and further apart; or, of course, there could be a limiting case between these two, successive approximations staying the same distance from the correct answer.   Fortunately in many important practical cases there is fairly rapid convergence; and this fact has been taken advantage of by Hartree in his application of the self-consistent field method to the problem of atomic structure, which we shall now describe.

Hartree approaches the atomic problem by assuming that N electrons move in the field of a nucleus of charge Ze (N of course equals Z for a neutral atom, but would be different for a positively or negatively charged ion).   The electrons themselves, of course, produce a space charge, and for reasons which we shall go into later, this space charge is approximately spherically symmetrical.   The total field acting on an electron is then produced not only by the nucleus, but by the other electrons, which have the effect of partially shielding the nuclear field, since they are oppositely charged.   Proceeding by analogy with the vacuum-tube case, we compute the potential of these other electrons by using electrostatics, starting with their assumed charge densities.   Then we have a resultant central field in which the electrons are assumed to move.   We now solve for the motions of the electrons in this central field; only now, since we are working on an atomic scale, we must use wave mechanics rather than classical mechanics to discuss this motion.   From the resulting wave functions of the electrons, we compute at once a charge density, which we can compare with the charge density with which we started.   If our field is self-consistent, the final density will agree with the originally assumed value, and Hartree has found that the procedure of successive approximations can be applied to the problem in a practical manner, the final density proving, in fact, to be a good deal closer to the correct solution than is the initial density.   By carrying through several stages of approximation, he has been able to find self-consistent fields, to a satisfactory degree of accuracy, and these have now been computed for a good many of the atoms in various stages of ionization.

There are a number of points in which we should make our discussion of Hartree's method more precise, and a number of respects in which the method is clearly incomplete. In the first place, an atom has relatively few electrons, whereas the space charge in a vacuum tube has a great many. In the vacuum-tube problem, we find the field acting on one electron by taking the charge density of all electrons, and finding its electrical potential, neglecting the fact that an electron does not act electrostatically on itself; to be strictly precise, we should find the field, not of all electrons, but of all but the one we are considering, but this is a practically meaningless distinction with the enormous number of electrons concerned. In an atom, however, this distinction is of considerable importance. Thus, to take the most extreme case, suppose we are working with the helium atom. Each electron actually moves in the field of the nucleus and of one other electron, not of two electrons, since it is not acted on by its own field. Hartree takes this correction into account, computing the field of all electrons except the one concerned, in finding the field acting on a given electron.

A very important point in which the description we have given so far of Hartree's method is incomplete is the following. We start with a central field and investigate the motions of electrons in this central field. We shall find that in the general central field, as in hydrogen, there are an infinite number of quantized energy levels, characterized by the quantum numbers n, l, and m. Which stationary state are we going to assume for each of the electrons in constructing our self-consistent solution? Clearly by taking different energy levels for the individual electrons, we will end up with different energy levels for the atom as a whole, so that we have the mechanism for finding approximate wave functions for various excited states of the atom. But suppose we are looking for the ground state, or state of lowest energy. Do we then put each electron into the state of lowest energy, which as in hydrogen is the $1s$ state, with $n = 1$, $l = 0$? The answer, as of course we know from our elementary knowledge of atomic structure, is no; for the Pauli exclusion principle operates to prevent this situation. The Pauli exclusion principle is an additional restriction, not demanded by quantum mechanics in its ordinary form, which must be assumed to apply to the behavior of electrons, in order to describe correctly the observed atomic structure; the most convincing experimental proof of the correctness of the principle comes just from the case we are about to consider, that of atomic structure, and its consequences regarding the nature of the periodic table.

The Pauli exclusion principle says, in its simplest form, that no two electrons can exist with the same wave function, or the same set of quantum numbers. We must understand from the outset that the wave functions must be exactly identical for the principle to apply; thus in particular, a wave function on one atom, such as a $1s$ function, and a function with the same quantum number on another atom, are not regarded as identical in this formulation. In building up a given atom, then, the exclusion principle forbids us to have more than one electron in each of the possible stationary states in the central field problem, and this automatically means that we can have only one electron in a $1s$ state, one in a $2s$, three in a $2p$ state (three because the quantum number m can take on the three values 1, 0, -1), and so on. Really these numbers must be doubled, on account of the existence of the electron spin, which we have only incidentally mentioned so far, and which we shall take up with more care in the next chapter. This spin, as it proves, can point in either of two possible directions in space, by a sort of space quantization (much as the angular momentum vector in a p state can point in three possible directions, connected with the three possible values of m). The two orientations of spin count as different wave functions, so that associated with each of the states so far mentioned there can be two directions of spin, and we are really left with the possibility of two electrons in each s state, six in each p state, ten in each d state, and so on.

In building up an atom, then, if we are in the ground state, we must assume that electrons go into their lowest energy levels consistent with the exclusion principle. This means that we shall build up shells of electrons in the atom; first a shell of two $1s$ electrons, which have the lowest energy, and as we shall see lie closest to the nucleus; then a shell of two $2s$'s; then six $2p$'s; and so on. It is this building of shells that leads to the periodic system of the elements, and we shall take it up in detail in a later section. But in the meantime it has a result which is of great importance in the use of Hartree's method. We saw in Sec. 5.3 that if we have a closed shell of electrons, one of each m value associated with a given l value, the resulting charge distribution is spherically symmetrical. Thus all the electrons of an atom which are in closed shells result in spherical symmetry of the resulting charge. We note that s electrons are also spherically symmetrical in their charge distribution. Hence if we are finding the potential of a distribution of electrons in closed shells, and s electrons outside the closed shells, the potential will be spherically symmetrical. This accounts in every case for almost all the electrons of the atom, so that Hartree's assumption of spherical symmetry is almost justified. If there are any remaining electrons which are not spherically symmetrical, Hartree arbitrarily averages their charge distribution over angle before computing their potentials, and to this extent his method is not a correct application of the self-consistent procedure. He does this for practical reasons: it is only with spherical charge distributions that we can easily find the potential, and only with spherically symmetrical fields that we can easily solve the wave-mechanical problem. It is in this way that we are led to a central field problem for atomic structure, and we see that it is an approximation, but ordinarily not a very drastic one.

We have now described Hartree's method; let us mention its principal shortcomings. We have just seen that it disregards the fact that some electron distributions are not spherically symmetrical. If we have an atom in which two or more electrons do not have spherical symmetry, this means that, if classical mechanics applied, the electrons would exert torques on each other, and their angular momenta would not stay constant. Corresponding things occur in wave mechanics, and this is the origin of the multiplet structure, which we shall discuss in the next chapter, and which really forms a first correction to the simple central field model. The other type of shortcoming is more serious, and much harder to remove by any simple expedient. It is the fundamental fact that electrons really exert forces on each other, which lead to correlations between their motions, rendering any method of separation of variables in principle impossible. The result of this correlation is that electrons really are not found in each other's neighborhoods as much as we should conclude if we assumed that they were statistically independent. Such a correlation is taken into account in the very accurate numerical solution for the helium atom which we have discussed earlier, and it makes a considerable difference in the final value of the energy of the atom: the best model which we can set up assuming statistical independence of the electrons has an energy in the ground state which is considerably higher than the correct energy, a result of the positive repulsive potential energy of interaction of the electrons during the time when this model would lead them to be closer together than they actually are. The more correct calculation, taking account of correlation, allows very satisfactorily for this effect. But unfortunately no one has suggested a very adequate way of introducing similar corrections for correlation into the study of the heavier atoms. This is an inherent shortcoming in our approximation method, and one to which we shall have to return, particularly in our study of solids, which we shall handle by similar methods; but it seems a small price to pay for an approximation which is so comparatively simple, and allows us to draw the great number of qualitatively correct deductions which we shall find following from the method of the self-consistent field.

In the present chapter we use the self-consistent method only for the problem of a single atom, where it leads to problems so nearly spherically symmetrical that we make only a small error by neglecting the departure from spherical symmetry. However, the ideas underlying the method of the self-consistent field are equally applicable to problems of any type, without spherical symmetry, and we shall be using them later, at least in a qualitative way, in discussing the structure of molecules and solids. This application is as valid in principle as that to atoms, but unfortunately in practice it is almost prohibitively difficult to carry through in exact detail. The reason is that, even though it reduces the problem of many bodies to a set of one-body problems, these one-body problems now no longer involve central fields, but instead involve potential energy functions so complicated that we have no straightforward way of solving them. It is this fact, perhaps more than any other, that makes the problems of molecular and solid-state structure so much more difficult than that of atomic structure.

6.3. The General Central-field Problem of Atomic Structure. The effect of the separation of variables resulting from the method of the self-consistent field is to lead to separate one-electron problems for each electron of the atom: each is supposed to move in a central field resulting from the nucleus and all other electrons, averaged over their wave functions. We first ask, then, what is the nature of the solution of a central-field problem in wave mechanics. We have already given a hint of the answer in the preceding chapter. There we pointed out, in Sec. 5.1 and Appendix 12, that in the hydrogen problem we can carry out a separation of variables, writing the wave function as a product of functions of r, θ, and φ. These satisfied one-dimensional wave equations which are given in (5.1.3). The reason for this separation, as we discussed it, was the constancy of angular momentum, the absence of torques on the electrons, since they move in central fields. But torques are still absent in the general central field, as in our present problem. As a matter of fact, examination of the methods of Appendix 12 will show that the separation of variables still proceeds in such a general problem just as in (5.1.3), and the equations for the functions of angle are unchanged. The equation for the function R, depending on r, is altered only in substituting the revised potential energy for the quantity $2Z/r$ which appears there. Thus all the conclusions of Chap. 5 regarding the quantization of angular momentum, and the properties of the quantum numbers l and m, will remain unchanged.

The only difference between our present problem and hydrogen will come in the details of the problem of finding $R(r)$. This function will have a different form, and we shall no longer be able to solve the problem by using a recursion formula like (5.1.9) and a series like (5.1.8). We shall then not expect to get the simple formula for the energy levels, $E = -Z^2/n^2$, which we found for hydrogen. We can still discuss the radial problem graphically, however, as in Fig. 5.2.1, and can still use the WKB method; and we shall come to these methods a little later, so as to discuss the radial problem in more detail. In Hartree's actual calculations the radial problem is solved by numerical integration of the differential equation, and the function R is presented in the form of a table of

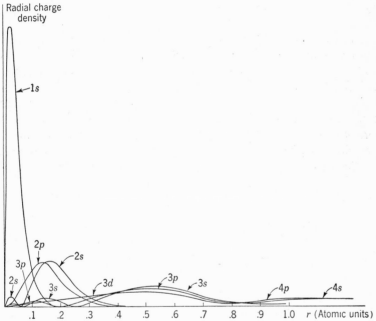

FIG. 6.3.1.   Radial charge density, for inner electrons of Rb, determined from self-consistent field.

values, or graphically. In Fig. 6.3.1 we give values of $y^2 = (rR)^2$ for the various wave functions occurring in the Rb atom, as calculated by Hartree's method, so as to indicate the type of results he obtains. This quantity, we remember from Sec. 5.2, measures the radial charge density, the amount of charge contained in a shell between r and $r + dr$, divided by dr.

It is now interesting to compare Fig. 6.3.1 with Fig. 5.2.3, showing the corresponding distributions for hydrogen. The differences are quite striking. The various wave functions for Rb are shrunk down to much smaller radii, so that all the electrons whose wave functions are shown in Fig. 6.3.1 can fit inside the atom, which has total dimensions not much greater than the hydrogen atom. The ground state of Rb, which has 37 electrons, has two $1s$ electrons, two $2s$, six $2p$, two $3s$, six $3p$, ten $3d$, two $4s$, six $4p$, and one $5s$.   Such a state of an atom, or configuration, is indicated by a symbol which in the present case would be

$$(1s)^2(2s)^2(2p)^6(3s)^2(3p)^6(3d)^{10}(4s)^2(4p)^6(5s).$$

To show the great discrepancy between the sizes of the wave functions in Rb and hydrogen, we give in Table 6.3.1 the radii at which y^2 has a maximum (that is, the radius of maximum radial density) for the $1s$, $2p$, and $3d$ orbits, and the corresponding value for hydrogen.   We must remember, however, that the Rb nucleus has a charge of 37 units, in contrast to hydrogen's unit charge, and we remember from Sec. 5.1 that the whole wave function has a scale inversely proportional to Z [Eqs. (5.1.8) and (5.1.9) can be interpreted as showing that R is a function of rZ].   Thus we might well expect that the various orbits in Rb would be 37 times as small as those in hydrogen.   To test this hypothesis, we give in a column of Table 6.3.1 the ratio of the radius for the maximum radial charge density of each hydrogen wave function, to the corresponding radius for Rb.

TABLE 6.3.1.   SIZES OF $1s$, $2p$, $3d$ ORBITS IN Rb

Orbit	Radius of maximum density, atomic units	Ratio of radius of maximum density, H to Rb
$1s$	0.0273	36.6
$2p$	0.122	32.8
$3d$	0.405	22.2

When we examine these figures, we see that they are by no means all equal to 37.   For the innermost electron, the $1s$, the figure approaches this value, but the numbers decrease as we go to larger wave functions. The reason for this is not a complicated one.   The $1s$ electron is so close to the nucleus that it is hardly shielded by the other electrons and feels practically the whole attractive force of the nucleus.   On the other hand, the outermost electrons spend most of their time outside the rest of the electrons, and thus feel a field of the nucleus of 37 positive charges, shielded by an electron cloud containing 36 electrons.   We remember the result of electrostatics, that a spherical distribution of charge produces the same field as if it were all concentrated at its center.   Thus the outermost electron, over most of its orbit, is in an effective field of only a single unit.   Intermediate electrons are in all intermediate situations between effective nuclear charges of 37 units and a single unit. We then arrive at the idea that each of the orbits is somewhat hydrogenlike, but corresponding to an effective nuclear charge somewhere between Z (that is, 37) and unity, decreasing as we go to the larger orbits. We shall examine this idea a little more carefully in a moment. First, however, let us consider the energies of the one-electron problems and see if they also have some resemblance to hydrogen energies.

In Hartree's calculations we have to find one-electron energies E_i, so chosen that the Schrödinger equations (6.1.3) have valid solutions, and the wave functions decrease properly at infinity, instead of increasing exponentially as r goes infinite. In the actual numerical calculations

TABLE 6.3.2. ENERGIES OF $1s$, $2p$, $3d$ ORBITS IN Rb

Orbit	Energy, Rydbergs	Square root of ratio of Rb to H energy
$1s$	1102.3	33.3
$2p$	132.2	23.0
$3d$	8.40	8.75

these energies are usually found by trial and error, but they could also be found approximately by the quantum condition and the WKB method. In Table 6.3.2 we give the energies found in this way, for the Hartree calculation, for Rb, again for the $1s$, $2p$, and $3d$ states, and the corresponding energies for the same wave functions in hydrogen. Here we find the energies in the Rb case to be much greater numerically than in hydrogen, and this again is what we should expect. We recall from Chap. 5 that the energy of a hydrogenlike orbit in an atom with atomic number Z is Z^2 times as great as in hydrogen, so that we might expect, by our argument of the preceding paragraph, that the square root of the ratio of the Rb energy to the corresponding hydrogen energy would vary from 37 for the $1s$ electron down to the order of unity for the outermost one. This supposition, as we see, is qualitatively fulfilled. However, when we compare the effective charges from Table 6.3.2, determined from the energies, with those from Table 6.3.1, determined from the sizes of the orbits, they do not agree very well. Part of the disagreement is simply a result of the fact that the Rb problem is really not like a hydrogenlike problem with an effective Z, but part is to be expected quite apart from this, for reasons which will be clear if we consider a little more carefully the nature of the potential energy acting on the electron in the Rb problem.

Let us assume that the total charge contained within a sphere of radius r is $Z(r)e$. This includes the nuclear charge Ze and the charge of those electrons inside the sphere, so that $Z(r)$ becomes equal to Z when r is zero, but decreases to zero as we go to the outer part of the atom. By electrostatics we then know that the electric field at distance r is what we should find if we concentrated the charge $Z(r)e$ at the origin, or it is $Z(r)e/4\pi\epsilon_0 r^2$.

Let us denote the electric potential by $Z_p(r)e/4\pi\epsilon_0 r$. If the field were a pure Coulomb field, $Z(r)$ would be constant, as would $Z_p(r)$, and they would be equal to each other. When $Z(r)$ really depends on r, however, the two quantities no longer are equal. We rather have, canceling the common factor $e/4\pi\epsilon_0$,

$$-\frac{d}{dr}\left[\frac{Z_p(r)}{r}\right] = \frac{Z(r)}{r^2}, \qquad Z(r) - Z_p(r) = -r\frac{dZ_p}{dr}. \qquad (6.3.1)$$

This shows at once the way the two quantities differ when Z_p depends on r; since Z_p will decrease with increasing r, $Z(r)$ is greater than $Z_p(r)$. In other words, there is some additional shielding which enters into $Z_p(r)$, or into the potential, which is not found in the expression for field. We can throw light on this additional shielding by recalling that according to electrostatics the field of a thin shell at external points is as if it were concentrated at its center, but inside the shell the field is zero. Thus the potential from a shell of thickness dr, containing charge $[dZ(r)/dr]dr$, is $\{[dZ(r)/dr]e/4\pi\epsilon_0 r\}dr$ at exterior points for which r is greater than the radius R of the shell, but is constant within the shell, equal to its value when $r = R$. Thus at a distance r from the origin the potential is made up of two sorts of contributions, those from the shells inside and outside r. It can be written

$$\frac{Z_p(r)e}{4\pi\epsilon_0 r} = \int_0^r \frac{dZ(R)}{dR}\frac{e}{4\pi\epsilon_0 r}\,dR + \int_r^\infty \frac{dZ(R)}{dR}\frac{e}{4\pi\epsilon_0 R}\,dR$$

$$= \frac{Z(r)e}{4\pi\epsilon_0 r} + \int_r^\infty \frac{dZ(R)}{dR}\frac{e}{4\pi\epsilon_0 R}\,dR, \qquad (6.3.2)$$

which we can compare with (6.3.1). If we multiply (6.3.2) by $4\pi\epsilon_0 r/e$, and differentiate, we at once verify that (6.3.2) is equivalent to (6.3.1).

In the expression (6.3.2), we see that the potential differs from the value which we should have from the nucleus alone for two reasons. First, $Z(r)$ is less than Z, the nuclear charge, on account of those electrons inside the sphere of radius r. This effect is called inner shielding. But second, the second term in (6.3.2), arising from electrons outside this sphere, is also negative, since $dZ(r)/dr$ is negative. This also diminishes the potential, and this effect is called outer shielding. The net result is that $Z(r)$ and $Z_p(r)$, which differ by the outer shielding, are quite different, as is shown in Fig. 6.3.2, showing these quantities for Rb as a function of r, as determined from Hartree's calculations.

Let us now ask what will be the effect of these terms on the wave function and energy of an electron. The wave function will depend essen-

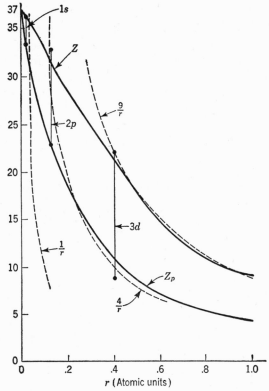

Fig. 6.3.2. Z and Z_p vs. r (atomic units) for Rb.   Also shown are hyperbolas n^2/r, which would intersect Z curve at radii of orbits, if they were hydrogenlike.   Vertical lines are drawn with r equal to the radius of maximum radial charge density of self-consistent solution.   Top point of vertical line indicates ratio of radius of maximum radial density, H to Rb, from Table 6.3.1, and bottom point indicates square root of ratio of Rb to H energy, from Table 6.3.2; these would equal Z and Z_p, respectively, if orbits were hydrogenlike.

tially on the field acting on the electron, just as the radius of an orbit in Bohr's theory would depend on the attractive force of the nucleus.   A constant correction to the potential energy, like that arising from the outer shielding, would have no effect on the wave function.   Thus we might well expect that the radii of the orbits, the values where y has its maximum value, would be given by $n^2 a_0 / Z(r)$, where we should put in the value of $Z(r)$ computed at the orbit's radius. In other words, we might expect that the radii of the orbits could be approximately found as the intersections of the curve giving $Z(r)$ as a function of r, and the hyperbola $Z(r) = n^2 a_0/r$. These hyperbolas are given in Fig. 6.3.2 for $n = 1, 2, 3$. We also indicate in the figure the values of r for which y actually has its maximum, as given in Table 6.3.1. The agreement, as we can see, is quite good, showing that in fact the orbits are not very far from hydrogen-like, if we choose the proper nuclear charge. The agreement is better for the $1s$, $2p$, and $3d$ orbits, which we have chosen, than for the others. The reason is that it is only for these wave functions, having no nodes, and corresponding to the circular orbits in Bohr's theory, that the formula $n^2 a_0/Z$ is exactly correct for the radius.

For the energy level of an electron in the potential field we must assume that the potential itself, and hence Z_p, is more important than the field; an additive constant in the potential energy, such as the outer shielding, would show itself as a corresponding change in the energy level. We thus might anticipate that if we take the value of r corresponding to the maximum value of y in the orbit, and find the corresponding value of Z_p, the result might agree approximately with the effective charge found in Table 6.3.2; or, putting it in an alternative way, that the energy would be approximately $-(Rhc/n^2)[Z_p(r)]^2$. To test this hypothesis, we have carried out the construction in Fig. 6.3.2, and have compared with the values of Z_p found from the formula above, given in Table 6.3.2. We see that here again there is approximate agreement. By this comparison, then, we understand why the effective charge associated with the wave function and its dimensions is quite different from that associated with the energy.

We have been speaking of the energy of the particle in its central field; but we have so far not tried to connect this with the energy levels of the whole atom. As soon as calculations by Hartree's method were first made, it was observed that these energy levels agreed rather accurately with the observed x-ray term values. To explain why this should be, we must first call attention to the meaning of these term values. They are the energies required to remove an inner electron from the atom. For instance, if a $1s$ electron is removed from Rb, we say that the required energy is the K ionization potential. If a $2s$ is removed, it is the L_I ionization potential. Removal of a $2p$ leads to two closely spaced levels, for reasons which will become clear in the next chapter; these are the L_{II} and L_{III} terms. Similarly, removal of a $3s$ leads to the M_I level, the $3p$ leads to the M_{II} and M_{III}, removal of the $3d$ leads to the M_{IV} and M_V, and so on. The x-ray emission lines occur after one of the inner electrons has been removed by electron bombardment. Thus if a $1s$

electron has been removed, any of the outer electrons can fall into this vacant place, and we have the lines of the K series emitted. It is clear that the $h\nu$ of the emitted radiation must be equal to the difference of two of the term values just considered, since before emission the $1s$ electron is missing, afterwards one of the outer electrons is missing. Similarly if a $2s$ or $2p$ electron is removed, and an outer electron falls into the empty space, we have one of the lines of the L series. Often the electrons with principal quantum number 1, 2, 3, etc., are called K, L, M, etc., electrons, as we have mentioned earlier.

Now let us ask how much energy we should expect it to take to remove one of the electrons from the atom. To get at this properly, we should have to set up two problems according to quantum mechanics, first the neutral atom, then the ion, find the energy of each as best we could, and subtract. To solve each one, we should use Hartree's method, and from that we should get separate wave functions for each electron. We should then multiply all these one-electron wave functions together to get an approximate wave function for the whole atom. This product of one-electron wave functions is a solution of the problem in which the interactions between electrons are replaced by the averaged-out central field of the self-consistent method, but it is not a solution of the real problem, whose Hamiltonian involves the Coulomb repulsive interactions of the pairs of electrons, as well as the attractions of the electrons for the nucleus. We know, however, from our study of perturbation theory, that the best way to get an energy value out of an approximate wave function is to take the average value of the correct energy operator, over the approximate wave function. We should then let the correct Hamiltonian operate on the approximate wave function, multiply this by the wave function, and integrate over the coordinates. In the next chapter we shall actually carry out this process. We should do this first for the neutral atom, then for the ion, getting somewhat different wave functions for each, and subtract. The result is a small difference of large quantities. It is very hard to carry out the process accurately, and as a matter of fact, the term values set up in this way are not very accurate. In Appendix 13 we give a further discussion of this process, showing that we can, in fact, set up analytical approximations to these various steps, and that while the final results obtained in this way are not very accurate, still they are good enough to be very useful.

This type of calculation, however, seems to have no resemblance to our energies of the one-electron problem. In Appendix 13 we show that there is in fact a connection, though it is rather involved to show it in detail. Here we can give a qualitative argument which shows in a general way why it is that we can expect the one-electron energies to approximate the term values.　The correct calculation of the energies of neutral atom and ion, which we have described in the preceding paragraph, provides the clue.　The Hamiltonian function for the ion differs from that for the atom in omitting the kinetic energy term of the removed electron, and all the potential energy terms of interaction of this electron with all other electrons and with the nucleus.　In finding the energy of the neutral atom, these terms are averaged over the wave function of the neutral atom, giving the average kinetic energy, and the average potential energy in the field of all the other electrons.　These terms, in other words, give just the one-electron energy of the removed electron.

But in addition, in finding the energy of the neutral atom, we average the remaining terms of the Hamiltonian over the wave function of the neutral atom, while in finding the energy of the ion we average the same remaining terms over the wave function of the ion.　The ion has quite different wave functions from the neutral atom, on account of differences in shielding.　Thus we might well expect the average of the Hamiltonian over these two wave functions to differ considerably, and the difference of them would appear as a correction term to the one-electron energy in calculating the energy required to remove an electron.　Here, however, the perturbation theory comes to our aid.　The wave function of the ion differs appreciably from the wave function which we should build up from the one-electron functions of the neutral atom, omitting the factor relating to the removed electron.　But we remember from perturbation theory that the difference between the mean value of the energy over the correct wave function (that of the ion) and over a somewhat different function (the function made up of the one-electron functions of the neutral atom) is a small quantity of the second order.　This leads, then, to the result that our one-electron energies will actually be correct values for the x-ray term values, correct to the second order of small quantities.

Let us now test this relationship between the one-electron energies and the x-ray levels by comparing the values for Rb.　We do this in Table 6.3.3; and we see that in fact the agreement is good.　It is not perfect; the discrepancies come partly, as is shown by more careful analysis, from the imperfections of the method, and partly from various corrections, such as multiplet structure and relativity corrections, which we have not yet considered.

In this section we have considered almost entirely the inner electronic shells of the atom, those which are occupied by electrons in the ground state.　These are the ones concerned in x-ray spectra.　We have not yet discussed the outer energy levels, in particular the excited ones, which are only occupied when the atom is in a higher state than the ground state.　These are the levels of importance in optical spectroscopy, and we shall take them up in a later section. In the meantime, however, the inner shells are the ones concerned in building up the atom from its constituents, and they are the ones responsible for the periodic table of the elements. Let us then carry out a comparison of the various electronic shells of the different elements and see how this leads us to an understanding of the periodic table.

TABLE 6.3.3.   COMPARISON OF HARTREE ONE-ELECTRON ENERGIES WITH X-RAY TERM
VALUES, FOR Rb

Electron	Hartree	X-ray
$1s$	1102.3	1119.4
$2s$	144.2	152.0
$2p$	132.2	137.0
$3s$	21.28	23.7 (estimated)
$3p$	16.64	17.4
$3d$	8.40	8.3 (estimated)
$4s$	2.707	2.3 (estimated)
$4p$	1.586	1.46

Note: The entries marked "estimated" are interpolated between measured values for other elements.

6.4. The Periodic System of the Elements. In the ground state of an atom of atomic number Z the lowest one-electron energy levels will be filled, enough being occupied to take care of all the electrons. We remember that according to Pauli's exclusion principle we can have just two electrons, one of each spin, in each stationary state. That is, we can have two electrons in each s shell, six in each p shell, and so on. Or, if we group the shells according to their total quantum number and use the x-ray notation K for the electrons of total quantum number 1, L for those with $n = 2$, and so on, we can have 2 electrons in the K shell, $2 + 6 = 8$ in the L shell, $2 + 6 + 10 = 18$ in the M shell, $2 + 6 + 10 + 14 = 32$ in the N shell, and so on. As electrons are added, in going from an atom of one atomic number to the next higher atomic number, we can see that there will be marked differences in properties: some atoms will have completed shells of electrons, others will have a few electrons outside closed shells, others will lack one or two electrons from closed shells. Our elementary knowledge of the periodic table tells us that the rare or inert gases have closed shell configurations, the alkali and alkaline-earth metals have one or two additional electrons, the halogens lack one electron of forming a complete shell, and so on. Let us now look into these facts with a good deal more care.

The first question we ask, in building up the periodic system, is **very** simple: for an atom of atomic number Z, what are the Z lowest energy levels? We have seen that the one-electron energy of a given state, in units of the Rydberg energy, is approximately $-[Z_p(r)]^2/n^2$, where Z_p is to be computed where the wave function has its maximum. From what we have seen so far, this would suggest that the levels of the same n value had the same energy, so that we should fill them up starting with $n = 1$, then $n = 2$, and so on. Closer examination, however, shows that this is not exactly right. Within a given shell, with a given n value, the s electron has the lowest energy, the p next higher, the d next, and so on; The reason for this is that the smaller the l value, the closer the wave function penetrates to the nucleus; we recall that the wave function varies for small r like r^l. Thus the electrons of small l value spend some of their time in a region of very high Z_p, and when we properly compute the energy, this has the effect of depressing the energy more than for the states of higher l value, or making them more stable. We shall look into this situation more closely when we discuss optical spectra in a later section. We shall then find that, for a given atom, those electrons with l greater than a given value do not penetrate into the interior of the atom at all. They find themselves in a field of unit charge (the nucleus shielded by all the other electrons), and have energies which are almost exactly hydrogenlike. Thus these wave functions are not occupied in the ground state of the atom.

We can show how these energies actually lie by giving values of the x-ray term values, or one-electron energies, for all the atoms, similar to the values given for Rb in Table 6.3.2. Such a tabulation is given in Table 6.4.1. We see that, as we should expect, the energy depends primarily on n; but we also see that the numerical value decreases as we go from s to p and d electrons. It is interesting also to see the sizes of the wave functions; and in Table 6.4.2 we give radii of maximum radial density for the atoms, similar to the values we have given for Rb in Table 6.3.1. We see clearly how the radii get smaller, the numerical values of the energies larger, as we go to heavier and heavier atoms, so that the outer orbits of the heavier atoms are not much larger than those of the lighter ones. The radii we have given are for the outermost maximum of each wave function, and these do not indicate the way in which the s electrons penetrate more than the p, and the p more than d. This behavior comes in the inner part of the orbit and, as we have seen, is responsible for the tighter binding of the s electrons.

To complete the interpretation of Tables 6.4.1 and 6.4.2, we must know how many electrons each atom has, and which stationary states they are in, in the ground state. This is shown in Fig. 6.4.1, where we give the periodic table in a form designed to show the electron orbits. The

TABLE 6.4.1.   IONIZATION POTENTIALS OF THE LIGHTER ELEMENTS (Rydbergs)

Element	K	L		M			N			O
	1s	2s	2p	3s	3p	3d	4s	4p	4d	5s
H	1.00									
He	1.81									
Li	4.80	0.40								
Be	(9.3)	0.69								
B	(15.2)	1.29	0.61							
C	(22.3)	1.51	0.83							
N	(31.1)	1.91	1.07							
O	(41.5)	2.10	1.00							
F	(53.0)	2.87	1.37							
Ne	(66.1)	3.56	1.59							
Na	(80.9)	(5.10)	2.79	0.38						
Mg	96.0	(6.96)	3.7	0.56						
Al	114.8	(9.05)	5.3	0.78	0.44					
Si	135.4	(11.5)	7.2	1.10	0.60					
P	157.8	(14.2)	9.4	(1.40)	(0.65)					
S	181.9	(17.2)	11.9	1.48	0.76					
Cl	207.9	(20.4)	14.8	1.81	0.96					
A	235.7	(23.9)	(18.2)	2.14	1.15					
K	265.6	(27.8)	21.5	(2.6)	1.2		0.32			
Ca	297.4	(31.9)	25.5	(3.1)	1.9		0.45			
Sc	331.2	(36.2)	30.0	(3.6)	2.7	0.54	0.50			
Ti	365.8	(41.0)	33.6	(4.2)	2.6	0.51	0.50			
V	402.7	(46.0)	37.9	(4.8)	3.0	0.50	0.52			
Cr	441.1	(51.2)	42.3	(5.4)	3.1	0.61	0.50			
Mn	481.9	(56.7)	47.4	(6.7)	3.8	0.68	0.55			
Fe	523.9	62.5	52.2	6.9	4.1	0.60	0.58			
Co	568.1	(68.5)	57.7	7.6	4.7	0.63	0.66			
Ni	614.1	74.8	63.2	8.2	5.4	(0.68)	0.64			
Cu	661.6	81.0	68.9	8.9	5.7	0.77	0.57			
Zn	711.7	88.4	75.4	10.1	6.7	1.26	0.69			
Ga	765.6	(96.0)	84.1	12.4	8.8	1.8	0.87	0.44		
Ge	817.6	(104.0)	89.3	13.4	9.5	3.2	1.39	0.60		
As	874.0	112.6	97.4	14.9	10.3	3.0	(1.6)	0.74		
Se	932.0	(121.9)	108.4	16.7	11.6	3.9	(1.7)	0.70		
Br	992.6	(131.5)	117.8	19.1	13.6	5.4	(1.9)	0.87		
Kr	(1055)	(141.6)	(127.2)	(21.4)	(15.4)	(6.8)	(2.1)	1.03		
Rb	1119.4	152.0	137.2	(23.7)	17.4	(8.3)	(2.3)	1.46		0.31
Sr	1186.0	162.9	147.6	26.2	19.6	9.7	2.5	(2.1)		0.42
Y	1256.1	175.8	159.9	30.3	23.3	13.0	4.7	2.9	0.48	0.49
Zr	1325.7	186.6	170.0	31.8	24.4	13.3	3.8	2.1	0.53	0.51
Cb	1398.5	198.9	181.7	34.7	26.9	15.2	4.3	2.5	(0.5)	(0.5)
Mo	1473.4	211.3	193.7	37.5	29.2	17.1	5.1	2.9	(0.5)	0.54

The ionization potentials tabulated represent in each case the least energy, in Rydberg units, required to remove the electron in question from the atom.   Data from optical ionization are taken from Bacher and Goudsmit, "Atomic Energy States," McGraw-Hill Book Company, Inc., New York, 1932.   Those for x-ray ionization are from Siegbahn, "Spektroskopie der Röntgenstrahlen," Verlag Julius Springer, Berlin.   Intermediate figures are interpolated.   Interpolated or estimated values are given in parentheses.

TABLE 6.4.2.   RADII OF ELECTRONIC ORBITS IN THE LIGHTER ELEMENTS (angstroms)

Ele-ment	K	L		M			N	
	$1s$	$2s$	$2p$	$3s$	$3p$	$3d$	$4s$	$4p$
H	0.53							
He	0.30							
Li	0.20	1.50						
Be	0.143	1.19						
B	0.112	0.88	0.85					
C	0.090	0.67	0.66					
N	0.080	0.56	0.53					
O	0.069	0.48	0.45					
F	0.061	0.41	0.38					
Ne	0.055	0.37	0.32					
Na	0.050	0.32	0.28	1.55				
Mg	0.046	0.30	0.25	1.32				
Al	0.042	0.27	0.23	1.16	1.21			
Si	0.040	0.24	0.21	0.98	1.06			
P	0.037	0.23	0.19	0.88	0.92			
S	0.035	0.21	0.18	0.78	0.82			
Cl	0.032	0.20	0.16	0.72	0.75			
A	0.031	0.19	0.155	0.66	0.67			
K	0.029	0.18	0.145	0.60	0.63		2.20	
Ca	0.028	0.16	0.133	0.55	0.58		2.03	
Sc	0.026	0.16	0.127	0.52	0.54	0.61	1.80	
Ti	0.025	0.150	0.122	0.48	0.50	0.55	1.66	
V	0.024	0.143	0.117	0.46	0.47	0.49	1.52	
Cr	0.023	0.138	0.112	0.43	0.44	0.45	1.41	
Mn	0.022	0.133	0.106	0.40	0.41	0.42	1.31	
Fe	0.021	0.127	0.101	0.39	0.39	0.39	1.22	
Co	0.020	0.122	0.096	0.37	0.37	0.36	1.14	
Ni	0.019	0.117	0.090	0.35	0.36	0.34	1.07	
Cu	0.019	0.112	0.085	0.34	0.34	0.32	1.03	
Zn	0.018	0.106	0.081	0.32	0.32	0.30	0.97	
Ga	0.017	0.103	0.078	0.31	0.31	0.28	0.92	1.13
Ge	0.017	0.100	0.076	0.30	0.30	0.27	0.88	1.06
As	0.016	0.097	0.073	0.29	0.29	0.25	0.84	1.01
Se	0.016	0.095	0.071	0.28	0.28	0.24	0.81	0.95
Br	0.015	0.092	0.069	0.27	0.27	0.23	0.76	0.90
Kr	0.015	0.090	0.067	0.25	0.25	0.22	0.74	0.86

The radii tabulated represent the distance from the nucleus at which the radial charge density is a maximum, and are computed from calculations of Hartree and coworkers, in the *Proceedings of the Royal Society*, and elsewhere.   Since only a few atoms have been computed, most of the values tabulated are interpolated.   The interpolation should be fairly accurate for the inner electrons of an atom, but unfortunately it is quite inaccurate for the outer electrons, so that these values should not be taken as exact.

general structure of the periodic table arises from the fact that the various shells and subshells are arranged, as far as their energy is concerned, approximately as shown in the following table, in which the first line gives the group, the second the number of electrons in the group, the

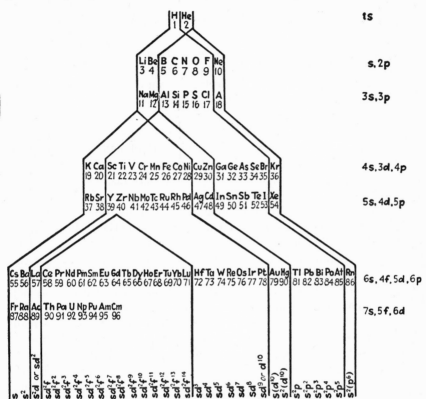

FIG. 6.4.1.   Periodic table of the elements, with electron configuration of lowest states.

third the total number of electrons in that group and all inside it, and the last the element completing the group, whose atomic number therefore stands just above it:

$1s$,	$2s$,	$2p$,	$3s$,	$3p$,	$4s$,	$3d$,	$4p$,	$5s$,	$4d$,	$5p$,	$6s$,	$4f$,	$5d$,	$6p$,	$7s$
2	2	6	2	6	2	10	6	2	10	6	2	14	10	6	2
2	4	10	12	18	20	30	36	38	48	54	56	70	80	86	88
He	Be	Ne	Mg	A	Ca	Zn	Kr	Sr	Cd	Xe	Ba	Yb	Hg	Rn	Ra.

The reason for the order is seen in Table 6.4.1, which of course follows from Hartree's calculations.

Let us now discuss the periodic table of the elements in terms of the structure of the various shells.   Since we have not yet taken up the theory of interatomic forces, we do not have a complete picture of what properties of an atom to examine; but we may anticipate and say that the essential feature, as far as chemical binding is concerned, is the existence of loosely bound electrons outside closed shells of electrons, or the possibility of joining electrons to the atom to form a negative ion with a closed shell. The electropositive atoms, with loosely bound electrons, tend to lose these electrons to form positive ions, or to share the electrons with other atoms in homopolar bonds; whereas the electronegative atoms, which can acquire electrons to form stable negative ions, tend to form ions in this way, or to attach themselves to electrons from other atoms in the form of homopolar bonds. We shall go into these forms of binding more in detail in later chapters.

Starting with the beginning of the elements, hydrogen has a single rather tightly bound electron and stands sort of halfway between an electropositive and electronegative element, sometimes losing and sometimes gaining an electron. Helium, the first inert gas, has a closed shell of two $2s$ electrons, very tightly bound (we note that the ionization potential is higher than for the outer electron of any other element), so that it has no tendency toward chemical combination. Lithium, the first of the alkalies, has a single very loosely bound electron in a large orbit, easily removed to form a positive ion. Beryllium has two rather easily removable electrons, boron has three, carbon four, and so on, leading to the possibility of positive ions; but the electrons are more and more tightly bound as we go along the series, and our later discussion will show that these elements actually are less and less likely to become really ionized, and more likely to share electrons with other atoms in homopolar bonds. As we fill up the L shell, completed at neon, the electrons get more and more tightly bound, and the orbits, and consequently the size, of the atom get smaller and smaller, until neon is an inert gas like helium. If we want to investigate the possibility of fluorine forming a singly charged negative ion, or oxygen a doubly charged ion, we have to determine the energy necessary to remove the last electron from the ion by indirect experiments, or by Hartree calculations of the negative ion. When we do this, we find that the F^- ion really is stable with respect to the F atom; that is, it requires a certain amount of energy, called the electron affinity, to remove the last electron from F^-, so that we can understand the tendency of this ion to form. Similarly O^- is stable with respect to O, but probably $O^=$ is not stable with respect to O^-. This would mean that the ion $O^=$ would not exist by itself; but we shall see later, when we study ionic binding, that in an ionic substance there is an additional electrostatic term in the energy, which stabilizes the ionic state of the positive and negative ions in comparison with the neutral atoms, explaining why the ions form.

The series of elements from sodium to argon repeats very much the same behavior found from lithium to neon. Potassium and calcium resemble the other alkalies and alkaline earths, having one and two easily removable valence electrons respectively; but after calcium we come to the first transition group of metals, in which the $3d$ electrons are being added to the atom. Comparison of Tables 6.4.1 and 6.4.2 shows that the $3d$ and $4s$ electrons have very nearly the same ionization potentials in these atoms, which explains why both shells are partly filled in some of these elements; but the wave functions are quite different, the radius of maximum density in the $3d$ electrons being much less than in the $4s$ electrons. The reason for this apparent anomaly cannot be seen if we use hydrogenic wave functions, but it is predicted satisfactorily by the more accurate calculations of Hartree. A consequence is that these $3d$ electrons in the transition-group elements are rather well shielded from outside influences, such as are present in the solid state and in chemical binding. We shall see later that these electrons have magnetic properties, somewhat as in individual atoms, and this is the origin of the magnetic behavior of the transition elements, among which the ferromagnetic elements are found. Furthermore, the $3d$ electrons do not take part in chemical binding to quite the same extent that the $4s$ electrons do, and as a result, these transition elements, which all resemble each other in their $4s$ shells, show somewhat similar chemical properties. The $3d$ shell is completed at Cu, and this element normally has only one electron in the $4s$ shell, easily removable, and giving the element some of the properties of an alkali metal, though it is really rather different, in that the valence electron is not as easily removable as in an alkali and does not have nearly as large an orbit, so that the inner, $3d$ shell has more effect proportionally on the properties. Furthermore, the state with nine $3d$ electrons, two $4s$, has very nearly the same energy as the ground state, and in this state Cu tends to lose two electrons, forming the cupric ion, quite unlike an alkali metal.

Beyond copper, the $4s$ and $4p$ electrons are added, forming a series of elements rather like those from sodium to argon, ending with the inert gas krypton. We then start with another alkali and alkaline earth, rubidium and strontium; but then we go into another transition group, from yttrium to palladium, as the $4d$ electrons are added; then a group from silver to xenon, resembling the elements from copper to krypton. Cesium and barium are like rubidium and strontium, but then, instead of building up the $5d$ group, which starts with lanthanum, we go into the series of rare-earth elements, in which the 4*f* electrons are being added. These have orbits well inside the atom, so that they are even more shielded from the outside than the *d* electrons being added in the transition groups. This shows itself in the remarkable chemical similarity of the rare earths, their outer electrons being practically identical, and in various properties arising from the 4*f* electrons, one of which is the existence of rather sharp absorption lines in the compounds of the rare-earth atoms. Ordinarily, as we shall see later, chemical compounds and solids do not have sharp line spectra like isolated atoms; the wave functions, and hence the energy levels, of the outer electrons, responsible for the absorption, are too distorted by the chemical binding to allow sharp lines. On the other hand, the 4*f* electrons of the rare earths are so far inside the atom that they are practically unaffected by the chemical state of the atom and show sharp spectra.

Joining continuously onto the group of rare-earth elements, which is substantially completed at lutecium, we enter another transition group in which the 5*d* shell is being completed, a group which is followed by gold and mercury, similar to silver and cadmium, and a series of elements in which the outermost shell, the 6*p*, is being filled, ending with the inert gas radon. We then start to fill the 7*s* shell, radium having two 7*s* electrons and being an alkaline earth, after which we begin to fill the 6*d*, and then the 5*f* shells, starting a new group of rare earths, to which presumably the transuranic elements neptunium, plutonium, americium, curium, and any further ones belong. This is not certain, since the spectra of these elements have not yet been analyzed in sufficient detail. After that, of course, the periodic system is terminated, not through any difficulty with the electronic orbits, but through radioactive instability of the nuclei. A situation does arise, however, which would terminate the periodic system near this point in any case: the *K* shell of the heaviest elements has grown so small that it comes rather close to bumping into the nucleus, and interaction between *K* electrons and the nucleus becomes increasingly likely as we get to the very heavy elements.

6.5. Valence Electrons and the Rydberg Formula. In the production of optical spectra the outermost electron of an atom becomes excited and undergoes transitions between one and another excited energy level, or between one of the excited levels and the ground state. Thus in the atom of Rb, which we have used as an illustration, the 5*s* electron can be excited to excited energy levels and carry out transitions. The wave functions and energy levels of these excited electrons are very different from those which we have been discussing in the preceding sections, which are characteristic of the inner, or x-ray, electrons. In the early days of spectroscopy it was discovered that the energy levels satisfy to a rather high degree of exactness the law

$$E = -\frac{Rhc}{(n - \delta)^2},$$ (6.5.1)

where n is the principal quantum number, and δ is a quantity called the quantum defect, a function of the azimuthal quantum number l, but not of n.   This is called Rydberg's formula, and it was regarded in the early days as a remarkable fact that the same Rydberg number R occurred in this formula for the spectra of many different elements.   The Rydberg formula holds most accurately for simple spectra such as the alkalies. For more complicated cases we shall see in the next chapter that the multiplet structure complicates the situation a good deal.   It is found that the quantum defects decrease rapidly as l increases, being quite large for s states, less for p states, and so on, until finally for those series in which the electrons do not penetrate the inner part of the atom, the quantum defect is almost zero, and the spectrum is hydrogenic.   We see, then, that the quantum defect is in some way a measure of the penetration of the electron into the atom.

The general order of magnitude of the quantum defect can be found by a simple rule.   For electrons of a given azimuthal quantum number, we know that some of the electrons are permanently incorporated in the atom.   Thus in Rb, the $1s$, $2s$, $3s$, and $4s$ electrons lie inside the atom, the $5s$ being the valence electron, and lying on the outside.   Similarly the $2p$, $3p$, $4p$ lie inside, and so does the $3d$.   We must then assume that the $5p$ and $4d$ would lie outside the atom, being unoccupied in the ground state, and easily removable.   Now the Rydberg formula (6.5.1) gives the Rydberg energy 13.54 volts if $n - \delta = 1$.   Thus for an easily removable electron we must have $n - \delta$ somewhat greater than unity.   Hence we must assume that for the s series, for Rb, δ is somewhat less than 4, so that for the $5s$ we shall have an ionization potential somewhat less than 13.54 volts.   In fact, from Table 6.4.1 we see that the term value for the $5s$ electron of Rb is about $0.31Rhc$, and if we fit this to formula (6.5.1), we find that $\delta = 3.21$.   This formula is not too bad even for the $4s$ electron, in which (6.5.1) would give an energy

$$\frac{-Rhc}{(4 - 3.21)^2} = -1.60Rhc,$$

compared with the actual value $-2.3Rhc$ from Table 6.4.1.   The experimental values of the δ's for the other series of Rb are about 2.70 for the p series, 1.23 for the d, and 0.02 for the f, showing the type of decrease with decreasing penetration which we have mentioned, with the non-penetrating f orbits showing almost hydrogenlike behavior.

Let us now try to understand how the Rydberg formula arises, from the atomic model. We may assume that the excited electron moves in the averaged field of the other electrons, following the self-consistent field method, and that the one-electron energy in that field measures the energy required to remove the electron from the corresponding stationary state, or the spectroscopic term value. To investigate these one-electron energies, we may solve the Schrödinger equation numerically, as Hartree does; but we may also get fairly accurate values by using the WKB method. By this means we can, as a matter of fact, derive the Rydberg formula as a first approximation and see how to get approximate values of the quantum defects. Before we can do this, however, we must investigate the application of the WKB method to the central field problem. A careful analysis of this problem involves rather advanced features of the WKB method, as it concerns the distinction between whole and half quantum numbers, and we shall have to leave certain features of our discussion in a rather incomplete state, in order to present it simply.

In Eq. (5.2.4) we have seen that Schrödinger's equation for the function y, equal to r times the radial part of the wave function for hydrogen, is like that of a one-dimensional particle whose potential energy is $-Ze^2/4\pi\epsilon_0 r + l(l + 1)h^2/8\pi^2mr^2$, where we express the result in mks rather than atomic units. Corresponding to this, we should be able to express the conservation of energy in the form

$$\frac{p_r^2}{2m} + \frac{l(l + 1)h^2}{8\pi^2mr^2} - \frac{Ze^2}{4\pi\epsilon_0 r} = E, \qquad (6.5.2)$$

where p_r is the radial momentum. Then we may write the radial quantum condition, using Eq. (2.3.2), in the form

$$2\int_{r_1}^{r_2} p_r\, dr = (n_r - \tfrac{1}{2})h, \qquad (6.5.3)$$

where r_1, r_2 are the turning points of the classical orbit, and n_r is an integer, which we may call the radial quantum number, and where p_r is to be determined from (6.5.2). The peculiar feature of the WKB method which we meet in this case, however, shows that this is not exactly right. Instead of using the expression $l(l + 1)$, which is the substitute for the classical value l^2, we find that we must use $(l + \tfrac{1}{2})^2$, which equals $l^2 + l + \tfrac{1}{4}$, whereas $l(l + 1)$ equals $l^2 + l$. With this minor modification, which we shall not try to justify, the radial quantum condition for hydrogen then proceeds in the following manner:

We may write our radial quantum integral from (6.5.3) in the form

$$2 \int_{r_1}^{r_2} p_r \, dr = 2 \int_{r_1}^{r_2} \frac{\sqrt{X}}{x} \, dx, \qquad \text{where } X = a + bx + cx^2,$$

$$a = -\left(l + \frac{1}{2}\right)^2 \frac{h^2}{4\pi^2}, \qquad b = \frac{2mZe^2}{4\pi\epsilon_0}, \qquad c = 2mE,$$

$$r_1, r_2 = \frac{-b \pm \sqrt{b^2 - 4ac}}{2c}. \tag{6.5.4}$$

From the integral tables, we find

$$\int \frac{\sqrt{X}}{x} \, dx = \sqrt{X} + \frac{b}{2\sqrt{-c}} \sin^{-1}\left(\frac{-2cx - b}{\sqrt{b^2 - 4ac}}\right)$$

$$- \sqrt{-a} \sin^{-1}\left(\frac{bx + 2a}{x\sqrt{b^2 - 4ac}}\right). \tag{6.5.5}$$

Here we have chosen the correct form of the integrals for the case we are considering, though there are alternative forms in terms of logarithms and inverse hyperbolic functions. At the upper and lower limits, respectively, the quantities whose inverse sines we are taking are ± 1, so that the differences of the inverse sines at the two limits are π; and the quantity $\sqrt{X}$ vanishes at both limits. Thus we have

$$\oint p_r \, dr = 2\pi \left(\frac{b}{2\sqrt{-c}} - \sqrt{-a}\right)$$

$$= 2\pi \left[\frac{mZe^2}{4\pi\epsilon_0 \sqrt{-2mE}} - \left(l + \frac{1}{2}\right)\frac{h}{2\pi}\right]$$

$$= (n_r - \tfrac{1}{2})h, \tag{6.5.6}$$

where we have written the quantum condition (6.5.3). We then solve for the energy, and find

$$E = -Rhc \frac{Z^2}{n^2}, \tag{6.5.7}$$

where the Rydberg is defined as in Sec. 1.2. Thus we see that the hydrogen energy levels are given correctly by the WKB method, modified as we have indicated to take care of the azimuthal quantum number.

We can now use these results to discuss a nonhydrogenic atom. The quantum condition is again given by (6.5.2) and (6.5.3), but now modified by using $Z_p(r)$ in place of the constant Z which appears there. The physical modification will come because an excited electron will spend part of its time in the region outside all other electronic shells, where the field is strictly hydrogenic, but also will spend part of its time penetrating into these inner shells, which then no longer shield the nucleus very completely, and hence expose it to a much greater negative potential energy, accompanied by a much greater kinetic energy and momentum. To show the nature of the modification, as it affects the WKB method, we plot in

Fig. 6.5.1 the quantity p_r as a function of r, for the hydrogenic case of Eq. (6.5.2), setting $Z = 1$. We give curves for two n values, with the same l, for comparison, the larger area, of course, corresponding to the higher quantum number, since the area of the curve of p_r vs. r is simply the phase integral $\oint p_r\, dr$. Then we also show, by shading, an additional area which would be added to the phase integral if the momentum were increased in the penetrating part of the orbit in the way we have just

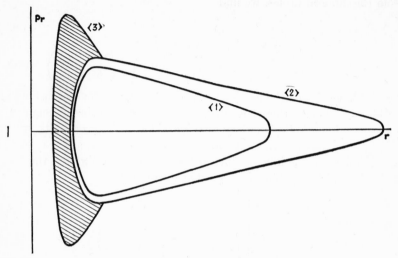

Fig. 6.5.1. Phase space and phase integral for r, penetrating and nonpenetrating orbits: (1) and (2) nonpenetrating orbits of same l, different n; (3) combined with (2) penetrating orbit, having same energy as (2), but in a non-Coulomb field, so that it has a different quantum number and phase integral. Shaded area represents the quantum defect δ.

described, calculated for the case of Rb. This additional area would come, as we see from the figure, in a region where the p_r of the hydrogenic functions is almost independent of the quantum number n_r; thus it will amount to an approximately constant addition to the phase integral for all orbits of the same l value.

We can now use the phase-integral method, coupled with the simple graphical situation seen in the figure above, to discuss the energy levels of the penetrating orbits. The phase integral $\oint p_r\, dr$ will be the hydrogenic value of this integral, plus a correction term depending to a first approximation only on l. Thus, using (6.5.6), we find

$$\oint p_r\, dr = 2\pi \left(\frac{mZ_0 e^2}{4\pi\epsilon_0 \sqrt{-2mE}} \right) - \left(l + \frac{1}{2} \right) h + \delta h$$
$$= (n_r - \tfrac{1}{2})h, \qquad (6.5.8)$$

where δh is the correction term, and where Z_0 is to be taken as unity if we are dealing with the valence electron in a neutral atom, two if we are handling the valence electron in a singly charged ion, etc; that is, it is the charge describing the hydrogenic field acting on the valence electron

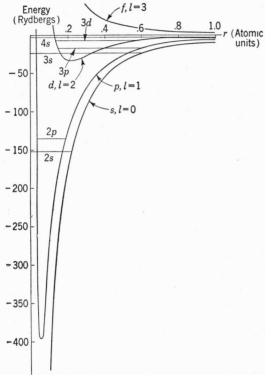

FIG. 6.5.2. Effective potential energy, $-2Z_p/r + l(l+1)/r^2$, for Rb. Lower energy levels shown.

in the nonpenetrating part of the orbit. When we solve for E, writing $n = n_r + l$ as in the hydrogenic case, we then find

$$E = -\frac{RhcZ_0^2}{(n-\delta)^2},$$

or the Rydberg formula, agreeing with (6.5.1). We thus see the origin of the quantum defects in the penetration of the orbits into the inner part of the atom and see that the quantum defects can be computed in a simple way as the difference between the phase integral $\oint p_r \, dr$ for the actual atom and for the hydrogenic case. The reason the quantum defect decreases with increasing l value is seen from Fig. 6.5.2, which shows the effective potential energy for different l values for Rb, similar to Fig. 5.2.1 for hydrogen.   It is clear that in this case the minimum in the curve, for the f levels, lies entirely outside the rest of the atom.   The quantity p_r, of course, is determined by the difference between this potential energy curve and the constant energy curve, as shown in the figure. Since this lies entirely outside the atom, in the region where Z_p is unity, the nonpenetrating orbits must be almost exactly hydrogenlike.

PROBLEMS

1. The K series in the x-ray spectra comes when a K electron is knocked out and an $L, M, \ldots$ electron falls into the vacant place in the K shell.   The lines are K_α (if an L electron falls in), K_β (an M), etc.   Write down the configurations before and after the K_α and K_β transitions of Mo.

2. Show that the frequencies of the lines of the K series are less than the frequency of light necessary to cause ionization of the K electron.   Compute the K ionization potential and the K_α line for Ca, and show that they fit in with the general case.

3. Moseley's law is that the square roots of x-ray term values (ionization potentials) form a linear function of the atomic number.   This would obviously be true if there were just inner shielding, for then the square root would be simply $(Z - S)/n$. Investigate how closely this is true when there is outer shielding as well, computing K and L term values for electrons from $Z = 10$ to $Z = 20$, by the methods of Appendix 13, and seeing how closely the square roots fall on straight lines.   Compare with the experimental values from Table 6.4.1.

4. Isoelectronic sequences are sets of ions, all of the same number of electrons, but with different nuclear charges, and hence different degrees of ionization.   Compute the ionization potentials, or term values, $1s^22s^22p \rightarrow 1s^22s^2$, $1s^22s^23s \rightarrow 1s^22s^2$, for the atoms $Z = 5$ to 10, indicating what ions they are (as $Z = 6$, $1s^22s^22p$ is C$^+$), using the methods of Appendix 13.   Investigate to see whether these term values follow Moseley's law that the square root of the term value is a linear function of atomic number.

5. Using the approximation that the radius of a shell is $n^2/(Z - S)$, where S is given by the methods of Appendix 13, draw curves giving the radius of each shell as function of Z for all atoms up to $Z = 20$ (compute only enough values to draw the curves).   Compare with the more accurate values of Table 6.4.2.

6. Assuming that the electrons are located on the surfaces of spheres of radius $n^2/(Z - S)$, and using the methods of Appendix 13, find and plot Z and Z_p for Na$^+$ as functions of r.

7. Use the potential of Prob. 6 to find the effective potential energy for s, p, and d electrons in the Na atom, as in Fig. 6.5.2.   Find which orbits are nonpenetrating.

8. Using the potential of Prob. 7 and Bohr's azimuthal quantum condition, compute the positions of $3s$, $4s$, and $5s$ levels.   To do this, evaluate the radial quantum integral, computing separately the parts inside and outside $r = 1$, set the sum equal to $(n_r - \frac{1}{2})h$, and solve for the energy, using numerical methods, if necessary, to solve the transcendental equation.   Find how closely the result fits with the Rydberg formula, computing quantum defects for each level.

9. In the field of Prob. 7 the d electrons do not have exactly the hydrogen energies, for their wave function is not zero in the region inside the L shell, where the potential is not hydrogenlike.   Compute the first-order perturbed value of the energies of $3d$, $4d$,

by using hydrogen wave functions as the starting point of a perturbation calculation and assuming the difference between the hydrogen potential and the actual one as perturbative potential.

10. Using the shielding constants of Appendix 13, we can set up effective nuclear charges $Z - S_i$ for the various electrons of an atom. It is then found that fairly good one-electron wave functions (better than hydrogenic wave functions) can be found as follows. For the $1s$, $2p$, electrons, we set up radial functions of the form $r^n e^{-(Z-S_i)r/n}$. For $2s$, this function, which has no nodes, is not orthogonal to the $1s$ function; but we can make a linear combination of it and the $1s$ function (noting that these two functions will have different exponential terms) which will be orthogonal to the $1s$. Show how this orthogonalizing process can be carried out.

11. Use the method of the preceding problem to set up $1s$, $2s$, $2p$ wave functions for Na. Compare the radii of outermost maxima of the charge density with those given in Table 6.4.2.

12. In a similar way, set up a wave function for the $3s$ electron for Na, making it up as a linear combination of the quantities $r^n e^{-(Z-S_i)r/n}$ for $n = 1, 2, 3$, choosing the coefficients so as to make it orthogonal to the $1s$ and $2s$. Plot this wave function as a function of r. Compare the radius of outermost maximum with that of Table 6.4.2.

CHAPTER 7

MULTIPLET STRUCTURE

We have seen in the preceding chapter that the central field model of atomic structure is only an approximation. If we have more than one electron outside closed shells in an atom, and if these are not s electrons, their charge distributions will depend on angle as well as on r. Each will then exert a torque on its neighbors, so that the separate angular momenta of the electrons will not stay constant. The situation that arises in this case leads to the formation of multiplets, which we shall take up in the present chapter. The torques are of several kinds: the largest ones come from electrostatic forces from nonspherical charge distributions, but also there are torques arising from magnetic forces. The individual electrons have magnetic moments, both on account of their rotation in their orbits, and on account of the electronic spins, and these exert magnetic forces on each other. The interactions of these angular momentum vectors lead to an involved problem in dynamics, but fortunately one which is not too hard to solve rather completely. This will interest us to some extent on account of its bearing on the spectra of individual atoms, where these multiplets form a conspicuous feature of the spectrum. For one whose main concern is the structure of molecules and solids, however, this application to atoms is of secondary interest, for the multiplet structure is completely changed by the forces of interaction between atoms. The more important reason for our interest in it, in connection with the theory of molecules and solids, is that the same principles encountered in atomic multiplets prove to operate in problems of molecular valence, and in fact underlie the whole theory of homopolar binding and the covalent bond. We shall consequently focus our attention on those parts of the theory which find more general application than just to atomic structure.

7.1. The Behavior of a Single Vector Quantity in an External Field.
One can get a very good understanding of most of the features of multiplet structure, though not of some of the very important ones, by a little use of classical mechanics, as applied to rotating vectors. Most of the theory was originally worked out in this way, and it has been a guide in applying the methods of wave mechanics. We shall, accordingly, start by describing the behavior of a single vector quantity in an external field according to classical mechanics, then take up its description in

wave mechanics. In later sections we shall then go on to the coupling of two such vectors, and finally to the coupling of many vectors, such as we have in the problem of multiplet structure, where each electron's orbit, and each spin, is a vector quantity coupling with all the others.

First we consider the effect of a torque on a single vector quantity, according to classical mechanics. The most familiar example of this effect is found in the elementary theory of the gyroscope. A gyroscope consists of a rotating wheel on an axle, supported by a pivot. It has an angular momentum vector along the axis of rotation, as in Fig. 7.1.1. When gravity acts on it, a torque is exerted, proportional to the sine of

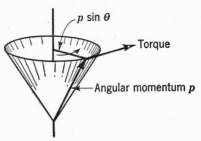

the angle between the axis and the vertical, tending to make the gyroscope fall. We apply Newton's second law of motion, in the form appropriate to the motion of rigid bodies; this states that the torque equals the time rate of change of the angular momentum, where both torque and angular momentum are to be considered as vectors. The torque, by hypothesis, is a vector along the axis about which it tries to produce rota-

FIG. 7.1.1. Angular momentum and torque for precessing motion of symmetrical rigid body.

tion, that is, the axis at right angles to the force and the lever arm. Thus the torque, in Fig. 7.1.1, is at right angles to the plane containing the vertical (the direction of the gravitational force) and the axis of the gyroscope, and hence it is at right angles to the angular momentum. If the time rate of change of angular momentum is at right angles to the angular momentum itself, then as the figure shows, the resulting motion must be a precession or rotation of the angular momentum vector about the vertical, so that the axis of the gyroscope moves in a cone. Such a precession is the normal effect of a torque on an angular momentum vector.

It is a simple and familiar calculation to find the rate of precession in this case. If the angle between the axis and the vertical is θ, and the magnitude of the angular momentum vector is p, the component of this vector in a horizontal plane is $p \sin \theta$. Let the distance out to the center of mass from the axis be r, and the mass m; then the gravitational torque is $mgr \sin \theta$. This is the time rate of change of the angular momentum. In the horizontal plane we have a vector of magnitude $p \sin \theta$ with a time rate of change $mgr \sin \theta$. This is as if the vector rotated with an angular velocity $mgr \sin \theta / (p \sin \theta) = mgr/p$. This then is the angular velocity of precession; it is interesting to note that it is independent of the angle θ.

A similar situation is met when an electronic orbit, which of course carries with it a magnetic moment, is placed in an external magnetic field. Let the external field be B, along the vertical direction in the preceding figure, and let the magnetic moment be μ. Then there is an energy $-\mu B \cos \theta$ giving the interaction between the magnet and the external field, the energy being a minimum when $\theta = 0$, or the magnet points parallel to the field; and the magnitude of the resulting torque is $\mu B \sin \theta$. The problem is almost precisely like that of the gyroscope, if we replace the torque $mgr \sin \theta$ by the value $\mu B \sin \theta$. Thus we find the angular velocity of precession to be $(\mu/p)B$. If now the magnetic moment μ equals $(e/2m)p$, or $(e/2mc)p$ (in the mks and Gaussian units, respectively), we see that this angular velocity is $(e/2m)B$ or $(e/2mc)B$, respectively, an angular velocity proportional to the external magnetic field. The corresponding frequency, $eB/4\pi m$ or $eB/4\pi mc$ depending on units, is called the Larmor frequency. It is a general result of electrodynamics that electronic systems of a rather wide generality will precess in a constant magnetic field with this frequency.

Now let us see how this situation is described in quantum theory. The magnitude of the angular momentum, p, will be $lh/2\pi$, where l is the azimuthal quantum number. The component $p \cos \theta$ along the axis will be equal to $mh/2\pi$, where m is an integer. Since the energy of the magnet in the external field is $-\mu B \cos \theta$, we may write this energy as $-(\mu B/p)(mh/2\pi)$. If we use the ratio μ/p above, this is equal to $-mh$ times the Larmor frequency. In other words, the rotating orbit can take up a space quantization with respect to the external magnetic fields, the possible energy levels being uniformly spaced, the spacing being h times the Larmor frequency. If now we have a transition between two energy levels differing only in m value, the energy difference will be equal to the difference in m multiplied by the $h\nu$ of the Larmor frequency. The emitted frequency of radiation associated with the transition will then be the difference of m multiplied by the Larmor frequency itself. Now it is possible to investigate the intensities of the emitted radiation corresponding to different changes of m by methods described in Sec. 5.4, and this leads to a very simple result for this case: the intensities are zero, unless the difference of m is unity. The effect of this selection principle is then that the emitted frequency, according to the quantum theory, is the Larmor frequency, or the same as the rotational frequency in classical mechanics. These frequencies can, as a matter of fact, be observed experimentally, under suitable conditions. If we put in numerical values, we find that for reasonable values of the magnetic field B they lie in the microwave region of the spectrum. Microwave experiments can be carried out, allowing radiation of these frequencies to fall on the atom.

and the radiation, as a matter of fact, is absorbed, provided the frequency is just right, as given by this condition.

The orbital angular momentum and magnetic moment are not the only kind met in atomic problems; we also have the electron spin. An electron has an intrinsic angular momentum of $(\frac{1}{2})(h/2\pi)$ and a magnetic moment of $(e/2m)(h/2\pi)$. That is, its ratio of magnetic moment to angular momentum is twice that for the orbital motion of an electron. As a consequence, its precession frequency in an external field is twice the Larmor frequency. The component of angular momentum along the axis is $\pm(\frac{1}{2})(h/2\pi)$, which we can write as $m_s h/2\pi$, where m_s takes on the values $\pm\frac{1}{2}$; to distinguish the cases of spin and orbital angular momentum, we shall from now on denote the component of $lh/2\pi$ along the axis as $m_l h/2\pi$.

As we get on with our study of multiplets, we shall see that an atom as a whole has an angular momentum equal to $Jh/2\pi$, where J is a quantum number, called the inner quantum number. This angular momentum is the vector sum of all the various orbital and spin angular momenta in the atom. Its orientation in space is quantized, just as that of a single angular momentum is quantized, and its component along the axis is $Mh/2\pi$, where M can go from $-J$ to J and is called the magnetic quantum number. Since the atom is made up partly of orbital and partly of spin vectors, the ratio of magnetic moment to angular momentum for the atom as a whole, sometimes called the gyromagnetic ratio, is some suitable mean of the value for orbital magnetic moments and for spins. It is usual to introduce a dimensionless factor g, equal to the ratio of the gyromagnetic ratio of the atom to that of an atom containing only orbital angular momenta; thus g is ordinarily between unity and two, though complicated arrangements of vectors can be set up which lead to g values outside this range. The quantity g is often called the Landé g factor, since Landé was very active in the study of the effects of magnetic fields on multiplet structure. We now see that the classical precession frequency of the atom would be g times the Larmor frequency ν_L, and the energy levels in the quantum theory would be given by $-Mgh\nu_L$. This gives a splitting of the levels in a magnetic field, which is called the Zeeman effect. The cases where g happens to equal unity are called the simple Zeeman effect, those where g is different from unity, the anomalous Zeeman effect; this notation is left over from the days before the existence of the electron spin was recognized, when any g value different from unity was regarded as anomalous. We shall later have a formula for the g value and shall see that its knowledge can lead to values of various quantum numbers of the atom; for this reason, an experimental study of the Zeeman effect is of great use in the analysis of a complicated atomic spectrum.

7.2. The Interaction of Two Vector Quantities. In an atom we have many vector quantities combining the properties of angular momenta and magnetic moments, as we have indicated in the preceding section. These vector quantities exert torques on each other; thus even in the absence of an external field, they are caused to precess. In the present section we shall take up the simplest possible case of such interaction, that in which we have two vectors exerting torques on each other. It is immaterial for the present purpose whether the vectors are orbital or spin angular momenta; we shall consider only the dynamics of their interaction. Then in the next section we shall come to the actual application of these ideas to the structure of complex atoms.

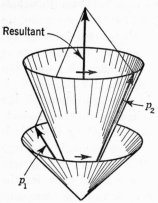

If there is no external field, the torques acting between the two vectors will be internal to the system, there being no torque on the system as a whole; and thus by Newton's second law the total angular momentum of the system will remain constant. In classical mechanics this then furnishes a fixed axis in space; as we can see from Fig. 7.2.1, if two angular momentum vectors add vectorially to give a constant resultant, the only motion possible to the vectors is for the plane containing them to precess around the fixed axis of total angular momentum. We can analyze this precession by methods analogous to those used in our earlier simpler case of the single vector in an external field and can show, as in that case, that the classical frequency of precession is closely related to the energy levels as determined by the quantum theory.

FIG. 7.2.1. Precession of two angular momentum vectors about their resultant.

When we examine the problem by the quantum theory, we find a number of interesting facts. Each of our two angular momentum vectors is assumed to be quantized; that is, to have a magnitude equal to an integral (or sometimes, as with the spin, half integral) multiple of the unit $h/2\pi$. But we also find that the resultant vector must be quantized. We find, in fact, that this resultant can take on all quantized values from the case where the two resultant vectors are parallel to each other, so that the resultant equals their sum, to the case where they are antiparallel, and the resultant is their difference. If for the sake of definiteness, we speak of the orbital angular momentum vectors l_1 and l_2 of two electrons, and their coupling to give a resultant which we may call L, then L can take on all values from $l_1 + l_2$ to $|l_1 - l_2|$. Each of these L

values in itself will represent a vector which can have space quantization, as described in the preceding section; its component along the z axis may be called M_L, and this can take on all values from L to $-L$. The levels with different L values will have different energies, for they correspond to different relative orientations of the vectors l_1 and l_2; in specific cases, where we know how the energy depends on the cosine of the angle between the vectors, we can set up formulas for the energy levels, as we shall show later. The levels with the same L, but different M_L, differing only in the orientation of the whole system in space, will have the same energy if there is no external field. On the other hand, if there is an external field, such as a magnetic field along the z axis, they will have different energies, and we shall have a Zeeman effect, as discussed at the end of the preceding section.

Let us now ask how by wave mechanics we proceed to get the energies corresponding to different L values in the absence of an external field. We proceed by perturbation theory, assuming that we have solved the problem of the uncoupled vectors, and imposing the energy of interaction between them as a perturbation. The perturbation problem is degenerate, with a high degree of degeneracy. In the absence of the perturbative energy, the space quantization of the vector l_1 leads to $2l_1 + 1$ orientations, described by the quantum number which we may denote as m_{l1}, each corresponding to a separate substate, all with the same energy. Similarly the quantization of l_2 leads to $2l_2 + 1$ substates. The quantum numbers m_{l1} and m_{l2} can be combined in any way in setting up unperturbed wave functions for the combined system; hence we have $(2l_1 + 1)$ $(2l_2 + 1)$ unperturbed wave functions, all degenerate. We must solve the perturbation problem for this degenerate system, involving a secular equation with $(2l_1 + 1)(2l_2 + 1)$ rows and columns. If it were not for simplifying features, the order of degeneracy is so great that it would probably be impossible to handle the secular equation and solve the problem. Fortunately, however, on account of the particular nature of the problem, things simplify enough so that a complete solution is possible. We may expect this simplification from our discussion of the vector model. For we have seen that we expect all sublevels with the same L value, but different M_L's, to have the same energy. Thus we expect in the perturbed problem that there will still be a great deal of degeneracy, there being only as many really distinct energy levels as there are L values; and this rather small number of distinct energy levels should make it easier to solve the secular equation.

There is one thing about this interpretation which we must verify at the outset. We know that after we have applied any perturbation calculation, we must have just as many perturbed wave functions as we had

unperturbed wave functions to start with. The number of unperturbed wave functions, as we have just seen, is $(2l_1 + 1)(2l_2 + 1)$. The number of perturbed wave functions, however, is determined from the statement **that** we have levels with values of L from $l_1 + l_2$ to $|l_1 - l_2|$, each having $2L + 1$ sublevels of different M_L. Thus, using the quantum numbers L and M_L appropriate to the perturbed system rather than the m_{l_1} and m_{l_2} appropriate to the unperturbed system, we find that there are

$$[2(l_1 + l_2) + 1] + [2(l_1 + l_2) - 1] + \cdots + [2(|l_1 - l_2|) + 1]$$

sublevels. Fortunately we can prove by simple algebra that this equals $(2l_1 + 1)(2l_2 + 2)$, so that the number of sublevels agrees in the two methods of description.

We can make a closer correspondence than this between the unperturbed and perturbed stationary states. The reason is that the z component of angular momentum of the whole system is conserved, whether the two vectors are interacting with each other or not, since the interaction does not involve any torque on the system as a whole. Thus in any case the angular momentum along the z axis will be quantized, and there must be a correspondence between the states with a given value of this quantity, with and without the interaction. This fact leads to far-reaching results in the way of simplification of the secular equation. For the total z component of angular momentum, in the original system of quantum numbers, is specified by $m_{l_1} + m_{l_2}$, and in the perturbed system by M_L. We should thus expect that all the perturbed states with a given M_L should be made up out of the unperturbed states with the same value of $m_{l_1} + m_{l_2}$. This proves in fact to be the case. The perturbative energy proves to have no matrix components between states with different values of $m_{l_1} + m_{l_2}$. Thus the secular equation factors, and we can essentially treat those states of a given Σm_l or M_L as if they formed a perturbation problem entirely independent of any other states. As a result of this, the complicated problem of degeneracy is broken down into a number of simpler separate problems.

The problem is further simplified by the fact that we have different energy levels only for different L values, a theorem which can be proved by general methods, and which, along with a number of other more detailed proofs, is discussed in Appendix 14. This allows us to use the diagonal sum rule, stated in Eq. (4.4.3), to carry out a complete solution of the degenerate problem by elementary means. That rule, we remember, states that the sum of the diagonal matrix components of energy for a number of unperturbed energy levels equals the sum of the perturbed energies for the same levels. Let us see how this is to be applied. There will be just one unperturbed, and one perturbed, state with the maximum value of M_L. It will correspond to m_{l_1} being equal to l_1, m_{l_2} equal to l_2; or alternatively to L being equal to its maximum possible value $l_1 + l_2$, and M_L being equal to L. Thus the degenerate problem associated with this value of M_L has only one state and is trivial: the unperturbed energy corresponding to these m_l values, including the diagonal matrix components of the interaction energy between the two vectors, will equal the perturbed energy of the level of maximum L value. Next, the next smaller value of M_L, given by $l_1 + l_2 - 1$, will have just two sublevels: we have either $m_{l_1} = l_1$, $m_{l_2} = l_2 - 1$, or $m_{l_1'} = l_1 - 1$, $m_{l_2} = l_2$; or alternatively we have $L = l_1 + l_2$, $M_L = L - 1$, or $L = l_1 + l_2 - 1$, $M_L = L$.

TABLE 7.2.1. DEGENERATE SUBLEVELS OF COMBINATION OF TWO VECTORS, WITH $l_1 = 1, l_2 = 2$

$\Sigma m_l = M_L$	m_{l_1}	m_{l_2}	L
3	1	2	3
2	$\begin{cases} 1 \\ 0 \end{cases}$	$\begin{cases} 1 \\ 2 \end{cases}$	3, **2**
1	$\begin{cases} 1 \\ 0 \\ -1 \end{cases}$	$\begin{cases} 0 \\ 1 \\ 2 \end{cases}$	3, **2**, 1
0	$\begin{cases} 1 \\ 0 \\ -1 \end{cases}$	$\begin{cases} -1 \\ 0 \\ 1 \end{cases}$	3, **2**, 1
-1	$\begin{cases} 1 \\ 0 \\ -1 \end{cases}$	$\begin{cases} -2 \\ -1 \\ 0 \end{cases}$	3, **2**, 1
-2	$\begin{cases} 0 \\ -1 \end{cases}$	$\begin{cases} -2 \\ -1 \end{cases}$	3, **2**
-3	-1	-2	3

Thus this degenerate perturbation problem has two unperturbed, and two perturbed, states. We can find the diagonal matrix components of energy, including interaction energy, for the two unperturbed states. This must equal the sum of the energies of the perturbed states. One of the perturbed states is that corresponding to $L = l_1 + l_2$, whose energy we have already found. Thus by subtraction we can find the energy of the other, corresponding to $L = l_1 + l_2 - 1$. We readily find that by an extension of this method to cases of smaller and smaller M_L, we can find the energies of the levels with all L values by subtraction.

To make these ideas clearer, let us take a specific example. We let $l_1 = 1$, $l_2 = 2$. The vector model would lead to $L = 3, 2, 1$. In Table 7.2.1 we arrange the degenerate sublevels, first according to the m_l's, next according to L. We see that, according to either method of description, there are 15 sublevels, broken up into seven separate problems corresponding to different values of M_L. Solution of the first problem, with only one level, gives the energy of the level $L = 3$; the next, with two levels, gives $L = 3$ and $L = 2$; the next three give $L = 3, 2$, and 1. Obviously there must be relations between the diagonal matrix components of the interaction energy in the various unperturbed states, in order that we may get the same energies out of each of these problems; the general theorems resulting from the conservation of angular momentum automatically bring it about that these relations are fulfilled.

The classification of energy levels corresponding to the interaction of two vectors l_1 and l_2 to give a resultant L is all we can derive from general principles; to go further, we must know something about the matrix components of the interaction energy. If we are dealing really with two orbital angular momentum matrices, or two electron spins, the interaction energy proves to be electrostatic, as we shall explain later, and the energy depends in a rather complicated way on angle, in a way which we shall take up in detail later in the chapter. However, if one of the vectors is an orbital angular momentum and the other a spin, the interaction energy is magnetic, coming from the interaction of the magnetic field produced by the orbital motion of the electrons and the intrinsic magnetization of the spin. This interaction energy proves to be proportional to the cosine of the angle between the two vectors, and in this case the matrix components are simple enough, as shown in Appendix 14, so that we can derive simple formulas for the energies of the various levels. Let us denote one of the vectors by L, representing an orbital angular momentum (which, as we shall see later, can represent a resultant angular momentum for several electrons in an atom), and let the other be S, representing a spin angular momentum (likewise a resultant of the effects of several electrons). Let the vector sum of these be called J. The dynamical problem of the interaction of these vectors is just like that taken up earlier, where we have discussed the interaction of l_1 and l_2. But now we can proceed by classical mechanics to find the cosine of the angle between L and S, and this gives us a guide as to the corresponding quantum-mechanical formula for energy.

From the law of cosines and the diagram of Fig. 7.2.2, illustrating how the resultant is made up from the two vectors, we see that

$$J^2 = L^2 + S^2 + 2LS \cos \theta,$$

from which

$$\cos \theta = \frac{J^2 - L^2 - S^2}{2LS}. \qquad (7.2.1)$$

The energy, being proportional to $\cos \theta$, should be proportional to this quantity; that is, the levels of different value of J and the same constant values of L and S should have energies proportional to J^2 plus a constant quantity independent of J. This is, however, another of the cases where a more careful discussion, based on the quantum theory, and discussed in Appendix 14, shows that we must modify the formula in a way suggesting half quantum numbers, the correct formula being

$$\cos \theta = \frac{J(J + 1) - L(L + 1) - S(S + 1)}{2LS}. \tag{7.2.2}$$

Formulas like (7.2.1) and (7.2.2) are often called Landé formulas, since their application to multiplet structure was first made by Landé. It is

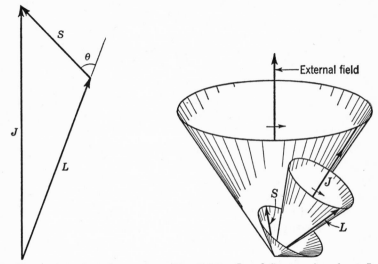

FIG. 7.2.2. Law of cosines for vector sum of L and S.

FIG. 7.2.3. L and S precessing about J, J precessing around external field.

actually found that in multiplets where the magnetic effect is the cause of the separation of levels with different J value, the energy is proportional to the quantity (7.2.2).

In the case of the coupling of an orbital angular momentum L and a spin angular momentum S, the arguments we have just used lead easily to the calculation of the Landé g factor, mentioned at the end of the preceding section, and concerned in the Zeeman effect. Let us consider classically how our two vectors, coupled together by magnetic forces, will behave in an external magnetic field. We assume that the interaction forces between L and S are large compared with the forces exerted on either vector by the external field. Then we may expect the motion to be as in Fig. 7.2.3. Here we see L and S precessing rapidly around their resultant under the action of their mutual interactions, and their resultant precesses much more slowly around the direction of the external field. This latter precession is the origin of the Zeeman effect, and is described in quantum theory by the statement that the levels with different orientation of J (that is, with different values of the quantum number M, giving the component of J along the axis) have slightly different energies. We wish to find the component of magnetic moment of the atom along the axis, for we know that that is what determines the magnetic energy in the external field.

From the dynamical system shown in Fig. 7.2.3, it seems fairly clear what will really happen. Each of the two vectors L and S will have two components, one along the direction of their resultant J, the other at right angles to this resultant. The component along J will have a fixed component in the direction of the z axis, for J always preserves a constant angle with respect to the z axis during its precession. On the other hand, the component at right angles to J will rotate rapidly, and its component along z will average to zero. Thus we can get the component of magnetic moment along z by first finding the separate components of magnetic moment of L and S along the resultant J, then finding the component of this quantity along z. We now recall that the g factor was defined to be a dimensionless quantity, equal to unity if all the magnetic moment resulted from orbital angular momentum, two if it were all from spin. We then see that we can compute it in a very simple way: it is the component of L along J, multiplied by unity; plus the component of S along J, multiplied by two; and divided by the value of J.

We can easily find a formula for this, and it is most easily done if for the moment we treat L, S, and J as vectors. We evidently have

$$g = \frac{(\mathbf{L} \cdot \mathbf{J}) + 2(\mathbf{S} \cdot \mathbf{J})}{J^2} = \frac{(\mathbf{L} + \mathbf{S}) \cdot \mathbf{J} + (\mathbf{S} \cdot \mathbf{J})}{J^2} = 1 + \frac{\mathbf{S} \cdot \mathbf{J}}{J^2}, \quad (7.2.3)$$

when we remember that vectorially $\mathbf{J} = \mathbf{L} + \mathbf{S}$. But

$$\mathbf{S} \cdot \mathbf{J} = \mathbf{S} \cdot (\mathbf{L} + \mathbf{S}) = LS \cos \theta + S^2,$$

where θ is the angle between L and S, given in (7.2.1). Thus, using (7.2.1), we find

$$g = 1 + \frac{J^2 - L^2 + S^2}{2J^2}.$$

We expect to find modifications of this formula produced by the quantum theory, similar to those encountered in going from (7.2.1) to (7.2.2); and as a matter of fact, the correct Landé formula is

$$g = 1 + \frac{J(J + 1) - L(L + 1) + S(S + 1)}{2J(J + 1)}. \quad (7.2.4)$$

When we recall that the Zeeman splitting is proportional to this quantity, we see that measurement of the Zeeman effect of a spectral line can lead to a value of g, and hence to a considerable amount of information about its quantum numbers. For this reason, the Zeeman effect is a valuable tool used in spectrum analysis of atomic spectra.

We have now investigated the nature of the interaction of two vectors to form a quantized resultant vector, and of the space quantization of this resultant, with splitting of the energy levels in an external field to remove the degeneracy. We shall now pass on to the more general question of the interaction of all the angular momentum vectors in a complete atom, treating that problem by methods similar to those we have already been using. There is one feature in which our calculation has been specialized, and we shall meet a similar specialization in our general problem. We have assumed that the magnetic energy of interaction between the vectors L and S was large compared with the magnetic energy in an external field. This obviously will not be the case if the external field is big enough. In Fig. 7.2.4 we show the actual way in which the energy

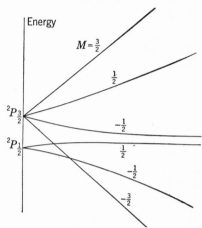

Fig. 7.2.4. Paschen-Back effect for multiplets arising from a single p electron, leading to $^2P_{3/2}$ and $^2P_{1/2}$; energy plotted as a function of magnetic field. The two levels with $M = \frac{1}{2}$ are the roots of a quadratic equation, and similarly for the two levels with $M = -\frac{1}{2}$.

levels of a simple multiplet split in an external magnetic field. We see that for small magnetic fields the displacement of each level is proportional to the field; this is the range in which the ordinary Zeeman effect calculation is appropriate. Here the energy is given by $-Mgh\nu_L$, where g is given in (7.2.4), and ν_L is the Larmor frequency, proportional to the magnetic field. However, when the splitting, as predicted by this theory, becomes comparable to the separation between levels of different J value, the linear relation between energy and field ceases, and the problem obviously becomes much more complicated. This case of large magnetic field is called the Paschen-Back effect.

Let us see why the Paschen-Back effect comes about, according to quantum mechanics. We can still carry out an analysis of the sublevels of the problem, according to the quantum number M (equivalent to the M_L of Table 7.2.1). However, we clearly no longer can assume that levels of different M_L's, but the same J value (corresponding to the L of Table 7.2.1), will all have the same energy. Thus we cannot use the diagonal sum rule, as in discussing the case of Table 7.2.1. Instead, if we take that particular case, the state with $M = 3$, $J = 3$, will still have an energy given by the diagonal matrix component computed for the unperturbed state (and hence containing a term linear in the magnetic field); but the two states with $M = 2$, $J = 3$ and 2, will have energies which are roots of a quadratic secular equation, and the three with $M = 1$, $J = 3$, 2, 1, will have energies which are roots of a cubic, and so on. The solutions of these quadratic and cubic equations will involve the magnetic field in complicated ways, leading to the type of result shown in Fig. 7.2.4. In a field strong enough so that the interaction between L and S is small compared with the interaction of either L or S with the external field, our unperturbed wave functions themselves give good approximations to the correct wave functions, since they correspond to the case where each of the two vectors separately is space quantized with respect to the external field. Thus the diagonal matrix components of energy, including the magnetic energy in the external field, computed for these unperturbed functions, will give good approximations to the energy in the case of very strong fields.

It is well to keep this case in mind in the calculations of the next section. There we shall see that in most atoms the largest interactions between vectors are of two sorts: electrostatic interactions which couple the orbital angular momentum vectors into a resultant L, and similar interactions which couple the spin angular momenta into a resultant S. The vector L then consists of a number of l vectors precessing rapidly around their resultant L, much as L and S precessed in Fig. 7.2.3. Similarly S consists of a number of spin vectors precessing around their resultant. Smaller in order of magnitude is the magnetic interaction between the resultant L and the resultant S, which we have just been discussing, and which leads to the vector sum J of these vectors being quantized. Still smaller is the interaction of J with an external magnetic field, leading to the Zeeman effect. But just as the magnetic field can sometimes be great enough to produce a Paschen-Back effect, so under some circumstances the magnetic coupling between L and S can become so great that it is comparable to the electrostatic coupling between the l's, or between the spin vectors, to produce the L and S. In this case the problem becomes much more complicated, and we shall avoid it in our discussion. These complications come up mostly in the heavy atoms; for the magnetic interactions between orbital and spin magnetic fields increase rapidly with atomic number, while the electrostatic interactions do not greatly change. The case of small magnetic interaction, which alone we shall treat, is called the case of *L-S* coupling, or of Russell-Saunders coupling, since its nature was first explained by Russell and Saunders. In the next section we shall go on to a study of the general nature of atomic multiplets obeying *L-S* coupling.

7.3. The Structure of Many-electron Atoms. At the end of the last section we have stated very briefly the main features of the multiplet structure of many-electron atoms. There are strong electrostatic torques between the orbital angular momenta of the various electrons, which cause them to be coupled into a resultant L, which is quantized. Similarly there are strong electrostatic torques between the spins, which couple them into a resultant S. We postpone until later an explanation of the origin of these torques. If we consider only electrostatic forces, however, there is no coupling at all between orbital and spin angular momentum, or between L and S. The magnetic torques arising from magnetic interaction between orbits and spins lead to such a coupling, and the result of this is that L and S couple to form a quantized resultant J, called the inner quantum number. Finally the component M of J along a fixed axis is quantized. This simple picture is the origin of the notation used to describe spectral terms. With a given L and S, we say that we have a given multiplet. There are $2S + 1$ relative orientations of L and S, from the maximum of $L + S$ to the minimum of $L - S$ (in the usual case where L is numerically greater than S; in the other case, where S is greater than L, there are $2L + 1$ orientations). That is, there are $2S + 1$ different J values corresponding to the multiplet. This number $2S + 1$ is called the multiplicity and is indicated by a superscript placed to the left of the symbol representing the multiplet term. The value of L is indicated by a letter indicating the term: by analogy with single electrons, we denote $L = 0, 1, 2, 3, \ldots$ by letters $S, P, D, F, G, H, \ldots$. Finally the value of J is indicated by a subscript to the right of the symbol. Thus $^2D_{3/2}$ (to be read: doublet d three-halves) indicates a level with $S = \frac{1}{2}$ (since $2S + 1$ equals 2), with $L = 2$, and with $J = \frac{3}{2}$. We note that such a term is still degenerate, since it has $2J + 1$ (in this case four) sublevels corresponding to the different values of M.

We remember the remarks made at the end of the preceding section about effects of various orders of magnitude in the energy. If we consider only electrostatic energy, all the sublevels of a multiplet [that is, $(2L + 1)(2S + 1)$ sublevels] are degenerate; but one multiplet differs from another in energy by a large amount, coming from electrostatic interactions. If we then introduce magnetic coupling, the sublevels of different J values split, by much smaller amounts. Finally if we introduce an external magnetic field, the sublevels of different M values split, and there is no degeneracy left. We show schematically in Fig. 7.3.1

what happens to the levels as these various perturbations are introduced in the course of the calculation.

Now we are ready to consider various typical cases, so as to become familiar with this procedure. A one-electron atom has a doublet spectrum; for its spin S arises from one electron only, which has a spin angular momentum of one-half unit. The value of L is that of the single electron. Thus, for instance, in hydrogen we have a spectrum of doublets, resulting in more complication than indicated in Chap. 5. However, as we mentioned in that chapter, the doublet separation in hydrogen is of the same

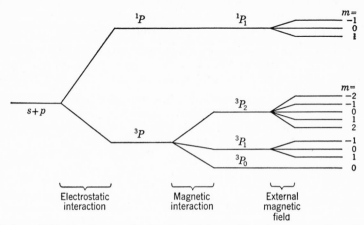

Fig. 7.3.1. Splitting of energy levels of multiplets arising from an s and a p electron, from electrostatic and magnetic interaction, and weak external magnetic field (schematic).

order of magnitude as the relativity separation, and the two effects are intimately mixed up. There are other one-electron spectra besides hydrogen, however; for one of the very important features of atomic structure which we have already mentioned, and which we shall consider in more detail, is that a closed shell of electrons has no net orbital or spin angular momentum, and hence has no effect on multiplet structure. Thus any atom with only one electron outside closed shells acts like a one-electron spectrum, and this means that the alkali metals have hydrogenlike spectra. The magnetic separation increases rapidly in magnitude as we go to the heavier atoms, so that the multiplet separation is of considerable size in the heaviest alkalies.

Next let us consider two-electron atoms. The two spin vectors can be combined either parallel, to give $S = 1$, or opposite, to give $S = 0$; thus a two-electron atom has triplet and singlet levels. The two l's can combine to give all L's from $l_1 + l_2$ to $l_1 - l_2$. Let us start with the simplest case, that of two s electrons, which therefore give $L = 0$, so that we have ^3S and ^1S levels; more precisely, we have $^3S_1$ and $^1S_0$. We note that although we write the first of these as a triplet, following the convention that the superscript is $2S + 1$, still there is only one J value, since in this case L is less than S, so that there is actually $2L + 1 = 1$ level, rather than the usual $2S + 1$. Let us now examine the nature of the perturbation problem which we must solve in order to find the energy levels of these multiplets.

In the unperturbed system of wave functions each sublevel can be characterized by the components of orbital and spin angular momentum of each electron along the axis. Since the orbital angular momentum is zero in this simple case, we have only the spin to consider. We can then take the values of m_s, the component of spin, for each of the two electrons, and, as in the preceding section, we can identify the sum of these with M_S, the component of S along the axis. The m_s's can then take on the values given in Table 7.3.1. In other words, there are four sublevels, as is

TABLE 7.3.1. SUBLEVELS FOR TWO s ELECTRONS

M_S	m_{s_1}	m_{s_2}
1	$\frac{1}{2}$	$\frac{1}{2}$
0	$\left\{ \begin{array}{c} \frac{1}{2} \\ -\frac{1}{2} \end{array} \right.$	$\begin{array}{c} -\frac{1}{2} \\ \frac{1}{2} \end{array}$
−1	$-\frac{1}{2}$	$-\frac{1}{2}$

correct for the $^3S_1$ and $^1S_0$ levels which the vector model would predict: the $^3S_1$ has sublevels with $M_S = 1, 0, -1$, and the $^1S_0$ has one sublevel with $M_S = 0$. The energy of the unperturbed state with $M_S = 1$ must then be the energy of the $^3S_1$, while the sum of the diagonal energies of the two unperturbed states with $M_S = 0$ must equal the sum of the energies of the $^3S_1$ and $^1S_0$, so that the energy of the latter multiplet can be found by subtraction.

This case is simple enough so that we can use it to get further insight into the nature of the perturbed wave functions, as well as the energy levels. The problem with $M_S = 0$ involves two states, one corresponding to $m_{s_1} = \frac{1}{2}$, $m_{s_2} = -\frac{1}{2}$, and the other to $m_{s_1} = -\frac{1}{2}$, $m_{s_2} = \frac{1}{2}$. These are degenerate states, with the same unperturbed energy. We know that in such a perturbation problem between two degenerate states the perturbed wave functions are the sum and difference of the unperturbed functions, as shown in Eq. (4.2.13). This will then be the case here; and this allows us to set up the correct wave functions for the various states of the $^3S_1$ and $^1S_0$ in this problem. We shall use this example later to demonstrate that, as far as the dependence of the wave function on the orbital motion of the electron is concerned, all three substates of the $^3S_1$, corresponding to $M_S = 1, 0, -1$, have the same wave function, from which the fact that they have the same energy follows at once.

We can now use this simple case to bring out a new result, which we have so far not mentioned. If our two s electrons had the same principal quantum number, or, as it is said, were equivalent, then the substate with $m_{s_1} = m_{s_2} = \frac{1}{2}$, or with $m_{s_1} = m_{s_2} = -\frac{1}{2}$, would be forbidden by the exclusion principle, for this principle says that no two electrons can have the same orbital and spin quantum numbers. Hence the states with $M_S = 1$ would be prohibited. Also the two states with $M_S = 0$ would become identical, so that there would really only be one such state. In other words, we are left with only enough sublevels to describe a $^1S_0$ state, with none for the $^3S_1$. Our conclusion is then that two equivalent s electrons can only form a $^1S_0$ multiplet, the $^3S_1$ being prohibited. This is the first example of a widespread set of restrictions according to which the exclusion principle forbids the existence of certain multiplets which would be predicted by the simple vector model, provided we are dealing with equivalent electrons. Also this is the first example where we can demonstrate the statement made previously, that a closed shell of electrons has neither orbital nor spin angular momentum, or in other words has a $^1S_0$ level; for two equivalent s electrons form a closed shell, as in the helium atom, or the K shell of heavier elements.

Next let us take a slightly more complicated case, that of an s and a p electron. We must have in this case $L = 1$, $S = 1$ and 0, so that the levels arising from the vector model are $^3P_2$, $^3P_1$, $^3P_0$, $^1P_1$. We can describe each unperturbed sublevel by the components m_{l_1}, m_{l_2} of orbital angular momentum along the axis, and by m_{s_1}, m_{s_2}. Of course, in this simple case, $m_{l_1} = 0$, so that we do not have to tabulate it separately. We then show in Table 7.3.2 the sublevels arising in this case.

We now have 12 substates; each combination of m_l's leads to a problem of degeneracy, resulting in a singlet and a triplet, as in the case of two s electrons. If we consider the expected levels $^3P_2$, $^3P_1$, $^3P_0$, $^1P_1$, we see that nine of the substates must be associated with the ^3P, three with the ^1P. Since we are not considering magnetic interactions, however, we do not have to use the quantum number J, or to assume that L and S are coupled together. Rather we may use M_L and M_S directly to describe the multiplets. Thus for the ^1P, in the absence of magnetic coupling, we should find $M_L = 1, 0, -1$, and $M_S = 0$; for ^3P, $M_L = 1, 0, -1$, and $M_S = 1, 0, -1$, leading to the nine sublevels. Comparison with Table 7.3.2 shows just the right number of levels with each combination of M_L and M_S. The comparison is perhaps shown more clearly in Fig.

7.3.2, in which we plot M_S as abscissa, M_L as ordinate, and at each point corresponding to one or more substates we give the number of such substates appearing in the problem. We give one such plot for the whole problem, and one each for the ^1P and ^3P, so that it is obvious that a superposition of the two will lead to the complete pattern.

Now let us state the various steps concerned in applying the perturbation theory in this case and arriving at the various energy levels. In the first place, we introduce the electrostatic terms in the interaction, coupling the l's together, and the spins together, but not introducing

TABLE 7.3.2. SUBLEVELS FOR AN s AND A p ELECTRON

M_L	M_S	m_{l_2}	m_{s_1}	m_{s_2}
1	1	1	½	½
1	0	1	{ ½ −½	−½ ½
1	−1	1	−½	−½
0	1	0	½	½
0	0	0	{ ½ −½	−½ ½
0	−1	0	−½	−½
−1	1	−1	½	½
−1	0	−1	{ ½ −½	−½ ½
−1	−1	−1	−½	−½

coupling between L and S. In other words, as a result of a perturbation problem involving only electrostatic energy, we expect that we shall get two energy levels for this problem: one corresponding to ^1P, the other to ^3P. In other words, in Fig. 7.3.2 all nine sublevels of the ^3P will have the same energy if we consider only electrostatic perturbations. We then see, either from Table 7.3.2 or Fig. 7.3.2, that we can use the diagonal sum rule in many ways to get the energies of ^1P and ^3P. We can prove, as in Appendix 14, that there are no nondiagonal matrix components of energy between states of different M_L, or of different M_S, so that the sublevels of a given M_L and M_S can be treated as a separate problem. Using this principle, the sublevel with $M_L = 1$, $M_S = 1$, is a sublevel of the ^3P, and there is only one unperturbed level with these quantum numbers; thus the energy of this unperturbed level is the energy of the ^3P. The sublevels of $M_L = 1$, $M_S = 0$, of which there are two, consist of one sublevel of the ^3P, one of the ^1P; thus by application of the sum rule to these unperturbed levels, we can get the energy of the ^1P by subtraction. It is obvious, as we have mentioned, that there are many other sublevels

which we could have used, and they must all lead to the same energies
for ^1P and ^3P. This implies far-reaching interrelations between the
unperturbed energies of the various sublevels, and these interrelations
must follow from fundamental principles, and are actually found when we
compute the required energy matrix.

The result of the electrostatic calculation, then, is two energy levels,
one corresponding to the three degenerate substates corresponding to the

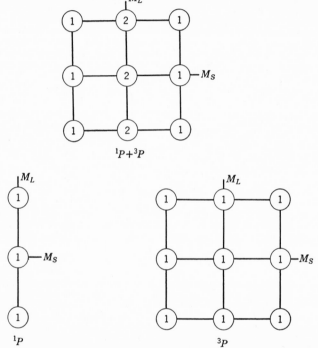

Fig. 7.3.2. M_L vs. M_S, for an s and a p electron combining to give ^1P and ^3P.

^1P, the other to the nine substates corresponding to the ^3P, as shown in
Fig. 7.3.2. Next we introduce the magnetic interaction between the
orbital magnetic moment, arising from the orbital motion of the electrons.
and the spin magnetic moment, arising because electrons have an intrinsic
magnetic moment. In the case of the ^1P this magnetic interaction is
absent, because the spin angular momentum S is zero, and there is no
spin magnetic moment. Thus the three substates of the ^1P do not split
up, even when magnetic interactions are introduced. With the ^3P,
however, we get a splitting into three levels $^3P_2$, $^3P_1$, $^3P_0$. The problem of
discussing this splitting is just like that taken up in Sec. 7.2. The total
component of angular momentum along the z axis, represented by the

quantum number M, remains quantized, and M has the same significance as $M_L + M_S$. Hence we can again use the sum rule to determine the energy levels. Thus, from Fig. 7.3.2, we see that we have one level with $M = 2$, which then must have the energy of the ${}^3P_2$; two levels with $M = 1$, so that the sum of the unperturbed energies must be the sum of the energies of ${}^3P_2$ and ${}^3P_1$; and so on. Furthermore, the interaction energy between the magnetic moments can be shown to be proportional to the cosine of the angle between them; hence when we evaluate these energy levels, they will be separated according to the Landé formula.

Finally, we may have the atom in an external magnetic field along the z axis. In this case the degeneracy will be completely removed. The magnetic interaction energy between the atom and the external field will depend on the z component of angular momentum or magnetic moment, and will be proportional to it. Thus we shall have a set of $2J + 1$ sublevels of each multiplet level, all with slightly different energies, proportional to the magnetic field. For instance, the ${}^3P_2$ will have five sublevels, corresponding to $M = 2, 1, 0, -1, -2$. The energies will be proportional to the component of magnetic moment along the z axis, and equal to $-Mgh\nu_L$.

Let us next go on to another problem which introduces some new features, that of two p electrons. The vector model indicates that the two orbital angular momentum vectors can combine to give $L = 2, 1, 0$, and the two spins to give $S = 1, 0$. Hence the multiplets should be ${}^3D, {}^3P, {}^3S, {}^1D, {}^1P, {}^1S$. In Table 7.3.3 we give part of the table, similar to Table 7.3.2, illustrating the substates.

TABLE 7.3.3.   SUBLEVELS FOR TWO p ELECTRONS

M_L	M_S	m_{l_1}	m_{l_2}	m_{s_1}	m_{s_2}
2	1	1	1	½	½
2	0	1	1	½	-½
				-½	½
2	-1	1	1	-½	-½
1	1	1	0	½	½
		0	1	½	½
1	0	1	0	½	-½
		1	0	-½	½
		0	1	½	-½
		0	1	-½	½
1	-1	1	0	-½	-½
		0	1	-½	-½
0	1	1	-1	½	½
		0	0	½	½
		-1	1	½	½
...	...	...	...	...	...

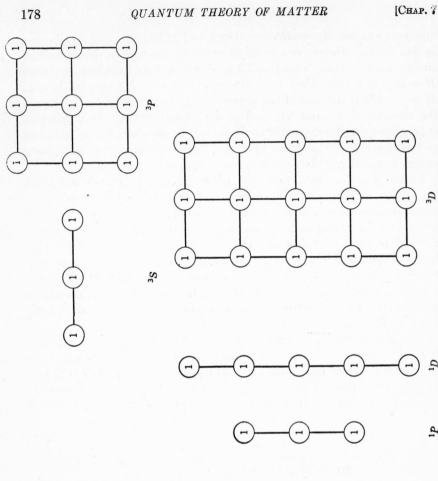

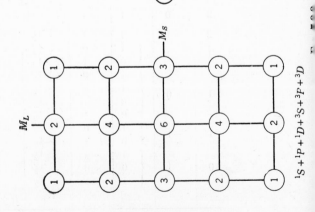

Fig. 8. M_S vs. M_L for two p electrons combining to give $^1S{}^1P{}^1D{}^3S{}^3P{}^3D$

$^1S + {}^1P + {}^1D + {}^3S + {}^3P + {}^3D$

Similarly, in Fig. 7.3.3 we give tabulations of all the substates, according to their values of M_L and M_S, and of the multiplets $^1S {}^1P {}^1D {}^3S {}^3P {}^3D$ arising from these two p electrons. Let us see how far we can go with the diagonal sum rule in evaluating the energies of these multiplets. The sublevel $M_L = 2$, $M_S = 1$, corresponds obviously to the ^3D; thus we can find its energy from the unperturbed wave functions. The two states with $M_L = 2$, $M_S = 0$, correspond to ^3D and ^1D; hence the energy of ^1D can be found by subtraction. The two sub-states with $M_L = 1$, $M_S = 1$, correspond to ^3D and ^3P, so that ^3P can be found by subtraction, and similarly, from $M_L = 0$, $M_S = 1$, we can find ^3S. The four substates $M_L = 1$, $M_S = 0$, correspond to ^3D, ^3P, ^1D, ^1P; we can then get ^1P by subtraction. Finally the six substates $M_L = 0$, $M_S = 0$, allow us to get ^1S. Thus this whole problem can be solved by means of the sum rule, as in the easier cases we have taken up so far.

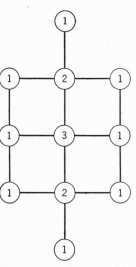

FIG. 7.3.4. M_L vs. M_S, for two equivalent p electrons combining to give $^1S {}^1D {}^3P$.

If our two p electrons are equivalent, many of the substates are forbidden by the exclusion principle, and many other pairs of substates become identical. Thus, of those shown in Table 7.3.3, the first and fourth are forbidden, and the second and third, the fifth and sixth, and many other pairs, become identical. When we take account of these forbidden or identical substates, we find that the remaining number of substates are as given in Fig. 7.3.4. We may then compare these with the patterns of the various multiplets shown in Fig. 7.3.3, and we see at once that we have enough substates to correspond to the multiplets ^3P, ^1S, ^1D, and that the other three, ^3S, ^3D, ^1P, are forbidden by the exclusion principle. We also can proceed by the sum rule to get the energies of the three allowed multiplets. This example shows us that the exclusion principle can operate in very complicated ways to exclude certain multiplets and to allow others. We can proceed by application of identical methods to more complicated multiplets formed from equivalent electrons, and we find that the allowed multiplets for various numbers of equivalent p and d electrons are as given in Table 7.3.4. The type of analysis carried out in the present section, as far as it leads to the exclusion of certain multiplets, is due to Hund, who was very active in the interpretation of the spectra of complex atoms.

There is one feature of multiplet theory which is rather simple: we find that a completed shell of equivalent electrons, lacking a certain number of electrons, has the same multiplet structure as an atom containing just the number of electrons missing from the shell. For instance, a shell of five equivalent p electrons has the same type of spectrum as a single p electron, and nine d's have a spectrum like a single d. This symmetry is shown in Table 7.3.4 and is a simple example of a general rule, which we shall encounter later in the theory of solids, that an electron missing from a full shell leaves that shell equivalent in many ways to a single electron.

These facts, while interesting in the spectra of the outer parts of the

TABLE 7.3.4. MULTIPLETS FOR EQUIVALENT p AND d ELECTRONS

p^1	^2P					
p^2	^1S		^1D	^3P		
p^3		^2P	^2D		^4S	
p^4	^1S		^1D	^3P		
p^5		^2P				
p^6	^1S					
d^1		$^2(D)$				
d^2	$^1(SDG)$		$^3(PF)$			
d^3		$^2(D)$		$^2(PDFGH)$	$^4(PF)$	
d^4	$^1(SDG)$		$^3(PF)$	$^1(SDFGI)$	$^3(PDFGH)$	$^5(D)$
d^5		$^2(D)$		$^2(PDFGH)$	$^4(PF)$ $^2(SDFGI)$	$^4(DG)$ $^6(S)$
d^6	$^1(SDG)$		$^3(PF)$	$^1(SDFGI)$	$^3(PDFGH)$	$^5(D)$
d^7		$^2(D)$		$^2(PDFGH)$	$^4(PF)$	
d^8	$^1(SDG)$		$^3(PF)$			
d^9		$^2(D)$				
d^{10}	$^1(S)$					

atom, are even more applicable to the x-ray spectra. Here we have removed an electron from an inner, complete shell. We must find, then, that the stationary state of the complete shell with an electron removed is like that of a single electron, and hence is a spectrum of doublets, the electron spin being oriented either parallel or opposite to the orbital angular momentum. The relative orientation of L and S affects the energy through magnetic coupling between the magnetic moment of orbital motion and the spin. This interaction is quite large for the inner, x-ray electrons; for it turns out to be proportional to the mean inverse third power of the radius of the orbit. Thus it comes about that the x-ray levels are split by quite appreciable amounts by magnetic interaction. It is this splitting which we mentioned in Sec. 6.3. There we mentioned that the state left by removing a $2p$ electron was split into two levels, called L_{II} and L_{III}; these are the two components of the ^2P level, given by the symbols $^2P_{3/2}$ and $^2P_{1/2}$. Such a splitting affects all the x-ray levels, except those arising from the removal of an s electron; we remember that the level $^2S_{1/2}$ has, in fact, only a single component, though it is formally regarded as a doublet. There is just one way in which this magnetic splitting in the x-ray spectra differs from that in the optical spectra, and this is characteristic of all cases in which we have electrons removed from a closed shell, rather than electrons outside closed shells. The levels of the multiplet are inverted, or upside down, as compared with the ordinary atomic multiplet, as if the magnetic interaction had the opposite sign. This is connected with the fact that it is really a missing electron, rather than a single electron, producing the doublet; the energy comes in, so to speak, with a negative sign. We shall meet more conspicuous cases of this same situation in considering missing electrons in solids, in which case these electrons too have an energy of opposite sign to what a single electron would have, a situation sometimes interpreted as saying that the electron behaves as if it had a positive rather than a negative charge.

A further very important result of Table 7.3.4 is the observation which we have already mentioned, that a completed shell of equivalent electrons (that is, two equivalent s electrons, six p's, ten d's) has only a ^1S multiplet in its spectrum. We have already seen the detailed reason for this in our discussion of two equivalent s electrons. The reason is very straightforward. With six p's, for instance, each of the three orientations of l, corresponding to $m_l = 1, 0, -1$, must be combined with each of the two orientations of the spin, to give the six electronic wave functions necessary to build up the closed shell. But then we have only one substate, with $M_L = M_S = 0$, clearly corresponding to a ^1S state. The importance of this fact is that a closed shell behaves as if it had no orbital or spin angular momentum; in other words, it acts like a spherically symmetrical system and does not take part in the multiplet structure of any electrons which may lie outside it. This is the feature which simplifies the problem of atomic, or for that matter molecular, spectra so greatly, in that only those electrons outside closed shells need to be considered in the vector model.

We shall now give a final example, in order to show the reader that we cannot always get our answers by use of the diagonal sum rule alone; the success of this method in the cases we have so far taken up might lead him to think it was always applicable. Let us take the simple case of three nonequivalent s electrons. This is a case which we should not often meet in atomic spectra, but the corresponding case is common in molecular problems. We have seen in Sec. 7.1 that we should then expect the third electron, added to the second, to result in a ^4S and two ^2S levels. That this is the case follows from Table 7.3.5. The substate with $M_S = 3/2$ will correspond to the ^4S, so that its energy will be found from the unperturbed functions. Of the three substates with $M_S = \frac{1}{2}$, we shall have representatives of the ^4S and of the two ^2S's. Subtraction of the ^4S energy from the energies of the three unperturbed states will then give the sum of the energies of the two ^2S's, but the diagonal sum rule cannot give their separate energies. We must instead set up non-diagonal matrix components of energy and solve the secular equation. This will be a cubic equation, but since we know one of its roots, the energy of the ^4S state, we can reduce it to a quadratic equation for the two ^2S's, as indicated in Sec. 4.4. This problem is one of the simplest in which the diagonal sum rule does not suffice, but there are many others,

TABLE 7.3.5. Sublevels for Three s Electrons

M_S	m_{s_1}	m_{s_2}	m_{s_3}
$\frac{3}{2}$	$\frac{1}{2}$	$\frac{1}{2}$	$\frac{1}{2}$
$\frac{1}{2}$	$\frac{1}{2}$	$\frac{1}{2}$	$-\frac{1}{2}$
	$\frac{1}{2}$	$-\frac{1}{2}$	$\frac{1}{2}$
	$-\frac{1}{2}$	$\frac{1}{2}$	$\frac{1}{2}$
...	...	...	...

as we get to more complicated atoms. In fact, we can see very simply that whenever by the vector model we find that there are several multiplets of the same L and S, we shall not be able to get their separate energies by the diagonal sum rule, but must solve a secular equation of degree equal to the number of such multiplets.

7.4. The Electrostatic Energy in Multiplet Structure. We have now surveyed the general theory of multiplet structure and have stated that the most important terms in the energy of multiplets are of electrostatic origin. We have seen that the essential quantities which our theory must give us are the values of the matrix components of electrostatic energy between the various unperturbed substates, each characterized by definite values of the quantum numbers m_l and m_s of each electron, giving the components of orbital and spin angular momentum along the z axis. If the diagonal sum rule suffices for finding the energy levels, we may be contented with diagonal matrix components of the energy, but in the more general case we need nondiagonal components as well. To find these matrix components, our procedure is in principle straightforward. We must first set up the unperturbed wave functions of the whole atom, corresponding to given n, l, m_l, m_s for each electron in it; then we must compute the matrix components of the energy operator with respect to these unperturbed wave functions, with appropriate values of m_l and m_s. This problem seems simple and straightforward; but when we look into it further, we find that it carries us very far into the theory under-lying the existence of the exclusion principle and its relation to electron spin.

To introduce the subject, we shall start with a simple example. It is not hard to understand why there should be an electrostatic coupling energy between the orbital angular momenta of two electrons. We have already seen, in Sec. 5.3, that the charge distributions of levels with the same l value, but different m's, are different, so that if the angle between the l's of two different electrons is varied, it is clear that the electrostatic energy of interaction between the two distributions will be different. The problem of the spins is less clear, however. We may well ask, why is it that the electrostatic energy differs by a large amount, depending on whether the spins of the two electrons are parallel or antiparallel? This will turn out to be a fundamental problem of atomic binding, and accord-ingly it is the case which we shall work out in detail. We consider two electrons, each in s states, so that there will be complete spherical sym-metry as far as the wave functions are concerned, and we ask why the energies of the singlet and triplet states differ by electrostatic terms. We shall assume first that the principal quantum numbers n of the two electrons are different; this removes any complication arising from the Pauli exclusion principle. In a later section, however, we shall take the case of two equivalent electrons with the same n as well as the same l and shall show that there is a very close connection between the applica-tion of the exclusion principle to such problems and the electrostatic energies which we are now considering.

The key to our understanding of these electrostatic effects of the spin is found far back in the theory of wave mechanics. Let us remember our arguments, in Sec. 6.1, regarding the Schrödinger equation for the many-body problem, and its solution by separation of variables for the case where the particles were independent of each other. We found in that case that if we had two electrons, one with coordinates $x_1y_1z_1$, the other with coordinates $x_2y_2z_2$ (which we shall abbreviate by x_1 and x_2 respec-tively), we could set up a wave function of the type $u_1(x_1)u_2(x_2)$, where u_1, u_2 are two different functions which may be associated with two differ-ent sets of quantum numbers. But now we note that we could equally well have set up a function $u_1(x_2)u_2(x_1)$, in which the role of the two electrons was interchanged, but in which no other changes were made. This would have been an equally legitimate solution of the problem, and since electrons are really indistinguishable from each other, there would be no way of deciding which function to use. We may go a step further and make use of the linear nature of Schrödinger's equation, which allows us to use sums or linear combinations of solutions, as well as separate solutions themselves; as a result of this, we find that the combinations $u_1(x_1)u_2(x_2) \pm u_1(x_2)u_2(x_1)$ are likewise appropriate solutions of that equation. The first of these combinations, with the plus sign, is called a symmetric function: interchanging the coordinates x_1 and x_2 makes no change in the function. The other function, with the minus sign, is called antisymmetric, since an interchange of x_1 and x_2 leaves the magnitude of the function unchanged but changes the sign.

Now the real Schrödinger equation for the atom is not (6.1.1); that involves no terms representing interaction between the atoms. If we put such interactions into the equation, of course, we can no longer get a solution as a product of functions of the two electrons; as we saw in Sec. 6.1, their motions are no longer statistically independent of each other. There will be modifications of the wave functions, getting greater and greater as the interactions become greater and greater. We may treat the effect of these interactions by the method of perturbations for degenerate systems, as discussed in Sec. 4.2. When we carry out such a perturbation calculation, we find that a small symmetrical interaction between the electrons (such as, of course, the repulsive force between them produces) leads to perturbed wave functions which are similar to the symmetric and antisymmetric functions above [as we see from Eq. (4.2.13)], but entirely different from the original functions, formed as products of one-electron wave functions. In fact, we can prove quite rigorously that the exact wave functions of the problem must be symmetric and antisymmetric, respectively, though they cannot be exactly expressed as the sum and difference of simple products, as we have written them above.

These two functions, the symmetric and the antisymmetric, no longer have the property that the two electrons are statistically independent of each other; they lead, in fact, to a strong correlation between their motions. Thus in the antisymmetric function, if $x_1 = x_2$, the function is automatically zero, and if x_1 is near x_2, or the electrons are close to each other, the function is very small. In other words, if the electronic motion is described by this antisymmetric function, there will be a strong tendency for the electrons to stay out of each other's way. It is not hard, by examining the square of the wave function, to show that the other case, the symmetric function, behaves in just the opposite way: there is a strong tendency for the electrons to get close to each other. These effects are bound to have an effect on the electrostatic energy. In the antisymmetric case, where the electrons stay out of each other's way, they will be less often found in the region where their repulsive energy, a positive term in the potential energy, is large; thus the energy of this wave function will be lower than if we had not considered this interaction effect.

Conversely, in the symmetric case, where electrons are found near each other, there will be a large positive term in the energy, coming from the interelectronic repulsions.

We thus see how it can be that we can get large electrostatic effects on the energy, depending on whether we have symmetric or antisymmetric wave functions. This is a completely nonclassical effect, not describable at all in terms of classical mechanics. But now we must ask what the relation is between the spin and this situation. We shall first state the answer, in a rather categorical manner; then in the next section we shall go a little further into the reason for it and shall show how closely this effect is tied up with the Pauli exclusion principle. Then, after considering the simple case of the two-electron atom, the simple example which we are now taking up, we shall go on to a more general discussion of the antisymmetry of wave functions and its relation to electron spin.

The thing which we shall find is very simple for the case of two electrons: if the two electronic spins are parallel, as they are in the triplet states, the electronic wave function of the two-electron problem must be antisymmetric, whereas if the spins are antiparallel, as in the singlets, the wave function must be symmetric. From the conclusions we have just drawn regarding the energy, we then find that the triplet state has a lower energy than the singlet, the difference being a result of electrostatic energies, and therefore of considerable magnitude. We see that the way the electrostatic effect of the spin orientation comes about is an indirect one: the spin orientation determines the type of electronic wave function, whether it should be symmetric or antisymmetric, according to the principles which we shall state in the next section; this in turn determines the correlation between the electronic motions and results in differences in electrostatic energy.

7.5. The Exclusion Principle and the Symmetry of Wave Functions.
If electrons had no spins, we should be able to state the Pauli exclusion principle in a very simple form in the language of wave mechanics: the wave function of a many-electron problem must always be antisymmetric in the coordinates of the electrons. That is, we should always have to have wave functions like the combination $u_1(x_1)u_2(x_2) - u_1(x_2)u_2(x_1)$. Why would this lead to the exclusion principle? Simply because we note at once that if $u_1 = u_2$, or if the wave functions, and hence the quantum numbers, of the two electrons are the same, the function is automatically equal to zero. In other words, if we use this postulate, states which do not satisfy the exclusion principle are automatically omitted from the solutions of Schrödinger's equation. If, for the moment, we forget about the spins, we may then state that this hypothesis that all wave functions are antisymmetric automatically leads to the exclusion principle, and

we find that we can impose this assumption as an additional hypothesis of the quantum theory in addition to Schrödinger's equation. Everything that we know about the behavior of electrons fits in with this hypothesis: that we must postulate that only those solutions of Schrödinger's equation which are antisymmetric in the coordinates of all electrons (that is, which change their sign when the coordinates of any two electrons are interchanged) have a physical significance in nature. We have considered only the two-electron case; it proves to be true that with many electrons we have not only symmetric and antisymmetric functions, but a variety of others with lower types of symmetry, but here too the hypothesis that only the antisymmetric function is to be used proves to be equivalent to the exclusion principle, and there is every experimental reason for thinking this hypothesis to be correct. We shall consider the general formulation of the antisymmetric wave function for any number of electrons in a later section.

Now let us see how the existence of the spin complicates the matter. It can be shown that the spin can be treated as an additional coordinate describing electronic motion, in addition to the three coordinates x, y, z; that we can set up wave functions which depend on this spin coordinate of each electron, as well as on the x, y, z's of each electron; and that when we proceed in this way, we can in fact state the exclusion principle quite generally in the form that the wave function expressed in terms of these four coordinates for each electron must be antisymmetric in the coordinates of all electrons. We shall give this method of writing the wave function in terms of spin coordinates in a later section. The argument reduces in the special case of two electrons to a very simple form, which appeals to our intuition. It states that if the two electrons have the same spin, they must have an antisymmetric wave function of the type we had been considering earlier, depending only on the xyz coordinates. This is to be expected: for this antisymmetry implies that the coordinate part of the wave function, or the ordinary orbital quantum numbers n, l, and m, must be different, and the ordinary formulation of the Pauli exclusion principle would imply that two electrons with the same spin would have to differ in orbital quantum numbers. On the other hand, it also states that if the two electrons have opposite spin, the orbital wave function must be symmetric. This is less obvious intuitionally, but it follows equally easily from the wave functions including the spin, as we shall see later. These are the results stated without argument at the end of the preceding section, which we showed to lead to the energy separation between the singlet and triplet states. We now see that these rules are a result of the hypothesis of the antisymmetry of the total electronic wave function involving the spin, a hypothesis which is a fundamental part of the quantum mechanics of electrons. We have seen that it leads to the Pauli exclusion principle as one of its consequences; but now we begin to realize that it is a good deal more general than that, leading also to definite predictions about energy differences between states of different multiplicities.

We shall now go ahead with the application of the general idea of antisymmetry of wave functions, and its relation to electron spin and the exclusion principle, to the general case of the atom with an arbitrary number of electrons, justifying many of the statements which we have made without proof so far. It is worth noting that most of the arguments we have used so far, and many of those we shall encounter, have not been based at all on the fact that our one-electron functions were solutions of a central field problem. In the next chapter we shall go on to the case of molecular structure, and we shall find that the same principles apply there. In particular, we shall find that levels of different multiplicities, and hence of different spin orientation, can differ profoundly in their electronic energy, and we shall also find that this has a very close connection to the whole problem of molecular binding.

7.6. Electron Spin and Antisymmetric Wave Functions. Our first step in generalizing the simple discussion which we have given so far will be to set up an antisymmetric wave function for the case of n electrons. In case these are all in different quantum states, there will be $n!$ different functions of the nature of $u_1(x_1) \cdots u_n(x_n)$, obtained by permuting the n sets of quantum numbers among the n electrons. These $n!$ functions will be degenerate, and all will be equally legitimate solutions of the central field problem. When we now consider the correct energy operator, in which electron interactions occur, we shall find that there are matrix components of energy between these degenerate functions, and we must then set up a perturbation problem between these $n!$ degenerate states. If we solve this problem of degeneracy, we shall find $n!$ linear combinations of the original functions, such that H has no nondiagonal matrix components between any of these combinations. It is too hard, in general, to set up and solve this general perturbation problem; but fortunately we can show that the antisymmetric combination of wave functions is one of the resulting linear combinations, and we can justify Pauli's hypothesis, according to which this combination is the only one of physical significance.

Of all the $n!$ linear combinations, just one is antisymmetric in the coordinates of all electrons, and it can be written in the form of a determinant,

$$\begin{vmatrix} u_1(x_1)u_1(x_2) & \cdots & u_1(x_n) \\ u_2(x_1) & \cdots & u_2(x_n) \\ \cdots \cdots \cdots \cdots \cdots \cdots \\ u_n(x_1) & \cdots & u_n(x_n) \end{vmatrix}. \qquad (7.6.1)$$

This determinant, by definition, is a linear combination of all possible products of the form $u_1(x_1) \cdots u_n(x_n)$, obtained by permuting the quantum numbers in all the possible $n!$ ways, each having a coefficient $+1$ or -1, according as an even or odd number of interchanges of rows or columns is necessary to bring the desired term to the principal diagonal of the determinant.   This is a linear combination of the desired sort, and we can see at once that it is antisymmetric, since interchange of two columns in a determinant (which is the same as interchanging two electrons) changes its sign, as we can see at once from the way of setting it up.   In our case of two electrons the determinant reduces at once to $u_1(x_1)u_2(x_2)$ $- u_2(x_1)u_1(x_2)$, the antisymmetric function discussed earlier.   Thus the determinant (7.6.1) is a natural generalization of that simple result.

Next we ask why this determinant, or antisymmetric function, must be one of the $n!$ linear combinations arising from our perturbation problem, or putting it more broadly, why there must be a solution of Schrödinger's equation for the many-body problem which is antisymmetric in the electron coordinates.   We can see this most straightforwardly from Schrödinger's equation involving the time $H\psi = -\dfrac{h}{2\pi i}\dfrac{\partial \psi}{\partial t}$, giving the time rate of change of ψ.   On account of the identity of electrons, the energy operator H must be symmetric in the electron coordinates (it involves identical Coulomb repulsive terms between all pairs of electrons, and identical attractive terms between each electron and each positive charge).   If then we have a wave function ψ which is antisymmetric in the electron coordinates at a given instant of time, $H\psi$ will be also antisymmetric, since interchange of the coordinates of two electrons will change the sign of ψ, leave H unchanged.   That is, the time rate of ψ will be antisymmetric, so that the increment of ψ in time dt is also antisymmetric.   Since the sum of two antisymmetric functions is also antisymmetric, ψ at time $t + dt$, which is the original ψ plus its increment, will also be antisymmetric, or this property of antisymmetry does not change with time.

There must then be a solution of Schrödinger's equation for the many-electron problem which is antisymmetric in the electron coordinates, and by a slight modification of this argument, there must be an antisymmetric combination of our approximate functions $u_1(x_1) \cdots u_n(x_n)$ which is the best approximation to the true antisymmetric solution which we can set up by making linear combinations of these functions.   As we have stated before, it is now the postulate of the exclusion principle that only this antisymmetric solution occurs in nature, and that we can disregard all other solutions.   This is fortunate, since those other solutions can be of much more complicated symmetry type and harder to work with.   And now we observe from this postulate that the exclusion principle follows at once. For if two of the functions $u_1, \ldots, u_n$ are equal, the determinant (7.6.1) will have two equal rows. But a determinant with two equal rows must necessarily be zero, since interchange of the rows in the first place must change the sign of the determinant, but in the second place cannot make any difference if the rows are identical, and these conditions are incompatible unless the determinant is zero. Hence no antisymmetric wave functions can be made up out of one-electron solutions corresponding to having more than one electron in the same stationary state, and the exclusion principle is automatically satisfied.

So far in this discussion we have omitted mention of the electron spin. Our discussion is correct just as it stands if all electrons have the same spin; in that case we know that the exclusion principle states that all electrons must have different orbital wave functions. When we consider spin, however, we find as we mentioned earlier that we must modify the discussion by introducing an additional coordinate describing the spin of an electron. When we take account of this properly, we shall find that we can still set up antisymmetric functions of the type (7.6.1) in the general case. We recall that the rule regarding orientation of an electronic spin in space can be stated as follows: the component $m_s h/2\pi$ of angular momentum along a fixed axis can take on only the two possible values $\pm (\frac{1}{2})(h/2\pi)$. Let us take as the coordinate describing the spin a quantity s, measuring the component of spin along the desired direction in units of $h/2\pi$. This variable s, then, can take on only two possible values $\pm \frac{1}{2}$, rather than an infinite continuum of values as x, y, z can. We have, then, one-electron functions $u(x,y,z,s)$, determined only for the two values $\pm \frac{1}{2}$ of s; that is, we have $u(x,y,z,\frac{1}{2})$ and $u(x,y,z,-\frac{1}{2})$.

The spin, as we have just seen, behaves like a coordinate. But at the same time, it also acts like a quantum number, and this is apt to be rather confusing. Let us consider an electron in a central field. The three quantum numbers describing the orbital motion are the total quantum number n, the azimuthal quantum number l, and the magnetic quantum number m_l. Of these, l measures the total angular momentum due to the rotation of the electron in its orbit, in units of $h/2\pi$, and m_l measures the projection of this angular momentum along a fixed axis, the z axis. But now the electron has an angular momentum on account of its spin, which, as we have seen, is $(\frac{1}{2})(h/2\pi)$. This spin, as we have just seen, can be oriented in two ways with respect to a fixed axis, either along it or opposite to it. It thus appears that this spin angular momentum should likewise have quantum numbers similar to the orbital angular momentum, one representing its total magnitude (which, being always $\frac{1}{2}$, need not be specially considered, since the spin angular momentum, unlike the orbital angular momentum, never changes its magnitude), and the other its projection along the z axis (which can be either $\frac{1}{2}$ or $-\frac{1}{2}$ units). This latter quantum number is m_s. Then to specify the stationary state of an electron, we must give the four quantities n, l, m_l, m_s, and the wave function should properly carry these four numbers as subscripts: $u_{n,l,m_l,m_s}(x,y,z,s)$.

We are now prepared to consider the physical meaning of the functions $u_{n,l,m_l,m_s}(x,y,z,\frac{1}{2})$ and $u_{n,l,m_l,m_s}(x,y,z,-\frac{1}{2})$. The square of the first gives the probability that, if the quantum numbers are n, l, m_l, m_s, the coordinates will be x, y, z, $\frac{1}{2}$. Suppose that $m_s = \frac{1}{2}$. Then we know that the spin must be along the positive axis. In this case there is no probability that the spin is along the negative direction, for we have information to the contrary. Thus $u_{n,l,m_l,\frac{1}{2}}^2(x,y,z,-\frac{1}{2})$ must be zero, since it measures the probability that the spin is along the negative axis. On the other hand, there is certainty that the spin is along the positive axis, so that $u_{n,l,m_l,\frac{1}{2}}^2(x,y,z,\frac{1}{2})$ merely gives information about the distribution in x, y, z of those electrons which have positive spin. A similar situation holds if $m_s = -\frac{1}{2}$, and the final result is

$$u_{n,l,m_l,\frac{1}{2}}(x,y,z,\frac{1}{2}) = u_{n,l,m_l}(x,y,z)$$
$$u_{n,l,m_l,\frac{1}{2}}(x,y,z,-\frac{1}{2}) = 0$$
$$u_{n,l,m_l,-\frac{1}{2}}(x,y,z,\frac{1}{2}) = 0$$
$$u_{n,l,m_l,-\frac{1}{2}}(x,y,z,-\frac{1}{2}) = u'_{n,l,m_l}(x,y,z), \qquad (7.6.2)$$

where $u_{n,l,m_l}(x,y,z)$ and $u'_{n,l,m_l}(x,y,z)$ are ordinary solutions of Schrödinger's equation without spin, which do not necessarily have to be equal to each other. These statements may be combined in a simpler form by defining a spin wave function $\sigma_{m_s}(s)$, which equals 1 if $s = m_s$, 0 if $s \neq m_s$; the function $\sigma_{\frac{1}{2}}(s)$ is often denoted as $\alpha(s)$, $\sigma_{-\frac{1}{2}}(s)$ as $\beta(s)$. In terms of this function, we may rewrite (7.6.2) in the form

$$u_{n,l,m_l,\frac{1}{2}}(x,y,z,s) = u_{n,l,m_l}(x,y,s)\alpha(s)$$
$$u_{n,l,m_l,-\frac{1}{2}}(x,y,z,s) = u'_{n,l,m_l}(x,y,z)\beta(s). \qquad (7.6.3)$$

Here $u_{n,l,m_l}^2(x,y,z)$ measures the space density of those electrons with positive spin, $u'^2_{n,l,m_l}(x,y,z)$ that of those with negative spin.

In case there are no magnetic energy terms in the Hamiltonian, we must expect that the space density will be independent of the spin, since there is no physical difference in the system depending on the spin orientation. In that case $u_{n,l,m_l}(x,y,z)$ and $u'_{n,l,m_l}(x,y,z)$ must be equal to each other, and we can rewrite (7.6.3) in the simpler form

$$u_{n,l,m_lm_s}(x,y,z,s) = u_{n,l,m_l}(x,y,z)\sigma_{m_s}(s). \qquad (7.6.4)$$

That is, in this case the variables are separated, so that the wave function is a product of a function of x, y, z, and a function of spin, as is natural when there is no interaction between coordinates and spin. If, on the other hand, there are magnetic terms in the energy, the separation is no longer possible, and we must use the more general form (7.6.3).

We have now seen, in (7.6.3) and (7.6.4), the way to set up a wave function of a single electron containing the spin, both as coordinate and quantum number. This can now be combined with the determinantal method (7.6.1) of setting up an antisymmetric function, to set up anti-symmetric functions depending on spin as well as orbital coordinates. It is in this enlarged sense that we postulate that the real wave functions occurring in nature must be antisymmetric in the coordinates of any pair of electrons. Let us go back to our simple case of two electrons, actually work out the determinants, and see what are the implications of our dependence of the antisymmetric wave functions on the spins.

We assume two orbital wave functions, which we symbolize $u_1(x)$, $u_2(x)$, where the subscripts stand for two sets of quantum numbers n, l, m_l, and where x stands for x, y, z. The unperturbed problem has no magnetic interaction between orbit and spin, so that from these we can make up two wave functions involving spin, $u_1(x)\sigma_{ms1}(s)$ and $u_2(x)\sigma_{ms2}(s)$, where m_{s_1} and m_{s_2} can each have either of the two values $\pm\frac{1}{2}$. We can then make up the antisymmetric combination

$$\begin{vmatrix} u_1(x_1)\sigma_{ms1}(s_1) & u_1(x_2)\sigma_{ms1}(s_2) \\ u_2(x_1)\sigma_{ms2}(s_1) & u_2(x_2)\sigma_{ms2}(s_2) \end{vmatrix}, \tag{7.6.5}$$

which is equal to $u_1(x_1)u_2(x_2)\sigma_{ms1}(s_1)\sigma_{ms2}(s_2) - u_2(x_1)u_1(x_2)\sigma_{ms2}(s_1)\sigma_{ms1}(s_2)$. The situation is now quite different, depending on whether the spin quantum numbers m_{s_1} and m_{s_2} are equal or not. If they are equal, we can rewrite the expression in the form

$$[u_1(x_1)u_2(x_2) - u_2(x_1)u_1(x_2)]\sigma_{m_s}(s_1)\sigma_{m_s}(s_2), \tag{7.6.6}$$

where m_s stands for the common value of m_{s_1} and m_{s_2}. In this case the wave function vanishes, unless both spins 1 and 2 have the appropriate value; in case they do, it is merely the antisymmetric function of coor-dinates which we have met earlier, vanishing if $u_1 = u_2$, and hence show-ing that if the two electrons have the same spin, the orbital quantum numbers must be different. On the other hand, if the spin quantum numbers are different, this situation no longer holds, and we cannot sim-plify the wave function, so that we conclude that if the spins are different, there is no prohibition against the orbital quantum numbers being the same. This agrees with our usual understanding of the exclusion prin-ciple. In a similar way, if $u_1 = u_2$, so that the orbital quantum numbers are the same, we can write the function in the form

$$u_1(x_1)u_1(x_2)[\sigma_{ms1}(s_1)\sigma_{ms2}(s_2) - \sigma_{ms2}(s_1)\sigma_{ms1}(s_2)], \qquad (7.6.7)$$

which is antisymmetric in the spin functions but symmetric in the orbital wave functions, just as (7.6.6) is antisymmetric in the orbital wave functions, symmetric in the spins. From (7.6.7) we see that if the orbital wave functions are the same, the spin wave functions are required to be different, for otherwise the whole wave function vanishes.

7.7. The Matrix Components of the Energy. In the perturbation treatment of multiplet theory, which is the subject of the present chapter, we start with determinantal wave functions, formed from one-electron wave functions, each characterized by its principal and azimuthal quantum number, its quantum number m_l giving the component of orbital angular momentum along the z axis, and its corresponding quantum number m_s giving the component of spin. When we set up these determinantal wave functions, we find degeneracy between them, since unperturbed states with different m_l's and m_s's have the same energy in the central field approximation. The degeneracy problem is greatly simplified, as we have stated, by the fact that there are no nondiagonal matrix components of energy between states with different $M_L = \Sigma m_l$ or different $M_S = \Sigma m_s$, as we prove in Appendix 14. As a result of these facts, we can separate the problem into a number of smaller problems, each dealing with only those states with a given M_L and M_S. We can then calculate the diagonal components of energy, in the unperturbed system, and can sum over all those unperturbed states corresponding to a given M_L and M_S. By the diagonal sum rule, this sum equals the sum of perturbed energies for the energy levels arising as linear combinations of these unperturbed states. In many simple cases a suitable use of this diagonal sum rule is enough to get the explicit values of the energies of the various multiplets; in other cases, though we must carry out a solution of the secular equation, the diagonal sum rule simplifies its application greatly.

Our main problem, then, is to find the diagonal and nondiagonal matrix components of energy, with respect to determinantal wave functions. The wave function may be expressed as

$$\frac{1}{\sqrt{n!}} \sum_{\substack{\text{permutations} \\ \text{of } x_i\text{'s}}} \pm u_1(x_1)u_2(x_2) \cdots u_n(x_n). \qquad (7.7.1)$$

In this expression, the u's are assumed to depend on spin as well as coordinates, and for the moment, $x_1, \ldots, x_n$ are supposed to symbolize spin as well as orbital variables. The u's are assumed to be orthogonal to each other, though later, when we treat molecular problems, we do not always have this orthogonality. The sum over permutations, using in each case the correct sign, is another way of writing the determinant. The factor $\sqrt{n!}$ in the denominator, where $n!$ is the number of permutations, or the number of terms in the determinant, is inserted to normalize the wave function.

Now let the energy operator H operate on the wave function u of (7.7.1), multiply by the conjugate u^*, and integrate over the coordinates of the various electrons (including a summation over the spin variables) in order to get the diagonal matrix component of H with respect to this wave function. We shall be summing over two separate permutations of the x_i's, one concerned in u, the other in u^*. However, if we take one single term of this double sum, corresponding to a particular permutation of x's in u, another particular permutation in u^*, and then perform the same further permutation on all x's in the whole expression (that is, on the x's in u, in u^*, and in the operator H), the result will be unchanged, for H depends in a symmetrical way on all the x's, since they refer to identical electrons, and we are integrating over all the x's. Thus, in our double sum, there will be $n!$ identical terms. This $n!$ cancels the $n!$ in the denominator, introduced in (7.7.1) for purposes of normalization, and reduces the matrix component to a single sum. We may, if we choose, write this as

$$\sum_{\substack{\text{permutations} \\ \text{of } i\text{'s}}} \pm \int u_1(x_1) \cdots u_n(x_n) H u_i(x_1) u_j(x_2) \cdots$$

$$u_p(x_n) dx_1 \cdots dx_n, \quad (7.7.2)$$

where we remember that the integrations really involve summation over the spins as well. We may, if we choose, abbreviate this diagonal matrix component as

$$\sum_{\substack{\text{permutations} \\ \text{of } i\text{'s}}} \pm (12 \cdots n/H/ij \cdots p). \quad (7.7.3)$$

Such a notation will be convenient when we come to the molecular problem.

In the atomic case the orthogonality of the functions $u_1, \cdots, u_n$ allows us to simplify the expression (7.7.3) greatly. The energy operator H is

$$H = \sum_i \left(-\nabla_i^2 - \frac{2Z}{r_i} \right) + \sum_{\substack{\text{pairs} \\ i,j}} \frac{2}{r_{ij}}, \quad (7.7.4)$$

where we use atomic units, and where r_i is the distance of the ith electron from the nucleus of charge Z units, and where r_{ij} is the distance from the ith to the jth electron. Let one of the terms in the first summation be called f_i, depending on the coordinates of only one electron, and let one of the terms $2/r_{ij}$ in the second be called g_{ij}, depending on the coordinates of only two electrons. In the integration of (7.7.2), if we are considering one of the operators such as f_1, the integral will be zero on account of orthogonality unless we have the same permutation in u^* and u; and in this case it will be a product of an integral $\int u_1^*(x_1)f_1u_1(x_1)dx_1$ and integrals $\int u_i^2(x_i)dx_i$, which will be unity on account of normalization. Thus if we abbreviate $\int u_i^*(x_1)f_1u_i(x_1)dx_1$ by $(i/f/i)$, the contributions of the terms f to the diagonal energy (7.7.3) will be simply the sum of terms $(i/f/i)$ over all i's. We note that in the definition of $(i/f/i)$ the integration over dx_1 is really supposed to include summation over the spin, and $u_i(x_1)$ is supposed to be the function including spin. However, when we write out this function, we find that the spin functions cancel out, and that we can express the quantity in terms of orbital functions alone. To see this, let us define a slightly more general integral, which we shall need later:

$$(i/f/j) = \sum_{\text{spin 1}} \int u_i^*(x_1,s_1)f_1u_j(x_1,s_1)dx_1,$$

where these u's depend on coordinates and spin. If we write

$$u_i^*(x_1,s_1) = u_i^*(x_1)\sigma_{ms1}(s_1),$$

as in (7.6.4), where now u_i^* is a function of coordinates only, we then find

$$(i/f/j) = \int u_i^*(x_1)f_1u_j(x_1)dx_1 \quad \text{if spin } i = \text{spin } j$$
$$= 0 \quad \text{if spin } i \neq \text{spin } j. \tag{7.7.5}$$

In terms of this definition, the contributions of all terms f_i will be, as we stated before, the sum of all integrals $(i/f/i)$.

Similarly for the operators like g_{12} we can introduce a quantity

$$(ij/g/kl) = \sum_{\text{spin 1}} \sum_{\text{spin 2}} \int \int u_i^*(x_1,s_1)u_j^*(x_2,s_2)g_{12}u_k(x_1,s_1)u_l(x_2,s_2)dx_1\,dx_2.$$

If we again write these wave functions in terms of functions of coordinates and functions of the spin and carry out the summations over the spins, we find

$$(ij/g/kl) = \int \int u_i^*(x_1)u_j^*(x_2)g_{12}u_k(x_1)u_l(x_2)dx_1\,dx_2$$
$$\text{if spin } i = \text{spin } k, \text{ spin } j = \text{spin } l,$$
$$= 0 \quad \text{otherwise.} \tag{7.7.6}$$

In terms of these integrals, we may write the contributions of all terms g_{12} to the diagonal energy as the sum of quantities $(ij/g/ij) - (ij/g/ji)$ over all permutations ij; the second term, which is called an exchange integral, and which, as we note from (7.7.6), is different from zero only if the spins of i and j are equal, arises on account of the permutation which involves an interchange of wave functions u_i and u_j, which does not drop out on account of orthogonality.

We see then that the diagonal matrix component of energy with respect to a determinantal wave function may be written

$$\sum_i (i/f/i) + \sum_{\substack{\text{pairs} \\ i,j}} [(ij/g/ij) - (ij/g/ji)], \qquad (7.7.7)$$

where we remember that the exchange integrals $(ij/g/ji)$ are different from zero only for pairs of states with parallel spins. This fact will later prove to be important in many applications, such as the theory of ferromagnetism.

By similar arguments we can find the nondiagonal matrix component of energy between two wave functions u add u', differing by some of the one-electron functions. The results are so simple to derive that we can state them without proof. If the function u' differs from u only in having one of the one-electron functions u_i replaced by another function $u_{i'}$, the nondiagonal matrix component proves to be

$$(i/f/i') + \sum_{k \neq i} [(ik/g/i'k) - (ik/g/ki')], \qquad (7.7.8)$$

where the various integrals are as defined in (7.7.5) and (7.7.6). Next, if u' differs from u by having two one-electron functions u_i and u_j replaced by two others $u_{i'}$ and $u_{j'}$, the nondiagonal matrix component is

$$(ij/g/i'j') - (ij/g/j'i'). \qquad (7.7.9)$$

Finally if u' differs from u by having three or more one-electron functions different, the matrix component is zero.

7.8. The Problem of Two s Electrons. Now that we have found our matrix components, let us illustrate their use by a very simple example, that of two s electrons, which we have already found to lead to multiplets ^1S and ^3S. We are now in position to work out in detail the arguments which earlier we could give only in general language. We assume that the electrons are nonequivalent, and that they have orbital wave functions u_1 and u_2. We then have four substates, which we may number I to IV, as follows:

m_{s_1}	m_{s_2}	M_s	
$\frac{1}{2}$	$\frac{1}{2}$	1	(I)
$\frac{1}{2}$	$-\frac{1}{2}$	0	(II)
$-\frac{1}{2}$	$\frac{1}{2}$	0	(III)
$-\frac{1}{2}$	$-\frac{1}{2}$	-1	(IV)

The diagonal energy of state I is $(1/f/1) + (2/f/2) + (12/g/12) - (12/g/21)$; that of states II and III is $(1/f/1) + (2/f/2) + (12/g/12)$; that of state IV is the same as I. The only nonvanishing nondiagonal matrix component of energy is between states II and III and is $-(12/g/21)$. Thus the secular equation is immediately factored into two factors $[(1/f/1) + (2/f/2) + (12/g/12) - (12/g/21)] - E$, coming from states I and IV, and showing that the energy of the triplet state is

$$(1/f/1) + (2/f/2) + (12/g/12) - (12/g/21); \qquad (7.8.1)$$

and into a determinantal secular equation of two rows and columns, involving states II and III, with diagonal energies $(1/f/1) + (2/f/2) + (12/g/12)$, and nondiagonal matrix component $-(12/g/21)$. By our usual solution for a problem of degeneracy, the perturbed energies equal the diagonal matrix component, plus and minus the nondiagonal matrix component. Thus one energy value is the same as given in (7.8.1), which then must correspond to the level $M = 0$ of the ^3S; and the other energy value is

$$(1/f/1) + (2/f/2) + (12/g/12) + (12/g/21), \qquad (7.8.2)$$

which must then be the energy of the ^1S. Thus in this example we have verified, rather than having to assume it or prove it by general theorems, that we have identical energy values for $M = 1, 0, -1$, as we must for the ^3S.

We have now found the separation of energies into the singlet and triplet, as a result of the perturbation. Next, it is interesting to work out the wave functions associated with each of our four perturbed states. For states I and IV, we have already found the functions in (7.6.6). For the singlet and triplet states arising from states II and III, we know from the perturbation theory of degenerate systems that the perturbed wave functions will be the sum and difference of these wave functions, divided by $\sqrt{2}$. When we work these values out, we have the following wave functions:

Triplet:

$$M = 1: \frac{1}{\sqrt{2}} [u_1(x_1)u_2(x_2) - u_2(x_1)u_1(x_2)]\alpha(s_1)\alpha(s_2)$$

$$M = 0: \frac{1}{\sqrt{2}} [u_1(x_1)u_2(x_2) - u_2(x_1)u_1(x_2)] \frac{1}{\sqrt{2}} [\alpha(s_1)\beta(s_2) + \beta(s_1)\alpha(s_2)]$$

$$M = -1: \frac{1}{\sqrt{2}} [u_1(x_1)u_2(x_2) - u_2(x_1)u_1(x_2)]\beta(s_1)\beta(s_2)$$

Singlet:

$$M = 0: \frac{1}{\sqrt{2}} [u_1(x_1)u_2(x_2) + u_2(x_1)u_1(x_2)]$$

$$\frac{1}{\sqrt{2}} [\alpha(s_1)\beta(s_2) - \beta(s_1)\alpha(s_2)]. \quad (7.8.3)$$

The constants are chosen in each case so that these functions are normalized. We now see that each of the three substates of the triplet has the same wave function as far as the coordinates are concerned, antisymmetric in the coordinates, but the three substates have different functions of spin, in each case symmetric in the spins. The identical orbital wave functions lead to the same energy for each substate of the triplet, provided there is no magnetic energy. The singlet has a wave function which is symmetric in the coordinates, and has its antisymmetry in the function of spins. It is in this way that our earlier statement, that the singlet has a symmetric function of coordinates, is verified.

7.9. Matrix Components and Energies for Orbital Degeneracy. The case which we have just taken up is the simplest example of what may be called spin degeneracy: the degeneracy arising from the possibility of different orientations of spins. In such a problem, the whole nature of the result depends on the way in which the spin enters into the wave function, and the results are independent of the nature of the orbital wave functions u_i. It is for this reason that we have been able to get results without using specific properties of these functions. It is also for this reason that these results are so useful in the theory of molecular structure, as we shall find in the next chapter. Most of the theory of valence binding and molecular structure is based on spin degeneracy, and on its effect on the electronic energy of the system.

On the other hand, when we have cases of orbital degeneracy, in which different orientations of the orbital angular momentum are essential to the problem, we must use the properties of the spherical harmonics which express the dependence of the wave functions of an electron in a central field on angle. This fact shows us at once that this orbital degeneracy will be of less importance in the molecular problem, since we no longer have a central field in a molecule. The details of the integrals $(ij/g/ij)$ and $(ij/g/ji)$ then become important, and they cannot be calculated without using detailed properties of the spherical harmonics. Since the calculation is rather specialized, we shall not give it here, but give it instead in Appendix 15. To carry out the integration of the product of r_{12} and various wave functions, we expand $1/r_{12}$ in spherical harmonics and inverse powers of r, and integration over angles then resolves itself into an integration over products of spherical harmonics, which can be performed, leaving only an integral over functions of r. These integrals cannot be evaluated without knowing the functions of r contained in the wave function, and it is often convenient to leave them as undetermined parameters in the solution. Then we can get all matrix components in terms of a few of these parameters, and can solve the perturbation problem.

When we do this, we find in the first place that all the levels of a multiplet come out automatically to have the same energy, as they should so long as we neglect magnetic energies. Further, we find that the various multiplets are displaced from the center of gravity of all mutiplets associated with the same configuration by amounts which are simple rational multiples of the various integrals, or parameters, which enter the problem. Thus, for instance, for two equivalent p electrons there is but one parameter, and the ^1S has energy 10 times the parameter, ^1D 1 times it, and ^3P -5 times it, all referred to the energy which we should obtain by the elementary theory, neglecting degeneracy and multiplet structure. That is, ^3P lies lowest, ^1D next, and ^1S highest, and the energy separations are in the ratio 2/3, a prediction which can be tested experimentally, even without knowing the numerical value of the parameter. In other cases there are often several unknown parameters, so that we cannot predict immediately the relative values of the various separations but still can get considerable information.

PROBLEMS

1. Prove by the vector diagram that an S level, no matter what the multiplicity, has only one sublevel (one J value), and that a P level never has more than three sublevels.

2. Discuss by the vector diagram the levels arising from a p and a d electron; two nonequivalent d's.

3. If the one-electron wave functions $u_1, \ldots, u_n$ are orthogonal and normalized, prove that

$$\frac{1}{\sqrt{n!}} \begin{vmatrix} u_1(x_1) & \ldots & u_1(x_n) \\ \cdots \cdots & \cdots & \cdots \cdots \\ u_n(x_1) & \ldots & u_n(x_n) \end{vmatrix}$$

is normalized.

4. Show that a system containing an odd number of electrons always has even multiplets, as doublets, quartets, etc., while one with an even number of electrons has odd multiplets, singlets, triplets, etc.

5. Discuss the spin degeneracy of two electrons, in the case where the one-electron functions u_1 and u_2 are not orthogonal, showing that the energies are

$$\frac{(12/H/12) \pm (12/H/21)}{1 \pm (12/1/21)},$$

the plus signs being for the singlet, the minus signs for the triplet, where the notation

$(12/H/12)$ stands for $\int u_1^*(x_1)u_2^*(x_2)Hu_1(x_1)u_2(x_2)dx_1\,dx_2$, $(12/1/21)$ for

$$\int u_1^*(x_1)u_2^*(x_2)u_2(x_1)u_1(x_2)dx_1\,dx_2,$$

etc., the functions and integrations including the dependence on spin.

6. Set up the perturbation problem of spin degeneracy for three nonequivalent electrons, and find the energy of the quartet terms, in the general case where the one-electron functions are not orthogonal.

7. Work out the problem of orbital degeneracy of two equivalent d electrons, showing that the only allowed levels are $^1(SGD)$, $^3(PF)$.

8. Prove that the vector diagram and the method of orbital degeneracy lead to the same set of levels for three nonequivalent p electrons. (*Hint:* In the vector method, first couple two of the l's together to form a vector, and then couple the remaining l to this to form L. Proceed similarly with the spins.)

9. Prove that three equivalent p electrons lead to $^2(PD)$, ^4S.

10. Use the results of Appendix 15 to find the energies of the multiplets resulting from three equivalent p electrons.

11. Use the results of Appendix 15 to find the energies of the multiplets resulting from two equivalent p electrons and an s electron.

12. Each of the one-electron wave functions in a central field has the property that it either is unchanged or changes sign but retains its magnitude if we make the transformation $x \to -x$, $y \to -y$, $z \to -z$. Show from this that the wave function for the complete atom either is unchanged or changes sign but retains its magnitude if we make a transformation $x \to -x$, $y \to -y$, $z \to -z$, for the coordinates of each electron. The two types of wave functions may be denoted by the symbols $+$ and $-$ respectively. This property of a wave function is called its parity. Prove that the matrix component of energy is zero between unperturbed wave functions of different parity, so that we need consider only a perturbation problem between wave functions of the same parity, in setting up the perturbed wave function for the atom.

13. Referring to the discussion of the preceding problem, prove that there is a selection principle stating that an optical transition induced by the electric dipole radiation can only occur between states of opposite parity.

14. The well-known D lines of sodium come from the transition $3p\,^2P_{\frac{1}{2},\frac{3}{2}} \to 3s\,^2S_{\frac{1}{2}}$. Work out the Zeeman patterns for the levels, including the g values, and from this deduce the Zeeman patterns of the resulting spectrum lines.

15. Set up the problem of the Paschen-Back effect for the levels $3p\,^2P_{\frac{1}{2},\frac{3}{2}}$ of sodium. To do this, first set up diagonal and nondiagonal matrix components of energy between the sublevels of different m_l, m_s values. The only energy in which the different sublevels differ is the magnetic energy, whose operator is proportional to the scalar product of orbital and spin angular momenta. Solve the resulting perturbation problem, and find the energy levels in the Paschen-Back effect.

CHAPTER 8

THE HYDROGEN MOLECULE

All of our work so far, on the structure of individual atoms, is really preliminary to the main purpose of our study, the understanding of the forces holding atoms together to form molecules and solids. There are many types of interatomic forces. The simplest ones are purely electrostatic. Two atoms which are ionized, to form a positive and a negative ion, will of course attract each other. A single charged ion will attract a neutral atom electrically, as a large charged object will attract an uncharged object, by inducing charges in the neutral atom and attracting those charges. Forces of this type are responsible for the binding of atoms into molecules, in a considerable number of cases. But there are other types of binding, called homopolar or covalent binding, resulting from electrons shared between two or more atoms, which are less simple to explain. There are also repulsive forces between atoms, as the repulsive forces between inert-gas atoms when they approach too closely, which are likewise not simple electrostatic forces. We fortunately meet examples of both these types of force in the simplest molecule, the hydrogen molecule H_2; consequently we shall study this molecule in the present chapter. The principles which we learn from it can then be used to give a general discussion of interatomic forces, which we take up in the next chapter.

We shall find that there are two rather different types of approximation which have been used for the hydrogen molecule, and for the study of molecular binding in general. Both are attempts to approximate the solution of Schrödinger's equation for the molecule, a much more difficult problem than that of Schrödinger's equation for a single atom. One of these methods is called that of molecular orbitals, the other that of Heitler and London. We shall take up both methods in the present chapter, for both have their uses. We shall also try to show that, though the two methods give different starting points for our approximate solution, their results converge to the same answer in the end. Either one is a legitimate approximation, if carried far enough; but in some cases one method leads more easily to desired results, and in other cases the other method is better. For this reason we can hardly dispense with either approximation method. We shall start with the method of molecular orbitals, which perhaps has a somewhat wider applicability in problems of molecular structure and the solid state.

8.1. Molecular Orbitals for the Hydrogen Molecule-Ion. As a preliminary step, we shall consider a simpler problem than the hydrogen molecule; namely, the hydrogen molecule-ion, composed of two protons, or hydrogen nuclei, and a single electron, leading thus to the ion H_2^+. This is much simpler than the hydrogen molecule, since it is only a one-electron problem. It can, as a matter of fact, be solved exactly; it is a piece of good fortune that by introducing ellipsoidal coordinates, with the two nuclei as the foci of the ellipsoids and hyperboloids forming the

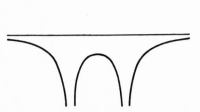

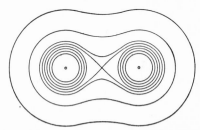

FIG. 8.1.1. Potential energy in field of two hydrogen nuclei, along line of centers.

FIG. 8.1.2. Potential energy in field of two hydrogen nuclei, equipotentials in plane containing nuclei.

coordinate surfaces, the variables can be separated in Schrödinger's equation, and the equation solved exactly. Thus this case forms a safe guide in problems of molecular structure, much as the hydrogen atom does in problems of atomic structure. We shall not, however, try to find this exact solution, which involves a good deal of complicated mathematics, but shall instead discuss its nature qualitatively, on the basis of our earlier elementary study of the solutions of Schrödinger's equation.

Let us first consider the potential energy acting on the electron. It is attracted by each of the two nuclei; if r_a, r_b are its distances from the two, the potential energy is $-2/r_a - 2/r_b$ in atomic units, with two infinitely deep minima at the two nuclei. Thus, as we see in Fig. 8.1.1, it is a potential energy function with two symmetrical minima, and as a result of this the solutions have the properties discussed in Sec. 2.5 and illustrated in Figs. 2.5.4 and 2.5.5. Of course, our present problem is three-dimensional, and this complicates the whole problem a good deal. In Fig. 8.1.1, we show merely the potential as a function of distance along the straight line joining the two nuclei, but to show it completely, we should have to indicate its behavior in three-dimensional space. This cannot be done in any convenient graphical way, but we can indicate the potential in a corresponding two-dimensional case by a contour map, as in Fig. 8.1.2.   Here we have drawn contours corresponding to constant values of the potential energy.   We see clearly the two potential wells, with a so-called saddle point between them (a point at which the potential energy has a maximum with respect to motion in one direction, toward the nuclei, but a minimum with respect to motion in the direction at right angles).   Some equipotentials surround only one nucleus or the other, while other larger equipotentials surround both nuclei.   The potential energy function, of course, is dependent on the distance between the nuclei, which we treat as a parameter: we are interested not only in the ion in its actually observed state, with the nuclei at the distance found in the actual ion, but also with arbitrary internuclear distance.   It is clear that if the nuclei are widely separated, the two wells will be far apart, and each will be like that around a single hydrogen nucleus; while in the limit, as the nuclei are brought together, the wells will coalesce into a single one which is like that around a helium nucleus (that is, a nucleus with a double charge).

Let us now try to predict the form which the wave functions and energy levels of the electron will take in the potential shown above, as the internuclear distance is changed.   At very large internuclear distances, it is obvious that there must be a very close analogy between this problem and that of the hydrogen atom.   There are, however, several very significant differences.   In the first place, we have the same situation taken up in Sec. 2.5, when we were discussing the problem of a particle in two wells: we have solutions which are either symmetric or antisymmetric in the mid-point between the attracting centers.   Thus, for instance, let us consider the wave function which goes to the $1s$ state when the nuclei are infinitely separated.   We know by our study of the hydrogen atom that the $1s$ wave function depends only on r, the distance from the nucleus, and in fact has the value e^{-r/a_0}.   Thus a wave function of an electron around the first nucleus would be represented by e^{-r_a/a_0}, and around the second by e^{-r_b/a_0}, where, as before, r_a is the distance from the first nucleus, r_b from the second.   But now more detailed study of Schrödinger's equation in such a case shows that the correct wave function must be symmetric or antisymmetric in the mid-plane between the nuclei.   We may deduce this either from the analogous case of two potential wells, taken up in Sec. 2.5, or from the perturbation theory.   The two functions, one concentrated around one nucleus and the other around the other, form two degenerate unperturbed solutions of the problem. Under these conditions, we know that the perturbation will introduce as perturbed functions the sum and difference of the unperturbed functions.

Thus for the perturbed functions we must approximately have $e^{-r_a/a_0} \pm e^{-r_b/a_0}$, the plus sign referring to the symmetric, the minus sign to the antisymmetric function.   Along the straight line joining the two nuclei, these two functions will then look like those given in Fig. 8.1.3.   We see that there is one significant difference between these functions, once the nuclei get close enough so that the functions coming from the two atoms separately begin to overlap.   The symmetric function is twice as high at the mid-point between the atoms as one of the functions separately would be; thus when we square it, to get the electronic charge distribution, the square is four times as great at this point.   On the other hand, the antisymmetric function is zero at the mid-point.   Hence

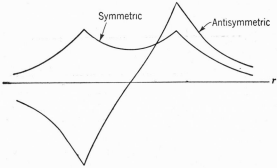

FIG. 8.1.3.   Exponential approximation to symmetric and antisymmetric wave functions of $H_2{}^+$ problem, along line passing through nuclei.

the symmetric function corresponds to an excess distribution of charge midway between the atoms, and the antisymmetric function to a deficiency of charge.

This difference between the symmetric and antisymmetric functions takes on considerable importance when we come to consider the energy level of the electron, as a function of the internuclear distance.   In the symmetric function the excess charge located between the two atoms finds itself at a lower potential energy than it would if the atoms were widely separated; the potential energy, as a matter of fact, has twice the negative value at the mid-point between atoms that it would have if only one nucleus were present.   Thus this wave function results in a lower potential energy than for infinite separation of the atoms.   We may say, if we choose, that the electronic charge shared between the atoms, as a result of the symmetry of the wave function, is attracted by both nuclei, decreasing the energy.   On the other hand, for the antisymmetric function, electronic charge will be forced away from this mid-position of lower potential energy, and must find its resting place at points away from the mid-point, in locations of higher potential energy.   Consequently the energy of the antisymmetric state will be higher than for the separated atoms.

We can investigate these trends of the energy levels in quite a different way: by asking what is the limiting energy of each of the levels as the two nuclei are pushed into coincidence, and the problem approaches that of a single electron moving around a doubly charged, or helium, nucleus. We know that the lowest state of this positively charged helium ion, its 1s state, has an energy $-4Rhc$ [the general formula for the levels being $-(Z^2/n^2)Rhc$]. Now the symmetric wave function of the two-center problem has no nodal surfaces anywhere; this is also characteristic of the 1s wave function of He$^+$. Thus it seems reasonable that these functions

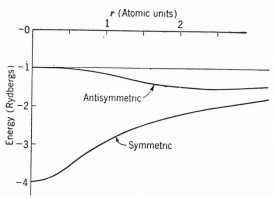

Fig. 8.1.4. Electronic energy of symmetric and antisymmetric states of H$_2$$^+$, as functions of internuclear distance (antisymmetric state is only schematic).

will merge smoothly into each other as the internuclear distance is varied, and this proves in fact to be the case. The energy of this level must then go from $-Rhc$ at infinite separation (the energy of the 1s state of hydrogen) to $-4Rhc$ at zero separation (the energy of the 1s of He$^+$), confirming our conclusion that the energy of the level would have to decrease as the nuclei are pushed together.

The case of the antisymmetric function is a little more involved. This function is zero at all points of the plane midway between the two nuclei, and this plane passes through the helium nucleus when the two nuclei are pushed into conjunction. The antisymmetric function must then join smoothly to a function of the He$^+$ problem which has this nodal plane. When we look at our hydrogenlike solutions, we see that this is one of the 2p functions. We remember, from our discussion of Sec. 5.3, that these functions have no nodes as far as the function of r is concerned, but the three spherical harmonics have the form x/r, y/r, z/r, respectively, for the three substates corresponding to $n = 2$, $l = 1$. If we choose the z axis to be the line joining the two nuclei, the function z/r then has the required property of being zero on the plane $z = 0$ and changing sign from one side to the other. Thus it must be that the energy level of our antisymmetric state, which has the value $-Rhc$ at infinite separation, goes also to $-Rhc$ at zero separation, for this is the energy of the $2p$ level of He^+. This argument shows only, then, that the trend of this energy level up or down, with decreasing internuclear distance, is not as extreme as for the symmetric case. As a matter of fact, the exact solution shows that the level starts down as the nuclei approach, but then turns up again as they come together.

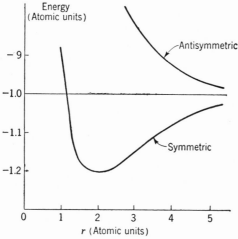

Fig. 8.1.5.   Total energy of symmetric and antisymmetric states of H_2^+, as function of internuclear distance (antisymmetric state is only schematic).

It is now interesting to derive from our study of the electronic energy levels as a function of internuclear distance, the curves for the energy of the whole molecule-ion as a function of internuclear distance. The energy levels which we have discussed so far, illustrated as a function of r_{ab}, the internuclear distance, are given in Fig. 8.1.4, and do not represent the whole energy of the molecule-ion. We have included the potential energy terms $-2/r_a - 2/r_b$ of interaction between the electron and the two nuclei in Schrödinger's equation; but we have disregarded the other term, $2/r_{ab}$, where r_{ab} is the distance between the nuclei, representing the repulsion between the two nuclei. This was justified, for it is a constant as far as the electronic motion is concerned and would not affect the wave functions. It must, however, be added in if we want the total energy of the ion. When we add this term in, we find, as illustrated in Fig. 8.1.5, that it causes the energy levels to become positively infinite as r_{ab}

approaches zero.   The energy of the symmetric state first falls as the internuclear distance decreases, goes through a minimum, and then increases without limit.   The antisymmetric function, on the other hand, has a sufficiently higher energy so that it never has a minimum at all.

These curves of total energy as a function of internuclear distance have a very great importance in the problem of interatomic forces.   The curve for the symmetric function is a typical interatomic potential energy curve for a case of a stable molecule.   We shall see later that this potential energy curve is the one which governs the vibrational motion of the nuclei in the actual molecule or ion. If there is no vibrational energy, then using classical mechanics, the internuclear distance would be at the minimum of the curve, r_0 in Fig. 8.1.6. At a higher energy, as E, the classical motion would correspond to a vibration whose range is determined by the two intersections of the energy curve and the line at height E.   In other words, this energy curve acts like a potential energy curve.   If the energy is zero in Fig. 8.1.6, the amplitude of oscillation becomes infinite, or the two nuclei fly apart from each other, and the molecule dissociates; D, therefore, represents the energy of dissociation. Of course, we must actually use the quantum mechanics to discuss the vibrations, but this will not alter the qualitative significance of r_0 and D.

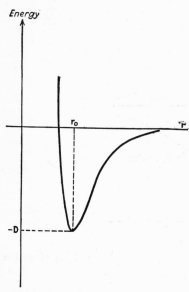

Fig. 8.1.6.   Morse potential curve, $De^{-2a(r-r_0)} - 2De^{-a(r-r_0)}$.

We shall come back to these questions of nuclear vibrations later, but in the meantime we can see that the existence of a potential energy curve like that above is such as to lead to a stable molecule.

It is often convenient to have an analytic form which approximately fits curves like that of Fig. 8.1.6.   A function of this type which is often very useful was introduced by Morse, and is known as a Morse curve. This is the function

$$\text{Energy} = D[e^{-2a(r-r_0)} - 2e^{-a(r-r_0)}]. \tag{8.1.1}$$

Here D and r_0 have the significance shown in Fig. 8.1.6, and a is a constant measuring the steepness with which the energy curve rises on both sides of the minimum.   We note that the first term of (8.1.1) represents a repulsive term, important at small values of r, and the second is an attraction, more important at large r's.

The antisymmetric function in H_2^+, returning to Fig. 8.1.5, leads to a potential curve without a minimum, and hence with no possibility of formation of a stable molecule; the two nuclei approaching each other classically, with their electron in this state, would approach to a certain minimum distance, reverse their motion, and fly apart again, performing a collision. This then is a repulsive energy level. Just as the attractive energy levels could be described by the Morse curve (8.1.1), a repulsive energy level can be described with fair accuracy by a single exponential term, similar to the first term of (8.1.1). It is common to describe our wave functions for the two-center problem as molecular orbitals and to denote the symmetric sort as a bonding orbital, the antisymmetric sort as an antibonding orbital. It is clear that a bonding orbital is one which contains electronic charge shared between the two atoms, which is in a position of lowered potential energy; whereas an antibonding orbital has a deficiency of charge between the two atoms.

In a way similar to what we have used, we can examine the higher wave functions of the hydrogen problem and ask whether they form bonding or antibonding orbitals. The principles are in each case the same that we have used already. Additional interesting features come in, however, when we begin to consider the $2p$ hydrogen functions. The various $2p$ functions, with their different angular dependence, will behave quite differently when it comes to their role in the molecule-ion. If the z axis is chosen as the line joining the nuclei, the function z/r will extend with maximum intensity along this axis, so that there will be large overlapping charge at the mid-point between the atoms. There will then be two functions, symmetric and antisymmetric in the mid-point, just as with the s functions, and the symmetric function will lead to bonding, the antisymmetric one to repulsion. The situation is quite different, however, with the functions x/r and y/r. These functions are automatically zero along the z axis, for which x and y are zero. Thus under any circumstances they correspond to having no charge density near the mid-point of the two nuclei. The electrostatic effects which cause attraction and repulsion with the symmetric and antisymmetric functions will then be considerably weakened in this case, and while these symmetric and antisymmetric functions will still exist, their energies will not depend very strikingly on the internuclear distance. As a first approximation, the curve for energy of the whole ion as a function of internuclear distance will resemble the average of the curves for the symmetric and antisymmetric s functions, though there will still be a somewhat lower energy for the function corresponding to increased density of charge in the mid-plane than for the other function.   Since these functions do not take part very strikingly either in bonding or in repulsion, they are sometimes called nonbonding.

There is another feature of these p functions, which is of only minor importance for most of our purposes, but which is nevertheless worth mentioning.   The total angular momentum of the electron is not constant in the molecule-ion problem, since the potential is not spherically symmetrical, and consequently it is not quantized.   However, the torque exerted by the nuclei on the electron has no component along the axis of the molecule, or along the z axis, and hence the component of angular momentum in this direction is conserved and is quantized.   When we examine the wave functions, we find that the functions formed by both antisymmetric and symmetric combinations of the s electrons of the separate atoms, and those formed from p functions having the angular dependence z/r, have no angular momentum along the axis; while those formed from the p functions x/r and y/r can lead to a single unit of angular momentum along the axis.   In this case we must use combinations $(x \pm iy)/r$, which can be rewritten so as to involve the factor $e^{\pm i\varphi}$, where φ is the angle around the axis, rather than using the functions x/r and y/r themselves, which have the characteristic of standing waves rather than of traveling waves rotating around the axis, which we need for having a resultant angular momentum.   The component of angular momentum along the axis is sometimes denoted by describing the terms by symbols involving Greek letters; thus the terms with no component of angular momentum along the axis are Σ terms, those with one unit of angular momentum Π terms, by analogy with S and P terms in atomic spectra.

8.2. Molecular Orbitals for the Hydrogen Molecule.   Let us suppose that we wish to apply the method of self-consistent fields to the hydrogen molecule.   Each of the two electrons will move in an averaged field of the other electron and in the field of the two nuclei.   Let us assume that the field of the other electron is symmetrical in the mid-point between the nuclei.   Then the electron we are considering will be moving in a field with two attracting centers.   These centers will not have the same potential energy function that we have considered in the preceding section, for each nucleus will be surrounded half the time by the other electron, so that roughly half of its effect will be shielded.   Nevertheless, the main features of the solution of the molecule-ion, taken up in the preceding section, will still be correct.   The wave function of the electron we are considering will still be either symmetric or antisymmetric in the mid-point, and the energy relations between the various stationary states will be roughly as before.   But now if the wave function is either symmetric or antisymmetric, its resulting charge distribution, being proportional to the square of the wave function, will be symmetric; and as a consequence, the potential resulting from it will be symmetric. Thus we have a consistent hypothesis if we assume each of the two electrons to move in a symmetric two-center potential, each having a wave function which is a molecular orbital for this type of problem. The method of molecular orbitals for the hydrogen molecule is the application of the method of self-consistent fields, proceeding along these lines.

Let us now see what picture of the hydrogen molecule we are led to by this process. First we consider the ground state of the molecule. The lowest one-electron energy level is the symmetric state formed from the 1s atomic function. By the principles learned in our study of atomic structure, we then presume that the ground state will be the one in which both electrons will have this wave function, but with opposite spins, so as to avoid trouble with the exclusion principle. This will be a singlet level. Since the one-electron energy of each of these symmetric wave functions will have a minimum, corresponding to the sharing of an electron between the nuclei, we may presume that this ground state will likewise have a minimum, arising from the sharing of the two electrons, one of each spin, between the nuclei. When we take the wave function and compute its energy by averaging the energy operator over the wave function, we find, in fact, that this is the case; and this forms the simplest case of the covalent, or electron-pair, bond, as described by the method of molecular orbitals.

We can also consider the excited levels of the molecule. Let one of the electrons be in the lowest state, but let the other one be excited. Then there will be the possibility of both a triplet and a singlet level, since we are dealing with a two-electron system; and by the general principles of the preceding chapter, we shall usually find the triplet having a lower energy than the singlet, since with the triplet the orbital part of the wave function must be antisymmetric in the coordinates of the two electrons, which then keep out of each other's way and reduce their repulsive energy. We must be very careful to keep clear the two types of symmetry and antisymmetry which appear in this problem: the symmetry properties of the one-electron wave function, or molecular orbital of a single electron, in the three-dimensional coordinates, with respect to the mid-point between the nuclei; and the symmetry and antisymmetry of the wave function of the two electrons, formed from these molecular orbitals, with respect to interchange of the two electrons.

The lowest of these excited levels will come when the excited electron is in the antisymmetric, or antibonding, orbital associated with the 1s atomic wave function, and the electron spins are parallel, leading to a triplet level. We shall then have one bonding, and one antibonding, electron; and closer examination of the energy shows that in this case there is no minimum in the potential energy curve of the whole molecule. This has an interesting result in the study of the molecule. If we have a hydrogen molecule in its ground state, at low temperature, there will be very little vibrational energy, and the interatomic distance will be found very close to that giving the minimum energy, as in Fig. 8.2.1. By absorbing light, we can raise the molecule into the excited state which we have just described, in which there is no minimum of potential energy. Once the electron is excited, we must use this new potential energy curve to describe the motion of the nuclei; and it is clear that the nuclei will immediately fly apart to infinite distance, or the molecule will be dissociated.

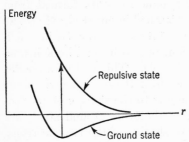

Fig. 8.2.1. Transition of hydrogen molecule from bottom of ground state to repulsive state by absorption of radiation.

There will be further excited states which arise from excited states of the atom, which can have minima. Thus we have noted that one of the $2p$ molecular orbitals is bonding. If the excited electron is in this level, both electrons will be bonding, and the resulting energy level of the molecule as a whole has a minimum and corresponds to a stable excited molecule. Many such stable excited states are known for hydrogen, as well as for other molecules, and the observed molecular spectra, or band spectra, arise from transitions between different such stable states. We cannot consider their detailed structure until we take up the study of the nuclear vibrations, which we shall not do until later. In addition to these spectra, the molecules also are observed to have continuous spectra, coming from the type of absorption to a repulsive state which we have just described.

All these predictions which we have described regarding the nature of the hydrogen molecule prove to be qualitatively correct, but to have serious errors when we consider them more carefully. Part of these errors come because all attempts to solve the two-center problem are very inaccurate. Unlike the central field problem, there is no straightforward way to do this. The exact solution for the hydrogen molecule-ion unfortunately cannot be generalized to apply to any other two-center problem. But quite aside from these errors, which arise from difficulties of exact calculation, there are errors of a more serious sort, which come from our fundamental hypothesis of the self-consistent field. These are errors of a type which we do not meet in applying the same method to atomic structure, and it is not hard to understand their origin. They come in in their most serious form in the part of the problem which we should think ought to be easiest to solve: the case where the two atoms are widely separated, when our physical intuition tells us correctly that the solution must reduce to that of two separated hydrogen atoms. Our molecular orbital method works in the following way with widely separated atoms: it tells us that each of the electrons should move in the field of the two nuclei and an averaged field of the other electron, which spends half its time surrounding each of the two nuclei. Thus the electron we are considering, according to this method, generally finds itself near a nucleus half shielded by a charge density equal in total amount to half an electronic charge. This, of course, is quite incorrect as a representation of the separated hydrogen atoms which we have under these circumstances, and the energy which we deduce is incorrect for the problem of two separated atoms. This tells us, in other words, that the method of molecular orbitals, as straightforwardly applied, can lead to results which are quite wrong for large interatomic separations. On the other hand, for distances near that found in the actual molecule, more careful examination of the wave functions and energies resulting from the molecular orbital method shows that they form quite good approximations to the correct values. It is for this reason that the method has many uses; but we must always be suspicious of it when the atoms are pulled far apart.

It is not impossible to correct these errors which we have just found for the case of large interatomic distance. We have only to apply perturbation theory, regarding the states we have already described as the unperturbed wave functions for a perturbation calculation. Suppose we consider simply the following low-lying levels of the hydrogen molecule, as described by the molecular orbital method: the ground state, a singlet, with the two electrons having opposite spin, each being in the symmetric orbital built out of $1s$ atomic functions; next, a triplet (lying lower) and a singlet (lying higher), in which one electron is in the symmetric state built from $1s$, and the other is in the antisymmetric state built from $1s$; finally the singlet state in which both electrons are in the antisymmetric $1s$ orbital. We can proceed to apply perturbation ideas merely to these states; the more highly excited states, in which the orbitals are built on higher levels of the atoms, will complicate matters but will not change the present argument. We then investigate first the diagonal matrix components of energy (we have already considered some of these, in discussing the energies of the various types of states), and the nondiagonal matrix components of energy. In Fig. 8.2.2 we give the diagonal energies as a function of internuclear distance; these are the energies of the states, as determined directly by the molecular orbital method without perturbations.   We observe the energy going to the wrong limit as the distance becomes large.

When we examine the nondiagonal matrix components of energy, we find that, by the type of argument used in the preceding chapter and by symmetry arguments, a number of these matrix components prove to

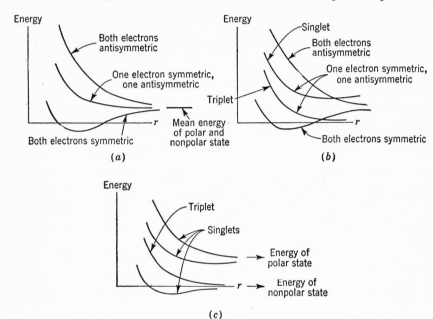

(a) (b)

(c)

FIG. 8.2.2.   Different stages in calculation of H_2 by molecular orbital method: (a) diagonal energies, without taking account of spin degeneracy; (b) energies after correcting state where one electron is in a symmetric orbital, one antisymmetric, for spin degeneracy; this separates the singlet and triplet and makes them go to the correct limits at infinite separation; (c) energies after applying perturbations to singlet states; all energies now go to correct limits at infinite separation.

be zero.   Thus the matrix component between a singlet and a triplet level automatically proves to vanish.   The only matrix component which is not zero, in fact, is between that singlet state in which both electrons are in the symmetric $1s$ state and that in which both are in the antisymmetric $1s$ state.   The resulting perturbation proves to be of most importance at large internuclear distances.   And when we carry out the calculation of wave functions and energy levels at large distances (this part of the calculation can, as a matter of fact, be made exact, and not dependent on the power-series approximation), we find that the correct energy levels reduce exactly to those which we know are correct for two separated hydrogen atoms, and the wave functions are just such combinations of symmetric and antisymmetric functions that, when we examine their meaning, we see that they predict that one electron will be in one atom, the other in the other. The perturbed energy levels, as well as the unperturbed ones, are given in Fig. 8.2.2, illustrating the situation.

We see then that the application of perturbation theory to the results of the molecular orbital method corrects the errors which we have earlier seen to be inherent in this method for large internuclear distances. On the other hand, while it leads to profound changes in the wave functions, as compared with the molecular orbital calculation without perturbations, for large distances, it still shows that at the actual internuclear distances the corrections to the unperturbed molecular orbital picture are relatively small, verifying our earlier statement that the molecular orbitals, without further correction, furnished a good approximation under the conditions actually holding in the molecule. At large distances, the corrections we are led to can be described as a certain admixture of states in which the electrons are in higher molecular orbitals, in order to get the best possible representation of the ground state.

8.3. The Heitler-London Method for the Hydrogen Molecule. From the discussion of the molecular orbital method which we have given so far, we see that while it is good for the description of the molecule with small internuclear distances, without the application of perturbation methods, still at large internuclear distances it is entirely incorrect, unless perturbation methods are correctly applied. We now consider another approximation, that suggested by Heitler and London, which is at its best in the other limit, that of large internuclear distance.

The Heitler-London method starts with the rather obvious observation that the correct wave function for two separated hydrogen atoms is that in which one electron has a hydrogenlike $1s$ wave function around one nucleus, the other a similar wave function around the other. These one-electron wave functions are not either symmetric or antisymmetric with respect to the nuclei, and hence they are not molecular orbitals in the sense of the preceding section; they are sometimes called atomic orbitals in discussions of this problem. As the atoms are brought closer together, this method assumes that the same wave functions can still be used as a first approximation; and then it proceeds by perturbation theory from there. Since the argument is rather subtle, we shall have to go through it in fair detail in order to give the essential points.

Let us denote a $1s$ hydrogen orbital about the first nucleus by $u_a(x)$, and a similar function about the second by $u_b(x)$. Then we could set up an approximate wave function for the problem of two electrons in the form $u_a(x_1)u_b(x_2)$, where x_1, x_2 symbolize the coordinates of the two electrons, and where this wave function implies that electron 1 is located on atom a, electron 2 on atom b. There is, however, an equally legitimate wave function with the electrons interchanged: $u_b(x_1)u_a(x_2)$. We must now consider the electron spins. According to the principles of Sec. 7.4, we know that if we have a two-electron problem like this, we can have either a singlet or a triplet state of the system, the first arising if the electrons have antiparallel spin, the second if the spins are parallel. Furthermore, from Sec. 7.4 we know that the wave functions for these stationary states must be symmetric and antisymmetric, respectively, in the coordinates. Thus they can be approximated by normalizing constants multiplied by

$$u_a(x_1)u_b(x_2) \pm u_b(x_1)u_a(x_2), \qquad (8.3.1)$$

where the plus sign goes with the singlet state, the minus sign with the triplet.

There is one significant difference between our present case and that of the atomic multiplets: the wave functions u_a and u_b are not orthogonal to each other. This is most easily seen from the fact that both u_a and u_b are everywhere positive, so that their product is also positive, and cannot integrate to zero. We assume that u_a and u_b are separately normalized, so that $\int u_a^2(x_1)dx_1 = 1$, etc., but we have

$$\int u_a(x_1)u_b(x_1)dx_1 = \alpha, \qquad (8.3.2)$$

a quantity different from zero, and very significant in the theory. The function u_a falls off rapidly as we go away from nucleus a, and u_b falls off as we go away from nucleus b; the main contributions to the quantity α will then be found in the region midway between the atoms. We may call α the overlap integral, since it measures the overlapping of the two wave functions. It will clearly be zero for very large internuclear distances but will increase as the nuclei approach, never getting larger than unity, which is the value it would have if the nuclei coincided and u_a and u_b became equal to each other.

Since u_a and u_b are not orthogonal, we cannot assume without further examination that the results of Chap. 7 are all valid, and as a matter of fact, the formulas given there for the energy of the singlet and triplet in this case, given in (7.8.1) and (7.8.2), do not hold in the present case. We examine the matter further in Appendix 16, where we take up the problem of determinantal wave functions formed from nonorthogonal atomic functions. There we show that even in the present case, though the formulas for energy are more complicated than in Chap. 7, nevertheless the wave functions for the problem of two s electrons, given in (7.8.3) and leading to orbital functions symmetric or antisymmetric in the electron coordinates, as in (8.3.1), are correct.   This seems reasonable on the basis of simple symmetry arguments.   Consequently, we may proceed now by taking the orbital functions (8.3.1), normalizing them, and computing the average value of the energy operator with respect to them, and we shall thus get the correct energy values.

First we normalize.   If we take either of the functions (8.3.1), square it, and integrate over the coordinates of the first and second electrons, symbolized by dx_1 and dx_2, and remember that u_a and u_b are normalized, but that their lack of orthogonality is indicated by (8.3.2), we find

$$\iint [u_a(x_1)u_b(x_2) \pm u_b(x_1)u_a(x_2)]^2 \, dx_1 \, dx_2 = 2(1 \pm \alpha^2). \qquad (8.3.3)$$

Thus, if we divide the functions (8.3.1) by $\sqrt{2(1 \pm \alpha^2)}$, the resulting functions will be normalized; and we assume this to be done.   For the average energy we then have, averaging over the wave functions of the singlet (with plus sign) or triplet (with minus sign),

$$E_\pm = \frac{1}{2(1 \pm \alpha^2)} \int\int [u_a(x_1)u_b(x_2) \pm u_b(x_1)u_a(x_2)]$$
$$H[u_a(x_1)u_b(x_2) \pm u_b(x_1)u_a(x_2)]dx_1 \, dx_2. \qquad (8.3.4)$$

We can now rewrite this in the form

$$E_\pm = \frac{(ab/H/ab) \pm (ab/H/ba)}{1 \pm \alpha^2}, \qquad (8.3.5)$$

where

$$(ab/H/ab) = \iint u_a(x_1)u_b(x_2)Hu_a(x_1)u_b(x_2)dx_1 \, dx_2,$$
$$(ab/H/ba) = \iint u_a(x_1)u_b(x_2)Hu_b(x_1)u_a(x_2)dx_1 \, dx_2, \qquad (8.3.6)$$

following a notation similar to that of Sec. 7.7.   The quantities $(ab/H/ab)$ and $(ab/H/ba)$ are diagonal and nondiagonal matrix components of the energy, with respect to the two unperturbed wave functions $u_a(x_1)u_b(x_2)$ and $u_b(x_1)u_a(x_2)$, which of course are degenerate unperturbed states, since they differ from each other only in the interchange of electrons between them.   The integral $(ab/H/ba)$ is an exchange integral, like those encountered in Sec. 7.7.

Let us now examine in more detail the terms $(ab/H/ab)$ and $(ab/H/ba)$ of (8.3.6).   The operator H is

$$H = -(\nabla_1^2 + \nabla_2^2) + \frac{2}{r_{ab}} - \frac{2}{r_{a1}} - \frac{2}{r_{a2}} - \frac{2}{r_{b1}} - \frac{2}{r_{b2}} + \frac{2}{r_{12}}, \qquad (8.3.7)$$

where we are using atomic units, r_{ab} is the distance between the nuclei, r_{a1} the distance from nucleus a to electron 1, etc., and r_{12} is the distance between electrons.   The function $u_a(x_1)$ satisfies the equation

$$-\nabla_1^2 u_a(x_1) - \frac{2}{r_{a1}} u_a(x_1) = -u_a(x_1), \qquad (8.3.8)$$

the ordinary Schrödinger equation for the ground state of hydrogen, with the energy -1 in atomic units. The other function u_b satisfies a similar differential equation. Now in the calculation of $(ab/H/ab)$ and $(ab/H/ba)$ we need the quantity $Hu_a(x_1)u_b(x_2)$. If we use (8.3.7) and (8.3.8), we find at once that this is

$$Hu_a(x_1)u_b(x_2) = -2 + \left(\frac{2}{r_{ab}} - \frac{2}{r_{b1}} - \frac{2}{r_{a2}} + \frac{2}{r_{12}}\right)u_a(x_1)u_b(x_2). \quad (8.3.9)$$

We now substitute into (8.3.6) and find

$$E_\pm = -2 + \frac{H_0 \pm H_1}{1 \pm \alpha^2}, \quad (8.3.10)$$

where

$$H_0 = \int\int u_a(x_1)u_b(x_2)\left(\frac{2}{r_{ab}} - \frac{2}{r_{b1}} - \frac{2}{r_{a2}} + \frac{2}{r_{12}}\right)u_a(x_1)u_b(x_2)dx_1\,dx_2,$$

$$H_1 = \int\int u_b(x_1)u_a(x_2)\left(\frac{2}{r_{ab}} - \frac{2}{r_{b1}} - \frac{2}{r_{a2}} + \frac{2}{r_{12}}\right)u_a(x_1)u_b(x_2)dx_1\,dx_2.$$

$$(8.3.11)$$

From (8.3.10) we find that the energy of the molecule, to the order of approximation to which we are working, differs from the energy -2 Rydbergs of two isolated atoms, on account of the terms H_0 and H_1, which as we shall shortly see, reduce to zero when the atoms are separated by an infinite distance. Thus we see that the Heitler-London method gives the correct answer at large distances of separation, as we expected that it should. We shall now examine the integrals H_0 and H_1.

The significance of H_0 is very simple. The first term can be simplified at once. The constant $1/r_{ab}$ can be taken outside the integral, and then, on account of normalization of the u's, the result is simply $2/r_{ab}$, the potential energy of the two nuclei, at distance r_{ab}, under the action of their electrostatic repulsion. The next term can also be simplified. We can integrate over x_2 and find that the term is $-\int u_a^2(x_1)(2/r_{b1})dx_1$. This is the electrostatic interaction between the positive charge on the nucleus b, and an electron 1 distributed on atom a with a charge density proportional to $u_a^2(x_1)$. The third term, similarly, is the interaction between nucleus a and electron 2 distributed on atom b. Finally the last term, which cannot be simplified, is the repulsive interaction between electron 1, distributed on atom a, and electron 2, distributed on atom b. These integrals can be worked out analytically from the known values of the u's; but we can deduce their general behavior from simple principles.

We remember that a spherical distribution of charge has a potential, at points outside the charge distribution, just as if its whole charge were concentrated at the center of the sphere. Thus at large interatomic distances, the interaction between the electron on atom a and nucleus b will be just as if the electron were concentrated at the nucleus a, and the interaction between electrons 1 and 2, the first concentrated on atom a and the second on atom b, will be as if each of the electrons were precisely at the corresponding nucleus. Thus in this limit the positive and negative terms of H_0 will exactly compensate each other; this compensation will not be disturbed until there begins to be penetration of one atom by the other. We can get a qualitative idea of the behavior at smaller distances from Fig. 8.3.1. Here the spheres are supposed to represent the electronic shells of the two atoms. As the shells begin to overlap,

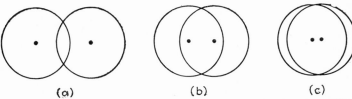

(a)   **(b)**   **(c)**

FIG. 8.3.1. Schematic representation of the overlapping of two atoms. The points represent the nuclei, the circles the regions occupied most densely by negative electronic charge distributions.

with decreasing interatomic distance, some of the electronic charge of each atom finds itself inside some of the charge of the other. Thus the electronic shells no longer completely shield the nuclei, as they do at large distances, and the electronic charge of each atom which penetrates into the other begins to be attracted by the unshielded nuclear charge of the other. Only at considerably smaller distances do repulsive forces come into play. If the distance is so small that the nucleus of each atom penetrates the electronic shell of the other, then each nucleus is repelled by the partially unshielded nuclear charge of the other. Finally, at small enough distances, this nuclear repulsion overcomes the attractions: the term in $1/r_{ab}$ in (8.3.11) can become infinite as r_{ab} goes to zero, while the other terms of (8.3.11) remain finite even in that limit, being interactions with extended electronic charge distributions. The net result is that H_0, as a function of r_{ab}, has the general character shown in Fig. 8.3.2. This in itself is the type of energy which we expect for a stable molecule, according to our previous discussion. However, we shall find that this effect forms but a small part of the whole energy. This term H_0 is generally called the Coulomb energy, for it is the electrostatic interaction energy between the two atoms, each regarded as a nucleus and a rigid electron cloud, as determined according to the Coulomb law.

Next we come to the term H_1 in (8.3.11). This is called the exchange energy, as we have mentioned earlier in referring to the related integral $(ab/H/ba)$ of (8.3.6). We can simplify this expression much as we did that for H_0. The first term is α^2 times the quantity $2/r_{ab}$, as if we had a charge αe located on each nucleus. The second and third terms are the energy of interaction between a charge whose charge density is $u_a(x)u_b(x)$ and a charge of amount αe located on one of the nuclei, and the last term is the energy of interaction of this charge with itself. Now α is the integral of the function $u_a(x)u_b(x)$ over the coordinates. Thus the whole exchange energy is what we should have if we had each of the elec-

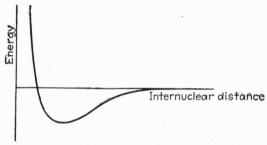

Fig. 8.3.2.   Schematic representation of the electrostatic or Coulomb energy of interaction of two overlapping rigid atoms, as shown in Fig. 8.3.1.

trons distributed with this function $u_a(x)u_b(x)$, a distribution of total amount $-\alpha e$, and found the electrostatic energy of interaction between these two electronic distributions, and charges αe on each nucleus. The distribution $u_a u_b$, as we have mentioned earlier, has its maximum intensity in the region midway between the nuclei. This charge distribution is sometimes called the exchange charge. When we come to examine the relative magnitudes of the terms, we find as with the Coulomb interaction that at moderate distances the exchange integral is negative, the attractions between the exchange charge and the nuclei more than balancing the repulsions between the nuclei, and between the two exchange charges. On the other hand, at small enough distances, just as with the Coulomb interactions, the nuclear repulsions become infinite, and the exchange energy becomes large and positive. In other words, the exchange energy, as a function of r_{ab}, has a form much like the Coulomb interaction, only it turns out to be several times as large.

When we now combine the exchange and Coulomb terms, according to (8.3.10), taking account of the term $1 \pm \alpha^2$ in the denominator, the resulting energy levels of the molecule look as in Fig. 8.2.1. We find, in other words, a singlet attractive level and a triplet repulsive level, in qualitative agreement with the results of the method of molecular orbitals.

We find furthermore that at infinite separation the levels go to the correct value. Thus in many respects the Heitler-London approximation is superior to that of molecular orbitals. When we examine it more carefully, however, we find that it too has its shortcomings. In the next section we shall look at it a little more critically and shall consider its relations with the method of molecular orbitals.

8.4. Comparison of the Heitler-London and Molecular Orbital Methods. The energy levels of the hydrogen molecule, as determined by the Heitler-London method, do not agree quantitatively with experiment, though they are all right qualitatively. We can really hardly expect a good agreement, particularly at small distances. If the two nuclei were brought into coincidence, so that the problem approached that of the helium atom, the Heitler-London wave functions would be obviously incorrect: they would indicate that each electron should move in a hydrogen $1s$ wave function surrounding the nucleus, quite different from a self-consistent wave function for the helium atom. Thus in this limit the result must be poorer than that found from the method of molecular orbitals, which in principle should reduce to the self-consistent solution for the helium atom in this limit of vanishing internuclear distance. The Heitler-London method, in fact, takes no direct account of the distortions of the electronic wave functions as the atoms are brought together, and it is clear from this that its results cannot have great quantitative significance.

There has been a great deal of use made of the Heitler-London method in the literature, particularly in writings on chemical binding, and much of this involves even greater errors than those inherent in the method. Most of the chemical writers on the subject have simplified Eq. (8.3.10) by neglecting the factor $1 \pm \alpha^2$ in the denominator. This, it is true, is nearly equal to unity for large interatomic distances, where α becomes small and α^2 is small of the second order; but consideration of the numerical values shows that this is no longer the case at the actual internuclear distance, and quite wrong results are obtained if one writes the energy as $H_0 \pm H_1$, or the Coulomb energy plus or minus the exchange energy. We can, of course, get qualitatively correct results in this way, but there is too much tendency, which should be guarded against, to ascribe numerical accuracy to such calculations, particularly when even the complete Heitler-London treatment is as inaccurate as it is.

The Heitler-London method seems quite different in its approach from the method of molecular orbitals. Nevertheless, it forms a first approximation, from which we can proceed by perturbation methods. Similarly, the method of molecular orbitals forms a different first approximation, from which we can calculate perturbations. If the perturbation method is correct and converges toward the correct answer, it should then be that the results of the Heitler-London and the molecular orbital methods should be more alike after we have carried out some perturbation calculations than in first approximation. This in fact is the case. We have already seen that if we appropriately combine the ground state, as determined in the first approximation by the molecular orbital method, with an excited state in which both electrons move in antisymmetric rather than symmetric molecular orbitals, the result at least agrees with the correct value at large interatomic distances. When we compare this final result with that of the Heitler-London method, we see that it is a closer approximation to the truth than is obtained by the Heitler-London calculation. We then naturally ask, can we not carry out a further approximation on the basis of the Heitler-London calculation and improve our answer further? The answer is that we can.

We can get an idea as to the wave functions which we should combine with the ground state of the Heitler-London method, in order to get a better approximation, by a simple comparison of the molecular orbital and Heitler-London wave functions. This comparison furthermore gives us a much increased insight into the relation between the two methods. Let $u_a(x)$ be a hydrogen $1s$ wave function around nucleus a, as before, and $u_b(x)$ a similar wave function around nucleus b. Then a fairly good approximation to the symmetrical molecular orbital would be $u_a(x) + u_b(x)$, and to the antisymmetric orbital $u_a(x) - u_b(x)$. These functions are not normalized; it is a simple calculation to show that the related normalized functions are the quantities given above, divided by $\sqrt{2(1 \pm \alpha)}$, where α is given in the preceding section. Let us now build up the two-electron function in which both electrons are in the symmetric, or both in the antisymmetric, orbital. This will be a singlet state; the wave function must then be symmetric in the electronic coordinates. When we set up this symmetric function, the factor $\frac{1}{2}$, brought about by the normalization, disappears, and we are left with a wave function

$$\frac{1}{1 \pm \alpha} [u_a(x_1) \pm u_b(x_1)][u_a(x_2) \pm u_b(x_2)]$$

$$= \frac{1}{1 \pm \alpha} \{[u_a(x_1)u_a(x_2) + u_b(x_1)u_b(x_2)]$$

$$\pm [u_b(x_1)u_a(x_2) + u_a(x_1)u_b(x_2)]\}. \quad (8.4.1)$$

The combination of these two functions, which we found to be the best wave functions which we can build up out of molecular orbitals arising from the $1s$ atomic state, will then be a linear combination of the functions with the plus and minus signs in (8.4.1). It will thus be some linear combination of the functions $[u_a(x_1)u_a(x_2) + u_b(x_1)u_b(x_2)]$ and $[u_b(x_1)u_a(x_2) + u_a(x_1)u_b(x_2)]$. The second of these is the singlet state used by the Heitler-London method, as given in (8.3.1); but the first function is of a type which so far we have not considered.

This first function clearly describes the case where both electrons are concentrated around the same nucleus. Thus in the function $u_a(x_1)u_a(x_2)$ both electrons are on nucleus a, and in $u_b(x_1)u_b(x_2)$ they are both on nucleus b. Such a state, in which both electrons are on one nucleus, making this negatively charged, and leaving the other one positively charged, is called a polar state; it results in the molecule having a dipole moment. In distinction to this, the other type of state, in which one electron is located on each atom, is called a nonpolar state. We thus see that the application of perturbation calculation to the method of molecular orbitals has led to the prediction that the best wave function is a mixture of polar and nonpolar functions. It is now clear that if we supplement the Heitler-London method by including polar states as well as nonpolar ones, and make suitable linear combinations of both sorts of states, we shall end up with the same result which we have found by superposing the molecular orbital wave functions, allowing the electrons to be in antisymmetric as well as symmetric orbitals. In fact, if we carry through the argument in mathematical detail, we come out with exactly the same answer, no matter which starting point we use.

It is now interesting to ask how the resulting functions, which are considerably better than either the molecular orbital or the Heitler-London functions without use of perturbation methods, behave as the internuclear distance is varied. At very large distances, we find that the Heitler-London functions are correct, without admixture of polar functions. This is natural; it requires a large amount of energy to ionize one hydrogen atom and attach the removed electron to another hydrogen atom to form a negative ion, provided the atoms are far apart, so that the ground state is certainly that without any trace of polar properties. As the internuclear distance decreases enough so that the atoms begin to overlap, however, this is no longer the case, and at the observed internuclear distance of the molecule, there is a quite large amount of polar state mixed in with the nonpolar function assumed in the simple application of the Heitler-London method. Thus the simple Heitler-London function is rather far from correct at these small distances. On the other hand, it is clear from (8.4.1) why the molecular orbital method is rather poor for large distances of separation: the symmetrical state there quite incorrectly mixes polar with nonpolar states in equal amounts, giving results not far from the truth at small distances, but very poor at large distances.

The comparison between the two methods of approximation which we have encountered here will prove to be of far-reaching significance in our later discussion of molecular binding.   In many problems involving interactions of atoms or shells at rather large distances, the Heitler-London method is preferable.   Thus, for instance, the theory of ferromagnetism involves the interaction of the inner shells of atoms: in iron, the $3d$ levels. Their wave functions are much smaller than the sizes of the atom as a whole, so that in the crystal they are rather widely separated.   It is not surprising then that one can build up a theory of ferromagnetism, using the Heitler-London methods.   For chemical binding the Heitler-London calculation is qualitatively good, though quantitatively inaccurate.   On the other hand, for the electrons in a metal, where we are largely concerned with small internuclear distances, the molecular orbital method, which there becomes the method of energy bands, becomes the most useful first approximation.   But in any case, if we carry our approximations a stage further than the first approximation, by perturbation methods, we shall come to a substantially common result, whichever starting point we may use.   Thus one can start with the molecular orbital method and end up with a satisfactory theory of ferromagnetism.   On the other hand, one can start with the Heitler-London method, include polar as well as nonpolar states, and get excellent results not only for molecular binding, but for the metallic state as well, though the results prove to be less convenient than those derived from molecular orbitals, if we wish to discuss electrical properties.

It is not a correct thing to imply that one method is right, the other wrong, in a particular case; neither one is complete, but both can be made satisfactory.   However, the steps in the calculation may look very different, depending on which starting point we use.   Thus, for instance, considering a molecular bond by the Heitler-London method, we may conclude that the bond is partly polar, partly nonpolar, and we may give precise numerical figures showing what fraction of the bond is polar, what fraction nonpolar.   These figures have a meaning only in comparison with the particular method of calculation used.   If we had discussed the same problem by the molecular orbital method, we could well have come out with exactly the same final wave function and energy level, but we should never have met the question of polar and nonpolar states at all.   We should rather have asked, to what extent is the final wave function made of bonding, and to what extent of antibonding, orbitals?

All these considerations have been developed from the simple problem of the hydrogen molecule; but we shall see in the next chapter that this problem forms a model which we can follow in our general discussion of interatomic forces.   We shall meet analogies to the hydrogen case not only in the study of electron-pair bonds, but also in quite a different direction: in the study of the repulsions of atoms or ions composed of closed shells. This problem is not met in precisely the same form in hydrogen; but we shall see that it is essentially like the repulsion found in the triplet state of hydrogen, which we have discussed both by the molecular orbital and the Heitler-London method.

PROBLEMS

1. Using the Heitler-London method, find an expression for the density of charge in the normal state of H_2 as a function of position. Show that the density is greater in the region between the atoms than if we simply added the densities of the two atoms.

2. Using the molecular orbital $(u_a + u_b)/\sqrt{2}$ (neglecting the fact that this is not exactly normalized), for H_2, and an internuclear distance of 0.8 A, find the charge density at points in a plane containing the nuclei. Draw a diagram with lines of constant charge density, which would be circles surrounding the nucleus for a single atom, but show that in this case some of the lines surround both nuclei.

3. Draw a diagram similar to that of Prob. 2 for the charge density of the repulsive orbital $(u_a - u_b)/\sqrt{2}$ for H_2.

4. Set up unperturbed wave functions, using the method of molecular orbitals for the hydrogen molecule. Approximate the symmetric and antisymmetric orbitals by the functions $(u_a \pm u_b)/\sqrt{2(1 \pm \alpha^2)}$. Set up functions corresponding to (I) the singlet state with both electrons in the symmetric orbital; (II) the triplet state with one electron in the symmetric, one in the antisymmetric orbital; (III) the singlet state with one electron in the symmetric, one in the antisymmetric orbital; (IV) the singlet state with both electrons in the antisymmetric orbital. From the form of these functions, state the energy value to which the diagonal energy of each function goes in the limit of infinite separation of the nuclei.

5. Show that the wave functions I and IV in Prob. 4 do not change sign when the subscripts a and b are interchanged (corresponding to turning the molecule end for end), while functions II and III do change sign. From this show that there are no nondiagonal matrix components of energy between either of states I and IV and either of states II and III. Hence show that the only nondiagonal matrix component of energy is between states I and IV.

6. Show that, in the limit of infinite separation, one of the correct perturbed combinations of functions I and IV of Prob. 4 is polar, the other nonpolar. Hence show the energy values approached by the perturbed energy levels at infinite separation, and justify the energy-level diagram of Fig. 8.2.2.

7. Set up the perturbation problem between states I and IV above, and solve it for arbitrary internuclear distance, expressing the result in terms of exchange integrals.

8. Show that if a perturbation problem is set up for the hydrogen molecule by the Heitler-London method, but including polar as well as nonpolar functions, the same stationary states result as discussed in Probs. 4 to 7.

9. The observed interatomic distance in the H_2 molecule at the minimum of the potential curve is 0.75 A, and the energy of dissociation is 4.45 ev. Assuming a Morse curve, plot the interatomic energy curve as a function of distance of separation.

CHAPTER 9

INTERATOMIC AND INTERMOLECULAR FORCES

Atoms by themselves have only a few interesting properties: their spectra, their dielectric and magnetic behavior, hardly any others.   It is when they come into combination with each other that problems of real physical and chemical interest arise.   Atoms act on each other with forces, in some cases attractive and in others repulsive, and in this chapter we shall consider the general nature of these forces, how they arise, and what their results are in their effect on the physical and chemical structure of the substance.   Interatomic forces, in the first place, hold atoms together to form molecules; this forms the province of chemistry.   But in turn, they hold molecules together in their various states of aggregation, as solids, liquids, and gases, and this is ordinarily considered to be part of physics.   The distinction, however, is purely arbitrary, and not at all general.   All the important interatomic forces of interest in the structure of matter are electrical.   We have seen simple examples of these forces in the preceding chapter, where we discussed the hydrogen molecule.   We shall now try to generalize the results we obtained there, so as to handle the general case of forces between atoms and molecules of all sorts.   As a first step, and the most straightforward problem after that of the hydrogen molecule, we consider the general diatomic molecule; later we go on to the differences encountered in polyatomic molecules and solids, and the nature of intermolecular forces.

9.1. Symmetrical Diatomic Molecules.   The fundamental problem of the force between two atoms is simple to state: we assume the nuclei of the two atoms to be held at an internuclear distance r_{ab}, with enough electrons surrounding them to make the molecule electrically neutral.   What are the energy levels of the resulting molecule, as functions of the internuclear distance?   In accordance with the methods of the preceding chapter, we shall assume that these resulting electronic energies, as functions of distance, form the potential energy functions governing the motion of the atoms as a whole; this is an assumption which we shall justify later, when we come to consider the motions of the atoms as a whole in molecules or solids.

The simplest case of diatomic molecules, and the one which has closest analogy to hydrogen, is the case of two like atoms, or the symmetrical diatomic molecule. We shall, accordingly, take up this case first, coming later to the case of unlike atoms. The problem is fundamentally very much like that of hydrogen, and like hydrogen we can handle it by either the method of molecular orbitals or the method of Heitler and London. Instead of carrying through our complete discussion first by the one method, then by the other, however, we shall use both together, but we shall arrange our treatment by atoms, proceeding from one atom to the next in the order of atomic number.

First after hydrogen we come to the case of two helium atoms; and we shall be disappointed, unless our theory predicts what we know to be a fact, that two helium atoms in their ground state repel each other, rather than form a stable molecule. Let us consider the problem first from the point of view of molecular orbitals. The lowest orbitals, just as with hydrogen, are the symmetric and antisymmetric orbitals formed from the atomic $1s$ functions; the orbitals formed from excited atomic functions all have sufficiently higher energy so that we do not need to consider them, as far as the ground state of the molecule is concerned. With the two atoms, we have four electrons to be disposed of; and these are just enough to fill the two orbitals, one electron of each spin going into the symmetric, bonding orbital, and one of each spin into the anti-symmetric, antibonding orbital. The resultant energy shows no minimum as a function of distance; the repulsion arising from the antibonding orbitals counteracts the attraction of the bonding orbitals, and a careful calculation of the interatomic force shows a repulsion, increasing as the atoms approach.

The Heitler-London method leads to the same result. A helium atom has, of course, a closed shell of two $1s$ electrons. When we combine two such atoms, each of these two $1s$ wave functions will be occupied by two electrons, one of each spin. In this case, as in the molecular orbital treatment, the state will be a singlet state; the resultant spin angular momentum is zero. But now we can examine the resulting wave function of all the electrons, as given by the Heitler-London method, and, in fact, show that it is essentially the same thing which we get by the molecular orbital method, so that in this case, unlike the hydrogen atom, we get just the same answer by either method. We shall first examine the mathematical reason why this should be, then take up its physical implications.

The first step in setting up the wave function for all the electrons is to consider the symmetry of this wave function. With our four electrons, there will be two of each spin. The two electrons with a particular spin must have different orbital wave functions; that is, since we now know that antisymmetry of the wave function is the mechanism for bringing about agreement with the Pauli exclusion principle, the wave function must be antisymmetric in the coordinates of the two electrons with positive spin, and also antisymmetric in the coordinates of the electrons with negative spin. If the two wave functions, one an atomic $1s$ function around the atom a, the other around the atom b, are called u_a and u_b, and if the electrons with positive spin have coordinates x_1, x_2, while those with negative spin have coordinates x_3, x_4, we can then show by the principles of Chap. 7 that the orbital part of the wave function for all four electrons can be written in the form

$$[u_a(x_1)u_b(x_2) - u_b(x_1)u_a(x_2)][u_a(x_3)u_b(x_4) - u_b(x_3)u_a(x_4)]. \quad (9.1.1)$$

But now suppose we set up a function, using the same principles, using not the functions u_a and u_b, but the symmetric and antisymmetric molecular orbitals formed from these functions. We know that we can approximate these by $u_a + u_b$ and $u_a - u_b$ (these will not be normalized, but we disregard that fact for simplicity). Thus we should set up the function

$$[u_a(x_1) + u_b(x_1)][u_a(x_2) - u_b(x_2)] - [u_a(x_1) - u_b(x_1)][u_a(x_2) + u_b(x_2)]$$
$$(9.1.2)$$

multiplied by a similar expression in terms of x_3 and x_4. If we multiply out the expression in (9.1.2), we find that it is equal to

$$-2[u_a(x_1)u_b(x_2) - u_b(x_1)u_a(x_2)],$$

or -2 times the first factor of (9.1.1). In other words, if we take care of the factor -2 by normalization, the properly symmetrized function set up by the method of molecular orbitals, in the problem of two helium atoms, agrees exactly with the corresponding function set up by the Heitler-London method, so that the two must agree in this case exactly, and not merely qualitatively.

We may well ask, why is it in this case that the methods of molecular orbitals and of Heitler and London agree exactly, while they differed considerably for the problem of the hydrogen molecule? The reason must be sought in the discussion which we gave in the preceding chapter about the errors in the method of molecular orbitals at large internuclear distances. The method of molecular orbitals in that case was incorrect, because it led to the assumption that a large amount of polar wave function was mixed with the nonpolar function, at large distance, a clearly incorrect situation. This came about because there was nothing in the wave function to prevent two electrons, in the singlet state in which the spins are opposite, from being located on the same hydrogen nucleus. This cannot happen in the case of two helium atoms, for a reason which was not present in hydrogen: the exclusion principle prevents it. The two electrons of positive spin are prevented by the exclusion principle from being on the same nucleus; one must be on one nucleus, the other on the other. Similarly, one of the electrons of negative spin is on one nucleus, the other on the other. The net result is that each helium atom carries just the two electrons required to fill up its closed shell. There is no possibility of formation of polar states, either in the method of molecular orbitals or the Heitler-London method, and the two methods lead to the same result, which behaves correctly at large distances as well as small.

We see that this argument is one which can be generalized, and it leads to a very important result. Whenever all the electrons of a molecular problem are in closed shells, the results of the molecular orbital and the Heitler-London methods will agree, and both methods will lead to correct results at large distances. Furthermore, if all electrons are in closed shells, the method of molecular orbitals will inevitably result in equal numbers of electrons in bonding and antibonding orbitals, and as in the case of two helium atoms, this will result in no net binding between the atoms, or in a net repulsion. Thus we have the general result that any two closed shells of electrons will repel each other. Closer examination shows that, as a matter of fact, this holds as well for a closed shell inside an atom which, in addition, has some electrons which are not in closed shells. We shall see an example of this next in the case of Li_2.

The qualitative argument which we have given shows that we shall have repulsion in the case of two helium atoms; it is not hard to get the quantitative value of the interatomic potential energy, though we shall not carry this through. All we have to do is to take the wave function (9.1.1) and compute the mean value of the energy operator with respect to this unperturbed wave function, following the methods of the preceding chapter. The result shows that there are certain exchange integrals coming into the total energy, essentially like the exchange integrals found in the hydrogen problem, but always with such sign as to bring about only the repulsive state, never the attractive state met in the hydrogen molecule. This result, involving exchange integrals of the Heitler-London type, of course applies in this case also to the molecular orbital method of calculation, since we have already shown that the wave functions found by both methods are equivalent. These results are discussed in more detail in Appendix 16, in which most of the results of the present chapter are presented in more quantitative form.

Now we are ready to go to our next symmetrical molecule, Li_2. From what we have just seen, the inner $1s$ shells of the two atoms will repel each other; but this repulsion will not begin until the interatomic distance is much less than is found in the ordinary state of the molecule, on account of the small size of the $1s$ shell. The $2s$ electrons, the valence electrons,

will behave substantially like the 1s electrons in the hydrogen molecule.
As in hydrogen, we could treat the problem either by molecular orbitals
or the Heitler-London method; and as in hydrogen, we should find a
ground state which showed molecular binding, on account of the sharing
of electrons between the nuclei.   The Li₂ molecule has, in fact, a ground
state of this sort, as is known from band spectra.

   The next symmetrical molecule, Be₂, would have only a repulsive state,
like the case of two helium atoms, if we assumed that all four electrons
outside the closed 1s shells went into 2s orbitals or wave functions.   But
the situation is really quite different from helium, in that the 2p wave
functions have energies only slightly higher than the 2s, whereas in

Fig. 9.1.1.   Crossing over of 2s2p (attractive) and (2s)² (repulsive) levels of Be₂
(schematic).

helium there is no other energy level near the ground state.   Consequently it is to be assumed that two of the outer electrons, one with each
spin, could go into the symmetric, bonding orbital formed from the 2s
wave functions, and the other two into the bonding orbital formed from
some of the 2p wave functions.   Presumably the lowest level, as indicated
in the preceding chapter, would come from those 2p functions which have
their maximum density along the line joining the two nuclei, called the
2pσ orbital, the σ indicating that the component of angular momentum
along the axis is zero.   The resulting state, with all electrons in bonding
orbitals, would have a potential energy with a minimum and would
correspond to a stable molecule.   An interesting point would arise, however, when we considered how the energy of this ground state would
behave for large internuclear distances.   If we described it by the Heitler-
London method, so as to get the best approximation to the correct behavior at large distances, we should find that this state at large distances
would go into the atomic states in which one outer electron of each Be
atom was in a 2s orbit, the other in a 2p; in other words, it would correspond to the configuration 2s2p.   This is not the ground state of the atom,
which is (2s)².   Thus we should have the situation shown in Fig. 9.1.1,
in which the repulsive energy level arising from the (2s)² configuration of
both atoms crosses the atrractive level coming from the 2s2p configuration of both atoms.   In the neighborhood of the crossing point of these

two levels the problem would be degenerate, to the approximation to which we are working. Application of the perturbation theory would show, in this case, that the correct wave functions were really a mixture of the two types, and that the correct energy levels would run something like the dotted lines in Fig. 9.1.1, indicating a large spread between the two levels at the place where they would cross in the unperturbed problem. We still get attraction in the ground state of the resulting molecule, but with a considerably smaller dissociation energy than if it had not been for this crossing of energy levels. Such a situation, in which the configuration responsible for the binding in the ground state changes into another configuration as the atoms are pulled apart from each other, proves to be not uncommon in molecular binding.

As we go on to the molecules B_2, C_2, we can continue with the same sort of process met in Be_2. We add two electrons in one of the nonbonding p orbitals in B_2, and two in the other nonbonding p orbital in C_2. These have comparatively little effect on the binding and leave us with a stable molecule, really with two electron-pair bonds in each case, and with the other electrons in orbitals which have no concentration of charge along the line joining the two atoms, and which are not greatly helping the binding. There are still two more pairs of electrons which can be added in these nonbonding orbitals, going into the antisymmetric wave functions (if the first electrons added went into the symmetric functions). These are added in N_2 and O_2; these molecules also have effectively two electron-pair bonds. With F_2 we no longer can maintain both electron-pair bonds. The electrons added in going from oxygen to fluorine must go into antibonding orbitals, reducing the number of electron-pair bonds to one; and when we come to Ne, the situation is as in He: all orbitals are occupied, with as many antibonding as bonding ones, and the net result is a repulsion between the atoms. We thus have gone through a complete group of atoms in the periodic table; as we go to further groups, similar situations repeat themselves.

9.2. Nonsymmetrical Diatomic Molecules. When we come to diatomic molecules in which the atoms are of different sorts, we meet a far greater variety of situations than we have seen with the symmetrical molecules. If we approach the problem by the method of molecular orbitals, we find that the orbitals must be the solutions of Schrödinger's equation for the problem of two unequal attracting centers, as shown in Fig. 9.2.1. There is a fundamental difference between this problem and that of two like centers: we no longer have the situation where all wave functions must be symmetric or antisymmetric in the mid-point between atoms. That symmetry requirement in the case of two like centers arose because of the degeneracy between the two states in which the electron

in question was in one atom or the other.   This degeneracy is no longer
present with unlike atoms: the energy levels are quite different, depending
on which atom the electron is in.   The wave functions therefore are concentrated almost completely around one nucleus or the other, representing
stationary states of an electron in one atom or the other.   Only if by
chance there happen to be almost identical energy levels in the two
atoms do we normally get splitting into symmetry and antisymmetry.
As we shall see presently, however, this chance may occur more often
than we might at first think.

There is one feature which we meet with nonsymmetrical molecules
which does not occur in the same way with symmetrical molecules.   This

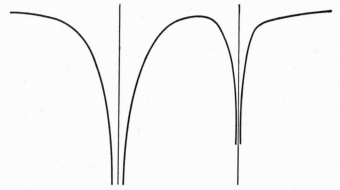

Fig. 9.2.1.   Nonsymmetrical potential energy curve for problem of unequal attracting
centers.

is the possibility that the stable state may correspond to a molecule with
a permanent dipole moment.   To meet this possibility in a particularly
straightforward form, let us consider an alkali halide molecule, such as
NaCl.   At large internuclear distances, the ground state is that formed
from neutral Na and Cl molecules, not from ions Na^+ and Cl^-; for the
ionization potential of sodium is greater than the electron affinity of
chlorine, so that it requires an absorption of energy to remove the valence
electron from the Na atom and place it on a Cl^- ion.   However, the
energy difference is not very great.   Now as the internuclear distance is
decreased, the energy of the ionic state very rapidly decreases, on account
of the electrostatic attraction of the oppositely charged ions for each
other.   Thus, as indicated in Fig. 9.2.2, the polar state soon crosses the
nonpolar state and becomes the most stable state.   In other words, at
distance less than this crossover point, the energy of the molecule formed
from neutral atoms decreases if we remove an electron from the sodium
atom and put it on the chlorine.   This crossing occurs at rather large

internuclear distances; so large, in fact, that the overlapping of the electronic wave functions of the two atoms or ions is very small.   As a result of this, the matrix component of energy between the two degenerate states, the polar and nonpolar, is very small, so that the admixture of one with the other, when we apply the perturbation method, is very small. We can say that at distances less than the crossover point, the ground state is polar, and at larger distances it is nonpolar.

As the internuclear distance decreases still more, we are interested in following the behavior of the polar ground state.   The energy will con-

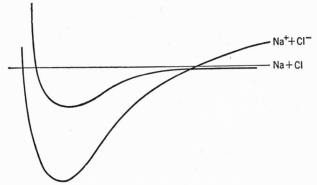

FIG. 9.2.2.   Crossing over of polar and nonpolar states of NaCl (schematic).

tinue to decrease, on account of the Coulomb attraction, until the outer shells of the two ions begin to get quite close together.   These outer shells both have inert-gas configurations, formed from closed shells.   Thus, as we have seen in the preceding section, they will exert a repulsion on each other, which rapidly increases with decreasing distance.   When we superpose this repulsion on the Coulomb attraction, we get a potential energy curve with a minimum, as shown in Fig. 9.2.2.   In this way we have a picture of the typical ionic bond, the attractive force coming from electrostatic attraction, the repulsion from the interaction of closed shells.

The case we have just considered is an extreme one.   It would clearly be possible for the energy of the polar state to be raised somewhat as compared with that in Fig. 9.2.2, so that the crossing of the energy levels of polar and nonpolar states would come near the position of equilibrium. Then the matrix component of energy between the two states would be large, and when we applied perturbation theory, the resulting ground state would be a mixture of polar and nonpolar states, neither one preponderating.   The ground state would then correspond to a dipole molecule, one with charge of one sign concentrated on one ion, that of the other sign on the other; but the effective charge on each ion would not be a whole electronic charge, as in Na^+Cl^-, but would be only a fraction of an electronic charge, the fraction depending on the amount of polar state admixed with the nonpolar state. We shall later have occasion to study the dipole moments of molecules, the product of the effective charge on the ion and the distance between the ions. We shall find that this is a quantity which can be measured experimentally. From these experimental values, we find that the intermediate case, such as we are considering in the present paragraph, is very common: the effective charges on the ions often correspond to the order of magnitude of a tenth of an electron, indicating rather small amounts of polar states mixed with nonpolar states.

This possibility of mixing polar and nonpolar states has a wider significance: it shows us that it is not usually possible to state uniquely whether a given molecule is held together by electron-pair bonds, usually called covalent bonds, or by ionic binding; more often it is a mixture of the two. Even in hydrogen we saw in the preceding chapter that this was the case: the bond was partly polar, though on account of the symmetry there was no net dipole moment, each atom being equally likely to be positive or negative. We shall find many cases in which there is an ambiguity of this sort. A typical example is an oxide of an alkaline earth, such as MgO. We could assume in the first place that this was formed from doubly charged ions Mg^{++} and $O^=$. We have already noted in an earlier chapter that $O^=$ is probably not a stable ion, in that its energy is higher than that of O^- and an electron; but that does not prevent us from setting up its energy at infinite separation, and then deducing the energy of this state at smaller internuclear distances, on account of the Coulomb attraction of the doubly charged ions. The resulting ions form closed shells, so that at small enough distances there will be repulsion and a stable state. On the other hand, there is another possibility which forms a competing energy level, which may lie lower, or which may be combined with the doubly charged polar state to form a resultant wave function which may be nearer the truth. We could form singly charged ions, Mg^+ and O^-, the first having one electron outside its closed shell, the other lacking an electron to form a closed shell. These ions would likewise have a Coulomb attraction, though it would be weaker on account of the smaller charges. But at the same time, they would have a covalent binding, of the variety which we shall discuss shortly. The resulting bond, then, would be a complicated mixture of ionic binding formed from ions somewhere between singly and doubly charged and covalent binding. Most real bonds are probably as complicated as this illustration would suggest.

Let us now consider how ordinary covalent binding can come about,

between unlike atoms, as in the illustration we have just given.   There is
one aspect of the formation of polar bonds in unlike atoms which we have
not considered so far.   As one of the atoms is positively charged, the
other negatively, the potential energies surrounding the two ions are
affected by the amount of charge which the ions carry: as an ion becomes
more positive, the potential energy of electrons in its neighborhood
decreases, and vice versa.   If we regard the amount of polar state present
as a variable quantity, we see that the heights of the potential wells, and
hence the energy levels of electrons surrounding the two nuclei, vary as
well.   Now, in general, the lowest energy levels of the two-center system

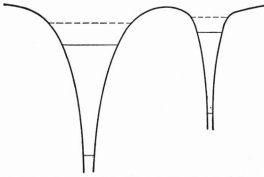

FIG. 9.2.3.   Occupied and unoccupied states (full and dotted lines, respectively) in
problem of unequal attracting centers (schematic).

will be occupied; thus if the energy levels happen to be as in Fig. 9.2.3,
occupied levels being shown as full lines, unoccupied ones as dotted, the
occupied levels will all lie below the unoccupied ones.   Consider, however, what will happen if part of an electronic charge goes over from one
atom to another, as it can do when we have a state which is partly polar.
It will not only help to fill up the level in the atom to which it goes, and
to empty the level in the atom from which it is removed, but at the same
time it will raise the potential energy function of the atom to which it
goes, and lower that of the atom which it leaves.   Thus there will be a
tendency to equalize the heights of those energy levels in the two atoms
between which the electron, so to speak, is trying to make a decision.
There will be a distinct tendency for just enough charge to be transferred
from one atom to the other, so that the energy levels in the two atoms will
become the same.   At this point, there really is degeneracy between the
two atoms, of the sort which we had in hydrogen, and there will be a
tendency to form molecular orbitals, some of which will have the characteristics of symmetric orbitals in hydrogen, some of which will be like
antisymmetric orbitals.   Just as in hydrogen, the symmetric orbitals will

correspond to sharing electronic charge between the atoms, and we have the mechanism for formation of a covalent bond.

In an actual molecule the situation presumably will be more complicated than this simple picture would suggest. Nevertheless, it is probable that it contains elements of truth, so that we can have covalent binding much as in hydrogen, but, in general, superposed on a certain amount of polar wave function, which will carry with it some ionic binding. The more nearly alike the two atoms are, the more easily covalent binding can occur without formation of a dipole moment.

9.3. Ionic and Covalent Binding in Polyatomic Molecules and Solids. When we have more than two atoms, in a polyatomic molecule or solid, we immediately ask whether the forces between pairs of atoms are just as in diatomic molecules, or whether the force between a particular pair of atoms depends on the presence of other atoms. In some cases we may certainly expect the second situation to hold; for we are familiar from chemistry with the phenomenon of saturation of valence, the situation by which, if an atom has already formed bonds with certain neighbors, its capacity for forming further bonds can be removed. It is this tendency which leads to the formation of molecules, groups of atoms which show very small attraction for further atoms; and it occurs, as we might well assume, in case we have covalent binding. In some other cases, however, there is no such saturation of valence, and atoms can continue to be added to a group already existing, without limit. Such a situation is met on the one hand in ionic crystals, on the other in metals; in either case, we form solids with no trace of molecular structure within them. We shall start by discussing the ionic crystals, which in many ways form the simplest example.

Let us consider a typical ionic substance, like an alkali halide, say NaCl. In discussing the diatomic molecule of this material, we have seen that at infinite separation the nonpolar state Na + Cl is more stable than the polar state $Na^+ + Cl^-$, but that as the interatomic distance is decreased, the electrostatic attraction between the ions lowers the energy of the polar state so much that this becomes the stable configuration; in other words, the energy of the whole system is lowered, at the actual internuclear distance, by removing an electron from a neutral Na atom and placing it on the neutral Cl atom, forming positive and negative ions. This same situation holds when we consider an aggregation of Na and Cl atoms. It is a somewhat complicated problem to sum the Coulomb electrostatic attraction energy resulting from a whole crystal of Na^+ and Cl^- ions[†]; but when this is done, the net result is not very different from

[†] See, for instance, J. C. Slater, "Introduction of Chemical Physics," McGraw-Hill Book Company, Inc., New York, 1939, Chap. XXIII, for this calculation.

that which we have already discussed in connection with the diatomic molecule. The forces holding the crystal together are then electrostatic attractions, which do not depend to a first order on whether there are any other neighbors present or not. The repulsions keeping the crystal from collapsing are the same repulsions between closed shells which we have already investigated with the diatomic molecules.

It is not entirely clear that these repulsions should be the same quantitatively that they are with diatomic molecules, and as a matter of fact, more careful calculation, based on the Heitler-London method, shows that they are not, in quantitative detail. In other words, we cannot write the repulsive energy just as a sum of repulsive terms between pairs of atoms, each term being like that met in a diatomic molecule; but the deviations from this assumption are not great. The deviations come mathematically on account of certain exchange integrals, in the Heitler-London method for a problem of many atoms, involving wave functions on more than two nuclei. We can understand physically how such an effect could come about by very simple models. For instance, suppose we considered the atoms to resemble rubber balloons, or soap bubbles, held together by some type of attractive force, but held from collapsing by an elastic surface with pressure inside it. If two such atoms are held together, the balloons or soap bubbles will be flattened on the interface between the atoms. This will somewhat modify the shape and elastic properties of the remaining parts of the surface of the atoms, and as a result, the atoms will present a slightly different repulsive effect to neighboring atoms or ions which are added. These deviations show themselves in one way which forms a very sensitive test as to whether the forces between atoms are central forces (as the repulsions would be if they acted between pairs of atoms, without mutual interaction) or are more complicated. There is a certain relation between the elastic constants of a cubic crystal, called the Cauchy relation, which can be shown mathematically to be satisfied if the forces are all central, but which in other cases is not generally true. The alkali halide crystals have elastic constants which, as a matter of experimental fact, do not satisfy the Cauchy relation. Hence we have a straightforward experimental proof that the presence of one ion near another affects the forces of interaction with a third ion. The careful treatment by the Heitler-London method, which we have mentioned, shows that the theory explains these deviations from the Cauchy relation quantitatively. In spite of these deviations from central field forces, however, the central field model forms a good first approximation, with ionic crystals.

Next let us go to the other extreme, the substance held by bonds which are as near pure covalent bonds as possible, where we meet the maximum possible effect of saturation of valence. After that we shall return to various intermediate cases. Let us start with the simplest possible case: the hydrogen molecule, with an additional hydrogen atom. Our chemical information tells us that, if we have two hydrogen atoms bound together to form a molecule, a third hydrogen atom will not be bound to the two to form a molecule H_3; the valence in H_2 is, in a sense, saturated, so that no further bonds can be formed.

We shall start by trying to analyze this situation in a little more quantitative language. The behavior of a diatomic molecule is described by our giving the energy of the molecule as a function of internuclear distance. We have mentioned a number of times that this curve really has two meanings. First, it represents the sum of electronic kinetic and potential energy, and the electrostatic interactions of the nuclei, as a function of distance. Second, it is the curve which plays the part of a potential energy curve for investigating the motions of the nuclei. Now in a similar way, if we have three atoms, we can investigate the energy as a function of the various interatomic distances. In this particular case the three distances r_{ab}, r_{bc}, r_{ac} between atoms a, b, c define completely the configuration of the molecule, or combination of three atoms. Of course, to prescribe the positions of three atoms requires nine coordinates, three for each atom, of which only three are the interatomic distances given above. Three more are the coordinates of the center of mass of the molecule, and the remaining three give the orientation of the molecule in space. The energy cannot depend on these six quantities, if there are no external forces acting on the molecule, so that what we really need to do to discuss our problem is to know the energy as a function of the three quantities r_{ab}, r_{bc}, r_{ac}. Let us now consider how much we know about this problem, and ask what further information we need to state the facts about the saturation of valence.

We certainly know that as any two of the three quantities r_{ab}, r_{bc}, r_{ac} become large, so that one of the atoms moves far away from the other two, these remaining two will be essentially independent of the existence of the third and will have an energy curve as a function of the remaining internuclear distance which will be essentially that which we have already found for a diatomic molecule. It is only as the third atom moves close to the other two that we may expect new effects. It is hard to visualize the situation geometrically, on account of the numerous variables involved; but we can take a special case which is typical of the general case, and later can consider the extension to the general case. The special case which we shall take up is that where all three atoms are in the same straight line, say in the order abc, so that $r_{ac} = r_{ab} + r_{bc}$. Then there are only two independent variables, r_{ab} and r_{bc}. In a plane in which these quantities are plotted as rectangular coordinates, we can then draw contours of constant energy. In Fig. 9.3.1 we give the sort of energy contours which are actually found in this case, by the application of the Heitler-London method, as given in Appendix 16. When r_{ab} is large, a molecule is formed from atoms b and c; we see from the figure that in this region the energy shows a minimum at a certain value of r_{bc}, the ordinary internuclear distance of separation. Similarly, when r_{bc} is

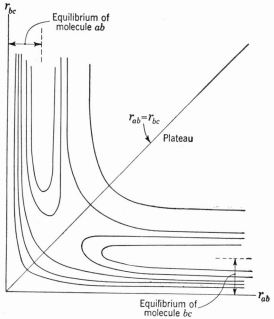

FIG. 9.3.1.   Potential energy contours for linear arrangement of three hydrogen atoms (schematic).

large, we see from the figure the energy minimum for the same value of r_{ab}. When both r_{ab} and r_{bc} are large, the energy rises to a constant value, or plateau, corresponding to large separation of all atoms. The figure is necessarily symmetrical about the diagonal line on which $r_{ab} = r_{bc}$, since interchanging r_{ab} and r_{bc} merely changes the triatomic molecule end for end, without changing its internal structure.

The part of the diagram which is interesting to us for our present purposes is that for which both r_{ab} and r_{bc} are small. Here the contours show that there is no point at which the energy is as low as the two minima, coming at large values of r_{ab} or r_{bc}, corresponding to a diatomic molecule and a distant atom. In particular, along the line $r_{ab} = r_{bc}$, the diagonal in the diagram, corresponding to a linear H_3 molecule with equal spacing between the atoms, we see that there is an energy minimum as we vary r_{ab} and r_{bc} together; but this point is really a saddle point, the energy decreasing as we go away from this apparent minimum by making the distances r_{ab} and r_{bc} different.   Another way to see that an H_3 molecule would not form is to go along the line corresponding to r_{ab} = constant, decreasing r_{bc}, keeping r_{ab} equal to the distance of separation in the stable diatomic molecule.   In this case, for large r_{bc}, the energy is in the bottom of the valley in the figure.   We see from the figure that as r_{bc} decreases, the energy begins to rise and rises without limit as r_{bc} goes to zero.   In other words, a third atom would be repelled by the diatomic molecule. This is the most straightforward way of describing the lack of binding between the molecule and the third atom.

Though we have considered only the case where the three atoms are in a straight line, one can carry out similar discussions for other configurations with the same result: the lowest energy level of the three atoms comes when one atom is at infinite distance, the other two forming a diatomic molecule.   For instance, we can consider the configuration with the atoms at the corners of an equilateral triangle; no value of interatomic distance, for this configuration, has as low an energy as the diatomic molecule with separated atom.

We have now surveyed the situation which proves to exist with three hydrogen atoms; let us try to understand how it comes about, in terms of our theories of interatomic forces.   The calculations of energy as a function of the three variables r_{ab}, r_{bc}, r_{ac}, such as we have been discussing, have in practice been made by application of the Heitler-London method, as we have stated earlier, and as is worked out in detail in Appendix 16. We shall sketch the procedure here in a qualitative manner.   We build up a wave function for the three-electron problem, taking proper account of the spins and the resulting symmetry of the wave function, starting with the assumption that the unperturbed wave functions are to be constructed from hydrogen wave functions.   We have several different multiplets arising from $1s$ atomic functions.   With two electrons the spins can be parallel or antiparallel, leading to a triplet and a singlet, as we have already seen.   When a third electron is added, it can be added to the vector $S = 1$ of the triplet, either parallel or antiparallel to that vector, resulting in $S = \frac{3}{2}$ or $\frac{1}{2}$, leading to a quartet and a doublet; it can also be added to the vector $S = 0$ of the singlet, resulting in $S = \frac{1}{2}$, another doublet.   There is a complicated problem of degeneracy to be solved between these two doublets, which prove to be the lowest energy levels; this problem leads to a quadratic equation for the energy, and as a result, the energy comes out to involve square roots of squares and products of various exchange integrals, rather than just a linear combination of exchange integrals as we have with the H_2 problem. The exchange integrals moreover are of several types: not only integrals of the sort met with H_2, in which two electrons change places with each other, but also integrals in which three electrons change places with each other, like an integral, similar to that of Eq. (8.3.11), but with the functions $u_b(x_1)u_c(x_2)u_a(x_3)$ before the $1/r$ terms, and the functions $u_a(x_1)u_b(x_2)u_c(x_3)$ after these terms. Such an exchange integral is generally small compared with the integrals of the more usual type, and a good deal of qualitative use is made of the assumption that such integrals can be neglected.

When we make such assumptions, we find that the resulting energy surface is similar to the one which we have been discussing. In particular, if the third atom, say atom c, is at a considerable distance from the molecule formed from atoms a and b, which are at approximately their equilibrium internuclear distance, corresponding to the stable diatomic molecule, we find that the exchange integrals coming in between atom c and atoms a and b come in in a repulsive way, much as the exchange integrals come in in the problem of two helium atoms. In both cases we can justify the following sort of interpretation of the repulsion. A covalent bond, coming from a shared electron or electrons between two atoms, arises because the electron or electrons really have the option of being located on either of the atoms. This was the case in the singlet state of H_2; each electron had a different spin, so that the Pauli exclusion principle was not brought into play, and each electron had two centers of attraction, in either of which it was welcome. In the process of oscillating, or resonating, between the two atoms, we found the typical wave-mechanical situation of the symmetric and antisymmetric wave functions, corresponding to slightly different energies. We could, if we had chosen, have combined these two wave functions with equal coefficients and have set up a wave packet. This wave packet would at one instant have represented a distribution of probability on one atom; then, as the two functions got out of phase with each other, on account of the different frequency of oscillation of the symmetric and antisymmetric wave functions, the packet would have shifted to the other atom, and so on, back and forth, representing an oscillation or beat between the two atoms. Such a beat, or resonance, phenomenon, however, would not represent the lowest energy; this would correspond to the symmetric state, as we have already seen. And the lowering of energy arising from this symmetric state, a result of the quantum-mechanical resonance between the two allowed sites of the electron, is the energy term which results in the stable molecule, as we have seen in the preceding chapter. Such cases of resonating structures, with resultant stabilization of the molecule, are of widespread occurrence in chemical problems, as has been emphasized by writers on chemical subjects.

Now let us see why this sort of situation does not occur in the case of two He atoms, or a H atom and a H_2 molecule. An electron from one He atom can find no place in the other atom; because each atom has a $1s$ electron of each spin, so that the electron from one atom visiting its neighbor already finds an electron there with the same spin, the exclusion principle is called into effect, and the electron is forbidden from entering the same orbital wave function, which means that it stays out of the other atom. This prevents the resonating action which occurs in H_2, with the resulting stabilization of the structure. A similar thing happens in the case of $H + H_2$. The electron from H, wandering into the neighborhood of H_2, finds that one of the electrons of the H_2 has the same spin that it does (since the H_2 has an electron of each spin). It thus is forced to stay out of its way. This effect is not so strong, however, as in He, because the electron of the same spin in the molecule is itself resonating between the two atoms and is found only half the time in each atom. This weakening of the repulsive effect is noted in the analytic treatment of the problem of three H atoms, in which it is, in fact, found that the exchange integral representing repulsion between the atom and the molecule comes in with a smaller coefficient than it would if this effect were absent.

The type of explanation which we have given for the phenomenon of saturation of valence is really a very general one and is not tied closely either to the molecular orbital or the Heitler-London theory. We shall now extend it to give a discussion of saturation of valence in various polyatomic molecules, including the organic molecules where it is particularly evident; and at the same time we can conveniently take up certain directional properties of covalent bonds, of the type which are evident in the structure of many molecules.

9.4. Directional and Saturation Properties of Covalent Bonds. As illustrations of molecules held by covalent bonds, though perhaps with some admixture of ionic or polar binding, we may take H_2O, NH_3, CH_4; a discussion of these simple cases will bring out a number of the points which we wish to make. The oxygen atom has six out of the possible eight wave functions for $2s$ and $2p$ electrons occupied. Thus there is the possibility of two additional electrons wandering in from neighboring atoms (which will be H atoms in the case of H_2O), without getting into trouble with the exclusion principle. These electrons could completely enter the O atom, forming a doubly charged $O^=$ ion, and leaving the H atoms positively charged; this would correspond to the extreme polar interpretation of the molecule, an interpretation which can be shown experimentally not to be correct, for the observed dipole moment is not nearly as large as it would indicate.   On the other hand, the electrons can spend part of their time in the O atom, part in the H atoms, resonating between them, and leading to covalent bonds between the oxygen and the two hydrogens, in the manner which we have just described.   Clearly, just two hydrogens can be bound to the oxygen in this way; if any other electrons tried to enter the oxygen atom, they would get into trouble with the exclusion principle, as we have already described in the preceding section.   In fact, we can see quite generally that the number of covalent bonds which can be formed with the mechanism we are describing is just the same as the number of ionic bonds which could be formed if the atoms were ionized to produce closed shells.   The same type of explanation will show at once why nitrogen can hold just three hydrogens, as in NH_3, and why carbon can hold four, as in CH_4.

These arguments do not give us complete information about the compounds, however.   It is known experimentally that the H_2O molecule is in the form of a triangle, the bonds between the oxygen and the two hydrogens coming at an angle of something over 90°.   The NH_3 molecule, similarly, is a pyramid, the nitrogen lying considerably outside the plane of the three hydrogens, which form an equilateral triangle.   And the CH_4 has the well-known tetrahedral form which we associate with organic compounds, the carbon being at the center of a regular tetrahedron, with the hydrogens at the four corners.   Why do the molecules have these forms?   If we adopted a completely ionic picture, the reason would not be obvious, though attempts can be made to explain the structures on this basis.   It would be hard, for instance, to see why the two hydrogens in H_2O, which presumably have no bond between them, and hence tend to repel, should not stay as far apart as possible, resulting in a linear molecule with the atoms arranged in the order HOH.   This however is not the case; and the idea of covalent bonds leads to a qualitative explanation which is fairly satisfying, though it is not as easy to make it quantitative as one might wish.

To understand this explanation, we must examine more in detail the atomic wave functions which take part in the binding.   These atomic wave functions are sometimes called atomic orbitals; by choosing the most suitable atomic orbitals in each type of molecule, we can understand why the binding between atoms is as strong as it is.   Let us consider the case of oxygen again.   This atom, as we have seen in previous chapters, has four types of atomic orbitals with $n = 2$: the $2s$ orbital, and three types of $2p$, whose angular functions can be written x/r, y/r, z/r, though linear combinations of these are sometimes used instead.   Two of these orbitals will be unoccupied and will form bonds with the hydrogen atoms, furnishing places into which the electrons from the hydrogen atoms can wander at will, leading to covalent binding. We naturally ask, which orbitals will these be? From our original discussion of covalent binding, we know that the whole existence of this type of binding is based on the overlapping of the appropriate orbitals in the region between the atoms. It seems reasonable then to assume that the strength of binding is a function of the amount of this overlapping, and that that bond will be most stable for which there is a maximum of overlapping. This criterion proves to be in rather good agreement with experimental facts. If we define the amount of overlapping of the atomic orbitals in the two atoms as the integral of the product of the orbitals over all space, it has been shown by comparison with experiment that this overlapping is closely related to the binding in a semiquantitative way which proves in practice to be very useful, whereas a full-scale application of the Heitler-London method is too complicated in these cases to be very useful.

We ask then what type of atomic orbital shows the maximum overlapping with a neighboring hydrogen atom? If the hydrogen atom is located on the x axis, the oxygen atom at the origin of coordinates, then the answer is obvious: it is that $2p$ oxygen orbital which extends along the x axis, which we may call p_x. We may expect then that this orbital will contain only one electron, which will form a covalent bond with the electron of the adjacent hydrogen. This covalent bond can be described either by the molecular orbital or by the Heitler-London method; but whichever mode of description we use, the p_x oxygen orbital and the $1s$ hydrogen orbital take the place of the functions u_a and u_b, representing $1s$ hydrogen functions on atoms a and b, which we used in discussing the hydrogen covalent bond in Chap. 8.

We have now made all the use we can of the p_x oxygen orbital, and by the general principles of saturation of valence, no further binding can be brought about by it. We still have p_y and p_z orbitals, however, which are equally suited for making bonds to hydrogen atoms. Let us suppose, for instance, that the p_y orbital contains only one electron. Then this is suited to making bonds along the $\pm y$ direction. If then the second hydrogen is located along the y axis, it can form a covalent bond with this p_y oxygen orbital, and we shall have a molecule of H_2O with an angle of $90°$ between the bonds. The remaining four electrons in the outer shell of the oxygen will be distributed two each in the $2s$ and the $2p_z$ orbitals, so that these will form essentially closed shells and can form no bonds with other atoms. Thus we arrive at a picture of the water molecule which is in essential agreement with the facts and predicts a definite angle between the bonds. The fact that the observed angle is somewhat greater than $90°$ presumably comes because the two hydrogen atoms are of finite size and tend to repel each other, increasing the angle slightly;

since they have no covalent bond between them, they tend to have a repulsive interaction, as we describe in Appendix 16. This effect, called steric hindrance, is small in this case, but it can be large in other cases, where larger atoms or groups of atoms are substituted for the H's.

The case of ammonia, NH_3, is handled in an entirely analogous manner. The nitrogen atom has its two $1s$ electrons and five additional electrons. We assume that two of these are in the $2s$ orbital and one each in the p_x, p_y, p_z. This leaves each of these free to form a covalent bond with one of the hydrogens, and the covalent bonds are at right angles to each other, so that there will be the maximum overlapping of wave functions, or lowest energy of the molecule, if the three hydrogens lie along three directions making right angles with each other, with respect to the nitrogen.   Of course, there is nothing special about the x, y, z axes; any three perpendicular directions can equally well be used for setting up the three bonding orbitals.   Here again steric hindrance spreads the hydrogens slightly apart, so that the observed angles between bonds are slightly larger than 90°.

When we come to methane, CH_4, we might suppose that three of the bonds would form from the orbitals p_x, p_y, p_z, as in NH_3, so that three hydrogens would be located along these axes; but that, in addition, the $2s$ orbital of the carbon had only one electron in it, so that this orbital could form a covalent bond with the fourth hydrogen.   Since the $2s$ has no directional properties, this fourth hydrogen could be located in any direction from the carbon; but steric hindrance would force it away from the other three hydrogens, so that it would lie more or less on the opposite side of the carbon from them, and the directions of the three would approximate the tetrahedral directions which are known to occur in methane.   If the bonds were formed this way, one of them would be different from the other three, being formed from the $2s$ rather than the $2p$ orbital.   This would seem, however, to be an obvious case for applying the idea of resonance, which we have discussed earlier.   If the hydrogens really arranged themselves in a regular tetrahedral way, we could describe the bond to any one of them as a $2s$ bond, those to the other three as very nearly $2p$ bonds (for the tetrahedral angles of 109° are not very different from right angles), but it would be arbitrary which of the four had the $2s$ bond.   Under these circumstances, we should expect that we could make linear combinations of the appropriate wave functions, such that the resulting ground state would indicate that each of the four bonds was partly $2s$, partly $2p$, with a net increase of strength of binding.

The method of discussion which we have just outlined would be a possible one, but an essentially equivalent and much simpler one can be given instead.   If we are going to mix up s and p wave functions, we might as well do this at the beginning, instead of going to all the trouble of setting up a description of the whole molecule and then mixing several such descriptions. The energies of the $2s$ and $2p$ atomic states of carbon are nearly enough the same so that we can almost neglect the energy difference in comparison with the energies involved in molecular binding. That is, we can with quite good justification take the $2s$, $2p_x$, $2p_y$, $2p_z$ orbitals as being degenerate with each other, and in this case we know that we are allowed to use any four orthogonal linear combinations of them, instead of the original wave functions. We show in Appendix 16 that a possible set of four such combinations consists of four orbitals,

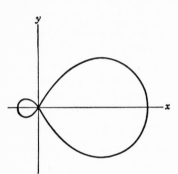

FIG. 9.4.1. Density of a tetrahedral orbital, shown in polar diagram.

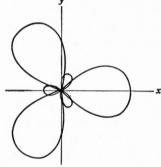

FIG. 9.4.2. Density of the three trigonal orbitals.

each extending along one of the tetrahedral directions, with a distribution of density as a function of angle given by Fig. 9.4.1. This density extends in one direction only, unlike the p_x, p_y, p_z orbitals; the density in the opposite direction is very much smaller. Thus these four tetrahedral orbitals are perfectly suited to making four bonds with hydrogens along the tetrahedral directions, and they are the ones concerned in the structure of methane and of the other organic compounds in which a carbon atom is surrounded tetrahedrally by its neighbors.

The tetrahedral wave functions are not the only combinations we can make; there are various other useful combinations, or hybrid wave functions, as they are often called. Probably the next most useful hybrid wave functions are the so-called trigonal wave functions. In these, three linear combinations of the s, p_x, and p_y wave functions extend out in three directions making angles of 120° to each other in the xy plane, with distributions of density indicated in Fig. 9.4.2. The fourth orbital is the ordinary p_z, extending in both positive and negative z directions. This type of orbital, as we shall see later, is found in cases involving double bonds, such as ethylene, C_2H_4, and also in the benzene ring. Still further types of orbitals sometimes are used, but they are much less common than the two which we have described.

9.5. Types of Substances Involving Covalent Binding.   The principles which have been illustrated in our simple cases of H_2O, NH_3, and CH_4 are clearly capable of being extended to a study of much more complicated molecules held by covalent binding.   As three general types of compounds in which this type of binding is important, we may mention organic compounds, silicates and silicon compounds, and inorganic radicals.   It is not our intention here to go far with the description of these substances, but merely to indicate how the principles already described can lead to their understanding.†

The characteristic feature of the organic compounds, the silicates, and the silicones, is the way in which long chains or other complicated structures of atoms can be formed, held together by covalent bonds.   This, of course, can happen if we have atoms like carbon and silicon, which can form four bonds in the tetrahedral directions; chains of carbons can form in the organic compounds, or of silicons in the silicones, with branching side chains.   Other atoms can, of course, also take part in the formation of chains; one of the most conspicuous of these is oxygen, and another is nitrogen.   In the silicates the chains are formed not of silicon atoms only, but of alternating silicons and oxygens.   In all these substances the same type of binding is evident which we have considered in the preceding section, and the same directional properties of the covalent bonds appear. These chains can terminate, resulting in molecules of a finite, though perhaps very large size, as in the organic compounds and silicones; or they can continue indefinitely, as in the silicates, resulting not in a finite molecule, but in a crystal, which really is a single great molecule.   Some very simple substances form such crystals, held together by covalent bonds.   A well-known example is carbon itself, in its two forms of diamond and graphite.   In diamond the carbon forms tetrahedral hybrid orbitals, each atom being bonded to four neighbors in the tetrahedral directions.   In graphite, the bonding is to three neighbors in a plane, making angles of 120°; the bonds are formed from the trigonal hybrid orbitals, and the orbitals at right angles to the plane form much weaker bonds with the atoms of neighboring planes, so that one plane slides over another very easily, resulting in the lubricating properties of graphite. Silicon has a structure like diamond; and similar structures are shown by SiC and a number of other compounds, as for instance BN.   This latter material could be described by assuming that the N atoms lost an elec-

† A somewhat more complete discussion of these materials is given in J. C. Slater, "Introduction to Chemical Physics," McGraw-Hill Book Company, Inc., New York, 1939, Chaps. XXIV–XXVI.

tron each, this electron was gained by the B atom, so that each type of atom had the same number of electrons as a carbon atom and could then form covalent bonds with the four neighbors in a diamond structure; but there would be additional binding on account of the ionic forces resulting from the charged ions, which would be partly canceled by the energy necessary to transfer the electron from the N to the B.   Thus it would be a mixture of covalent and ionic binding.

There are features which we have not yet discussed, which are of great importance in the structure of organic compounds.   These concern the formation of double and multiple covalent bonds.   A typical example of

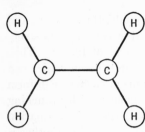

a double bond is found in ethylene, C_2H_4, which has a structure as shown in Fig. 9.5.1. We may use the trigonal orbitals for the carbons, the two carbons being linked by one of the trigonal orbitals of each, and the other two trigonal orbitals being linked to the hydrogens. This leaves one electron in the p_z orbital of each of the carbons.   The p_z's of the two carbons do not overlap very much, but still there is some overlapping, provided the hydrogens attached to both carbons lie in the same

FIG.   9.5.1.   Structure   of ethylene.

plane, so that the z axes are defined in the same way for the p_z's of both atoms.   Thus these p_z orbitals will form a weak additional bond between the carbons, as well as the bond formed by the trigonal orbitals extending from one carbon to the other; and this is the origin of the double bond.

We see that this picture gives information regarding the possibility of free rotation about the bonds which proves to agree with experiment. In the case of two carbons held by a single bond, as for instance in ethane, C_2H_6, the evidence indicates that free rotation about the bond is possible: one group of three hydrogens can rotate, about the bond direction as an axis, with respect to the other three, without appreciable resisting forces, except the small ones which come from steric hindrance between the two sets of hydrogen atoms.   On the other hand, a group of two hydrogens in ethylene does not rotate freely about the bond; it seems to be restrained by forces much greater than those of steric hindrance.   This is clearly to be expected from the picture we have given, in which the binding between the two p_z orbitals constrains the molecule to lie in a plane.

A further point connected with double bonds arises in the case of the benzene ring, the foundation of all aromatic compounds, and in many other cases.   It is well known that there are two possible ways of writing the single and double bonds in the benzene configuration, shown in Fig.

9.5.2, which are equally legitimate.   In either case we use the trigonal orbitals, as in ethylene, and the double bonds signify covalent bonds between p_z orbitals attached to neighboring carbons.   But now, since either of the structures of Fig. 9.5.2 is equally correct, they correspond to two degenerate unperturbed states of the system.   In any such case, we know that the correct wave function is a mixture of the two degenerate functions, and in general there are two possible combinations, one resulting in lower energy than the other.   Furthermore, if we combine the two wave functions, each with its appropriate frequency factor, we are led to an oscillatory or beat phenomenon, representing a process by which the system passes from one of the wave functions to the other.   This is the same process which we have earlier described as resonating between the two states, and this resonating occurs here too.   As in all such cases, that combination of wave functions which is more stable, or corresponds to lower energy, is a combination of the two, so that in this case of the

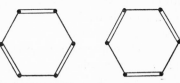

FIG. 9.5.2.   Alternative arrangements of double bonds for benzene molecule.

benzene ring we say that neither of the structures drawn above is the correct one, but the correct structure is a mixture of the two, each occurring with equal probability.   And by the process of forming the mixture, the resulting energy is lowered or the structure made more stable than if the resonance were absent.

As we have mentioned, there are many cases of resonance which occur in the structure of organic molecules.   This is only one example of the situation, which by now we have observed a good many times, in which various alternative descriptions can be given of the binding in a given compound, and in which the true situation is actually a combination of the various alternatives.   Thus we have seen similar choices in cases where a bond could be described as ionic or convalent.   In all such cases, the perturbation theory operates in such a way that the final energy tends to be lower than any one of the individual descriptions would indicate.   The structure of atomic multiplets, in which the interactions gave one multiplet with lower energy and one with higher energy than we should have otherwise found, was the first example which we saw of this sort of interaction.

This very brief sketch will suffice to describe some of the important features of covalent binding as underlying the compounds of carbon and silicon.   We have already mentioned that another type of substance in which covalent binding is important is found in some inorganic radicals.   As an illustration let us take the sulphates.   In these substances the group $(SO_4)^=$ exists as a well-defined radical, presumably really carrying the two negative charges which its formula indicates, and the compounds formed from the radical have the properties of ionic compounds. The sulphate group has a tetrahedral symmetry, with the sulphur at the center of the regular tetrahedron. We could, of course, adopt a strictly ionic picture of the radical, assuming that the sulphur atom had lost all six outer electrons, to form a negative ion with six charges, while these six electrons, and the other two which are incorporated in its structure to form the negative ion, would be enough to add to the oxygen atoms and make each of these negatively charged with a double charge, leading to a closed shell for them. This extreme structure seems highly improbable, however, on account of the very large amount of energy that would be required to ionize the sulphur atom so highly. Much more likely would be a partly covalent structure, in which the eight electrons would resonate between the atomic orbitals on the sulphur and the atomic orbitals on the oxygen, resulting in much smaller ionic properties associated with the atoms. Similar considerations can apply to many similar radicals.

There is one point of view regarding these radicals which finds other applications as well, and which we have not mentioned so far. Suppose we started with the extreme ionic picture of the sulphate ion, which we have described above. We should then have a sulphur ion, carrying six positive charges, surrounded by four oxygen ions each with two negative charges. The strong positive charge on the sulphur would exert electrical attractions on the electrons in the oxygen ions and would tend to pull them over toward it. So far we have not considered the effect of an external electric field on an atom or ion, but its effect is simple and is just what we should expect: it tends to distort the cloud of electrons, pulling it in the direction of the electrostatic force. Solutions for the behavior of an atom in an external electric field, leading to quantitative descriptions of this effect, can be found without great difficulty. The net effect of an external field is to produce a dipole moment in the atom, measured by the product of the amount of charge displaced and the distance through which it is displaced, which is proportional to the external field. The polarizability, or ratio of dipole moment to field producing it, is a measure of how easily the atom is distorted. The theory shows that this polarizability is roughly proportional to the volume of the atom or ion, large atoms being easily polarized. We should then certainly expect a large distortion, or polarization, of the oxygen ions under the action of the sulphur ion in the sulphate radical, and this would have the effect of pulling electronic charge from the oxygens toward the regions midway between oxygen and sulphur. This is very similar, in actual electrical distribution, to our picture of covalent bonds between atoms with smaller net charges; for these covalent bonds would also correspond to a distribution of charge between the atoms.   This modification of the ionic picture by the addition of polarization effects really represents a higher stage of approximation than the simple ionic picture we have considered so far; and the fact that it approaches the covalent picture is another illustration of the situation which we have often found, that if we approach a problem in molecular structure by two quite different first approximations but carry each one through further stages of approximation, we often find the final results converging toward each other and, as we hope, converging toward a true representation of the facts.

9.6. Intermolecular Forces in Molecular Compounds.   We have seen in the preceding sections that it is possible to have molecules in which the atoms are held together by cova-lent bonds, and in which all the va-lences are saturated, so that further atoms or groups of atoms approach-ing such a molecule will not be bound to it but will instead be repelled. These are the typical molecular com-pounds, in which the existence of molecules is a physical reality, quite

Fig. 9.6.1.   Intermolecular potential energy curve.

in contrast to ionic crystals on the one hand, metals on the other, in which we cannot distinguish separate molecules.   A molecular compound commonly can exist as a solid, the molecules being held together by inter-molecular forces of a type which we shall discuss in a moment; it can melt into a liquid, the molecules remaining as distinct entities, but the inter-molecular forces being weak enough so as to let the various molecules flow past each other freely, though still with enough binding to hold them together; and finally it can vaporize, the molecules breaking apart from each other.   We now ask, what is the nature of the intermolecular forces which are responsible for these various physical states of which such sub-stances are capable?

It is obvious that the energy of interaction of two molecules, as a function of distance of separation, must be given by a curve like that given in Fig. 9.6.1, the familiar type which we have already met a number of times.   The minimum then corresponds to the distance of separation found at the absolute zero of temperature or in the crystal; the depth of this minimum will be related to the heat of vaporization.   Of course, with large molecules of complicated shape, we must consider the energy as a function of orientation as well as of distance of separation, but this does not change the general situation.   It is also obvious that the heat of vaporization, determined by the depth of the minimum, must be considerably smaller than the energy of dissociation of the molecule, the energy necessary to remove an atom from it; for if this were not the case, the molecule would fly apart when it got enough energy to vaporize, and we should have a case of a substance that dissociated as easily as it vaporized.   Such substances exist, but they are not the typical molecular compounds which we wish to discuss at the moment.

The intermolecular forces of the type described above are made up of two parts: an attraction, operating at moderately long distances, and a repulsion, preventing the molecules from coming too close together. These are often called the Van der Waals attraction and the Van der Waals repulsion, from the occurrence of such forces in Van der Waals' equation, describing the equation of state of the gaseous and liquid phases of such a material.†   We have already found the explanation of the Van der Waals repulsion: it is simply the repulsion which an atom feels when it approaches a saturated molecule, such as we described for a hydrogen atom approaching an H_2 molecule, in Sec. 9.3.   We are left then with the Van der Waals attraction, which must still be explained. There are several different mechanisms which can be responsible for it, under different circumstances.   All of them, however, represent different types of attractions between electrical dipole moments on the two molecules.

In the first place, the molecules may have permanent dipole moments, and these may interact with each other.   An example is water, where the H_2O molecule, on account of its triangular shape, has a considerable dipole moment.   In such a case it is clear that two molecules will attract each other if they are so oriented that the positive end of one of them is near the negatively charged end of the other, that is, in the water molecule, if the hydrogen of one molecule is near the oxygen of another. These forces are so strong in water, and in some similar cases, that at any ordinary temperature they prevent the free rotation and motion of the molecule, not only in the solid, but in the liquid as well.   Water molecules line themselves up in a roughly regular arrangement, each oxygen atom having near it not only the two hydrogens belonging to its own molecule, but also hydrogen atoms attached to two neighboring molecules.   The electrostatic attractions arising in this way are those holding the liquid or solid together.   There are many other substances in which such dipole-dipole interactions are important in determining intermolecular forces. If they are strong enough to be the main feature in holding the liquid and solid together, they are also strong enough to ensure a fairly regular

† This equation and its interpretation in terms of intermolecular forces are discussed in J. C. Slater, "Introduction to Chemical Physics," McGraw-Hill Book Company, Inc., New York, 1939, Chaps. XII and XXIV.

arrangement of the molecules, in spite of temperature agitation. In some other cases, where they are weaker, the regularity imposed by their action can be diminished by temperature agitation to a point where they are relatively unimportant at higher temperatures.

There is a second effect which a molecule with a permanent dipole moment can have. When a charged object approaches a polarizable object, it polarizes it, attracting toward itself some charge of opposite sign. We have already seen this effect in our discussion of the polarization of oxygen ions by a positively charged sulphur ion. Once it has produced this polarization, an attraction ensues; for the induced charge of opposite sign to the charge inducing it is always closer to it than the induced charge of the same sign, as shown in Fig. 9.6.2, so that the resulting attraction is always greater than the repulsion. This is the same effect by which an electrically charged body attracts a pith ball or other uncharged but polarizable object; or, applied to magnetic forces, by which a magnetic pole attracts a polarizable but unmagnetized iron filing. This type of

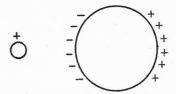

FIG. 9.6.2. Polarizable atom polarized by neighboring charge.

attraction does not depend on favorable relative orientations of the molecules, and hence can be important even at temperatures so high that molecules are rotating freely. It is not hard by a simple argument to see how it depends on the distance between molecules, the permanent charge or dipole moment inducing the polarization, and the polarizability.

To make this calculation, let us assume that a molecule with electrical dipole moment μ is at a distance r from another molecule with polarizability α. The field produced by a dipole is proportional to the inverse cube of the distance; thus the field produced by the first molecule at the location of the second is proportional to $\mu/4\pi\epsilon_0 r^3$. The dipole induced in the second molecule by this field is then proportional to $\mu\alpha/4\pi\epsilon_0 r^3$. This dipole, in turn, will produce a field at the location of the first molecule proportional to $(\mu\alpha/4\pi\epsilon_0 r^3)/4\pi\epsilon_0 r^3$, or to $\mu\alpha/(4\pi\epsilon_0)^2 r^6$. The force exerted by this field on the dipole moment of the first molecule is proportional to the dipole moment and to the gradient of the field. Thus it is proportional to $\mu^2\alpha/(4\pi\epsilon_0)^2 r^7$. The related term in the energy, whose gradient or derivative gives this force, is then proportional to $\mu^2\alpha/(4\pi\epsilon_0)^2 r^6$. This simple calculation gives the result correctly, except for a simple numerical constant. We see then that this type of attraction falls off rapidly with distance and is greater for molecules with large dipole moment and large polarizability.

The type of attraction we have just been considering is not nearly as important or general as a type which we have between any pair of molecules whatever, quite apart from the question whether they have a permanent dipole moment or not. We note that the formula we have derived above for the attractive energy involves μ^2, the square of the dipole moment. Now any molecule has an instantaneous dipole moment, even if the molecule has perfect spherical or other symmetry, like a CH_4 molecule, or a spherically symmetrical atom like He or Ne. For at any given instant, the electrons in their motions will not happen to be distributed in the symmetrical way in which they are in their time-average behavior. The average dipole moment will, it is true, be zero in such a case. But if we take the instantaneous dipole moment, square it, and then average this square, the result will not be zero. And it proves to be the case that we must use this mean-square dipole moment in considering the force between two such molecules which have no average dipole moment. The instantaneous dipole moment of one molecule polarizes the other, this produces a field which reacts back on the first one and attracts it, and the resultant term in the energy is just the one given in the preceding paragraph, if we interpret μ^2 as meaning the mean-square dipole moment. This leads to the type of Van der Waals attraction between molecules which is completely general, and which in most cases is the important effect in holding molecules together in liquids and solids, and in leading to the deviations from the perfect gas law in the gaseous state. If we are interested in getting numerical values of the attractive potential energy, we can use the formula above or an alternative formula due to London, amounting to the same thing, but expressing the quantities μ^2 and α in terms of various matrix components and energy-level differences encountered in the atoms of the molecule. We shall discuss these matters in more detail in a later chapter, taking up the behavior of dielectrics.

9.7. Interatomic Forces in Metals. In the present chapter we have put our major emphasis on two types of materials: ionic crystals, in which the attractive forces are electrostatic, and molecular compounds, in which we have covalent forces. These by no means exhaust the types of materials, however. By far the greatest majority of the elements are metals; and the study of the metals, of alloys, and of intermetallic compounds, furnishes a subject which is almost parallel in importance to the study of all the other types of substances combined. It furnishes the basis for the science of metallurgy, as the other compounds furnish the basis for inorganic and organic chemistry. The study of the metallic bond is distinctly different from either the ionic or covalent bond. Forces between metallic atoms are homopolar, in the sense that the atoms do not carry net charges, so that we cannot explain the binding in an ionic way.

Thus the metallic bond has some aspects in common with the covalent bond. On the other hand, it has many features in which it differs from the covalent bond. There is nothing resembling the saturation of valence; more and more atoms can be added, there is no molecular structure, and the typical state of a metal is the crystal, or its related liquid or vapor. Furthermore, there is no very decided preference for one position rather than another for an atom. It is true that the metals form crystals of definite form; but they are easily ductile, at least in some cases, atoms being able to be displaced from their ideal positions in the lattice without great impairment of the structure. Quite aside from these features affecting the mechanical structure of metals, perhaps their most characteristic feature is their electrical conductivity, which they possess in rather complete contrast to the ionic and molecular compounds. All these features are so different from the ones we have been considering that we must start practically from the beginning in discussing the properties of metals, and this will form the subject of the next chapter. In spite of these differences, however, we shall see that we can tie metallic structure up to the covalent binding which we have been considering, in a way which correlates all the various typical properties of metals: the metallic bond is essentially an unsaturated covalent bond. Its unsaturated nature allows new atoms to be added practically at will; the new atoms have considerable freedom of choice as to where they will be bound, since they have more than one available orbital to tie to; and the freedom of motion of the electrons, as they oscillate or resonate from available locations in one atom to another, leads to the electrical conductivity. We shall bring out these parallels between metallic and covalent bonds; but we shall also see that to describe many important metallic properties, particularly the electrical ones, an approach based on the method of molecular orbitals is more appropriate than the approach which we have mainly used in our discussion of chemical binding in the present chapter, largely based on atomic orbitals and the Heitler-London method.

PROBLEMS

1. In a Morse curve, where the interatomic energy is given by the formula

$$D[e^{-2a(r-r0)} - 2e^{-a(r-r0)}],$$

applying to a molecule formed by covalent binding, we can set up simple empirical rules giving fairly accurate values of r_0 and a in terms of atomic constants. First we set up for each of the two atoms the "radius" of the outer shell, equal to $n^2/(Z - S)$, where n is the principal quantum number, S the shielding constant, as given by the rules of Appendix 13. The value of r_0 is then found empirically to be approximately the sum of the atomic radii, provided the outer electrons are p electrons, and 1.4 times this value if they are s electrons. The constant a is found to be approximately $3/r_0$.

Compute by these approximate laws the distance of separation r_0 of the atoms in the normal states of the valence compounds given below, and compare with the experimental values tabulated:

Compound	r_0, angstroms
C_2	1.3
CN	1.17
CO	1.15
H_2	0.76
I_2	2.66
NO	1.15
O_2	1.21
SiN	1.57

2. Compare the distance of separation of atoms in the metallic crystals tabulated below with the sum of the quantities $n^2/(Z - S)$ for the two atoms.

Metal	Distance, angstroms
Na	3.72
K	4.50
Ca	4.97

3. The polarizability of an atom or ion can be approximately computed empirically as follows: We know that the polarizability divided by $4\pi\epsilon_0$ has the dimensions of a volume, and that the polarizability of an atom in Gaussian units or the polarizability divided by $4\pi\epsilon_0$ in mks units is of the order of magnitude of the cube of its radius. Now the radius of an electron's orbit can be approximated by $n^2/(Z - S)$. Thus we might imagine that the polarizability of an atom could be approximated by the sum of cubes of such terms for all electrons. More accurately, one finds empirically that the contribution of an electron to the polarizability proves to be approximately

$$\left(\frac{n^2 a_0}{Z - S}\right)^3 \times \begin{cases} 4.5 & \text{if } n = 1 \\ 1.1 & \text{if } n = 2 \\ 0.65 & \text{if } n = 3, \text{ etc.} \end{cases}$$

Here we have inserted the radius a_0, to convert from atomic to practical units. Compute by this approximation polarizabilities for the following ions, and compare with the experimental value tabulated:

Ion	Polarizability/$4\pi\epsilon_0$, cubic angstroms
O^-	1.60
F^-	0.868
Ne	0.398
Na^+	0.292
Mg^{++}	0.173
S^-	5.91
Cl^-	3.33
A	1.67
K^+	1.12
Ca^{++}	0.785

4. Compute the interatomic potential energy for NaCl at large distance, assuming it is composed of Na^+ and Cl^-, so that there will be the ionic force, and at the same time, a polarization force, the sodium polarizing the chlorine. Show that the polarization of sodium by chlorine can be neglected. Using the polarizabilities of Prob. 3, show that the potential energy is $\left[\dfrac{-27}{r/a_0} - \dfrac{302}{(r/a_0)^4}\right]$ ev.

5. The repulsive energy between two closed shells proves empirically, as far as order of magnitude is concerned, to be approximately a constant times $e^{-4(r/r_0)}$, where r_0 is defined as in Prob. 1. The observed interatomic distance in the NaCl molecule is 2.73 A. Compute C and a in the repulsive potential Ce^{-ar}. Find a by the rules we have used, and determine C so that the sum of the repulsive potential and the attractive potential of Prob. 4 will have a minimum at the required distance.

6. In the text we show that the Van der Waals attraction energy is proportional to $\mu^2\alpha/(4\pi\epsilon_0)^2 r^6$; we shall later show that the correct formula is this value multiplied by $\frac{3}{2}$ [see Eq. (13.5.5)]. Furthermore, it can be shown that μ^2 equals $\alpha\,\Delta E/2$, where ΔE is the difference of energy of that transition from the normal state which contributes most to the refractive index and dispersion [see Eq. (13.5.2)]. Find the potential energy between two helium atoms, using our approximate methods for calculating Van der Waals and repulsive forces, and compare with the more accurate value

$$\left[7.7e^{-2.43r/a_0} - \frac{0.68}{(r/a_0)^6}\right] \times 10^{-10} \quad \text{erg.}$$

The polarizability of helium is $1.43a_0^3$ Gaussian units, or $1.43a_0^3(4\pi\epsilon_0)$ mks units, and its ionization potential $1.80Rhc$. Compare these with simple calculated values.

7. Using the potential of Prob. 6, compute the equilibrium distance of separation between two helium atoms, and find the energy of dissociation, in ergs and in electron volts. Compare the equilibrium distance with the mean distance in the liquid, which has a density of 0.14, assuming atoms to be spaced on a regular lattice, so that the mean distance will be $1/\sqrt[3]{n}$, if n is the number of atoms per cubic centimeter.

8. Find a radius of the helium atom for use in kinetic theory, assuming that two helium atoms at temperature 300°K, with kinetic energy of $\frac{1}{2}kT$, collide head on. Find how close they come before they stop, and compare this molecular diameter with the distance r_0.

9. Set up the secular equation for the two doublet states in the problem of the molecule composed of three nonequivalent s electrons, as treated in Appendix 16, and solve for the energies of the levels.

10. Find the wave function and charge density in a tetrahedral atomic orbital as a function of angle, and plot the charge density in a polar diagram.

11. Plot the charge density of a trigonal orbital in a polar diagram.

12. Show how to set up wave functions for a polar model of LiF, composed of Li⁺ and F⁻. Show also how to set up wave functions representing a covalent bond between the neutral atoms, using a Heitler-London method.

13. Set up the perturbation problem for interaction between the polar and nonpolar models of LiF, as set up in Prob. 12, and show how this problem would be solved.

14. An approximate wave function for a molecule is set up by making a linear combination of two wave functions, each representing a particular way of describing the binding (resonance). Show that if the two unperturbed wave functions are orthogonal to each other, the lowest energy level of the perturbed problem will be lower than the diagonal energy of either of the unperturbed states.

CHAPTER 10

THE METALLIC STATE

At the close of the preceding chapter, we mentioned that the characteristic properties of the metallic state can be described by saying that the metallic atoms are held together by unsaturated covalent bonds. In the following section we shall describe this point of view. But it is not a point of view well suited to discussing the problem of metallic conductivity, and we shall then proceed to the method of energy bands and Brillouin zones, an adaptation of the method of molecular orbitals to a periodic lattice, and shall show that this method is appropriate for discussing electrical problems and can be used for mechanical problems as well.

10.1. The Metallic Bond as an Unsaturated Covalent Bond. Let us start our discussion with the simplest metal, Li, which of course will behave like the other alkali metals; and let us go through an argument, starting with a diatomic Li_2 molecule, then considering the addition of a third Li atom, to see in what way this problem differs from the superficially similar case of hydrogen, which we have already considered, and where we have found a saturation of valence and a typical molecular formation. In Sec. 9.1 we took up the case of Li_2. We mentioned that the $2s$ electron in Li was similar to the $1s$ in H, so that the problem of Li_2 was, in fact, much like that of H_2: it could be treated by either the method of molecular orbitals or the Heitler-London method, and by either argument the ground state of the molecule should be a singlet state showing covalent binding. Now we must assume that a third Li atom approaches the diatomic molecule so formed, and we must ask why this atom is not repelled, as a similar hydrogen atom would be if it approached a hydrogen molecule, as described in Sec. 9.3.

The profound difference between the two cases is that in Li we have the $2p$ atomic orbitals, corresponding to energy so little higher than the $2s$ that the energy difference can be almost disregarded; whereas in H there are no other orbitals than the $1s$ with anything like the same energy, the orbitals corresponding to $n = 2$ being so much higher in energy that they are of no importance in problems of molecular binding. Thus if we have a Li_2 molecule and let a third Li atom approach it, it is true that the electron of this approaching atom must have the same spin as

256

one of the two electrons in the molecule. But we have a choice of other atomic orbitals into which the electron of the approaching atom can go, without getting into trouble with the exclusion principle. It can then resonate between the atom to which it was originally attached and the one it approaches, and so can lead to a covalent bond between them. There are so many unfilled atomic orbitals in the Li atom that practically as many atoms can be bound to it as can physically find space in its neighborhood. Of course, there would be trouble, not with the exclusion principle, but with electrostatics, if all the electrons in the covalent bonds formed with the neighbors surrounding a Li atom in a metallic crystal should happen to be simultaneously located on this atom, in connection with their oscillations from one atom to another; for this would put a very large charge on this atom. But this would be very unlikely, for the various electrons would oscillate back and forth more or less independently of each other and, on the average, the net charge found on each atom at any time would be just enough to make it electrically neutral. Fluctuations of charge are allowed, however, and in this respect a metal is quite different from a molecule held by saturated covalent bonds, in which charge fluctuations are ironed out.

We can see very easily, by a little arithmetic, why there is no saturation of valence in metallic Li. Lithium, and the other alkali metals, crystallize in the body-centered cubic structure, each atom being surrounded by eight nearest neighbors. Let us assume that a bond is formed between each atom and each of its eight nearest neighbors, and count up to see how many electrons are associated with each of these bonds. Each bond may be visualized as a line joining two atoms. Eight of these will be terminating on each atom, but since each bond has two ends, there will be four bonds per atom. Since each atom has one available valence electron, there will be one-fourth of an electron available at any instant to constitute each bond. This electron will presumably resonate between the two atoms at the ends of the bond and contribute to the binding, just as if it were forming a covalent bond. However, a covalent bond is ordinarily formed of two electrons, one of each spin. Thus in the alkali metals there is only one-eighth of the charge available in each bond that there would be in a complete covalent bond. It is clear why additional charge can easily move onto any given atom, without producing saturation of valence.

It is also clear that we can have several times more charge per atom than we have in the alkali metals, without interfering with this situation of the free mobility of charge and the lack of saturation of valence. Thus most of the alkaline-earth metals crystallize in the hexagonal close-packed or the face-centered cubic structures, in each of which an atom has twelve nearest neighbors. There are then six bonds per atom; and with two valence electrons per atom, we have only one-third of an electron per bond. Similarly, many metals with three electrons per atom crystallize in these close-packed structures, and they have one-half of an electron per bond. A few with as many as four electrons per atom do likewise, with two-thirds of an electron per bond. Included in the types we have already mentioned are the great majority of the metals, provided we include the metals of the various transitions groups.[†] It is suitable to include the transition metals, for they have either one or two *s* electrons in their outer shells, as well as a number of *d* electrons in inner shells. Toward the beginning of the transition groups, there are few enough of these *d* electrons so that we still have a very unsaturated situation, whereas toward the end of the transition groups, the *d* electrons are so far inside the atom that they are not available to take part in covalent bonding with their neighbors to any large extent.

The metals with more electrons per atom than these, as pointed out in the reference just mentioned, generally do not crystallize in the cubic or hexagonal structures, but in other structures with far fewer neighbors. Thus, for instance, Ge, and one form of Sn, crystallize in the diamond structure, with four nearest neighbors. Thus there are only twice as many bonds as atoms, and with four outer electrons per atom, we have two electrons per bond, or a saturated covalent structure. In fact, as far as electronic structure is concerned, these elements are not essentially different from diamond, which of course is a nonconductor. We meet here one of those cases in which this picture of shared electron bonds in a crystal fails to give correct information about electrical properties; for as a first, rough approximation, we should say that in cases where covalent bonds are not saturated there is the possibility of mobility of electrons, and hence of conductivity, whereas with saturated bonds, as in molecular compounds, we expect no conductivity. We shall see later how the energy-band theory shows itself more powerful than the electron-bond structure, and can give correct descriptions of these exceptional cases. There are, in fact, a number of other metals which act in many ways like structures with saturated covalent bonds. Well-known examples are As, Sb, and Bi, discussed in the reference above. Though they are metals, in spite of their covalent binding, it is well known that they have very unusual properties, and we shall later get some insight into these properties, from their energy-band structure.

Several deductions can be drawn from the unsaturated nature of the

[†] For the crystal structures of the various metals and other related information about metals, see J. C. Slater, "Introduction to Chemical Physics," McGraw-Hill Book Company, Inc., New York, 1939, Chap. XXVII.

shared-electron bonds in most metals. For one thing, each such bond must obviously be much less strong, contribute much less to the binding energy, than if there were two electrons forming the bond, as in a saturated covalent bond. This is clear, since it is the presence of electronic charge in the region between the atoms which leads to the binding, and obviously one-fourth or one-third of an electron, on an average, can do much less than two electrons. When we investigate the heat of vaporization of a metal, per bond, and compare it with the heat of dissociation of molecules held with covalent binding, per bond, we find that this difference is in fact observed. In addition to this, we have already pointed out that the directional effects of covalent bonds are almost completely lost in a metal. The orbitals of a given atom are so far from being filled with electrons that a new atom approaching from almost any direction can share its electron with the atom with equal ease. Thus the packing of atoms in a crystal of a metal is determined almost entirely by geometrical convenience, and not by directional effects of the binding. It is this, as we have pointed out, which makes it possible to deform the crystal of a metal so greatly, without impairing its strength. Finally we have pointed out the rather obvious connection between the unsaturated nature of the valence and the possibility of electrical conductivity, as electrons wander practically at will from one atom to another, without being impeded by the exclusion principle.

These qualitative features of metallic structure can be deduced with ease from the shared-electron picture of a metal. However, we can get much further from the energy-band picture, which we shall present next. This comes from a straightforward application of the molecular orbital type of solution of the self-consistent field problem to a metal. In it, as we shall see, the molecular orbitals correspond to wave functions in which an electron is free to wander throughout the whole metal. Since the free mobility of the electrons is such a characteristic feature of a metal, it is not surprising that this is a valuable approach to the problem, in contrast to ordinary problems of molecular structure and covalent binding, where electrons presumably actually do tend to be localized on a given atom and its immediate neighbors, without possibility of much motion.

10.2. Wave Functions in a One-dimensional Periodic Potential. If we approach the problem of a metal from the self-consistent field point of view, we meet at once the fact that the potential energy function is periodic, with the period of the crystal lattice. Instead of having one or two centers of attraction, as in the cases we have considered so far, we have an infinite number, or practically infinite, spaced in a regular way. We then naturally look for a solution of the self-consistent problem in which we start with such a periodic potential, find wave functions for the electrons in it, distribute charge according to these wave functions, determine a potential from this charge distribution, and demand that the final potential agree with the initial potential. This is a practical program of calculation to carry through, though it is too hard to do it in the detail that Hartree has used for atoms. It is a procedure that has been made the basis of most of the detailed work which has been done on the structure of metals. And clearly the most important part of it is the discussion of the wave functions of an electron in a periodic potential, such as we meet in a metallic crystal. We start consideration of that problem in the present section.

When we wished to consider the wave functions of an electron in a two-center problem, as the hydrogen molecule, we used as a simple analogy the one-dimensional problem of an electron in a potential having two identical wells. Similarly, here we can derive many of the properties of our solution by taking up the Schrödinger problem of an electron in a

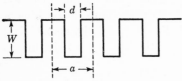

FIG. 10.2.1. Periodic potential problem.

potential of the type shown in Fig. 10.2.1, with an infinite number of identical potential wells, corresponding to a crystal with a "unit cell" as shown. Fortunately this problem can be carried through exactly, since we can solve Schrödinger's equation by piecing together sinusoidal or exponential functions in each of the unit cells. Thus we can use the solution of this problem to suggest the sort of results to be expected in the more general case of a three-dimensional crystal with potential minima such as we actually find in a metallic crystal. Let us inquire about the nature of the solution which we shall get in the case of the potential above.

We start with a given energy E and build up a wave function within a unit cell; then we shall consider how to fit together the functions in different unit cells. The first thing to notice is that for each energy, we can build up two independent solutions of the Schrödinger problem, one symmetrical and the other antisymmetric in the central point of the unit cell. That is, the first one is a cosine function, the second a sine, within the potential well; each then joins onto a sinusoidal or exponential function, with continuous value and derivative, at the boundary between the well and the barriers at the side. By the time we reach the two edges of the unit cell, each of these functions, the cosinelike and the sinelike, will have definite values for the function and its derivative. Let the value of the cosinelike function at the right-hand boundary of the cell be C; then it will have the same value at the left-hand end. Similarly, let its derivative be C' at the right-hand end. Symmetry then demands that its slope at the left-hand end be $-C'$. Let the values of the sinelike function at the right-hand and left-hand boundaries be S and $-S$ respectively; the slopes will be the same, S', at each boundary, as we see in Fig. 10.2.2.

We must now consider how to combine these functions, the cosinelike and sinelike, to form an acceptable solution. Neither function by itself is in general appropriate; that is, we could not use, for instance, the cosine-like function in each of the unit cells, and hope to have them satisfy the boundary conditions. The functions C would be continuous, but the derivatives would not; for we have seen that the derivative at the right-hand end of the cell is C', while that at the left-hand end is $-C'$, so that the derivative of the function at the right-hand end of one cell would not fit smoothly onto the function at the left-hand end of the adjacent cell (except in the special case where C' was zero). Similarly with the S function alone, the slope would be continuous, but the function would not.

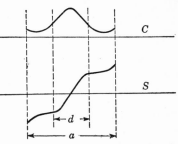

FIG. 10.2.2. Symmetric (C) and antisymmetric (S) functions in a single cell; periodic potential problem.

It would be possible to start in a given cell with, say, just the C function. Then in the next cell to the right we could set up a combination of the C and S functions which would have the required function and slope at the left-hand boundary of that cell. This combination, in turn, would have a definite value and slope at the right-hand boundary of that cell, and so on. This process of fitting functions and derivatives at each cell boundary is in principle possible, but in practice it would lead to an infinite complication and would be of no value. Fortunately we can use a much simpler and more straightforward procedure, which gives us complete information.

The idea behind this straightforward procedure will at once occur to anyone familiar with the electrical problem of the transmission of signals down a loaded electrical transmission line or network. Suppose we have an infinite set of identical four-terminal networks, each containing resistances, inductances, and capacitances, connected together as shown in Fig. 10.2.3. It is not hard to show that the mathematical problem of setting up the disturbances in such a transmission line is mathematically very similar to our problem of the periodic potential. In the electrical case the whole problem is greatly simplified by noting that, for disturbances of a given frequency, there are two particular solutions of the problem of wave propagation that have particularly simple significance. These correspond essentially to simple propagated waves, one traveling to the right, the other to the left. In some cases these waves are propagated without attenuation, while in other cases they are attenuated. In any case, however, both current and voltage at the set of terminals at a distance x, measured along the line, may be written as $e^{\pm\gamma x}$ times the current and voltage at $x = 0$. Here γ is pure imaginary if we have real propagation, while it is complex if there is also attenuation. The two signs of the exponent correspond to propagation in the two directions. The solution of the problem of propagation in a transmission line is that

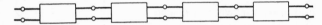

FIG. 10.2.3.   Infinite electrical line formed from four-terminal networks.

of finding γ as a function of frequency.[†]   For a network without resistances, it can be proved that γ is either real or pure imaginary.   For those ranges of frequency where it is pure imaginary, we have propagation of the wave without attenuation; such ranges of frequencies are called pass bands.   In between these ranges, where γ is real, the transmission line attenuates, without real propagation.   It is obvious that such a network acts like an electric filter, allowing only certain ranges of frequency to be propagated.   The solution we have spoken of is for pure propagated waves traveling in the two directions; to get a general solution, we need only superpose the waves traveling in both directions with arbitrary phases and amplitudes, getting a standing wave of some type.   All solutions can be written in this form.

In an entirely analogous way, we can set up solutions for traveling waves traveling to left and right, in our case of the periodic potential, and can build up the most general solution corresponding to a given energy by superposing waves traveling to left and right with arbitrary phases and amplitudes.   Here, as in the resistanceless electrical case, we prove to have certain ranges of energy in which propagation is possible; these are known as the energy bands.   Between these energy bands only an attenuated wave exists, falling off so rapidly that ordinarily we can neglect its existence and say that these regions of energy are forbidden, and that no electrons can occur with those forbidden energies.   The existence of such allowed and forbidden energy bands, with their related properties of propagation of electron waves, is the fundamental feature of the solution of Schrödinger's equation in a periodic potential.

† See, for instance, J. C. Slater, "Microwave Transmission," McGraw-Hill Book Company, Inc., New York, 1942, Sec. 1, for a discussion of this problem.

We can now sketch the mathematical steps by which these allowed and forbidden energies come about, in the Schrödinger equation which we are concerned with. The characteristic of our special solutions corresponding to propagated waves is that both the wave function and its slope (which can be shown to behave mathematically like the voltage and current in the electrical case) must be multiplied by $e^{\pm \gamma a}$ when we go along distance a, the length of the unit cell. It is not hard to show that this condition leads at once to the equation

$$\cosh \gamma a = \frac{S'/S + C'/C}{S'/S - C'/C},$$
(10.2.1)

where S, S', C, C' are as defined above. To have a specific example to work on, we can compute these quantities for the problem of the potential wells, shown in Fig. 10.2.1, and can express the right-hand side of (10.2.1) in terms of the dimensions of the potential wells. This is a straightforward problem, though it involves some little calculation. We can show that its result is

$$
\begin{aligned}
\cosh \gamma a &= \cos\left(\frac{2\pi}{h}\sqrt{2mE}d\right)\cos\left[\frac{2\pi}{h}\sqrt{2m(E-W)}(a-d)\right] \\
&\quad - \frac{E-W/2}{\sqrt{E(E-W)}}\sin\left(\frac{2\pi}{h}\sqrt{2mE}d\right)\sin\left[\frac{2\pi}{h}\sqrt{2m(E-W)}(a-d)\right] \\
&= \cos\left(\frac{2\pi}{h}\sqrt{2mE}d\right)\cosh\left[\frac{2\pi}{h}\sqrt{2m(W-E)}(a-d)\right] \\
&\quad - \frac{E-W/2}{\sqrt{E(W-E)}}\sin\left(\frac{2\pi}{h}\sqrt{2mE}d\right)\sinh\left[\frac{2\pi}{h}\sqrt{2m(W-E)}(a-d)\right],
\end{aligned}
$$
(10.2.2)

where the first form is to be used when $E > W$, the second when $E < W$.

We shall discuss the implications of this formula in a moment; first let us check it by considering its limiting values when the potential becomes constant, and when the solution must reduce to a sinusoidal function. We can first let the potential become constant by letting W go to zero. Then the expression becomes equal to

$$
\begin{aligned}
&\cos\left(\frac{2\pi}{h}\sqrt{2mE}d\right)\cos\left[\frac{2\pi}{h}\sqrt{2mE}(a-d)\right] \\
&\quad - \sin\left(\frac{2\pi}{h}\sqrt{2mE}d\right)\sin\left[\frac{2\pi}{h}\sqrt{2mE}(a-d)\right] = \cos\left(\frac{2\pi}{h}\sqrt{2mE}a\right).
\end{aligned}
$$

Thus in this case we have $\gamma = (2\pi i/h)\sqrt{2mE}$, which is just the right value for the sinusoidal function associated with a free particle of kinetic energy E. Similarly we can let d become equal to a, in which case the result above again comes out to be correct; or we can let d become zero, in which case the expression in (10.2.2) becomes

$$\cos [(2\pi/h) \sqrt{2m(E - W)}]a,$$

the appropriate value for that case, when we remember that the zero of energy in that case would come at W.

We have checked (10.2.2) in the simple case of a constant potential; let us now ask what it leads to in the general case. The function is too complicated for us to visualize it without actually plotting it. We therefore give in Fig. 10.2.4 a graph of the right side of (10.2.2), as a function of

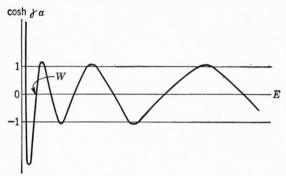

Fig. 10.2.4. Function cosh γa as function of E, from Eq. (10.2.2).

energy, for a special case: we have chosen $d = a/2$, and we have chosen such a value of W that there will be one bound state lying well below the top of the well. The value of W is shown in the graph. We now note from the structure of (10.2.2) that it is very important to know whether cosh γa is greater than or less than unity in absolute magnitude. If it is greater than unity, γ is real, and we have attenuation of the wave rather than propagation. On the other hand, if it is less than unity, we can rewrite it as cos ka, where $k = i\gamma$, and k will be real, or γ pure imaginary, leading to a propagated wave without attenuation. Thus the allowed energy bands come in those regions where cosh γa lies between $+1$ and -1.

Examination of the figure shows that the situation is quite different, depending on whether E is less than or greater than W. For E less than W, the amplitude of oscillation of the curve of cosh γa vs. E is very large, so that the curve cuts the axis very steeply and is between $+1$ and -1 only for a very small range of energy. Thus in this case we have very narrow energy bands. We shall see in a moment that these bands come just about at the position where the energy levels would come in an infinitely deep potential well. Furthermore, it can be shown that the energy breadth of the band is comparable to the energy separation between the symmetric and antisymmetric states in the problem of two potential wells, which we have already taken up. On the other hand, for E greater than W, the curve lies between $+1$ and -1 for almost its whole range; it is only at its extreme maxima and minima that it goes outside this range. Thus almost all energies are allowed; there are just small forbidden energy ranges near the places where cos ka goes to ± 1, or where ka is an integral number times π. We shall examine these forbidden ranges in the next section. It is not hard to carry out an approximate discussion of (10.2.2), for the case where E is large compared with W, to show that these forbidden ranges are actually quite small as we go up in energy.

To get the position of the allowed bands for E less than W, we may ask where the curve for cosh γa crosses the axis; the allowed band will be so narrow that it will be concentrated very close to this point. Let us then set cosh γa equal to zero in (10.2.2) and take the limiting case where W is very large compared with E. The general case of cosh $\gamma a = 0$ is given by

$$\tan\left(\frac{2\pi}{h}\sqrt{2mE}d\right) = \frac{\sqrt{E(W-E)}}{E-W/2}\coth\left[\frac{2\pi}{h}\sqrt{2m(W-E)}(a-d)\right].$$

In the limiting case where W becomes infinite, the right side of this expression goes to zero, so that $(2\pi/h)\sqrt{2mE}d$ must be an integer times π. This is just the condition for energy in an infinitely deep potential well of depth d, verifying our statement about the position of these allowed bands. If the well had been much deeper than in our example, so that there would have been more allowed bands in the well, we should have found in Fig. 10.2.4 that there would have been correspondingly more periods of the curve with very large amplitude, corresponding to very narrow bands.

In the other limit, for E large compared with W, we approach the situation where $W = 0$, which we have already discussed, and in which $ka = (2\pi/h)\sqrt{2mE}a$, $k = (2\pi/h)\sqrt{2mE}$, or

$$E = \frac{k^2h^2}{8\pi^2m},\tag{10.2.3}$$

as for a free particle. The approximate discussion which we have mentioned, for the case where E is large compared with W, shows that (10.2.3) actually furnishes a good approximation to the energy for large E, except in the immediate neighborhood of the energy gaps, which, as we have seen, come for ka near $n\pi$, where n is an integer.

10.3. Periodicity Properties in the One-dimensional Problem. We shall now consider the results which we have been discussing, in respect to their properties of periodicity as a function of k. This involves us in considerations which prove to be very important in the whole theory of energy bands. These properties come only in the allowed bands, and arise on account of the periodicity of the function cos ka which is substituted for cosh γa on the left side of (10.2.2), in case this quantity is less than unity. On account of the periodicity of cos ka, it is clear that

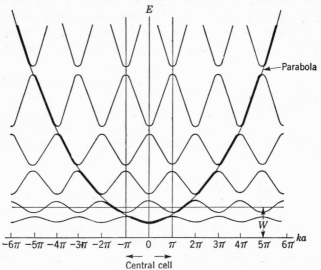

FIG. 10.3.1.   Energy as function of propagation constant ka, for periodic potential of Fig. 10.2.1.

for a given energy, and hence a given value of cos ka, an infinite number of values of ka are possible, differing from each other by integral multiples of 2π. Furthermore, cos ka will have equal values for positive and negative values of ka, on account of the fact that it is an even function. Hence, rephrasing, we see that the energy E will be a periodic function of k, with period $2\pi/a$, and furthermore will be an even function of k. These very important properties, we note, are quite general for any one-dimensional periodic function, since they follow from (10.2.1) as well as (10.2.2); this expression depends only on the individual unit cells being symmetrical about a point, and as a matter of fact, it can be shown that the present results do not even depend on that special condition.

We can now exhibit our results in a very interesting form by plotting the energy E as a function of k. The results are as in Fig. 10.3.1. We note several things about this plot. In the first place, the periodicity with period $2\pi/a$ is obvious.   Next, the energy gaps are shown as ranges of E in which the curve indicates no value of k; we understand why, since we know that in these ranges k is imaginary.   The allowed energy bands for the bottom band, and to some extent the next level, are very narrow.   The higher ones, however, fill most of the range of energy. Particularly interesting is the behavior for large E, where we know that the energy should be approximately given by (10.2.3), a parabola.   This parabola is drawn in the figure; and we see that the parabola does in fact lie close to one of the branches of one of the periodic curves of E vs. k, in each energy band, shown by heavier lines.

On account of the periodic nature of the energy as a function of k, it is convenient to divide the k axis, like the x axis, into unit cells.   Clearly such a unit cell will have a length $2\pi/a$ along the k axis.   We may, if we choose, take such a cell to extend from $k = 0$ to $k = 2\pi/a$; though for reasons of symmetry it is often more convenient to take it as extending from $k = -\pi/a$ to $k = +\pi/a$, and to consider the other unit cells to be displaced from this central cell by integral multiples of $2\pi/a$.   We shall find that the wave function, as well as the energy, has the same periodicity in k, so that by considering the problem only within the unit cell, we really have obtained a complete picture of energy and wave function as functions of k.   On the other hand, to understand the relationship to the behavior of free electrons, as in Fig. 10.3.1, we must use many unit cells in the k space.   We shall see in a later section that this periodicity with k is very closely related to the reciprocal lattice and reciprocal space generally used in discussions of x-ray diffraction.

This relationship to x-ray diffraction is made clearer if we try to get an understanding of why the energy as a function of k shows the breaks it does in the neighborhood of the values $k = n\pi/a$.   From the meaning of k, we see that it equals $2\pi/\lambda$ where λ is the wave length of the function e^{ikx}, which, as we have seen in the preceding section, determines the phase of the wave function at corresponding points in different unit cells.   Thus our equation $k = n\pi a$ is equivalent to

$$n\lambda = 2a. \tag{10.3.1}$$

This will be recognized as similar to the Bragg law, $n\lambda = 2d \sin \theta$, governing x-ray diffraction.   In the Bragg law θ is the glancing angle of incidence, equal to $\pi/2$ for normal incidence, for which case $\sin \theta = 1$. We see, then, that (10.3.1) is just the Bragg law for waves diffracted at normal incidence from a set of planes with spacing a.   Let us inquire why we should get this relationship.   It comes about essentially not through x-ray diffraction, but through electron diffraction, which follows the same laws.   Electron diffraction is precisely an example of our present problem.　We have been interested in our problem of electrons in a periodic potential on account of its application to the tightly bound electrons in a metal; but fast electrons, such as are used in electron diffraction, form precisely the case of large E where the energy gaps become narrow.　Our one-dimensional problem, of course, corresponds to normal incidence in a three-dimensional problem.　Now let us inquire what feature of electron-diffraction theory leads to our energy gaps.

The theory behind the Bragg law is very simple: the law is simply the statement that there is constructive interference between direct and reflected waves.　A reflected wave has traveled a round trip distance of $2a$ for each lattice spacing that it has traversed; we have constructive interference if this is an integral number of wave lengths, as demanded by (10.3.1).　But there is a more complicated theory than this, called the dynamic theory of x-ray or of electron diffraction, which leads to exactly the energy gaps which we have discovered by our theoretical treatment. In the case of electron diffraction we can state its essential features very easily.　The dynamical theory becomes a perturbation theory, applied to the interactions between the direct and the reflected waves, regarded as two unperturbed solutions of Schrödinger's equation.　The correct, or perturbed, wave functions become linear combinations of direct and reflected waves.　If the Bragg condition is precisely satisfied, the direct and reflected waves will be combined with equal amplitude, and we shall have complete reflection; if it is approximately but not exactly satisfied, we shall have strong reflection, approaching complete reflection the closer we get to the Bragg condition.　Let us set up the problem in a simple way and see why these statements should be true.

Let us assume that we are dealing with fast electrons, for which a reasonable first approximation is to treat them as being perfectly free, so that they will have wave functions e^{ikx}, corresponding to an energy $k^2h^2/8\pi^2m$.　We then introduce the periodic potential as a small perturbation and ask about the reflected waves produced by this perturbation. Let the potential be $V(x)$, a periodic function with period a.　We know that we can write such a periodic function as a Fourier series, and it is convenient to write this Fourier series in a complex exponential form,

$$V(x) = \sum_{h=-\infty}^{\infty} V_h e^{2\pi ihx/a}, \qquad h = \text{integer.} \qquad (10.3.2)$$

This must be periodic with period a, since increasing x by a leaves each of the exponential functions unchanged.　Since V must be a real function, we must have $V_{-h} = V_h^*$, the components corresponding to equal positive and negative values of h being complex conjugates of each other.　Now we shall ask for the matrix components of the perturbative potential between two of the unperturbed wave functions e^{ikx}, for we remember that these are the essential things in discussing the perturbation problem.

The component V_{ij} between two states $e^{ik_i x}$ and $e^{ik_j x}$ is

$$V_{ij} = \int e^{-ik_i x} V(x) e^{ik_j x} \, dx. \tag{10.3.3}$$

We use the expansion (10.3.2) for V and find

$$V_{ij} = \sum_h V_h \int e^{i(k_j - k_i + 2\pi h/a)x} \, dx. \tag{10.3.4}$$

The integral is here an integral of a sinusoidal function of x. We shall not at the moment ask further regarding the range of integration; this question will be taken up in a later section. But we shall find that the integration is to be taken essentially over the whole sample of crystal, and the integral of such a sinusoidal function over a large region is zero, the sine averaging to zero, except in the special case where the exponent is zero, or where

$$k_i - k_j = \frac{2\pi h}{a}. \tag{10.3.5}$$

In other words, there will be no matrix components of perturbative energy except between states whose propagation constants k differ by the amount (10.3.5).

This result has two important consequences. In the first place, we remember from our study of perturbation theory that the perturbed wave function is a linear combination of unperturbed wave functions, the coefficients being the matrix component of energy between the two states, divided by the difference between the unperturbed energies [Eq. (4.3.7)]. In our case this shows that to get a correct perturbed wave function, starting with the unperturbed function $e^{ik_i x}$, we must use only those functions $e^{ik_j x}$ satisfying (10.3.5); that is, the perturbed wave function is a series of terms $e^{i(k_i - 2\pi h/a)x}$, or is a product of $e^{ik_i x}$ and a series of terms $e^{-2\pi ihx/a}$. But such a series, just like the series (10.3.2), is a periodic function of x, with period a. Thus we see that our correct perturbed function is a product of $e^{ik_i x}$ and a periodic function of period a. This important result, due originally to Bloch, provides us with an alternative proof of our result of the preceding section that the wave function must be multiplied by the factor e^{ika} when we go along the x axis a distance a. For the factor $e^{ik_i x}$ is obviously multiplied by this factor (if we identify k_i with k), and the periodic function is unchanged.

The second consequence of our results (10.3.4) and (10.3.5) comes when we consider the amplitudes of the various waves $e^{ik_j x}$ which go to make up the perturbed solution.   If we assume that many coefficients V_n, of (10.3.4), have considerable magnitudes, we shall still find that the amplitudes of these waves depend on the difference of unperturbed energies of the states with propagation constants k_i and k_j.   Only if the energies are almost the same will the amplitudes be large.   Now we show in Fig. 10.3.2 the allowed values k_j corresponding to different values of h, in (10.3.5).   These are just the values at corresponding points of all the cells along the k axis, as shown in Fig. 10.3.1.   The only way in which the

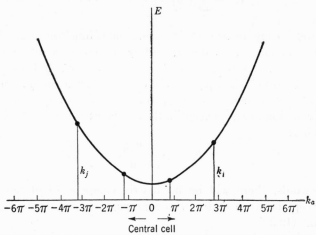

FIG. 10.3.2.   Corresponding points in different cells, with unperturbed energy determined from parabola.

energy corresponding to two k values fulfilling these conditions can be approximately equal is for one k to be approximately the negative of the other, as we see from Fig. 10.3.2, where we show also the parabola corresponding to the unperturbed energy.   If k_j is exactly $-k_i$, the two unperturbed states in question will have exactly equal energy, the unperturbed problem will be degenerate, and the perturbed wave function will correspond to a combination of the two unperturbed functions with equal amplitudes.   This will be the case when

$$k_i - (-k_i) = \frac{2\pi h}{a}, \qquad k_i = \frac{2\pi}{\lambda} = \frac{\pi h}{a},$$
$$h\lambda = 2a,$$

which is just the same as the Bragg relation (10.3.1) which we have already stated.

Let us then consider the interpretation of our results.   The complete solution corresponds to a superposition of the original function $e^{ik_i x}$, which we may consider as a plane wave of electrons, with other waves obeying the relation (10.3.5). These must be considered as scattered or reflected waves. The amplitude of these reflected waves is large only if they correspond to approximately the same wave length as the incident wave, and the more closely they satisfy this condition, the more closely they also satisfy the Bragg relation. The amplitude of the reflected wave clearly depends on the matrix component V_h of perturbing energy.

At the same time, our perturbation theory shows that the energy of the perturbed state will no longer be the unperturbed energy $k^2 h^2/8\pi^2 m$, but will be modified. From Eq. (4.3.6) we see that the perturbation effect on the energy is a small quantity of the second order in the matrix components, or the V_h's, and the only large contributions come between states whose energies are almost the same. That is, we shall have appreciable perturbations only when the Bragg conditions are almost fulfilled, as shown in Fig. 10.3.2. The perturbation will be such as to push the upper energy of the two which are interacting with each other still further up, and the lower one further down. Just at the point where the Bragg conditions are satisfied, there will be the maximum perturbation of energy, and it will take the form of a spreading apart of the two energy levels. In other words, we shall end up with energy gaps, of just the form shown in Fig. 10.3.1.

Exactly at the values $k = h\pi/a$, where the Bragg conditions are fulfilled, the two waves, the direct and reflected, which are degenerate with each other, must be combined with equal amplitudes, so that only a standing wave can represent the correct solution of Schrödinger's equation. The standing wave has certain nodes, positions at which the amplitude is zero, and loops, positions where it has a maximum value. Nodes will come a half wave length apart; thus, by (10.3.1), there will be n nodes in the lattice spacing a. In our particular case of the potential wells, we can have two possible types of standing waves, one with nodes at the centers of the wells (which then are antisymmetric functions), and the other with loops at the centers (which then are symmetric functions). In other words, just at these values of k where the Bragg conditions are satisfied, the symmetric or antisymmetric functions C or S of the preceding section form exact solutions of the problem, without having to set up linear combinations of them, so that we can correlate our present type of solution with the earlier type. These two functions will have different charge distributions, so that they will correspond to different values of the energy; this explains physically the existence of the two energies corresponding to the same value of k.

The dynamical theory of electron diffraction leads to the description we have just given of the perturbed wave within a crystal, and to the existence of the forbidden bands of energy. It deals, of course, with those electrons which are reflected back from a crystal lattice. Thus it handles the boundary conditions at a surface of separation between a crystal and empty space. Inside the forbidden range of energy, between energy bands, only an attenuated wave can exist within the crystal, carrying no net flow of electrons. Thus it must be that electrons striking the crystal, in this range of energies, will be totally reflected, never penetrating into the crystal. Thus the dynamical theory predicts that there will be a finite range of energies for reflection, rather than the infinitely narrow range predicted by the Bragg law. This identification of the forbidden bands with the condition for total reflection of electrons from the crystal gives a good physical picture of their meaning. The dynamic theory of x-ray diffraction leads similarly to a finite range of wave lengths for diffraction but in the x-ray case the corrections to the Bragg theory are smaller in magnitude than for electrons. The actual situation of electron diffraction is in practice much more complicated than we have indicated, on account of the large absorption of electrons in a crystal. This has the effect of broadening the Bragg lines much more than the dynamical effect which we have just been describing.

When we consider the low-lying energy bands, for $E < W$, rather than the high ones for $E > W$ which we have just been discussing, we can make interesting comparisons with the low-lying levels in the problem of two potential wells, which was discussed in Sec. 2.5. In that problem we found two wave functions, one symmetric, the other antisymmetric in the mid-point between the wells, the symmetric case corresponding to the lower energy. Similarly, in our present case the lowest energy band extends from its lowest energy, corresponding to $k = 0$, to its highest energy, coming at $k = \pi/a$. Going from one cell to the next, the wave function is multiplied by e^{ika}. For $k = 0$, this factor is unity; this then corresponds to the symmetric wave function of the two-center problem. For $k = \pi/a$, the factor is $e^{i\pi} = -1$, the wave function changing sign from one cell to the next, as in the antisymmetric wave function of the two-center problem. The extreme limits of the energy band then correspond to these two cases; but in the periodic problem we have an infinite number of possible energy values between, with appropriate changes of phase between 0 and π from one cell to the next.

10.4. The Finite Crystal and Periodic Boundary Conditions. In the preceding sections we have been taking up the infinite one-dimensional crystal, or periodic potential problem. Actually, of course, we are always dealing with a finite crystal; and we shall show in this section that this leads to a finite number of energy levels, one per atom of the crystal for each energy band, rather than the continuum of energy levels in an energy band which we have found for the infinite crystal. This is an important distinction in connection with the Pauli exclusion principle, where we must know the number of available energy levels. There are two methods which we can use to discuss the finite lattice. In the first place, we really consider the boundaries of the crystal, impose suitable boundary conditions on the solution of Schrödinger's equation, and determine the stationary states in that way. In the second place, we can use what are called periodic boundary conditions, a device which does not exactly represent the physical situation, but is approximately equivalent to the correct boundary conditions, and is considerably easier to apply. We shall illustrate the difference between these two methods by considering free electrons, in which case the problem of solving Schrödinger's equation is trivial.

Suppose we have a free particle in a box of width L, with an infinitely high potential barrier at each end of the box, representing the wall which keeps the particle in. We have already considered this problem. We know that, if x is the coordinate measured from one end of the box, the wave function is of the form $\sin [(2\pi/h) \sqrt{2mEx}]$. This function automatically satisfies the boundary condition that it vanish at $x = 0$, as it must do at an infinitely high wall. In order to have it vanish at $x = L$, we must have $(2\pi/h) \sqrt{2mEL} = n\pi$, where n is an integer. This quantum condition then determines the energy E as

$$E = \frac{n^2h^2}{8mL^2},$$

as we have found earlier. We note that if L is large, the energy levels are close together. In fact, if L is of the dimensions of ordinary samples of matter, the energy levels are so close together as to form practically a continuum.

The method we have just used deals with sine functions. We might, however, prefer to use wave functions $e^{\pm ikx}$, where $k = (2\pi/h) \sqrt{2mE}$. Such solutions are equally good solutions of Schrödinger's equation and have a closer analogy to the traveling-wave type of solution which we have been using for our periodic potential problem. Let us assume an infinite lattice; but let us impose the quite artificial boundary condition that the function be periodic with period L, that is, that the wave function have the same value at $x = L$ that it does at $x = 0$. Then we can show that this leads to the same distribution of energy levels that we got by the correct boundary conditions. If the function is to be periodic, it is clear that kL must be an integral multiple of 2π. This condition, $k = 2\pi n/L$, is at first sight different from that determined above, which may be rewritten $k = \pi n/L$. However, we can show very easily that the two results are effectively equivalent. We note that in either case we have the statement that allowed stationary states are described by equally spaced values of k, the spacing being $2\pi/L$ in the one case, π/L in the other, the spacing being twice as great in the case of periodic boundary conditions. On the other hand, there is something we have overlooked: with the actual boundary conditions, n takes on only positive values, while with periodic boundary conditions both positive and negative values of k are to be used, since we have waves traveling both to the left and the right. Consider a given range of k values, corresponding to a given energy range. With the actual boundary conditions we consider just a positive range of k's, corresponding to positive n's; with the periodic boundary conditions we have twice as great a range, on account of using negative as well as positive k's, but energy levels are spaced twice as far apart. Thus in either case we find the same number of energy levels per unit energy range, and it is this quantity that is significant.

With the periodic potential problem the periodic boundary conditions are more appropriate, since we are using functions modulated according to the factor $e^{\pm ikx}$. We may demand, just as with the free particle, that the wave function be periodic with period L. Then we shall find, just as before, that we do not have allowed states for any arbitrary value of k, but only for discrete values, spaced by the amount $2\pi/L$. Now we have seen that the unit cell along the k axis has a length $2\pi/a$. Obviously only those values of k within the unit cell will contribute different energy levels, corresponding points in other unit cells merely repeating the same energy levels and wave functions. Thus there will be

$$(2\pi/a)/(2\pi/L) = L/a$$

different energy levels per energy band. But this is just the number of unit cells in the length L. Thus we have established the important result: the number of discrete energy levels in a crystal, in a given energy band, is equal to the number of unit cells in the crystal. We shall find later that this result holds in the three-dimensional case, as well as in our present one-dimensional problem.

Consequences of this are obvious, when we consider small numbers of cells in the crystal. Thus if there is only one atom in the crystal, we have but one energy level per energy band; the energy bands do not really exist at all. If there are two atoms, we have the problem of two centers. There are two energy levels, corresponding to $k = 0$ and $k = \pi/a$; we have already seen that these are the symmetric and antisymmetric wave functions, respectively. For three atoms there are three energy levels, and so on. As the number of atoms becomes very large, these energy levels, which are quite discrete for a few atoms, become so numerous that they form practically a continuum. They are not really a continuum, however. And we may anticipate the results of the application to the molecular orbital model of the crystal, and the use of the exclusion principle, by pointing out that we are allowed to have just as many electrons per energy band, of one spin, as there are atoms in the crystal; that is, we may have just one electron per atom per energy band with each spin.

In the preceding section, in Eq. (10.3.4), we had occasion to calculate a matrix component of energy, involving integrating over a range of x which we did not specify at that time. Now that we have considered the boundary conditions in the crystal, we can take care of this omission. We wished to integrate the quantity $\exp i(k_j - k_i + 2\pi h/a)x$ with respect to x. It is now clear that we should use periodic boundary conditions for this problem, since we are dealing with the exponential type of wave function, and that we should integrate from 0 to L. From what we have seen in the present section, we see that the only k_i's which are admissible are those such that $e^{ik_i x}$ is a periodic function with period L. Furthermore, the function $e^{2\pi i h x/a}$ is periodic with period L, since L/a is an integer, the number of atoms in the crystal. Hence our whole exponential is periodic with period L, and this is all that is needed to make the integral in (10.3.4) vanish exactly if it is integrated over the distance L.

10.5. The Three-dimensional Periodic Potential; the Reciprocal Lattice. We can now go on to the case of the three-dimensional lattice. Here we cannot solve any special cases as easily as we could handle the case of periodically spaced potential wells taken up in the preceding sections; but we can give general proofs of the periodicity properties of the solutions, without the need of carrying through a particular case. Let us proceed, using only the fact that the potential has a threefold periodicity, and using the perturbation method of Sec. 10.3, treating the problem like an electron-diffraction problem with Bragg reflection.

The characteristic of a periodic lattice, such as one has in a crystal, is that there are three vectors, a_1, a_2, a_3, determining the unit cell, such that if the crystal is displaced through any one of these vectors it coincides with its initial configuration. Thus more generally a translation $m_1 a_1 + m_2 a_2 + m_3 a_3$, where m_1, m_2, m_3 are integers, will move the lattice into coincidence with itself. The potential energy then must be unchanged when such a translation is made. Let us try to find a Fourier expansion of the potential $V(x,y,z)$, similar to (10.3.2), expressing this periodicity. To do this, it is convenient to introduce three vectors b_1, b_2, b_3, satisfying the relations

$$a_i \cdot b_j = 0 \qquad \text{if } i \neq j,$$
$$= 1 \qquad \text{if } i = j. \tag{10.5.1}$$

These vectors b are called reciprocal to the a's, in that, from (10.5.1), the products of the a's and b's in a sense are unity. Then we can write

$$V(x,y,z) = \sum_{h_1h_2h_3} V_{h_1h_2h_3} e^{2\pi i(h_1b_1+h_2b_2+h_3b_3)\cdot r}, \tag{10.5.2}$$

where h_1, h_2, h_3 are integers which go from $-\infty$ to ∞, and r is the radius vector of components x, y, z. This obviously reduces to (10.3.2) in the one-dimensional case, where r reduces to x, b is a scalar equal to $1/a$. The periodicity of V follows at once if we let r increase by $m_1a_1 + m_2a_2 + m_3a_3$, using (10.5.1). It is sometimes convenient to imagine a space, called a reciprocal space, in which we set up a lattice, the reciprocal lattice, based on the vectors b_1, b_2, b_3, just as the space lattice is based on the vectors a_1, a_2, a_3. Each lattice point of the reciprocal lattice then is associated with a set of integers h_1, h_2, h_3, and one of the Fourier components $V_{h_1h_2h_3}$ is attached to each lattice point.

The unperturbed wave functions, representing plane waves, then can be written in the form $e^{ik\cdot r}$, where k is now a vector, in the direction of the wave normal (or momentum of the particle), and whose magnitude is $2\pi/\lambda = 2\pi p/h$, p being the momentum of the particle, and λ the wave length of the wave. Let us now find the nondiagonal matrix component V_{ij} of the potential energy between two waves with wave vectors k_i and k_j, as we found for the one-dimensional case in (10.3.3) and (10.3.4). When we use the expansion (10.5.2) for the potential energy, we find at once

$$V_{ij} = \sum_{h_1h_2h_3} V_{h_1h_2h_3} \int e^{i[k_j-k_i+2\pi(h_1b_1+h_2b_2+h_3b_3)]\cdot r} \, dx \, dy \, dz. \tag{10.5.3}$$

Here, as in Sec. 10.3, the integral will be zero if we sum over the finite crystal (using periodic boundary conditions in analogy with the method of Sec. 10.4) unless the exponent is zero, which demands

$$k_i - k_j = 2\pi(h_1b_1 + h_2b_2 + h_3b_3). \tag{10.5.4}$$

The general conclusions from this result will be exactly analogous to the one-dimensional case of Sec. 10.3. First, we conclude that the perturbed wave function consists of a sum of functions with propagation vectors $k_j = k_i - 2\pi(h_1b_1 + h_2b_2 + h_3b_3)$, which can be expressed as a product of the function $e^{ik_i\cdot r}$ and a periodic function of x, y, z, with the periodicity of the crystal lattice. This is Bloch's theorem for the three-dimensional case. Second, the amplitude of the perturbed wave will be large only if the energies of the waves with propagation vectors k_i and k_j are very nearly the same. For maximum amplitude, we must have these energies equal, and this means, since the energy is equal to $k^2h^2/8\pi^2m$, that k_i^2 must equal k_j^2. Thus the condition for scattering is as shown in Fig. 10.5.1: a sphere whose radius is $|k_i|/2\pi = 1/\lambda$ in the reciprocal space, with center at the origin, must pass not only through the point $k_i/2\pi$, but also through another point $k_j/2\pi$ which has a similar position in another cell of the reciprocal space. This is the usual way of stating the Bragg condition in the reciprocal lattice.

We can easily get the relation between this statement and the more conventional formulation of the Bragg condition. This demands setting

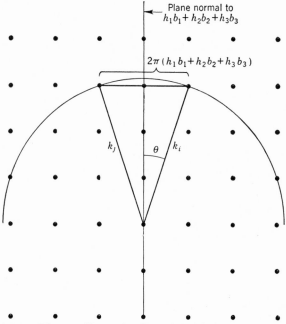

FIG. 10.5.1. Diagram illustrating Bragg's law in the reciprocal lattice.

up an infinite set of parallel planes which contain all the lattice points $m_1a_1 + m_2a_2 + m_3a_3$. The set of planes given by the linear equation

$$(h_1b_1 + h_2b_2 + h_3b_3) \cdot r = \text{integer} \qquad (10.5.5)$$

will obviously satisfy this condition. This will be a set of planes normal to the vector $h_1b_1 + h_2b_2 + h_3b_3$, and with a spacing given by d, where

$$|h_1b_1 + h_2b_2 + h_3b_3|d = 1. \qquad (10.5.6)$$

In Fig. 10.5.1 we can then set up the plane through the origin normal to the vector $h_1b_1 + h_2b_2 + h_3b_3$, as shown, and it will be parallel to the family of lattice planes in question. We show on the figure the glancing angle of incidence θ; and it is clear that we have

$$\sin \theta = \frac{2\pi|h_1b_1 + h_2b_2 + h_3b_3|}{2|k_j|},$$

which at once leads to

$$\lambda = 2d \sin \theta. \qquad (10.5.7)$$

This is the Bragg law $n\lambda = 2d \sin \theta$, except for the omission of the integer n. To introduce this integer, we note that Eq. (10.5.6) really introduces an infinite number of spacings d, all related to planes with the same wave normal. The wave normal is in the direction of the vector $h_1b_1 + h_2b_2 + h_3b_3$, but we have an infinite number of allowable vectors of this type, all in the same direction, since if we have one set of integers h_1, h_2, h_3, we can multiply them by any integer without changing the direction of the vector. Let us define a spacing d_0 by choosing the h's to give the smallest such vector; then the other allowable values of d are given by the equation $nd = d_0$. In terms of d_0, (10.5.7) becomes

$$n\lambda = 2d_0 \sin \theta, \qquad (10.5.8)$$

which is Bragg's relation in the usual form.

We have now used our electron-diffraction picture to investigate the properties of the solution of the periodic potential problem in three dimensions. Our perturbation solution shows that the wave function will be a sum of plane waves satisfying the relation (10.5.4); that is, their k vectors will be located at corresponding points in different unit cells of the reciprocal lattice. It is not a very great extension of this to show that, as in the one-dimensional case, this results in a periodicity of the energy in the k space, or the reciprocal space, so that a central cell of reciprocal space contains complete information regarding the energy.† We find energy bands, as in one dimension, though the existence of three dimensions proves to lead to complications not present in the one-dimensional case. For instance, it can well happen that energy bands corresponding to different types of wave functions can overlap, in such a way as not to leave any energy gaps. This turns out to be characteristic of excited energy levels, and to have an important bearing on the metallic state. Nevertheless, the general situation is as in the one-dimensional case.

The effect of the finite size of the crystal, or of having periodic boundary conditions, likewise is as in the one-dimensional case. We may assume a three-fold periodicity of boundary conditions, the wave function repeating after a distance L_1 along the direction of a_1, L_2 along a_2, etc. Then we

---

† For a general discussion of this problem, see J. C. Slater, "The Electronic Structure of Metals," *Rev. Mod. Phys.* **6**, 209 (1934). This reference contains further development of many subjects treated in the present chapter.

find in an obvious way that the stationary states are represented by a network of points in the reciprocal space, very closely spaced, such that the spacing along the b_1 direction is $1/N_1$ of the spacing of the unit cell in the b_1 direction, and so on, for the other directions, where $N_1 = L_1/|a_1|$, or that it is the number of cells in the distance L_1, etc. The total number of such lattice points in unit cells of the reciprocal lattice is then $N_1N_2N_3$, or the number of unit cells in the repeating volume determined by the distances L_1, L_2, L_3. Thus we arrive at the same result found in the one-dimensional case, that the number of energy levels per energy band just equals the number of unit cells in the crystal. If, instead of using periodic boundary conditions, we apply real boundary conditions to the actual crystal, we find that the mathematical difficulties are greatly increased, on account of the possibility, which does not come in in one dimension, of having different shapes for the crystal. It can be proved, however, that even in this general case the same result holds regarding the relation between number of energy levels per energy band and number of unit cells in the crystal.

10.6. The Nature of Energy Bands in the Metallic Crystal. We now have a general picture of the principal properties of the wave functions and energy levels in a periodic po-tential in three dimensions. Let us proceed to the specific case of a metallic crystal and try to get some understanding of the type of energy bands which we find in that case. First it is worth while saying a little about the methods which

FIG. 10.6.1. Periodic potential in a metallic crystal.

have been used for approximate solution of Schrödinger's equation for this case.

The potential energy function met in a metal combines the aspects of periodicity characteristic of the crystal lattice and of spherical symmetry characteristic of an individual atom. Near the nucleus of a given atom, the energy of interaction of the electron with that atom is so much greater than that with any other atom that we can neglect the others, and we have only the central field of the Hartree approximation for that atom. On the other hand, in the region intermediate between atoms, several neighboring atoms will exert comparable forces, and the potential is modified accordingly. In a line cutting through the centers of a row of atoms, the potential will have the aspect shown in Fig. 10.6.1; but the potential minima will be arranged on some sort of periodic lattice in three dimensions. We can now solve Schrödinger's equation in the interior of one of the atoms. In that region it is a central field problem, which we know how to handle.   However, we need to know the solution for arbitrary energy, just as in the one-dimensional problem of potential wells we needed solutions for all energies.   A solution of Schrödinger's equation satisfying a suitable boundary condition at the nucleus of the atom, but with the wrong energy to represent a stationary state, would in general go exponentially infinite as we went out to infinity; but this does not concern us in the present case, for we need merely impose the condition that the function and its derivative be continuous in going from one atom to another.   In the one-dimensional case this was very simple to accomplish, for we had a boundary condition at only one point between each pair of

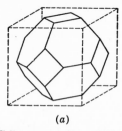   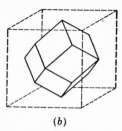

(a)   (b)

Fig. 10.6.2.   Cells surrounding single atom in crystal: (a) body-centered cubic structure; (b) face-centered cubic structure.   Dotted lines represent unit cells, containing two atoms for the body-centered structure, four for the face-centered.

potential wells.   In the three-dimensional case, however, it is very difficult.   We can carry out an approximate solution, in the following manner.

Let us take a given atom in a metallic crystal and draw the lines joining such an atom to its nearest neighbors.   Draw the planes bisecting these lines perpendicularly.   These planes will enclose a cell of fairly complicated shape, surrounding the atom in question; for example, in a body-centered cubic crystal, such a cell is in the form of a cube with its corners cut off.   Such cells for the simplest crystal structures met in ordinary metals are shown in Fig. 10.6.2.   These are not unit cells of the crystal; in most cases, even of the simple metallic structures, there are two atoms in a unit cell.   They form, however, volumes such that an infinite number of similar volumes, regarded as blocks, could be stacked together to fill all space.   Furthermore, they have a single atom at the center, and, being cubes with the corners cut off, or similar structures, do not depart widely from a sphere.   They are, in fact, the solids which would be formed by stacking balloons or rubber balls in the same way as the atoms of the crystal, and squeezing these balloons until they touched along flat planes, leaving no spaces between.

Inside one of these cells we have a single potential well at the center; outside this, the potential becomes relatively constant as we reach the potential maximum between one cell and another. We have seen that we can solve Schrödinger's equation within such a cell for any arbitrary energy. We can, in fact, find an infinite number of solutions of Schrödinger's equation in the cell, for each energy, for we can have solutions for all values of the quantum numbers l and m, which we met in discussing the atomic problem. This infinite variety of solutions is the analogue, in the three-dimensional case, of the existence of two solutions, the symmetric and antisymmetric, in the case of the potential well in the one-dimensional problem. The correct solution then can be built up by making a linear combination of all these solutions for the same energy, but with all l's and m's. The infinite number of arbitrary constants arising in this way can be used to satisfy the condition that the function and its slope be continuous at all points where one of the cells joins its neighboring cells, just as in the one-dimensional case we were able to attain continuity at the two edges of the cell by use of the two available functions.

It is obvious that it is not practicable to use this infinite number of functions and to satisfy the boundary conditions all over the surface of the cell. An approximation which has proved practicable, and which gives some sort of approximation to the correct solution, is to use enough functions to satisfy boundary conditions at the mid-points of the various plane faces of the cell. This has been carried through in a practical way, and its final result is a determination of the wave functions and energy, as functions of the vector quantity k. The mathematical relations come out in forms suggesting Eq. (10.2.1), relating the quantity k to certain ratios of derivatives of wave functions to the values of those functions at the edge of the cell; the functions concerned are those associated with different l values, or the s, p, d, etc., functions. The correct periodicity properties come out automatically, and while the resulting energy bands are certainly rather far from the truth, they still give qualitative indication of the true nature of the energy as a function of k. They also indicate one important fact: the final wave functions cannot be characterized by the quantum number l; they are not s, p, etc. levels, but mixtures of these. In other words, the various atomic wave functions become combined, as in the perturbation theory, to lead to wave functions in the crystal.

The results of these calculations are in the form of energy as a function of k, for each of the energy bands. These are not dissimilar functions to those which we have found in our one-dimensional case. The energy has a minimum or maximum in the center of the reciprocal space. We can divide this reciprocal space into cells, just as we can divide real space into cells. In both spaces there are several points, often two, per unit cell, of identical properties, on account of the crystal symmetry; for instance, it can be shown that if the crystal is body-centered cubic, the reciprocal space has face-centered cubic symmetry properties, and vice versa. The central cell of reciprocal space, of such a shape that we can subdivide the whole space into an infinite number of such cells, is often called a Brillouin zone. Then if the energy has a minimum or maximum at the center of this Brillouin zone, it likewise has a similar behavior in every other zone; it is a periodic function, repeating in each. It always has a value which approaches a maximum or minimum as we approach

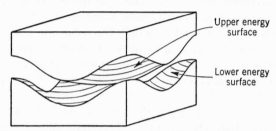

Upper energy surface

Lower energy surface

Fig. 10.6.3. Two energy surfaces, energy plotted vertically as function of x and y components of momentum, showing how it is possible to have no energy gap between two bands, even though the energy surfaces do not cut each other. The case shown in the figure is simpler than that existing in any real crystal.

the boundary of the zone along the normal to the boundary, on account of its periodicity. Just as in the one-dimensional problem, we shall have an infinite number of different values of energy as a function of k in the Brillouin zone, each corresponding to a different energy band. Each energy band has enough separate stationary states, in a finite crystal, to accommodate one electron (of each spin) per atom of the whole crystal. But now, in contrast to the one-dimensional case, it no longer necessarily follows that there is an energy gap between different energy bands. We can describe the reason for this more easily in terms of a two-dimensional model, in which there are two components of k, rather than three, so that we can plot energy E as a function of k_x and k_y, in an ordinary three-dimensional space.

When we do this, we can speak of energy surfaces, lying at different heights. These can be indicated as in Fig. 10.6.3. In general, these surfaces, associated with different energy bands, do not cut each other. Nevertheless, it is quite clearly possible for some parts of an upper energy surface to extend down below the topmost part of a lower energy surface, so that there is no value of energy between them for which there is no allowed value of k, and yet without crossing of the energy surfaces. This situation very often occurs, particularly at higher energies. We shall see that, as in the one-dimensional case, the lower energy bands are very slightly spread out; but the upper ones are spread more and are likely to overlap, so that above a certain energy it generally comes about that all higher energies are allowed values for waves propagated with one value or another of k.

We are now ready, in the next section, to consider a little more specifically the nature of these energy bands for some particular cases. It is most valuable here to consider the total extension of the energy bands, as a function of the internuclear distance in the lattice. In other words, we imagine the lattice to be expanded or contracted, going in the limit to infinite separation of the atoms, but without change of crystal structure. At infinite separation we naturally have the energy levels characteristic of the separated potential minima, or sharp energy levels. These may not necessarily agree exactly with the energy levels of the separated atoms, if we make the same sorts of errors in setting up our potential functions that we did in considering the molecular orbital model of the hydrogen molecule. Nevertheless, in a general way we shall have energies similar to the various atomic stationary states. As the atoms are brought closer together, however, the bands will widen, until finally they will overlap at small distances.

10.7. Energy Bands as Function of Interatomic Distance. An example which has been fairly thoroughly worked out is the sodium crystal. In Fig. 10.7.1 we show the way some of the energy levels of the atom broaden out as the interatomic distance decreases. The $2p$ level stays as a practically infinitely narrow band down to very small distances; it will not begin to broaden until the $2p$ wave functions in the separated atoms begin to overlap, and this hardly happens at all at the actual internuclear distances. The same thing holds for the $1s$ and $2s$ levels, which lie lower than those shown in the diagram. In other words, these levels, which form the inner shells of the sodium atoms, are practically not affected by the fact that the atoms are in a crystal. Each of these levels is capable of holding just as many electrons per atom as in the separated atoms, and we know that there are enough electrons in the separated atoms to fill these bands completely.

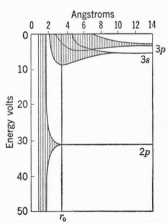

Fig. 10.7.1. Energy bands of metallic sodium as function of internuclear distance.

The $3s$ and $3p$ levels, however, broaden out at much larger interatomic distances. The reason for this, of course, is that the atomic wave functions are much more extended and begin to overlap at larger distances. The actual interatomic distance in the metal corresponds to about the minimum of the 3s band, in the figure. Now the 3s band, of course, can accommodate two electrons, one of each spin, per atom, and the 3p can accommodate six, three of each spin. In the actual crystal we have but one electron per atom to go into these levels. If we count up from the bottom of the 3s band to see how high we must go to get one electron per atom, we come about halfway up this 3s band. In the actual metal, since the lowest wave functions are occupied, all levels up to this halfway mark are full. We can show, even from this very simple diagram, in a general way why it is that the sodium crystal has its minimum energy, and finds a stable state, at about the minimum of this 3s band. Clearly, there will be a connection, though it is by no means a simple one, between the average energy of the electrons in their occupied levels, in the diagram, and the energy of the crystal as a whole; we go further into this connection in Appendix 17. And clearly, the occupied energy levels all dip, as we reduce the internuclear distance of separation, their center of gravity having a minimum at about the same place as the minimum of the 3s band, and then rise again. In Appendix 17 we say something about all the terms that come into the calculation of the energy of a metallic crystal and show that this picture is oversimplified; nevertheless, the energy terms we have indicated in this way are the most important ones in finding the crystal energy, and this simple argument is, in a general way, correct in showing the nature of the binding energy of the crystal, and in showing why the stable structure comes where it does.

If we add another charge to the nucleus, and have magnesium, we shall not greatly change the nature of the energy levels. Now, however, we shall have two electrons per atom in the 3s or 3p shells. At large distances, these will fill the 3s band, leaving the 3p band empty. At smaller distances, however, we see that there is a sort of overlapping of these two bands, leaving no gap between them. The two electrons per atom will then fill the combined band part way up, leaving empty levels immediately above the filled one, as in sodium. This situation is very similar to that which we discovered, in the preceding chapter, where we discussed the Be_2 molecule. There, as here, it was the overlapping of the s and p levels which allowed the valence electron to be partly in a p state at the actual internuclear distance, though at large distance it would be entirely in the s state. And here, as there, the net result of this possibility is to lower the electronic energy in the neighborhood of the internuclear distance, and to make binding possible.

As we go to heavier and heavier atoms, the energy levels will change only gradually, and we see that we shall continue to have our combined 3s and 3p band partly filled with electrons, leaving unoccupied levels immediately above them, until we have eight such electrons per atom, or until we come to the inert-gas configuration.   At that point, we should have no binding, since the center of gravity of the energy levels of the electron would tend steadily upward as the interatomic distance was decreased, and there would be no minimum.   Thus this picture correctly describes the repulsion of inert-gas atoms for each other.   At the same time, we see that there is an empty gap immediately above the filled

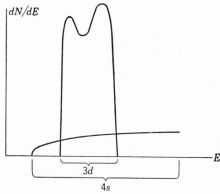

FIG. 10.7.2.   Energy bands for transition-group element showing broad 4s band, narrow 3d (schematic).

bands.   We shall see shortly that this is the mark of an insulator; this ties in with the fact that a collection of inert-gas atoms would not be a conductor.

The features which we have been discussing are those met in a good many metals.   Additional interesting situations arise in the transition-group metals and in the rare earths.   In the iron group the 4s, 4p, and 3d levels have bands somewhat as in Fig. 10.7.2, which is rather schematic. The energy levels of these various bands at large internuclear distance are not far apart.   However, the 3d wave functions are so much less extended than the 4s and 4p that their energy band does not begin to be broadened out at nearly such large internuclear distances as for the 4s and 4p.   Thus it can come about that the 3d band at the actual internuclear distance is rather narrow, and yet is capable of holding 10 electrons per atom, while the 4s and 4p, which can hold another eight electrons, are very much broader.   If we adopt this energy-band picture, we must assume that in the various elements of the iron group, there will be enough electrons in 4s levels to fill up the bands to the level of the 3d (a fractional number of electrons; this of course merely means that the correct wave function is made up of linear combinations of wave functions corresponding to different integral numbers of electrons in this state), plus enough 3d electrons to make the atom neutral. We shall see later that the partly filled 3d band leads to the magnetic properties of the iron-group elements, and from magnetic measurements we shall see how one can get rather accurate experimental values of the number of electrons in the 3d band. Similar things occur in the other transition groups, and in the rare earths the 4f band is even narrower than the 3d band in the iron-group elements.

10.8. Distribution of Energy Levels. At a given internuclear distance, in particular at the observed distance in the crystal, it is clear that there will be certain energies occupied by energy levels, and other gaps where there are no energy levels. It is now interesting to go one step further, and ask how many energy levels there are per unit energy range in the energy bands. As a first step in investigating this distribution, we can consider the corresponding problem for free electrons. The energy of a free electron, in terms of the propagation constant k, is given by $E = k^2 h^2 / 8\pi^2 m$. In a three-dimensional space in which k_x, k_y, k_z are plotted as coordinates, so that $k^2 = k_x^2 + k_y^2 + k_z^2$, the surfaces of constant energy will then be spheres. We have already seen that, in a crystal satisfying periodic boundary conditions, with periodic length L_1 along the x axis, L_2 along y, and L_3 along z, there will be a lattice of points in the k space, each representing a stationary state, the spacing being $2\pi/L_1$ along k_x, etc. We may then say that each rectangular volume of dimensions $2\pi/L_1$, etc., or of volume $(2\pi)^3/L_1 L_2 L_3 = (2\pi)^3/V$, where V is the volume of the crystal, will contain one stationary state, or will accommodate two electrons, one of each spin. The number of energy levels whose energy is less than E will then be the volume of k space inside the sphere corresponding to this energy, divided by the volume associated with a single state. Thus, since the volume of a sphere of radius k is $(4/3)\pi k^3$, we have

$$N(E) = \frac{4}{3}\pi k^3 \frac{2V}{(2\pi)^3} = \frac{8\pi}{3}\frac{(2mE)^{3/2}}{h^3} V. \tag{10.8.1}$$

The number of electrons with levels between E and $E + dE$ is then

$$\frac{dN}{dE} dE = 4\pi \frac{(2m)^{3/2}}{h^3} E^{1/2} V \, dE. \tag{10.8.2}$$

This important result shows us that the quantity dN/dE is proportional to the volume of the crystal, as, of course, it should be (since we expect the number N of electrons to be proportional to the volume), and that it varies with E in the parabolic way shown in Fig. 10.8.1. If we had an actual crystal whose electrons are substantially free, we could

then find the maximum kinetic energy of its electrons, resulting from the
Fermi distribution, by using (10.8.1), putting in for N/V the known
number of electrons per unit volume. We should see in this case, solving
(10.8.1) for E as a function of N/V, that E, the breadth of the occupied
energy band, would increase as V decreased, proportionally to $V^{-\frac{2}{3}}$.

Now as a matter of fact this free-electron approximation proves to be
a very good one for the alkali metals, and not very bad for a good many
other metals. When we actually compute the wave functions and their
distribution in energy levels for the electrons of sodium coming from their
$3s$ and $3p$ levels, for instance, the wave functions prove to be remarkably
like free-electron wave functions, except
in the immediate neighborhood of the
nuclei of the ions. The energy as a
function of k, for this band, is given
rather closely by the free-electron formula, except immediately at the edges
of the Brillouin zone, where, of course,
there is an energy gap. Thus we get
a good approximation to the height of
the maximum energy resulting from
the Fermi distribution, often called the
Fermi level, from (10.8.1), and for the

FIG. 10.8.1.   Energy-level distribution for free electrons.

energy distribution from (10.8.2). We shall then have occupied energy
states up to the energy E_F, the Fermi energy and unoccupied states above
that. In the alkaline earths the situation is somewhat similar, but not
so simple; we shall describe the difference in a moment. In the iron
group the situation again is not very different from this if we leave the
d electrons out of account.

The energy-band distribution of energy levels can simulate the free-
electron distribution, in the case of the alkalies, because the bands overlap so much that almost all evidence of the band edges is lost. On the
other hand, the situation is quite different for a band which does not overlap its neighbors. It is a slightly complicated, but by no means insoluble,
problem to investigate the distribution of states in an isolated band, and
the general result proves to be as shown in Fig. 10.8.2. The quantity
dN/dE rises as $E^{\frac{1}{2}}$, or as a parabola, at the lower edge of the band (where,
of course, E is to be measured from the bottom of the band), but similarly,
it falls again as a parabola at the top of the band. We can prove quite
generally, by simple geometrical arguments, that this general type of
behavior will occur. Now if several such bands overlap, as in the alkali
halides, the resulting curve can simulate a single parabola; this demands,
of course, that there be more and more bands at the higher energies, but

this is in fact the case.   On the other hand, in the alkaline earths, it proves to be the case that there is almost a gap between the lowest band, arising from the *s* levels, and the next higher bands, arising from the *p* levels.   The bands overlap only slightly, as shown in Fig. 10.8.3.   It is for this reason that we stated above that this case is more complicated than for the alkali metals.   Again, in the iron group the *d* band practically intrudes itself into the middle of the *s* and *p* bands, as we saw from our earlier Figure 10.7.2, and corresponds to a very high, narrow band.   It must be very high, because its area, which, of course, measures the total number of electrons in the *d* band, must amount to 10 per atom.

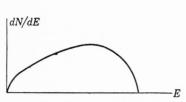

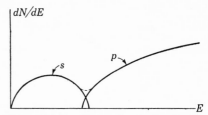

Fig.   10.8.2.   Energy-level distribution for energy band (schematic).

Fig.   10.8.3.   Energy-level distribution for slightly overlapping *s* and *p* bands, as in the alkaline earths (schematic).

There are a number of indirect methods of investigating these distribution functions of energy bands experimentally; fortunately also there is one rather direct method, the study of the soft x-ray emission spectra. Let us illustrate this by using the energy-level diagram of the sodium bands as a function of internuclear distance, given in Fig. 10.7.1.   Suppose a sodium crystal is bombarded by an electron beam, and that an electron is knocked out of the $2p$ shell of one of the atoms, or out of the $2p$ band, which at the ordinary distance of separation is not broadened at all by atomic interactions.   Then one of the electrons in the $3s$ band can fall down into the $2p$ band and emit radiation.   For transitions of this general variety, in many metals, this radiation is in the soft x-ray region, the wave lengths being in the range of 100 A.   Naturally the electron falling to the lower level can be coming from any part of the occupied energy band.   Hence there will be a variety of energy differences, and consequently a variety of emitted wave lengths, and the distribution of intensity in the resultant band of emission will be a measure of the quantity dN/dE, and its breadth a measure of E_F.   Such measurements have been carried out for a number of the lighter elements, and in general, the results check the calculations made by the energy-band method.

There are, however, several complications in making this comparison. In the first place, the intensity of emission depends not only on the number of electrons which can make a given transition, but also on the transition probabilities from one state to another, and we have seen that these depend in turn on the matrix component of electric moment between the two levels.   If we are considering, for instance, the transition from electrons in a 3s band of sodium to the 2s level, the matrix component will be quite different from that to the 2p level, for there is a selection principle, according to which transitions between two levels of the same l value are forbidden, or have zero matrix component.   On the other hand, the levels in the energy band are not pure wave functions of a given l value, as we saw earlier.   Even in the 3s band, there will be some admixture of 3p wave functions, as well as of other l values.   And this 3p part

Be   Na   Al

FIG. 10.8.4.   Intensities in soft x-ray emission spectra, following Skinner and O'Bryan. Top of energy band corresponds to right side of diagram.   Sharp drop of curves for Na and Al at right indicates Fermi level; more gradual drop for Be indicates decrease of density between s and p bands, as in Fig. 10.8.3.

of the wave function will contribute to a nonvanishing matrix component for the optical transition to the 2s level.   This transition probability will then depend on what part of the energy band we are dealing with, for the percentage of 3p level in the 3s will vary rather strongly from the bottom to the top of the band.   In other words, the intensity in the soft x-ray emission spectrum will measure not dN/dE, but a combination of this quantity and a transition probability depending on E, which can be estimated from theory, but which makes the results less conclusive than they otherwise would be.   Another complication which proves experimentally to arise in these soft x-ray emission spectra is that there proves to be considerable radiation of lower frequency than would be expected from the theory, in the form of a "tail" on the expected distribution curve, extending to long wave lengths.   The origin of this "tail" is not thoroughly understood, and this interferes with the interpretation of the results.   Nevertheless, in spite of these two difficulties, the results of the method, as we have stated, are in general agreement with theory and furnish a very valuable experimental confirmation of the theory of energy bands.   In particular, they check well with the expectation that the value of dN/dE at the bottom of a band falls off parabolically, while the distribution of occupied levels at the top of the band falls off sharply to zero; this is seen clearly from Fig. 10.8.4, showing some experimental curves.   In other words, the Fermi level E_F can be seen in a very straightforward way from the results. And in cases like the alkaline-earth metals, the dip between the 3s and 3p bands, which we have described from the theory, is found experimentally.

Situations like the one we have just described, where the density of states dN/dE falls to a very low value at a point where two bands just overlap, have been used by Hume-Rothery to explain the stability of some types of intermetallic compounds. There are some such compounds which crystallize in complicated structures, with a number of atoms in the unit cell. When the Brillouin zone is analyzed, and when we investigate to see how many electrons are located in the central zone, taking proper account of the number of conduction electrons originating from the various types of atoms, which may have different numbers of valence electrons, it is found in a number of such cases that there are very closely enough electrons just to fill the levels of this first Brillouin zone. On the other hand, an alloy with slightly different composition, involving more electrons per atom on the average, may have considerably less stability. The suggestion then is that there are essentially enough electrons in the stable intermetallic compound to fill the distribution up to the very deep minimum of the dN/dE curve. Adding additional electrons at this point would make a considerable change in the energy; if dN/dE is small, dE/dN, or the increase of energy per added electron, would be large. Though this argument has not been worked out in complete quantitative detail, it seems to correlate a good many apparently disconnected experimental observations and presumably has considerable truth.†

10.9. The Difference between Metals and Insulators. We shall postpone until later a thorough discussion of electrical conductivity; but the qualitative features of the distinction between conductors and insulators can be very easily stated, and they have far-reaching implications. When we study conductivity, we shall ask how the energy levels change under the action of an applied external electric field. The change is fairly complicated; but one feature of it would be almost obvious from the outset and is really all we need to use for our present purposes. An electric field acting on a classical electron accelerates it, increasing its velocity, and hence its kinetic energy. In a similar way an electric field acting on an electron in a crystal lattice proves, in general, to increase its energy, by a small amount dependent on the field. For electrical conductivity to be possible then, there must be energy levels very slightly above the highest occupied levels, which are unoccupied, and hence available for the electrons near the Fermi level to be accelerated into. This will always be the case if the electrons partly fill a band. On the other hand,

† For discussion, see N. F. Mott and H. Jones, "The Properties of Metals and Alloys," Oxford University Press, New York, 1936, p. 170.

if there are just enough electrons to fill a band completely, leaving an energy gap above them, there is no possibility for them to pick up small amounts of energy from the external field, and this field cannot produce a current. We shall later see the detailed mechanism by which this comes about, but the net result fits in with this simple picture, showing that a substance in which all energy bands are either completely filled or empty, with energy gaps between, will be an insulator.

This criterion fits in well with our previous discussion of the metallic

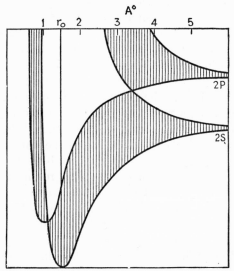

FIG. 10.9.1.   Energy bands in diamond.   The lower band is occupied, the upper one unoccupied, illustrating the energy gap above the occupied levels.

state from the point of view of the Heitler-London method. We saw there that the essential feature for electrical conductivity was unsaturated bonds, allowing free motion to the electrons. Our partly filled energy bands are really only another aspect of this same situation. We see from the present point of view, as previously, that if all electrons are held in electron-pair bonds, we shall have an insulator. An example is diamond, in which each atom is surrounded tetrahedrally by four neighbors and forms a single covalent bond with each, just using up all the electrons. The energy bands for this material have been computed, with results qualitatively like those in Fig. 10.9.1. An energy gap proves to be left between the levels arising from the 2s and some of the 2p levels, and the higher levels. On account of the nature of the crystal structure, it proves to be the case that the lower energy band is large enough to accommodate just four electrons per atom, so that in the crystal this band will be filled, the higher one empty, and the material will be an insulator. A similar situation holds in silicon and germanium, which have the same structure; but the gap is known to get narrower and narrower as we go to the heavier elements. Silicon and germanium are, in fact, semiconductors, whose properties we shall describe in more detail in a moment. The next heavier element of the same structure is one of the modifications of tin, which, as far as is known, is metallic in its behavior. It must be assumed, if this is really the case, that the gap has closed by the time this element is reached. This is an example of a way in which a gradual change in atomic properties can bring about a sudden change from insulating to conducting properties. A similar situation has already been mentioned, in the elements As, Sb, and Bi. These have a structure which would suggest that they were held by saturated covalent bonds, and yet they are metals. The situation proves to be that for them the energy bands, the lower one corresponding to the covalent bonds, and the next higher one, overlap by an extremely small amount; by chance we seem to be in a region of internuclear distance where only a very slight increase of spacing would cause the bands to separate and open a gap between them, resulting in the substances being insulators. It is this very small amount of overlapping, resulting in a very small value of dN/dE at the top of the Fermi distribution (much smaller than with the alkaline earths) which is responsible for the exceptional properties of these three elements, particularly for Bi, whose anomalies are most extreme.

We have mentioned that silicon and germanium, which have small but not vanishing gaps between the top of the occupied band and the bottom of the next empty band, are semiconductors. Let us explain this term in a qualitative way, putting off for a later discussion the more quantitative treatment. At the absolute zero of temperature an insulator will have its lower band entirely filled, its upper band entirely empty, and will carry no current. As the temperature is raised, however, a certain number of electrons will be raised to excited energy levels on account of thermal excitation. Such excitations involve so-called Boltzmann factors, of the nature of $e^{-\Delta E/kT}$, where ΔE is an energy difference, k is Boltzmann's constant, and T is the absolute temperature. If the temperature is high enough so that kT is comparable to ΔE, this can indicate a large number of electrons in the excited levels; in such a case these electrons can carry current as in a metal, and an insulator would conduct metallically at sufficiently elevated temperatures. This generally does not happen, for the ΔE's concerned in energy gaps are of the order of magnitude of several volts, whereas kT for room temperature is only about $\frac{1}{40}$ volt, so that the temperature necessary to bring about such conductivity would be enough to melt and vaporize the material. If the gap is small enough, however, appreciable conductivity can be produced at temperatures not too high above room temperature. Such a material is called an intrinsic semiconductor. Silicon and germanium have small enough gaps so that they show considerable intrinsic semiconductivity at temperatures a few hundred degrees above room temperature.

There is an additional feature generally met in semiconductors, however, which is responsible for most of their conductivity at room temperatures. They contain appreciable numbers of impurity atoms. It can be shown that these impurity atoms give rise to electronic energy levels,

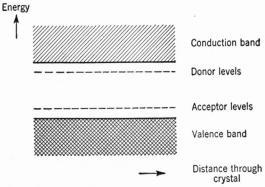

FIG. 10.9.2.   Schematic arrangement of energy levels for semiconductors.

associated with the impurities, which lie within the energy gap between the empty and filled bands. To raise electrons from these impurity levels to the upper band requires then a much smaller ΔE than the width of the gap; in some cases the necessary energy can be as small as $\frac{1}{10}$ volt, or smaller. The Boltzmann factor then indicates that a considerable number of electrons will be raised to the empty level at room temperature and leads to a conductivity of appreciable amount, rapidly rising with temperature, coming from these electrons raised from the impurity atoms to the upper band. Such a material is called an n-type semiconductor (n-type standing for negative charge, the electrons being negative), and the impurity atoms are called donors, since they give up electrons. In other cases there can be impurity levels only slightly above the lower, filled band, which are normally unoccupied. A small temperature can raise electrons from the lower, filled band to these impurity atoms, which are then called acceptors, leaving a few empty energy levels in the lower band. It can be shown that the conductivity arising from these empty levels (or rather, from all the remaining electrons in the band) resembles conductivity produced by fictitious, positively charged electrons; hence such a material is called a p-type semiconductor (p-type for positive charge). Different types of impurities can result in making a given intrinsic semiconductor into either an n-type or p-type semiconductor. Positions of donor and acceptor energy levels are shown in a schematic way in Fig. 10.9.2. It can be shown that many of the important properties shown by semiconductors, such as their rectifying properties, arise as a result of the type of distribution of energy levels derived from such a model. We shall discuss such matters further in a later chapter.

From the discussion which we have given, we see that in a metal the partly filled energy band is responsible both for conduction and for the binding together of the atoms. This band is usually called the conduction band. In an insulator or semiconductor, however, the conduction takes place largely on account of electrons excited to a higher, normally empty band. This is called the conduction band in such a case, and the lower band, normally filled, and responsible mainly for the binding of the substance, is called the valence band.

PROBLEMS

1. Taking the dimensions of a copper crystal lattice, and assuming one conduction electron per atom, find the maximum kinetic energy, in volts, of the conduction electrons, on the assumption that they act like free electrons in a box.

2. To compress a metal at the absolute zero, we must squeeze the electrons into smaller volume, therefore increase the kinetic energy, and do work. This accounts for the larger part of the resistance to larger compressions. Find the formula for pressure as a function of volume, assuming only this repulsive effect.

3. Show that the formula for pressure as a function of volume, found in Prob. 2, is the same that one would get by ordinary gas theory for the adiabatic compression of a gas with the same kinetic energy as the electron gas.

4. A simple model of a metal may be made by assuming the repulsion of Prob. 2, and an ionic attraction, giving a potential inversely proportional to the grating space. Using such a potential, determine its arbitrary coefficient by making the grating space agree with the observed value, and compute the compressibility in terms of the constants of the system.

5. Apply the method of Prob. 4 to the case of copper. Compare the resulting compressibility with experiment.

6. Verify Eqs. (10.2.1) and (10.2.2).

7. Compute the curve of cosh γa vs. E for a case similar to that worked out in the text, and find the curve of E as a function of ka, as in the text.

8. Work out the wave function for one of the lowest energy bands, using the assumptions of Sec. 10.2, for a small value of ka, such as $ka = \pi/8$. Find the real part of this wave function, plot it, and show the significance of the wave length given by $k = 2\pi/\lambda$.

9. Assume that a particle moves in a potential $V = A \cos 2\pi x/a$, in one-dimensional motion. Set up the Schrödinger equation for this problem; it is of a form called Mathieu's equation. Set up a solution in the form of a sum of complex exponential functions, as in Sec. 10.3. Set up the secular equation for determining the coefficients

regarding this as a perturbation problem between the various plane waves, considered as unperturbed functions.

10. Assume in Prob. 9 that A is small in comparison with the energy of the state considered. In this case, set up the perturbation problem by power-series methods. Find the second-order perturbation correction to the energy in the neighborhood of the k values leading to Bragg reflection.

11. Very near a Bragg reflection, in Prob. 10, the two unperturbed energy levels which would become equal if the Bragg condition were fulfilled will be so close together that the perturbation problem between them must be treated by the perturbation method appropriate to a degenerate system. Carry through such a discussion, showing that it leads to the existence of the energy gaps.

12. Putting together the information from Probs. 9 to 11, construct a curve of energy vs. k for the potential $V = A \cos 2\pi x/a$, where A is small.

CHAPTER 11

MECHANICAL, CHEMICAL, AND THERMAL PROPERTIES
OF MATTER

We have now made a preliminary survey of the type of wave functions required to describe the electronic motions in a variety of substances and are ready to start using this information to answer questions about important physical properties of matter. In the course of these applications, we shall carry our fundamental theory further than we have already gone, but it is well to have our goals distinctly in mind in the further development of the subject. There are a great many types of properties of matter in which we may be interested; but they divide themselves rather naturally into two main classes, more or less on the basis of the traditional classification of physics into its branches of mechanics, sound, heat, electricity and magnetism, and optics. The first group of properties are the mechanical and thermal ones, which we shall take up in the present chapter. The second group includes the electrical, magnetic, and optical properties, and those will be postponed until later chapters. When we consider practical applications, the properties of the first type are more important when we consider the uses of substances as structural materials, the second type more important for electrical and optical applications.

Along with the mechanical and thermal properties of matter we naturally group the ordinary chemical reactions, to the extent to which they are produced by heat rather than by light or other such means (as in photochemical processes). We naturally consider such questions as the elastic constants of materials, and their dependence on temperature; in other words, their equations of state. These problems relate to the different phases of matter, solid, liquid, and gaseous, and we are concerned with the coexistence of these phases, and their equilibrium relations. In addition to the equation of state, there are a variety of irreversible phenomena of great importance: viscosity, heat conduction, diffusion, and, in the case of solids, the breaking strength, plasticity, creep, and related subjects. Then in materials capable of undergoing chemical change, whether in the solid, liquid, or gaseous phase, we have problems of chemical equilibrium and of the rate of chemical reactions. This leads us to a very wide field, sometimes called chemical physics, and we can do no more than touch on some of its aspects in a single chapter.   Many of its problems are dealt with in much more detail in J. C. Slater, "Introduction to Chemical Physics," McGraw-Hill Book Company, Inc., New York, 1939. All of the problems of this field depend quite as much on thermodynamics and statistical mechanics as on quantum theory.   What we shall try to do in the present chapter is to give a qualitative survey of many of the most important problems of chemical physics, to try to give a brief account of the methods used to solve the problems, and in particular, to point out the nature of the quantum-theoretical background of the various problems.

11.1. The Relations between Nuclear and Electronic Motions.   The whole problem of the structure of matter is very profoundly influenced by the fact that the atomic nuclei are so very much heavier than the electrons.   This influence comes in in two ways: in relation to quantum mechanics, and to statistical mechanics and thermodynamics.   First we take up the situation regarding quantum mechanics.   We saw in our first chapter that the de Broglie wave lengths for electrons in atomic problems were of the same order of magnitude as atomic dimensions, so that it was absolutely essential to use quantum mechanics in discussing electronic motion; whereas the de Broglie wave lengths for nuclear motion were small enough so that in many cases we were just on the edge of the region where we could use classical mechanics to discuss their motion.   A corollary of this is that the electronic energy levels are widely spaced, as we have seen in our discussions of atomic and molecular energy levels; on the other hand, the energy levels of the nuclear motion are so close together that they can almost be considered to be continuous.

Once we have established the very different nature of the spacing of electronic and atomic energy levels, we come to a relation between our problem and statistical mechanics.   The most fundamental result of statistical mechanics is that the probability of finding a system in an energy level E is proportional to the so-called Boltzmann factor $e^{-E/kT}$, which we have met before in our discussions.   If the spacing of energy levels is comparable to or smaller than kT, which is the case with the energy levels of the nuclear motion at ordinary temperatures, many successive energy levels will be more or less equally populated, the population gradually decreasing as we go to higher energies.   In case we have this gradual variation of population from one state to the next, we can justify one of the very important results of classical statistical mechanics, the principle of equipartition of energy: the mean kinetic energy associated with each degree of freedom is $\frac{1}{2}kT$.   On the other hand, if the spacing of levels is much larger than kT, as ordinarily with the electronic energy levels, the chance of finding the system in any state but the ground state is very small. In this case, naturally, the equipartition does not hold, for changes of temperature, in this range, make hardly any change at all in the population of the states or in the mean energy of the system, and hence the kinetic energy is almost independent of temperature. We then have approximate equipartition between the motions of the nuclei, under ordinary conditions, but no resemblance to equipartition at all when we are dealing with the electronic motions. We find, in fact, that the kinetic energies of electronic motions in the ground state are exceedingly large. The virial theorem allows us to find the relation between the mean kinetic energy and the total energy of a system. From this theorem, assuming that all forces are electrostatic, or vary inversely as the square of the distance, as we have in atomic systems, it can be proved that the kinetic energy is numerically equal to the total energy, but of opposite sign, the kinetic energy, of course, being positive and the total energy negative. Since we have studied atomic structure enough to know that the total energy of the electrons is numerically of the order of a good many volts, this shows us how large the electronic kinetic energy must be, in proportion to kT, which equals $\frac{1}{40}$ volt at room temperature.

The electrons in a piece of matter, in other words, have much more kinetic energy than the nuclei. Even if there were equipartition between electrons and nuclei, the electrons, having a much smaller mass, would have to have much higher velocity. But with the departure from equipartition, there is a very much greater disparity in velocity, so much so that the electrons move with speeds several orders of magnitude greater than the nuclei, under ordinary circumstances. The only exception to this situation would come if we were dealing with problems of atoms moving with really extremely high velocities, as, for instance, the fragments released in nuclear fission; in such cases it is possible for the atomic velocities to be comparable with, or even greater than the electronic speeds of the outer electrons, though not of the inner electrons. If we disregard such problems, however, and consider only atoms in thermal equilibrium at laboratory temperatures, or even temperatures a good deal above those attainable in the laboratory, we still are justified in considering the electrons to move exceedingly rapidly in comparison with the nuclei. This difference in speed is the basis of the whole approximate treatment of the solution of the Schrödinger problem of the motion of electrons and nuclei.

So far, we have tacitly treated the nuclei of atoms or molecules as being at rest, with the electrons moving around them. The justification for this is really the argument we have just gone through: the electrons can make so many revolutions about the nucleus of an atom in the time that it moves a small fraction of an angstrom that we commit no serious error if we assume that it is standing still.   We can make a mathematical argument out of this and really justify our method.   We can set up an approximate solution for the problem of Schrödinger's equation for the electrons and nuclei in the following way.   We assume the electrons have a wave function of the type we have been considering for many chapters, a function of the positions of the electrons, but with the positions of the nuclei as parameters, so that the electronic energy is also dependent on the nuclear positions.   We then assume the nuclei to have a wave function as if they moved under the action of a potential energy function, which was simply this total electronic energy (including electrostatic interactions between nuclear particles), regarded as a function of nuclear positions.   We try the effect of building up an approximate solution of Schrödinger's equation by multiplying the wave functions of the electrons, involving the nuclear positions as parameters, by the nuclear wave function.   When we substitute this combined wave function into Schrödinger's equation, we can show that, in fact, it makes a good approximate solution, which becomes better as the nuclear motions are slower with respect to the electronic motions.   This theorem, which is not very hard to prove, is really the foundation of the whole treatment of the structure of matter by quantum theory, and we have used its results constantly.   It is discussed further in Appendix 18.

The type of solution we have been speaking of has a close relationship to adiabatic processes in statistical mechanics.   We recall that an adiabatic process is one in which the entropy does not change.   When we formulate statistical mechanics in terms of quantum mechanics, we find that the entropy is defined in terms of the amount of spreading of systems into the various stationary states: if systems are widely dispersed between stationary states, the entropy is high, whereas if they are concentrated into a few states, the entropy is low, and in particular if they are all in one state, as the electrons ordinarily are at low temperatures, the entropy is zero.   If, in a given process, the probability of finding the system in each stationary state does not change, the entropy does not change, and the process is adiabatic.   This distinction is often used, in a somewhat restricted way, in discussions of the quantum theory.   If a certain parameter governing a mechanical problem is slowly changed, we can investigate the mechanical motion by quantum mechanics, and we find that the system will, in general, remain in the same stationary state, though the properties of this state may continuously vary.   Thus, for instance, a linear oscillator has an energy $(n + \frac{1}{2})h\nu$, as we have often seen.   The frequency ν depends on the linear restoring force.   Let this restoring-force constant be gradually changed by some sort of external action.   Then the so-called adiabatic theorem of quantum mechanics shows that the quantum number n will not change during the process; consequently the energy of the oscillator will change to make up for the change in ν. This result, as a matter of fact, is not limited to quantum mechanics; it holds in classical mechanics as well, where there is a purely classical theorem that the phase integrals $\oint p \, dq$, which have a classical as well as quantum significance, do not change in an adiabatic process. This adiabatic theorem holds if the change in parameters is sufficiently slow: the criterion is that the change in frequency produced by the change of parameter must be a small fraction of the frequency itself, in the time of one period. If, on the other hand, the parameters change too fast, the situation is quite different: the system will no longer be able to follow adiabatically in the same stationary state, but probabilities of transition to other stationary states will arise, increasing with the rate of change of the parameters, and as a result of the transitions occurring for this reason, the systems will become dispersed through a number of stationary states, and the entropy will rise. Such a process is irreversible, whereas an adiabatic process is reversible, as we learn from the statistical interpretation of the second law of thermodynamics.

We now see the relationship between this adiabatic theorem and our separation of the electronic and nuclear motions. What we are doing is to treat the motion of the electrons adiabatically, as the force fields acting on them change on account of the nuclear motions. This is allowed so long as the nuclear motions are as slow as they ordinarily are. The only exception would come with exceedingly rapidly moving particles. We have already mentioned, for instance, that a fission fragment can move with a velocity comparable to the outer electrons of an atom. We may anticipate, then, that a fission fragment passing through matter can cause electronic transitions, producing nonadiabatic changes in the electronic motion. This, as a matter of fact, is true: fission fragments can ionize atoms through which they pass, as can also alpha particles and other rapidly moving heavy ions encountered in nuclear problems. The energies which they must have to do this, however, are of the order of magnitude of millions of electron volts, for it is only at such energies that they move with speeds comparable with electrons; in contrast, electrons of a few volts energy can ionize atoms which they strike, simply on account of their much greater velocity at a given energy.

The other side of our problem is the one of particular concern to us in this chapter: the fact that the total kinetic and potential energy of the electrons, plus the potential energy of interaction between nuclei, forms a potential energy function to use in discussing the nuclear motions. This, of course, is very plausible: if we are dealing with adiabatic motions of the electrons, then any motion of the nuclei will automatically cause a change in the kinetic energy of the electrons, as well as in the various potential energy terms, and this will then act as a potential energy term as far as the nuclei are concerned. We are then justified in taking our energy curves for the energy of diatomic molecules, polyatomic molecules, and so on, as functions of nuclear position, as being the potential energy curves for the nuclear motions which we must consider in the theory of the equation of state, chemical reactions, and similar problems of the present chapter.

Just one problem remains to be discussed, before we can go on to consider the nuclear motions in more detail. We have a different energy function as a function of nuclear position for each stationary state of the electrons. What energy level are we to assume that the electrons take up, in calculating the nuclear potential energy? In some cases the problem is simple: there may be a unique ground state, with excited electronic states so far above it that they could not possibly exist at the temperatures considered, on account of the Boltzmann factor. This would be the case if we were dealing with a single atom. But in systems of molecules, metals, etc., we often meet cases where this is not true. For instance, in a metal, electrons have excited levels very slightly above the occupied levels, and they can be excited into these levels by thermal excitation. In such a case we naturally should use the equilibrium distribution of electrons characteristic of the temperature concerned, finding a suitable average of the nuclear potential energy curves for the various electronic states concerned in the average. This is the reasonable thing to do in case we are sure that we have reached thermal equilibrium under the conditions of the problem, and the thermal equilibrium of electrons is ordinarily reached in an exceedingly short time, provided we are dealing with relatively good conductors. Thus any departure of charge distribution from uniformity in a metal will dissipate itself in a time which can be calculated by elementary electrical theory, and the time turns out to be of the order of magnitude of ϵ/σ, where ϵ is the permittivity (proportional to the dielectric constant), σ is the electrical conductivity. With the kind of conductivity which we have in a metal, the times prove to be of the order of 10^{-15} sec or thereabouts, so that we can assume in practically all problems that the electrons are in a state of thermal equilibrium.

When we go to poorer conductors, however, the time taken for the electrons to reach equilibrium may become appreciable. In a semiconductor, for instance, if we have produced excess electrons in the conduction band, and holes, or missing electrons, in the valence band, this situation will persist until the holes and electrons neutralize each other, and the evidence is that this process can be slow enough to be comparable with times met in laboratory experiments in the radio-frequency range. And in insulators the times taken for charges to come to equilibrium can become very long indeed. It is well known that a good insulator like quartz can carry a charge for long periods of time before it leaks off. Thus, in the case where we are dealing with good insulators, we must reckon with the possibility that the electrons may for long periods of time remain in stationary states which are not the ground state. Such an excited state which nevertheless has a long lifetime is called a metastable state. Clearly, the larger the system is, the longer a metastable state can persist; charges of opposite sign at opposite ends of a body will move toward each other and neutralize each other more rapidly, the closer together they are. We shall expect to meet examples of such metastable electronic states principally in ionic substances, and in those held by covalent bonds, for they tend to be the best insulators. Such situations actually are known to occur. For instance, in ionic crystals, electrons can become "trapped" in certain potential minima, of a variety which we shall describe later, in which they can persist in metastable states for long periods of time, showing their presence by modifying the optical properties of the substance. And in substances held by covalent bonds, as, for instance, in complicated organic compounds, electrons can become displaced to positions of metastable equilibrium, resulting in excited or ionized states of the molecule which can persist for long periods. When we have such problems of insulators to deal with, we must consider the appropriate metastable electronic configuration in determining the energy as a function of nuclear coordinates, to be used as a potential energy function; but in the other cases, where electronic equilibrium is rapidly reached, we use the thermal equilibrium state of the electrons in setting up our potential function.

11.2. The Physical States of Matter and the Equation of State. We are so much in the habit of thinking of the three states of matter, solid, liquid, and gas, that we forget the great complication really hidden under those terms. Let us think a little about the general nature of these three phases and their variants, and of the equation of state of each; then we can consider the equilibrium between them. The theory has been able to deal much more successfully with solids and gases than with liquids, but we shall give some consideration to each.

Solids, as we know from our discussions of preceding chapters, are largely of three sorts: metals, ionic crystals, and the solids held together by covalent bonds. An important distinction is whether the solid is formed of molecules or not. The solid phase of an organic compound, for instance, is composed of molecules, in which the interatomic forces are of a covalent nature, and hence quite strong. Molecules are held to each other by Van der Waals forces, which are much weaker.   The result is that when the material is heated, the molecules are separated from each other.   If it is heated enough, it vaporizes, and the molecules travel around separately in free space, their Van der Waals attraction and repulsion resulting in their equation of state as an imperfect gas.   With less heating, the material forms a liquid, in which the molecules are still held to each other by their Van der Waals attractions, but in which they are not lined up as in the crystal.   There still is a tendency toward ordering of the arrangements of the molecules, neighboring ones tending to line up, leading to what is called short-range order, but the long-range order characteristic of the solid phase is missing.   The liquid ordinarily has a lower density than the solid; there tend to be open spaces between the molecules, to some extent, and this open space permits the flow characteristic of the liquid, a molecule being able to move into the open space near it, another molecule moving into the space so liberated, and so on.   At the same time that the molecules as a whole are moving around, there are internal motions within a molecule; we can by no means treat them as rigid objects.   Sometimes these motions are of the nature of vibrations, sometimes rotation of part of the molecule with respect to the rest.   We shall consider these motions later, when we take up atomic and molecular motions in solids, liquids, and molecules.

The detailed problems of the equation of state of such materials are very largely parts of statistical mechanics.   We must start with the interatomic and intermolecular forces of the type we have taken up in preceding chapters, but then proceed from that point by statistical methods.   At the absolute zero of temperature, of course, statistical mechanics is not necessary; the crystal which forms under those circumstances will have an energy which is a function of lattice spacing, and which can be found by straightforward application of quantum mechanics, though the problem is too hard to get more than approximate results, using, for instance, the Heitler-London method to discuss the interatomic forces, and the theory of Van der Waals attractions for intermolecular forces.   At higher temperatures we must consider the nuclear motions, and we shall go into these a little more deeply in another section, though we shall not handle any of these questions more than superficially.   The equilibrium between phases, as we know from statistical mechanics, is determined by equality of free energy between the various phases, and the calculation of free energy is an intricate problem of statistical mechanics.   For the solid and gas this can be handled with fair success; for the liquid, a number of approximate methods of treating it have been proposed, but none is completely satisfactory.

One of the more suggestive approaches treats the liquid as essentially a mixture of molecules and holes. By having a molecule surrounded by fewer neighbors than in the solid, the energy of the liquid is greater than the solid, the increase being the latent heat of fusion; the increased randomness associated with the many possible ways of arranging the molecules and holes leads to the increased entropy of the liquid. We know from thermodynamics that the entropy of melting equals the latent heat of melting divided by the absolute temperature of the melting point; thus if we can calculate both latent heat and entropy of melting, we can find the melting point. In principle, we could carry this program through, if we knew the interatomic and intermolecular forces. In practice, it is so formidable that hardly more than a beginning has been made at such calculations. Eventually, no doubt, the theory of the equation of state of such materials will be far enough advanced to need to use the best calculations of interatomic and intermolecular forces which quantum mechanics can provide, but so far it is in a sufficiently elementary state so that ordinarily calculations are made using semiempirical laws of force, determined, for instance, by comparison with diatomic molecules. Quantitative study of the equation of state of molecular substances, based on quantum mechanics, is still rather far in the future.

There are a good many solids, held together largely by covalent forces, whose general properties we can understand from our knowledge of the nature of the covalent bond and of the Van der Waals attraction, but for which almost no quantitative attempt has been made at discussing the equation of state. Thus in the silicates there are bonds, partly covalent and partly polar in character, extending throughout the crystal. In some cases these forces extend through a three-dimensional region, so that the whole crystal is firmly held together, without suggestion of molecular structure; quartz is an example of this situation. In others, like mica, the bonds extend through two-dimensional sheets, the sheets being more loosely held together by Van der Waals forces; the easy cleavage of mica arises from this source. In still others, like asbestos, the bonds extend only through one-dimensional filaments, which can be separated into strands. In the case of the three-dimensional structure, like quartz, it is easy, by adding impurities, to terminate the valence bonds at many points throughout the structure. In such cases an irregularity is introduced into the structure, and a looseness of binding in some parts of it, which can lead to a gradual softening of the solid at high temperatures, as these impurity atoms find the possibility of migrating from point to point. Such materials are the glasses. A characteristic of these substances is that they show no sharp melting point, but a gradual transition from solid to liquid phase. On the basis of the sort of picture we have described, this is not very hard to understand: some parts of the material may have the strong binding characteristic of a quartzlike solid, while others, where the bonds are not continuous, are more easily broken, and are softened at a much lower temperature than the melting point of quartz. With sufficient fluctuations in behavior from point to point of the glass, a gradual transition is the only thing we could well anticipate. Substances like these, with essentially very large molecules, extending throughout the larger part of a large-scale solid, naturally cannot vaporize as can a molecular solid with small molecules. The single unit held loosely to its neighbors by Van der Waals forces is too large to act as a molecule in the gaseous phase. If such a material is heated, we can expect that it will take a high temperature, high enough to break some of the covalent bonds, to vaporize it; the vapor pressure will then be low, the vaporization temperature high, and the vapor will have a different structure from the solid or liquid, relatively small molecules existing in the vapor phase.

The situation of the metals and ionic crystals, in which no molecules form in the solid phase, is quite different from the materials which we have just been discussing. In the solid phase we have regular crystals, which at high temperatures become somewhat distorted by temperature oscillations, but without serious change in their structures. The liquid phase is one which, as in the molecular substances, differs from the solid phase in having short-range order, but not long-range order; spaces open up between the atoms or ions, allowing fluidity, and resulting in the increase in both energy and entropy found in the liquid. In the liquid phase of a metal, there does not have to be any special arrangement of the atoms. Our whole picture of metallic binding indicates that there are no particular directional properties to the binding; an atom can be held to about as many neighboring atoms as can find place in its immediate neighborhood, without regard to exact directions or numbers. Thus the arrangement in the liquid is determined mostly by the maximum number of atoms which geometrically can find space around any given atom; the actual number will approximate this, though leaving some gaps to give the possibility of fluidity.

In the ionic compound, on the other hand, the binding is a result of electrostatic attractions. Thus in the liquid the ions of one sign will tend to be surrounded by ions of the opposite sign, though there will be no preferred arrangements of these ions. In the gaseous forms of these substances, of course, we shall have atoms or molecules. In a metal we may well have an equilibrium mixture of single atoms, diatomic molecules, and molecules with various numbers of atoms. We have seen that the characteristic of a metal is the way in which more and more atoms can be joined to an individual one, without limit; it is obvious in such a case that molecules of any arbitrary number of atoms can exist, and there is no reason to suppose that these will not all be present in the vapor. In the gaseous phase of an ionic compound we shall, of course, not ordinarily have single ions; it would require much too high a temperature to break the positive and negative ions apart. Instead, we shall have neutral molecules (such as NaCl molecules, in that substance), and we may well have molecules of a compound variety in equilibrium with them, composed of several neutral molecules joined together in appropriate orientations by the stray electrostatic fields extending out from the molecules, which in the nature of the case must have strong dipole moments.

11.3. Mixtures of Phases; Physical and Chemical Equilibrium. A very large part of the study of chemical physics, or physical chemistry, is devoted to a study of phase equilibrium: the study of solutions, phase diagrams, chemical equilibrium, and similar problems. A very great part of the theory of these subjects is purely a part of statistical mechanics, and as such is not our primary concern here. The aspects of the subject which particularly depend on quantum mechanics are two: the study of the energy relations involved in mixtures or solutions or chemical compounds, which are problems of interatomic and intermolecular force of the type which we have already considered in a general way; and the enumeration of stationary states, required to compute the entropy, in cases where the motion of the nuclei must be handled by quantum mechanics, so that we cannot use a classical computation of the entropy. We shall not touch on this second aspect of the problem at all, but it is worth while saying something about the first part, the study of energy.

Treatments of such problems as chemical equilibrium, in physical chemistry, introduce as empirical constants the heats of reaction, or differences of energy between different forms of material, as between two atoms and the same atoms formed into a molecule. From our discussion of the structure of molecules and solids, it is clear that quantum mechanics can allow us to calculate these energies. On the other hand, unfortunately in most cases such calculations have been too difficult to have been carried out with any accuracy. A good deal of semiempirical use has been made of the general ideas of quantum mechanics, for instance of the Heitler-London scheme, suggesting forms for the binding energy in terms of exchange integrals, and finding empirical values of exchange integrals from certain observations, then applying the results to other compounds. Such applications are certainly useful in the way of correlating experimental data, and suggesting the general lines which it would be profitable to follow with later, more quantitative calculations. Chemistry is such a vast subject, and the detailed calculations on the basis of quantum mechanics are so hard, that it is obvious that it will never be worth while to try to calculate values for all the constants that can be measured. The value of making a certain number of fairly accurate calculations is to establish the correctness of the general principles, and make sure that we understand what is going on in at least a general way, so that semiempirical methods can be used with more assurance that their results would prove to be verified if more exact calculations were made.

The classical type of problem in physical chemistry is one in which the total energy, or free energy, is a sum of such quantities computed for the various phases present, each phase having a free energy proportional to the amount of that phase. A good many problems, however, are more complicated than this, in that there is a surface energy at the boundaries between the phases which is of importance in the problem. This situation arises whenever the material of one phase is finely dispersed within the other, so that there is a great deal of surface. An extreme example of this is seen in such problems as order-disorder transformations in alloys. It is well known that there are certain alloys in which the atoms of two metals are arranged on a simple lattice, but in which there is a possible ordered structure, in which atoms of, for instance, two types are regularly alternating in the crystal, while there is also a disordered structure, with the atoms of the two types arranged at random. Here we have the maximum possible dispersal of one type of material through the other, and the theory of such situations, including the variation of the degree of order with temperature, involves as parameters the interaction energies between adjacent pairs of unlike atoms. Obviously the calculation of these energies is a problem for quantum mechanics. We see in such a case the conditions under which the dispersal takes place: if the energy between unlike atoms is lower than that between like atoms, the atoms will tend to alternate, whereas in the opposite case they will tend to segregate into regions partly of one type, partly of the other. This reason, based on energy, for the system to prefer the dispersed structure, is in addition to the reason, based on entropy, which holds at high temperatures: greater randomness, or greater entropy, is possible with a dispersed than with an ordered structure, whether the ordered one is a segregated structure or an alternating one. Resemblances of such problems to those met in the theory of solutions, and in particular of solutions with strong electrolytes, are obvious, but we shall not go further into them. All such theories involve hypotheses about interatomic or intermolecular forces; the rest of the treatment is entirely statistical; and though quantum mechanics, in principle, could tell us about the forces, in practice it has not been carried far enough in most cases to be very valuable. Nevertheless, important beginnings have been made in a number of directions in making application to such problems, and further such applications should be a rewarding field for future work.

11.4. Nuclear Motions in Molecules and Solids. We have seen that there are two ways in which quantum mechanics touches the problems of chemical physics: in its prediction of the energy of a piece of matter as a function of the positions of its atoms or their nuclei, and in the dynamics of the nuclear motions themselves. The first half of this problem is the one which we have been sketching in the preceding sections of this chapter, and to which most of the earlier chapters have been devoted. Let us now turn our attention to the second question, the nuclear motions. At the outset we remind the reader that the departures from classical mechanics in this part of the problem are not great, and that they come in principally in the region of low energies, or low temperatures. Thus we do better to start with classical mechanics and consider the relatively small deviations from it, rather than to start from the beginning with a quantum-mechanical description, as we must do in treating the electronic motions.

Let us arrange our discussion by starting with monatomic substances, then diatomic, then substances consisting of more complicated molecules, finally coming to crystals which do not contain molecules. The typical monatomic substances are the inert gases. Their atoms can engage in translational motion, which can be handled completely classically, except at the very lowest temperatures, for the only one of them which remains gaseous at these extremely low temperatures, helium. One can analyze the question whether quantum mechanics enters the problem of their equation of state in an appreciable way by setting up a parameter, equal to the ratio of the de Broglie wave length of the atom when its kinetic energy has some characteristic value, say the value found at the critical point, to a characteristic dimension of the atom, say its radius as determined by the kinetic theory of gases. For almost all gases this ratio is negligibly small; but for helium it is of considerable size, for here all factors conspire to make it large. The critical point comes at such low temperature that the atoms are traveling very slowly, and hence have small momentum and large de Broglie wave length; the mass of the atom is very small, again leading to small momentum; and the radius of the atom is very small, increasing the ratio of de Broglie wave length to atomic radius. For the isotope He^3 the ratio is even smaller than for the usual isotope He^4, principally on account of the smaller mass, so that He^3 is the most nonclassical gas known, as far as its equation of state is concerned. The effect of the quantum mechanics comes in when we consider the behavior of a collision between two atoms, leading to the repulsive term in Van der Waals' equation, or in a more correct equation of state.   Such a collision really must be handled by quantum mechanics. It is a two-body problem which can be reduced to a one-body problem, each atom being effectively repelled by a force acting from the center of mass of the two atoms.   If we have a problem of a particle in a repulsive field, the wave function will go practically to zero at the distance at which the classical collision would occur and will rise to a maximum approximately a quarter wave further out, as shown in Fig. 11.4.1.   Thus the distance between each particle and the center of repulsion will be very seldom found to be less than the sum of the classical distance and an extra quarter wave length of the de Broglie wave; the effect of quantum mechanics is to keep the atoms farther apart than they are classically. Such an effect occurs in helium, whose density in the liquid phase, for instance, is much less than we should conclude by applying classical statistical mechanics to the interatomic potential energy curve, as found from Heitler-London theory.   This great tendency for the helium atoms to stay apart from each other results in the extraordinary mobility of the atoms in

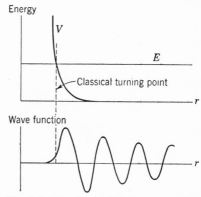

FIG.1 1.4.1.   Wave function near classical turning point of orbit.

liquid helium, which has an extremely low viscosity.   The anomalous low-temperature phase of liquid helium, He II, with extraordinary properties of superfluidity, is presumably a result of the application of Bose-Einstein statistics to He^4, an additional quantum-theoretical effect which we shall not go into.   The fact that helium does not solidify at atmospheric pressure, even at the absolute zero, is presumably a result of the anomalously large interatomic distance arising from wave mechanics; the Van der Waals attraction, which is responsible for holding the other inert gases together in their liquid and solid phases, is overcome by this extra apparent repulsion arising from the large de Broglie wave length.

There is another way in which quantum mechanics affects the equation of state of monatomic gases, which by now has become so commonplace that we hardly notice it, but which furnishes the answer to a puzzle which existed in the classical statistical theory of the perfect gas.   If we treat a monatomic gas by classical statistical mechanics, treating each atom as a small rigid sphere, each atom has six degrees of freedom.   To describe its state completely, we need to know the three coordinates of its center of mass, and three angles determining its orientation in space, two of which may be latitude and longitude angles of some particular axis in the atom (like the north pole of the earth), the third being an angle of rotation about this axis. Such angles are shown in Fig. 11.4.2. In classical statistical mechanics we can show by the theorem of equipartition of energy that each of these six degrees of freedom will have a mean kinetic energy of $\frac{1}{2}kT$, so that the internal energy of the gas, per atom, would prove to be $3kT$. Actually, from the specific heat, it is known to be very close to $\frac{3}{2}kT$, indicating that the translational degrees of freedom have the classical kinetic energy, but that the rotational degrees of freedom have no kinetic energy. The quantum theory provides the explanation of this discrepancy. We have mentioned that the equipartition does not hold if the energy levels are widely separate. Now the energy levels associated with the angular variables are those corresponding to different angular momenta of the atom about its axis. These angular momenta, for a single atom, must arise from electronic motions, since the nucleus is at the center and cannot contribute to rotational motion. We know that the electronic energy levels corresponding to different angular momenta are those of different l values, corresponding to large electronic excitation, and large energy separation, of the order of magnitude of volts. Thus rotational states will not be excited at ordinary temperatures, and will not contribute to the internal energy.

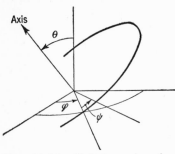

FIG. 11.4.2. Euler's angles, for describing orientation of rigid body. θ is angle between axis fixed in body and vertical (colatitude angle), ϕ is longitude angle, ψ angle of rotation of body about its axis.

We have seen, then, two effects of the quantum theory on the behavior of a monatomic gas: an effect on translation, which is important only in helium, and an effect on rotation, which means that a monatomic gas can be treated as a gas of point masses, without the possibility of rotation, for all practical purposes. Next we go to the diatomic molecules. Here, in the first place, the quantum effect on translation is almost completely negligible. Examination of the equations of state for such gases shows that for H_2 this effect is barely observable, but for other gases can be left out of account. The rotational effect, however, comes in in quite a different way. A diatomic molecule has an axis determined by the line passing through the two nuclei. Rotation about the axis would imply no motion of the nuclei, but only of the electrons, and just as in the monatomic gases this would imply a very high electronic energy level, so that under ordinary circumstances this type of motion would not be excited in temperature agitation. On the other hand, rotation of the atoms of the molecule (change of the angles φ and θ in Fig. 11.4.2) would imply motions of the atomic nuclei, which, on account of their much higher masses, would result in energy levels spaced closely together, so that classical mechanics would almost be applicable. As a matter of fact, for the great majority of diatomic molecules we find experimentally, as this would suggest, that the internal energy is approximately $\frac{5}{2}kT$ per molecule, corresponding to a classical behavior of these two rotational degrees of freedom. On the other hand, for H_2, where we would expect the greatest deviation from classical behavior on account of the small mass of the atoms, the internal energy is found to decrease from $\frac{5}{2}kT$ at high temperatures to $\frac{3}{2}kT$ at very low temperatures. This suggests that the spacing of the rotational energy levels for this molecule is comparable to kT for a rather high temperature, and this, as a matter of fact, is the case. We saw in Chap. 1 that the energy of a rotator is given by $n^2h^2/8\pi^2I$, where n is the quantum number, I the moment of inertia. When we put in the known numbers for these quantities, we find that the separation between the ground state and first excited state of rotation of the H_2 molecule does, in fact, correspond to kT for a very considerable temperature, and more elaborate theory shows that we can account for the observed specific heat by application of statistical mechanics to the predicted energy levels. This application is very considerably complicated by the separation of the rotational levels into two groups, called ortho- and parahydrogen, as a result of interaction between rotational motion and the spins of the nuclei, an effect whose theory would demand going into a good deal more detail than we are able to in an elementary treatment of this sort. Calculation of the spacings of rotational states for the other diatomic molecules shows that the quantum effect should be much less than for hydrogen, and when we couple this with the fact that the others all have higher boiling points, and consequently are in the liquid state at the low temperatures where these effects could be observed, we see that quantum effects on the translation and rotation of diatomic molecules are not of widespread occurrence.

There is another effect coming into the motion of diatomic molecules, however, which is of great importance in studying their behavior. To describe completely the position of the two nuclei of a diatomic molecule requires six coordinates. We have mentioned five: the three determining the position of the center of mass, and the two determining the orientation of the axis. The remaining one is the internuclear distance. Motion in which this quantity changes is the vibrational motion of the molecule, each atom moving toward and away from the center of mass, under the action of the interatomic potential energy curve of the type we have often discussed.   For small energies this potential energy curve resembles a parabola, meaning that the force is approximately a linear restoring force, pulling the atoms back to the equilibrium distance given by the minimum of the curve.   If ν is the vibrational frequency associated with motion under the action of this restoring force, the energy levels are then determined by the familiar quantum condition $(n + \frac{1}{2})h\nu$.   The vibrational frequencies found in most diatomic molecules, as determined from their spectra, prove to be such that $h\nu$ corresponds to a temperature, through the equation $h\nu = kT$, rather large compared with room temperature, though in a few very easily dissociated molecules they are comparable with room temperature. Thus in most cases the molecules are found in their ground states up to room temperature and beyond, and the vibrational motion does not contribute to the internal energy. At higher temperatures, however, excited vibrational levels begin to be occupied, with corresponding contributions to the internal energy and specific heat.   At temperatures high enough for these vibrational levels to be fully excited, there would be a contribution of $\frac{1}{2}kT$ to the internal energy coming from kinetic energy, and an equal contribution from potential energy, since the mean potential energy of a linear oscillator equals its mean kinetic energy.

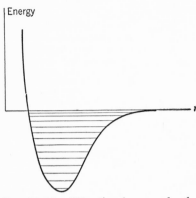

FIG. 11.4.3.   Vibrational energy levels of diatomic molecule (schematic).

At temperatures somewhat above those at which the vibrational levels become excited, we have to consider the possibility of dissociation of the molecule.   The vibrational energy levels are equally spaced, as for a linear oscillator, for the lower levels, for which the restoring force is linear.   For higher energies the spacing decreases, as we see from Fig. 11.4.3, but at sufficiently high energy we meet the situation of oscillation with very high amplitude, and somewhat above this point we have dissociation of the molecule.   It is a problem in statistical mechanics to consider the equilibrium of the diatomic molecule in its various vibrational levels with the single atoms into which it dissociates; but the net result is that the observations are in agreement with the theory, and that as the temperature is raised, dissociation in general increases, though the pressure, as well as the temperature, enters in an important way into the final result.

Next let us consider polyatomic molecules, still in a gas. All three angles are really needed to describe the orientation of the molecule in space, unless the molecule is a linear molecule (all the nuclei in a straight line), and the rotation of the molecule as a whole involves moments of inertia of such value that the energy levels associated with the rotation are close together, and the rotational energy behaves essentially classically. Thus equipartition holds for the rotational as well as the translational energy, and the kinetic energy associated with these two types of motion is $3kT$. The vibrational situation, however, is more complicated than with a diatomic molecule. It is a well-known result of the theory of vibrating systems that if we have a number of particles held together by linear restoring forces, we can introduce what are called normal coordinates, each one being a linear combination of actual coordinates, such that the normal coordinates are independent of each other as far as the equations of motion are concerned. That is, the classical equations of motion break up into a set of separate equations, one for each normal coordinate, each one being just like the equation of a linear oscillator of appropriate frequency.† Correspondingly, it can be shown in wave mechanics that if we have the same problem of a set of particles held by linear restoring forces and introduce the classical normal coordinates as a change of variables, the Schrödinger equation becomes separable, so that we can write the wave function as a product of functions, one of each normal coordinate. The separate differential equation for each of the factors then becomes the Schrödinger equation for a linear oscillator. Each of the normal coordinates will then lead to a contribution $(n + \frac{1}{2})h\nu$ to the energy, where n is the appropriate quantum number, and ν the frequency associated with that normal coordinate; the total energy is the sum of such terms, for all normal coordinates. With a molecule with N atoms, there will be $3N$ variables necessary to determine the positions, of which six are required to determine the position and orientation of the molecule as a whole. The remaining $3N - 6$ variables then represent vibrations, and each of these will be associated with a normal coordinate and a corresponding term in the energy. Just as with the diatomic molecule, the frequencies are generally large enough so that these vibrations are not much excited at room temperatures, but come in at higher temperatures.

It is only for small amplitudes of oscillation that the restoring forces

† See J. C. Slater and N. H. Frank, "Mechanics," McGraw-Hill Book Company, Inc., New York, 1947, Chap. VII, for further discussion of normal coordinates.

are linear, and that we can introduce normal coordinates. For larger amplitudes we meet the complicated situation for the energy as a function of interatomic distances which we sketched in our discussion of the interaction of three hydrogen atoms. The energy will be a function of some sort of the $3N - 6$ variables necessary to determine the configuration of the molecule. At one point in a $3N - 6$-dimensional space in which these variables are plotted as coordinates, the energy will have a minimum; this is the equilibrium configuration. In its neighborhood the energy will be a quadratic function of the displacement from the position of equilibrium, and it is in this region that the normal coordinates can be introduced. If we consider the energy as being plotted as a function of the coordinates, and describe this as an energy surface (as if there were only two coordinates), the energy surface would have an ellipsoidal configuration in the neighborhood of the minimum, and it is shown in the theory of normal coordinates that these normal coordinates are simply axes measured along the directions of the major and minor axes of the ellipsoid. As we go further away from the minimum, however, the energy will rise to various types of plateaus, corresponding to infinite values of one or another of the coordinates, representing the cases in which one or another of the atoms may have been removed from the molecule. This corresponds to the case with the diatomic molecule, in which the atoms dissociate from each other at a quite finite energy. In this complicated situation the Schrödinger equation cannot be solved in any easy way, and we cannot get far at predicting the wave functions and energy levels. However, in these cases the quantum theory is not very important for many purposes, as we have seen, and we can get rather far by a classical discussion of the nuclear motions. We shall describe some applications of this fact in a later section.

In a solid, the situation is much like that of a polyatomic molecule with an enormously large number of atoms. We still have $3N - 6$ vibrational degrees of freedom; and since N is now of enormous size, equal to the total number of atoms in the crystal, the number six is negligible in comparison, and we may say that there are three degrees of freedom per atom. We then have essentially $3N$ normal coordinates, each with an appropriate term in the energy, provided the amplitude of oscillation is small. Each of these normal coordinates can be shown to correspond to a certain standing wave of mechanical vibration in the crystal. Some of these waves are of the nature of acoustical or sound waves: the whole crystal undergoes compressions or shears as in a longitudinal or transverse sound wave. Since we can have only a finite number of such degrees of freedom, these waves cannot have any arbitrary length; it proves to be the case that there is a minimum length, in which the wave length is equal to twice the spacing of the unit cell of the crystal.   There is in fact a far-reaching analogy between these mechanical vibrational waves and the Schrödinger waves which we have found to be associated with the propagation of an electron in a periodic lattice.   We can describe the mechanical waves in the same way by giving their propagation constants in the reciprocal lattice; we have the same sort of periodicity with respect to this propagation vector.   We have frequency bands, instead of energy bands.   We have a certain number of allowed frequencies, associated with the normal coordinates, and amounting to one per unit cell of the crystal, just as we have a certain number of allowed energies in the electronic problem.†   The lowest frequency band corresponds to these acoustic oscillations and is called the acoustical branch of the frequency spectrum of the normal coordinates.   There are, in addition, a finite number of higher branches in the spectrum, corresponding to higher energy bands in the Schrödinger case, just enough to include the appropriate number of normal coordinates.   These higher vibrations correspond to internal vibrations within the molecules, or groups of atoms within the unit cells of the crystals, without motions of the centers of gravity of these groups of atoms as a whole.   The acoustical branch has frequencies extending down to zero, corresponding to real sound waves, whereas the other branches, called the optical branches, have high frequencies, just as molecular vibrations do.

There is then quite a difference between the thermal behavior of the acoustical branch and the optical branches of the vibrational spectrum. In the acoustical branch there are many modes of oscillation with frequencies so low that their $h\nu$'s are small compared with any reasonable kT.   Thus we can use a classical calculation for the energy of these modes.   On the other hand, some of the acoustical modes will have higher frequencies, and must be handled by quantum theory.   Debye's theory of specific heat takes account of this distribution of frequencies and leads to a formula for internal energy and specific heat of the acoustical modes. With the optical modes, the problem is essentially as in molecules, and the internal energy in both these problems can be handled by Einstein's theory of specific heat.   In a polyatomic solid, or solid with several atoms per unit cell, we shall have a sum of Debye and Einstein terms in the internal energy and specific heat.   The result, at high temperatures, where these modes are all fully excited, will be that the kinetic energy will be $\frac{3}{2}kT$ per atom, with an equal contribution to the potential energy, since we are dealing with linear oscillators; that is, we have an internal energy of $3kT$ per atom, leading to a specific heat of $3k$ per atom, or the

† This situation is taken up in J. C. Slater, "Introduction to Chemical Physics," McGraw-Hill Book Company, Inc., New York, 1939, Chaps. XIV and XV.

so-called Dulong-Petit law of specific heats, which proves to be well obeyed experimentally by those solids whose vibrational frequencies are small enough so that we can have the vibrations entirely excited at temperatures which we can reach.

There are some solid-state problems aside from internal energy which depend on this type of calculation. Thus the theory of thermal expansion can be set up in terms of the nuclear vibrations. If we dealt only with the linear terms in the restoring force, we should have no thermal expansion; for a linear oscillator in vibration has an average position which agrees exactly with its equilibrium position, and the dimensions of a crystal made of exactly linear oscillators would not depend on whether the atoms were vibrating or not. On the other hand, if we take into account the nonlinear terms, we see why we should have expansion. In a diatomic molecule in an excited energy level, according to quantum mechanics, or vibrating with fairly high energy, according to classical mechanics, the average internuclear distance will be greater than the equilibrium value, gradually increasing to infinity at the point of dissociation. Grüneisen has set up a theory of thermal expansion depending on the nonlinear terms in the restoring force, which agrees well with experiment.

Another problem depending on nuclear vibrations is that of thermal conductivity. Suppose we had a localization of high temperature somewhere within a crystal. This would mean that the atoms in that region were vibrating with much more amplitude than the average. Now we can set up a theory of the radiation of acoustical energy in a solid, and this would show that a vibrating atom in a nonvibrating solid would send out a spherical wave, gradually dissipating its energy as this wave traveled outward with the velocity of sound. This would spread the energy out through the solid. If it were a perfect propagation of sound, the energy would spread like radiation, however, and not, as heat does, by diffusion. The thing that makes heat conduction resemble diffusion is that the sound waves in an actual crystal are scattered by imperfections in the crystal, and this scattering makes the propagation of energy resemble diffusion and satisfy the correct differential equation for heat conduction. This simple description suggests that anything which tends to scatter acoustical waves of high frequency will decrease the heat conductivity of a solid. This type of thermal conductivity, by the propagation of acoustical waves, is the only mechanism present in insulators, but in conductors the same electrons which carry electric current also can carry heat, and this electronic thermal conductivity is much greater than the other type. This is the reason for the good thermal conductivity of metals, as contrasted with insulators.

The problems of nuclear vibration which we have considered in this section are those in which the atoms are not allowed to depart far from the situation of a linear restoring force.   However, there is an important class of phenomena in which the essential feature is that the atoms can get entirely out of one potential minimum, perhaps into another, thus departing widely from the behavior of a linear oscillator.   We meet such questions in studying the flow of viscous liquids and plastic solids, in chemical reactions, and in many other places.   We shall now consider some of these quite different problems.

11.5. Nuclear Motion in Viscosity and Plastic Flow.   As an initial problem to introduce the type of nuclear motion in which the particle

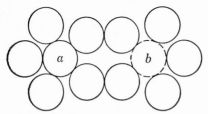

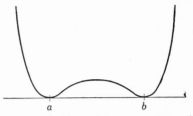

FIG. 11.5.1.   Hole *b* into which atom *a* could move by squeezing through aperture.

FIG. 11.5.2.   Potential energy of atom in case of Fig. 11.5.1.

escapes from a region of linear restoring force, let us consider the motion of an atom in a monatomic liquid, when it happens to be next to an unoccupied hole in the liquid.   We have already noted that the existence of such holes is an essential feature of the liquid state.   Let us have several atoms, as shown in Fig. 11.5.1.   The atom marked *a* will be in a position of equilibrium where it is located.   It, like any atom in a liquid or solid, is acted on by its neighbors, each exerting forces of the general type found in a diatomic molecule.   Thus the potential energy acting on it is something like a sum of ordinary diatomic molecular potential energy curves, one depending on the distance from the molecule in question to each of its neighbors, so that the potential energy goes infinite as the atom gets too close to any of its neighbors and will have a minimum at its position of equilibrium.   In the case shown above, however, by symmetry, there will be an equally good position of equilibrium *b*.   In the mid-position between these two points, the potential energy will be decidedly higher than at either of the positions of equilibrium, for the atom will have to squeeze between other atoms to get through.   Thus there will be a maximum of potential energy there.   If we draw the potential energy as a function of distance along a line drawn through the centers of positions *a* and *b*, we shall have a curve with two minima, as shown in Fig. 11.5 2.

Let us now consider what happens to an atom oscillating in one of these minima with an energy too low to escape to the other minimum.

Our problem is the same problem of two centers which we have approached a number of times from the standpoint of quantum mechanics. We know that if we attack it classically, the particle can oscillate with the same energy on either side of the potential barrier but will never pass over the top, unless its energy is great enough. In quantum mechanics, however, we remember that we get the symmetric and antisymmetric wave functions and combine them to get a wave packet, which resonates back and forth between the two potential wells. The way by which it passes the barrier is called the tunnel effect: it is as if it went through the mountain in a tunnel. The probability of passing the barrier by the tunnel effect gets rapidly smaller as the barrier gets higher or wider. And if we look into the magnitudes involved, we conclude that at ordinary temperatures, with atoms of ordinary size and barriers of an ordinary height, the tunnel effect is in fact of very small importance in this problem of the motion of atoms in a liquid, and that we are almost entirely justified in treating the problem classically, assuming that the particle will not pass through the barrier.

We have forgotten something, however, if we assume that the particle will never surmount the barrier. Proceeding directly by classical statistical mechanics, we remember that the energy of our atom a will fluctuate, on account of the Boltzmann distribution of energies. Sometimes, by virtue of a series of successful collisions with its neighbors, it may happen to pick up enough energy so that it can pass over the barrier. We can, in fact, make a very simple statement: the number of times per second when the atom will pass over the barrier (that is, the probability that it will pass over in unit time) equals the number of times it will hit the barrier per second (or the frequency of oscillation in its potential well) multiplied by the probability that when it hits it will have sufficient energy to surmount the barrier. This probability is of the order of magnitude of $e^{-E/kT}$, where E is the height of the barrier above the bottom of the potential well.

There is thus a quite finite probability of surmounting the barrier, which may be written approximately as $\nu e^{-E/kT}$, where ν is the frequency of oscillation. This probability increases rapidly as the temperature increases, on account of the exponential function. Furthermore, it is a quantity which can take on an extraordinary range of values, with quite ordinary values of ν and E. Ordinarily the frequencies ν of atomic vibrations are of the order of magnitude of 10^{13} cycles/sec. If then $e^{-E/kT}$ equals 10^{-13}, the probability of surmounting the barrier will be unity; that is, in 1 sec the chances are even that the particle will cross the barrier, or it takes a time of the order of 1 sec before it crosses. This happens when $E/kT = (2.303)(13) = 30$, approximately. If we are considering room temperature, where $kT = \frac{1}{40}$ volt, this means that $E = \frac{3}{4}$ ev, approximately. On the other hand, very small increases or decreases of either E or the temperature will make large changes in the probability. Thus, for instance, to double the probability of surmounting the barrier, we need change E/kT by only $\ln 2 = 0.693$, so that if $E/kT = 30$, this means a change of only $0.693/30 = \frac{1}{43}$. In other words, a change in the temperature of only this amount (less than $10°$ at room temperature), or of E by about 0.02 volt (if $E = 0.75$ volt) is enough to double the rate of crossing the barrier. Putting it the other way, if we go from E equal to 0.75 volt to double this amount, the probability of surmounting the barrier will go from 1 per second to 10^{-13} per second, while if it goes to 0.37 volt, half the preceding value, the probability will go to something like 10^6 to 10^7 per second, showing that a time of less than 1μsec will elapse before the particle traverses the barrier. This great range of times, from microseconds or less to times of geologic proportions, shows that in some cases such processes will occur very rapidly compared with laboratory experiments, while in other cases, for all practical purposes, they will never occur at all.

If the two minima a and b are entirely symmetrical, there will, of course, be no preference for one position over the other. Sometimes an atom at a will happen to acquire enough energy to jump to b. It has a considerable chance, at its very first collision with its neighbors at site b, to lose enough energy so that it will not be able to jump over again and return to site a. On the other hand, at some later time it is equally likely to pick up enough energy to return from site b to a. Thus there is no one-sided flow. We can, however, change the conditions of the problem slightly, in such a way as to make one direction of flow more likely than the other, and this is the basis of the theory of viscous flow, and of other types of irreversible processes. Let us suppose that one miminum, say b, is slightly lower than the other; that is, the height of the barrier above minimum a is E, but above b is $E + \Delta E$. Then the probability that an atom in a will pass the barrier is $\nu e^{-E/kT}$, but if it is in b the probability of returning to a is $\nu e^{-(E+\Delta E)/kT}$. Then if in a statistical situation we are equally likely to have the atom in positions a or b, there will be a net probability that the atom will leave minimum a and pass to b, this probability being

$$\nu e^{-E/kT} - \nu e^{-(E+\Delta E)/kT} = \nu e^{-E/kT}\left(1 - e^{-\Delta E/kT}\right) \sim \nu e^{-E/kT}\frac{\Delta E}{kT}, \quad (11.5.1)$$

where the last step comes by expanding the exponential, treating $\Delta E/kT$

as a small quantity. This gives, in other words, a net flow proportional to the difference in height between the two minima. It gives an expression for the rate at which, on the average, the particle would go from the shallower to the deeper minimum, assuming that initially the particle was equally likely to be found in either minimum. Of course, this flow, on the average, would continue until the deeper minimum had a number of particles greater than the shallower one by the factor $e^{\Delta E/kT}$, at which time the flows would equalize, and equilibrium would be attained. This is just the factor necessary to adjust the Boltzmann factors for the two minima; the average number of particles in each minimum, under a condition of thermal equilibrium, will be given by Boltzmann factors involving the energy of the minimum, as measured from some absolute value, and these factors would differ by the amount mentioned above.

We shall find a number of problems in which a continuous flow is possible, the rate of flow being determined by (11.5.1). Before we look for the physical situations underlying these problems, let us consider a little the nature of the function (11.5.1). In the first place, it indicates a rate of transition or flow proportional to ΔE; thus, if particles are equally likely to be found at sites of higher and lower energy, the flow to the sites of lower energy will be proportional to the difference of energy. Furthermore, the function involves the exponential factor $e^{-E/kT}$, increasing very rapidly with increase of temperature or decrease of the height of the barrier. This type of variation is experimentally found for a great many processes depending on thermal activation, and the energy E is called the activation energy. Commonly one plots the logarithm of the rate of whatever process we are considering as a function of $1/T$; the resulting curve will be a straight line, from whose slope we can find the activation energy.

Now let us examine some of the physical cases where we may expect to find an equation similar to (11.5.1). Suppose we have a viscous liquid, flowing with a velocity gradient, one part moving past another. In a liquid the atoms or molecules fit together on a microscopic scale more or less as they do in a solid, though there is no large-scale regularity of structure. It is not easy then for one part of the liquid to flow past another, for the molecules of one part get caught in the molecules of the other. At any given instant, there will be a certain restricted number of atoms or molecules which happen to be caught worse than others: they will be interfering with progress, pushed in opposite directions by the opposing flows of liquid, and tending to hold back some molecules behind them. It may well be that such a molecule, by squeezing through a narrow opening, could get into a more favorable position where it would not hold up the procession. In such a case we have the necessary elements for application of our general discussion. The molecule is being pushed in one direction by an excess of stress, of the nature of pressure, behind it. It is being prevented from going in the direction it wants to by molecules forming an opening which is too narrow for it to get through without excess energy. That is, if it squeezed through the barrier, it would find at the barrier a higher potential energy than in the location where it is. On the other hand, if it succeeded in getting through, it would find itself in a new potential minimum, lower than the one where it is located. The new minimum would be lower, because the molecules around it, in this new location, would not be pushing it so hard; and neighboring molecules, by pushing against a given molecule, increase its potential energy, as we can see from the elementary fact that the increase of potential energy equals the work done by the neighboring molecules in pushing closer to the molecule in question. Thus our molecule in the difficult position will have a chance of squeezing through, from the position, like a in Fig. 11.5.1, where it is under pressure, to the position like b, where it is not, and the probability of squeezing through will be $\nu e^{-E/kT}$. Once it is in the easier position, its probability of going back will be only $\nu e^{-(E+\Delta E)/kT}$, where ΔE is the difference in depths of the minima. Out of a great many molecules in the liquid then, some in positions where they are squeezed, others in positions where they are not, there will be a net flow, given by (11.5.1), from positions where they are squeezed to the easier positions.

Most of the resistance offered to the flow, with the velocity gradient, will be localized at molecules such as we have been describing, which find themselves under unusually large stress. The pressure, or stress, behind one of these molecules will be proportional to the shearing stress applied to the sample as a whole; this over-all stress will be divided up, so to speak, among the molecules supporting unusually large stresses. But the stress on one of the molecules will be proportional to the energy difference ΔE between the position where it is and the more favorable position which it could move to. Thus the rate of flow will be proportional to the stress, the familiar law governing viscosity. The rate of flow of the key molecules, the ones holding the flow back, of course, will determine the flow of the others, which do not happen to be subject to such obstacles. And the coefficient of viscosity, defined as the stress per unit velocity gradient, will contain the factor $e^{E/kT}$, very high at low temperatures, but rapidly decreasing as the temperature increases.

From the discussion we have already given, it is clear that small changes in E can lead to very large variations in the rate of viscous flow; thus we must be prepared to find materials varying all the way from very non-viscous liquids to materials which are practically solid and yet are capable of very slow flow.   Liquid helium, at one extreme, is the most nonviscous liquid known.   Even in its ordinary phase (not the anomalous helium II) its viscosity at a temperature of a few degrees absolute is exceedingly small, pointing to an extremely small value of E.   This arises, as we have already mentioned, because the quantum effect keeps the atoms so far apart in the liquid that the repulsions between atoms are very small, and there is almost no obstacle to an atom's moving from one position to another.   At the other extreme we have, for instance, the glasses.   These, in some ways, are definitely liquids.   They do not have a regular crystal structure, though they do have short-range order, as we have mentioned before.   At high temperatures they flow, though with a good deal of viscosity.   As the temperature decreases, the viscosity increases so much that at room temperature they act, for all practical purposes, like solids, and yet they have not gone through any discontinuous change in properties.   And furthermore, at room temperature a long-continued stress, at least with some glasses, can result in creep, a permanent change of form, which essentially is a viscous flow at a very slow rate.

We have been speaking so far about liquids; and we have found that the mechanism of their flow is dependent on having a certain number of empty sites into which atoms or molecules under pressure can flow, under action of applied stress, in such a way as to relieve the stress.   This type of mechanism, as we can see, would apply as well to amorphous solids; glass, of which we have just spoken, is an example of such an amorphous solid.   The characteristic of such materials is that their atoms or molecules do not fit together as perfectly as in a crystal; though there may be microscopic regions of regularity, there are also regions of imperfect arrangement of atoms, and such regions necessarily involve gaps, allowing flow of the type we have been describing.   On the other hand, it is known that crystalline solids can be deformed plastically, showing the phenomenon of creep, or gradual change of dimensions under the continued action of a stress.   We may well ask, what is the mechanism of such deformations of solids?   It is known, for instance, that a single crystal of a solid, under the action of a shearing stress, will shear along certain planes determined by the crystal symmetry, called slip planes, so that it appears that whole planes of atoms have slid bodily over the next adjacent plane.   This slipping under many circumstances occurs with surprisingly small stress.   As the crystal becomes more deformed, however, by making many such slipping deformations, it becomes hardened: further stress produces much less deformation.   One of the early applications of the theory of interatomic forces was an attempt to calculate the limiting stress necessary to produce such slipping.   The calculations, unfortunately, came out wrong by many orders of magnitude.

The calculations which were at first made proceeded in a very simple way. Suppose the regular crystal has atoms arranged as in the schematic picture on the left of Fig. 11.5.3. Then to make one plane slip along its neighbor, we should have to assume that the upper part of the crystal was displaced with respect to the lower part, as indicated in the diagram to the right, in order that the atoms could rise over their neighbors in the plane below and fall down into another position of equilibrium one atom further along. It would require the expenditure of energy to get the crystal into the form shown in the figure at the right, for in that position each atom would be attracted by fewer neighbors than in the regular equilibrium position, so that certain bonds would have to be broken.

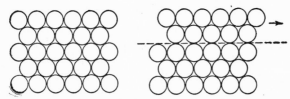

Fig. 11.5.3.   Deformation by slipping of one plane of atoms across another.

It is a straightforward problem to assume that the crystal is held together by interatomic forces of suitable sort, electrostatic, Heitler-London, or whatever is appropriate to the material being considered, and to find what stress would have to be applied to produce this deformation. When the calculation is made, the resulting stress comes out, without the possibility of serious error in the approximations, to be thousands of times as large as the observed stress necessary to produce the deformation.

When this fact was discovered, it was obvious that the mechanism pictured above could not be responsible for plastic deformation under the action of a shear. Instead, we should have to imagine some mechanism in which, instead of having to break a whole set of atomic bonds along a plane at the same time, the deformation could proceed by a step process, only one or a few atoms moving at any instant of time. In this way we could concentrate the stress at a few points, as in the mechanism of viscous flow which we have been discussing, and at these points temperature agitation could result in a rapid rate of flow. In other words, the material which actually does the flowing must have much the same amorphous nature which we have already considered. It is now the general view that slip and plastic deformation of solids occur only in the presence of amorphous regions, perhaps of appreciable size, perhaps on an atomic scale, and that the type of slipping which would involve a whole plane of atoms suddenly jumping over their neighboring plane does not occur.

We wish, then, to consider the possible types of amorphous regions which can lead to the flow of solids.   One such obvious region is a grain boundary.   Ordinary metals are made up of many small crystal grains, with different orientations of their crystal structures; where they join, naturally the structures do not match perfectly, and there must be a joining layer, presumably only one or a few atoms thick, in which there are many atomic imperfections.   This has the characteristics of an amorphous region, and we should assume that, at a suitable temperature, flow can occur in it, as in a liquid.   There seem to be cases in which this is in fact observed.   This mechanism, however, is probably not the one commonly found in plastic deformation.

We have spoken of slip planes; shortly we shall explain how they can come about.   Assume, however, for the moment that we are dealing with a metal in which slip has already occurred along a certain plane.   No matter what the mechanism of this slip has been, it seems almost obvious that one half of the crystal, having been displaced bodily with respect to the other half, will not be able to join perfectly again.   Over considerable areas the atoms may fit exactly, but there are almost certain to be regions of bad joining, in which there are errors of alignment of atoms.   These regions would be in a sense amorphous; and at a suitable temperature they would be able to flow and contribute to plastic deformation.

Let us now try to understand how slip planes can come about, by a process involving one or a few atoms jumping at a time, rather than a whole plane of atoms.   A possible mechanism for such slip has been suggested which reminds us of the way in which a piece of paper can be torn.   If we try to pull apart a piece of paper bodily, breaking it across its whole width, we find it is very strong and difficult to pull apart.   However, if we have started a tear, and proceed to tear it, essentially the whole stress we apply to it is concentrated at the point at which tearing is occurring.   This allows us to apply a very large stress to this spot, and the tear increases in length.   As this happens, the stress is applied to the new position of tear, and thus the tear propagates across the paper with relatively small application of stress.   In similar ways a crack, once formed in a solid and extending for some distance into it, concentrates any stress applied to it at the end of the crack, which then tends strongly to extend itself.   In a similar way, the explanation we can give of the mechanism of slip, suggested by Orowan, Taylor, and others, shows how a slip plane, once started and extended for some distance across a crystal, can propagate itself by concentrating the stress at its ends.

We can indicate the situation schematically as in Fig. 11.5.4.   Here the lines represent rows of atoms.   In the unstrained crystal they would be assumed to be vertical.   However, it is assumed that a shearing stress has been applied, leading to the strain represented by the tilting of the lines. In a certain region, along a plane represented by the dotted line, slip has already occurred: the atoms below the plane have moved one atom distance to the left with respect to those above the plane. We then observe that two regions of unusual stress are left at the two ends of this region of slip. These regions are of a type usually called a dislocation, a position where a row of atoms comes to an end. It is then clear that the atoms at these dislocations can relieve their local stress by jumping in the directions indicated by the two arrows. They will get to positions of

lower potential energy by making these jumps, for they will join a relatively unstressed part of the material, leaving a region of high stress. Furthermore, they will have to cross a barrier to make the jump, for if we look at the problem microscopically, as we did earlier, we see that they will have to rise up over atoms on the opposite side of the dotted line, which are in their way. Thus we have the same sort of situation which we have discussed earlier, and under the action of thermal agitation the

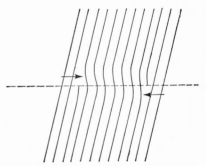

FIG. 11.5.4. Schematic view of two dislocations. The lines indicate lines of atoms, the dotted line being the line along which slip will occur.

atoms indicated by arrows will probably make the jump, in a time which is smaller, the higher the temperature, as indicated in (11.5.1). But the net result of this is that the dislocations will have moved away from each other, and the region of the plane along which slip has occurred will have increased by one atom at each end. This mechanism, then, automatically leads to an extension of the slip plane, once it has started.

It is clear that the two dislocations in the figure above are essentially independent of each other. The point is merely that at the end of a region where slip has occurred there must geometrically be such a dislocation, and stress applied to it will cause it to propagate. To account for the formation of slip planes, then, we need only explain how they start. The general assumption is that, even in apparently very perfect crystals, there are a certain number of dislocations or other irregularities already present, which can initiate slip. The fact that slip experimentally occurs along certain definite planes, separated by distances large enough to observe with a microscope, suggests that a chance fluctuation or irregularity is necessary to initiate slip, and that it is those planes which thus happen to be weakened which slip.

A part of the mechanism described above is the existence of a plane, determined by the crystal orientation, along which slip can occur easily. If we did not have this, even the presence of dislocations might not be enough to make slip possible. We may expect, then, that slip will proceed through the interior of a crystal grain but will stop where it meets a crystal boundary or other amorphous region. This tends to be the case. In particular, if a plane on which slip has already occurred tends to be amorphous, another slip plane propagating in another direction, and meeting such a slip plane, is likely to be stopped there. Thus as more and more slip has occurred in a crystal, so that more and more slip planes crisscross over it, further slip is likely to be stopped sooner, and further plastic deformation is decreased. This is probably a crude explanation of work-hardening, the phenomenon by which a material gets more resistant to plastic flow if it has been deformed to a certain extent. Again, if there are irregularities of the lattice as a result of impurity atoms or intrusions of crystals of other types of materials, we expect that the propagation of slip planes will be impeded, and again the material is hardened.

The description we have just given implies that as a metal is cold-worked, it will acquire more and more irregular regions in its crystal lattice. These regions are all necessarily regions of high stress, even in the absence of any over-all stress applied to the sample as a whole. There will thus be a tendency for atoms in such regions, which may happen to find neighboring sites free, to jump over barriers to such more advantageous sites, provided that helps to relieve the stress. The new sites presumably will correspond to a more nearly perfect crystal. Such a process is a simple picture of the annealing or healing of a metal after it has been deformed. It is known that this happens, and that its rate is governed by an equation of the general form of (11.5.1), including an energy of activation. We have already noted that such an equation leads to a very rapid change of the rate of the process with temperature. This is in line with the fact that metals show a fairly definite annealing temperature: within a rather narrow range of temperatures we go from a temperature so low that annealing for all practical purposes does not occur, to a temperature where it occurs very rapidly.

This process of annealing, or of gradual relaxation of a stress present in a solid, is one of the two principal ways in which the jumps of atoms from stressed to unstressed positions enter into the dynamics of a solid. The other is the viscous type of behavior, in which we have a stress proportional to the rate of flow, as well as the ordinary stress proportional to the strain, which is given by Hooke's law. One can set up a generalized equation describing the behavior of a solid, involving both these effects, which proves to give a fairly satisfactory description of the time-dependent behavior of a solid.   By studying the behavior of solids under stresses which vary sinusoidally with time, Zener has shown that it is possible to get quantitative information about the various rates involved in these phenomena.

11.6. Rates of Chemical Reactions.   The study of chemical reactions, from the point of view of physical chemistry or chemical physics, involves two aspects: chemical equilibrium and the rate of chemical reactions. Chemical equilibrium can be approached from either of two points of view, a thermodynamic and statistical, or a kinetic, approach.   The statistical approach requires only a knowledge of the free energies and various properties of the molecules to give complete information about equilibrium. On the other hand, we can also discuss equilibrium by balancing the rates of opposite reactions in a kinetic way, arriving at the same results.   It would then seem at first sight as if we should be able to work this argument backward and from knowledge of the equilibrium find the rates of reactions.   We find, however, that this is not the case: the information we need about rates of reactions in order to derive the equations of equilibrium is very limited, not nearly enough to reverse the argument and find the rate of reaction.   The kinetic method, as applied to a gas reaction, deals with the number of collisions of the molecules which are going to react, correctly concluding that they cannot react unless they first collide, so as to be close enough to have influence on each other.   If, however, we measure experimentally the rate of reaction and compare this with the rate of collisions of the reacting molecules, we find that in only a very small fraction of the times when two such molecules collide are they able to react.   And we find that this fraction varies with temperature according to a factor $e^{-E/kT}$, involving an activation energy, and suggesting that in order to react, a barrier must somehow be surmounted, which requires unusually large thermal energy.   This picture proves to be correct, and we shall now consider a very simple case, illustrative of the way in which this barrier comes about.

Probably the simplest chemical reactions to discuss are bimolecular gas reactions, in which two molecules collide, are transformed into one or more other molecules, and the resulting molecules separate.   The simplest case of two single atoms colliding does not ordinarily lead to the formation of a molecule at all.   For then the atoms act on each other according to the type of interatomic potential curve with which we are familiar from our discussions of molecular binding.   Considering the atoms as moving according to classical mechanics in this potential field, we see that if they start toward each other from infinity with finite kinetic energy, they will approach to a minimum distance, separate, and finally go to infinity again, with the same kinetic energy as before.   The only way for them to become bound would be for them to lose vibrational kinetic energy when close together, at a distance approximately equal to that giving the minimum of the interatomic potential curve, so that they would begin vibrating about this position. This could conceivably happen if they happened to be in an excited electronic state and radiated while close together, but calculation shows this to be most improbable. Actually the only important mechanism by which such binding occurs is a collision by a third particle, or with the wall of the vessel, part of the kinetic energy being imparted to this particle or to the wall, resulting in the recombination of the atoms to form a molecule. Thus this reaction is not of the simple type we wish to consider.

One can really get bimolecular reactions, however, if at least one of the colliding molecules is diatomic. For example, it would be possible for HBr, colliding with H, to change into H_2 and Br, or vice versa. And such reactions can occur without change of electronic quantum number, the electrons always staying in their lowest state. To understand them, we need merely consider the potential energy function as it depends on the coordinates of all three atoms. This is a problem like that already taken up in discussing the interactions of three H atoms in Sec. 9.3. We know from our discussion of that case that the energy is a function of three coordinates, the distances between the three pairs of atoms. As in that case, let us simplify our discussion by assuming the atoms to be in line, in the order H-H-Br, so that we have only two independent interatomic distances to consider. Then we can indicate the potential energy by contour lines in a plane in which the H-H and H-Br distances are plotted as coordinates, and the result will be somewhat as shown in Fig. 11.6.1. We see one valley of potential energy corresponding to the stable HBr molecule, extending out to infinite values of the H-H distance; another valley corresponding to the stable H_2 molecule, extending to infinite values of the H-Br distance. Between these is a pass, the same saddle point which we discussed earlier in considering the problem of three hydrogens.

To discuss the dynamics of nuclear motion in such a case as this, we can use a very convenient picture, which is justified by the laws of motion of classical mechanics. We can imagine our potential surface to be actually constructed in space, the height being the potential energy, as a function of the two distances. Then we may imagine a small ball to roll around such a surface. The motion of such a rolling ball will, in fact, correspond very closely to the actual motion of the point representing the system. The reason is that the ball has a gravitational potential energy proportional to its height, or to the potential energy we are considering, and its translational kinetic energy is proportional to its total kinetic energy (translational plus rotational). If we can disregard its vertical component of motion as far as it affects its kinetic energy (which we can do if the energy surface is constructed with only gradual inclines), then the ball has the same relation between kinetic and potential energy as the actual particle and, consequently, moves according to the same laws.

Let us, then, start with a molecule of HBr and a H atom approaching it. This means that the rolling ball, representing the system, may well

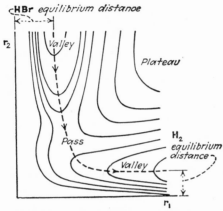

FIG. 11.6.1.   Potential energy of H-H-Br as function of H-Br distance (r_1) and H-H distance (r_2) for all three atoms in line.   Dotted line indicates reaction HBr + H → H_2 + Br, the height of the pass above the first valley being the activation energy. (*Curve from H. Eyring and M. Polanyi, by permission.*)

be moving along the dotted line in Fig. 11.6.1. We have drawn it for the case where the HBr molecule does not have appreciable vibrational energy, so that the H-Br distance is not changing with time. The rolling ball is moving in the bottom of the HBr valley, rolling along the valley toward the pass, which corresponds to the situation where all three atoms are close together. The direction of motion is toward the junction with the other valley, corresponding to H_2 + Br. If the ball is going fast enough, it will be able to rise over the pass separating the two valleys and roll down the other side, resulting in the reaction we are interested in. We see, then, that we have two separate valleys, representing the initial and final states of the reaction, with a pass or barrier between; and to surmount this barrier, the incident H atom must have kinetic energy greater than E, where E is the height of the pass above the valley in which the motion starts, at the beginning of the collision. As in our preceding cases, the probability that it will have this energy will involve the Boltzmann factor $e^{-E/kT}$, so that E will be the energy of activation of the reaction.

Though this is a very simple example, it illustrates satisfactorily the situation met in the general case of chemical reactions. At the same time we can see why the study of chemical equilibrium cannot give us information about the rate of reaction. The rate of the reaction from $H + HBr$ to $H_2 + Br$ has a factor $e^{-E/kT}$, where E is the height of the pass above the HBr valley; the inverse reaction has a factor $e^{-(E+\Delta E)/kT}$, where $E + \Delta E$ is the height of the pass above the H_2 valley. The kinetic argument proves to depend on the ratio of these rates of reaction, which is $e^{\Delta E/kT}$, independent of E itself. Thus it comes about that equilibrium theory depends only on the difference of energy between the two equilibrium states, and that the height of the barrier between them does not enter. To get experimental information about the absolute value of the rate of reaction, we must actually measure reaction rates; to study them theoretically, we must construct surfaces giving the energy as a function of the interatomic distances, which, as we have seen earlier, we can do by use of the Heitler-London method. This method leads in fact to qualitatively correct energy surfaces; but we naturally cannot expect accurate calculations of the actual reaction rates, since we have seen how very sensitive they are to small changes in the activation energy.

PROBLEMS

1. The probability of finding an atomic or molecular system in a stationary state with energy E_i, at temperature T, is given by the Boltzmann statistics as being $e^{-E_i/kT} \Big/ \left(\sum_i e^{-E_i/kT} \right)$. Thus the average energy is $\left(\sum_i E_i e^{-E_i/kT} \right) \Big/ \left(\sum_i e^{-E_i/kT} \right)$.

Find the average energy of a linear oscillator for which $E_i = (n_i + \frac{1}{2})h\nu$. Show that at high temperatures this leads to a limiting value of kT, as required by equipartition. Describe the situation holding at low temperatures.

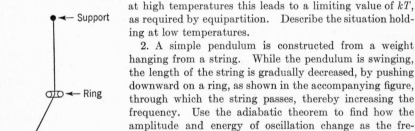

2. A simple pendulum is constructed from a weight hanging from a string. While the pendulum is swinging, the length of the string is gradually decreased, by pushing downward on a ring, as shown in the accompanying figure, through which the string passes, thereby increasing the frequency. Use the adiabatic theorem to find how the amplitude and energy of oscillation change as the frequency changes. If the energy of oscillation changes, where is the work done which maintains conservation of energy?

3. Find the de Broglie wave length of a He^4 atom moving with the velocity given by the equipartition kinetic energy corresponding to 4°K, and compare this with a reasonable value of the radius of the atom. Make a similar calculation for He^3; also for a H_2 molecule at 20°K.

4. Einstein assumed that a crystal with N atoms had $3N$ vibrational degrees of freedom (corresponding to vibration of each atom along x, y, and z), all with frequency ν, so that the vibrational or thermal energy consisted of $3N$ terms of the form given in Prob. 1. Differentiate with respect to temperature to get the Einstein specific heat curve, and discuss the qualitative nature of this curve. Show that at high temperatures the heat capacity of N atoms approaches $3Nk$, which is the Dulong and Petit law.

5. Given a crystal whose energy at the absolute zero is $-K/\delta + b/\delta^n$, where δ is a linear dimension, b and n are constants, find the compressibility at zero pressure as a function of K, δ_0, and n.

6. In rock salt ions of Na^+ and Cl^- are arranged alternately on a cubic lattice, the equilibrium distance between successive Na^+ ions being 5.7×10^{-8} cm. If δ is chosen as the distance between successive Na^+ ions, so that $\delta_0 = 5.7 \times 10^{-8}$, the energy in the cube of volume δ^3 may be approximated $-K/\delta + b/\delta^n$, where $K = 13.94e^2$, if e is the charge on an electron in electrostatic units, and if cgs units are used. It is found that $n = 8$, approximately. Find the compressibility at the absolute zero, in reciprocal dynes per square centimeter, comparing with the observed value (between 3 and 4×10^{-12}).

7. Using the figures of Prob. 6, compute the energy required to break up 1 gm-mole of NaCl into Na^+ and Cl^- ions (that is, to make δ infinite). Compare with the experimental value, in the neighborhood of 180 kg-cal/g-mole.

8. Using the Dulong-Petit law, compute the specific heat at ordinary temperatures of copper and lead, and compare with the experimental values.

9. Calculate the breaking strength of a solid according to a simple model in which each atom on one side of a boundary exerts a force on its neighbor on the opposite side of the boundary, given by a Morse curve. Assume an atom per area of 4 square angstroms, and let the Morse curve correspond to $D = 4$ ev, $r_0 = 2$ A, $a = 3/r_0$. Find the maximum force which would have to be exerted per unit area in pulling the two surfaces apart. The experimentally observed forces are actually much smaller than this calculated value.

10. Solve the problem of the vibrational levels of a molecule whose potential energy is $De^{-2au} - 2De^{-au}$, where $u = r - r_0$, without rotation. If R is r times the radial wave function, and $y = e^{-au}$, set up the differential equation for R, using y as independent variable, showing that it is

$$\frac{1}{y}\frac{d}{dy}\left(y\frac{dR}{dy}\right) + \frac{8\pi^2\mu}{a^2h^2}\left(\frac{E}{y^2} + \frac{2D}{y} - D\right)R = 0,$$

where $\mu = m_1 m_2/(m_1 + m_2)$, if m_1, m_2 are the masses of the atoms. Treat this equation like Schrödinger's equation for the hydrogen atom, letting $R = e^{-dy}(2dy)^{b/2}F(y)$, where $d = (2\pi\sqrt{2\mu D})/ah$, $E = -a^2h^2b^2/32\pi^2\mu$. Obtain the differential equation for F, showing that the series solution breaks off to give a finite polynomial if the energy is given by

$$E_n = -D + \left(n + \frac{1}{2}\right)h\nu - \left(\frac{h^2\nu^2}{4D}\right)\left(n + \frac{1}{2}\right)^2,$$

where ν is the frequency of classical vibration about r_0, equal to $\dfrac{a}{2\pi}\sqrt{\dfrac{2D}{\mu}}$.

11. If three atoms interact by valence forces, it can be proved by the methods of Appendix 16 that the following formula gives approximately the energy of the lowest

state: $\sqrt{\frac{1}{2}[(\alpha - \beta)^2 + (\beta - \gamma)^2 + (\gamma - \alpha)^2]}$, where α, β, γ, are the energies of binding of the pairs 1 and 2, 2 and 3, 3 and 1, respectively, if in each case the third atom is removed to infinity, so that α, etc., are given as functions of the three interatomic distances r_{12}, r_{23}, r_{31} by curves of the nature of Morse curves. This formula is used in constructing Fig. 11.6.1. Show that the formula approaches the correct limit as any one of the three atoms recedes to infinity. Show that a single atom approaching a molecule is repelled, by assuming atoms 1 and 2 to be at the equilibrium distance, forming a molecule, so that α is large and negative, β and γ much smaller and also negative, increasingly so as the third atom approaches, and expanding the square root in binomial series in the small quantities β and γ.

12. Find the energy for three hydrogen atoms on a line at arbitrary distances apart, using the formula of Prob. 11 and the hydrogen interaction energy from Prob. 9, Chap. 8.

13. Taking the energy expression of Prob. 12, let the distances r_{12} and r_{23} be equal, and $r_{13} = r_{12} + r_{23}$, so that the corresponding point is on the 45° diagonal of Fig. 9.3.1. Compute energy as a function of r_{12} or r_{23}, and find graphically the energy of the pass (the minimum of this curve). Compare with the energy at the bottom of either valley, and so find the activation energy of the reaction in which a hydrogen atom approaches a hydrogen molecule, knocks off one of the atoms from the molecule, and itself becomes bound.

CHAPTER 12

ELECTRICAL CONDUCTIVITY

In earlier chapters we have seen how it comes about that a metal, with unsaturated bonds, is a conductor, whereas an ionic or covalent substance, with saturated bonds, is an insulator. We have stated that the best and most straightforward way to approach these questions quantitatively is through the use of energy-band theory: if we have a partially filled band, we have conduction, whereas if the band is filled, it conducts no current. In the present chapter we shall also take up the intermediate case between the conductor and insulator, the semiconductor, in which, as we have already mentioned, the conductivity is a result of the presence of impurity atoms. Our first problem will be the straightforward one: to investigate the effect of an electric field on the type of wave function, and energy level, which we have found to occur in the problem of an electron in a periodic potential.

12.1. An Electron in a Periodic Potential and an Electric Field. The behavior of the wave functions of an electron in a periodic potential, which we have discussed in Chap. 10, when an additional electric field varying slowly with position is superposed, such as we have in electrical conductivity, is derived in terms of two theorems of wide applicability. These theorems are not easy to prove rigorously, but we can easily make them very plausible by arguments which prove to be legitimate when they are examined in more detail. We start with the description of the energy band in which we give the energy E as a function of the quantities k_x, k_y, k_z. It will be more convenient to express the k's in terms of components of a momentum p, with components p_x, p_y, p_z, by the equations

$$p_x = \frac{k_x h}{2\pi}, \qquad p_y = \frac{k_y h}{2\pi}, \qquad p_z = \frac{k_z h}{2\pi}, \qquad (12.1.1)$$

where p is then the momentum of a free particle whose wave function would be multiplied by the same phase factor in going from one unit cell to the next. Let us then assume that we know E as a function of p_x, p_y, p_z for the problem of the periodic potential without an additional external field. We then superpose an additional field, given by a potential energy $V(x,y,z)$ which is assumed to vary slowly with position. This would be the case with any electrostatic potential concerned in current flow.

333

Under the action of this perturbing potential, we may expect a perturbation of a type not ordinarily considered in perturbation theory. For one thing, the unperturbed energy levels form practically a continuum, so that we do not have the necessary conditions for application of the ordinary perturbation theory for a nondegenerate system; the levels are too close together. We can get a guide as to the type of result we hope to get by considering what this perturbative potential would do classically, if the electrons were free. It would accelerate them; and we wish to get a quantum-mechanical description of this acceleration. The best way to consider such a problem is by means of wave packets; in our first chapter we stated that a wave packet describing a free electron, under the action of an external force, will be accelerated according to quantum mechanics, just as the particle would be accelerated according to Newton's equations of motion. Let us then set up a wave packet in our problem; only, instead of having the potential V act on a free electron, we shall consider its effect on the electrons moving in the periodic potential.

To set up a wave packet, we know that we must superpose waves of a variety of wave lengths or energies. Let us, however, choose the energies to be fairly well localized within the band. In fact, let us set up a wave packet out of waves whose p vectors are fairly well concentrated in the p space. The resulting packet will not be perfectly localized in coordinate space. The principles of Fourier resolution, which in this case become identical with Heisenberg's principle of uncertainty, tell us that if the packet is made up of waves extending through a region of dimensions Δp_x, Δp_y, Δp_z in the p space, the extension of the corresponding packet in coordinate space will be of the order of magnitude of Δx, Δy, Δz, where

$$\Delta p_x \, \Delta x = h, \qquad \Delta p_y \, \Delta y = h, \qquad \Delta p_z \, \Delta z = h. \qquad (12.1.2)$$

This uncertainty principle is not unduly restrictive in our case; we can choose our packet so that its extension in p space is small compared with the whole Brillouin zone, and its extension in energy small compared with the whole energy band. Then the extension of the packet will be large compared with a single lattice cell, as we can find by examination of the relations. For from (12.1.1), relations (12.1.2) can be written $\Delta k_x \, \Delta x = 2\pi$, etc. Now we know that the extension of k_x associated with the whole Brillouin zone is $2\pi/a$, where a is one of the unit vectors of the lattice. Thus our condition that Δk_x is small compared with the extension of the Brillouin zone shows that it is small compared with $2\pi/a$; and (12.1.2) shows that Δx is then large compared with a. But even if the packet is as large as this, it need not trouble us, as long as it is small compared with the scale of variation of V, or as long as V is approximately constant over the packet, which will be the case if V is the type of potential concerned with a macroscopic electrical potential.

Our theorems, which we mentioned above, now tell us what the effect of the perturbing potential V is on the time variation of the coordinates $\bar{x}$, $\bar{y}$, $\bar{z}$ of the center of the wave packet, and on the time variation of the values $\overline{p_x}$, $\overline{p_y}$, $\overline{p_z}$ of momentum at the center of the packet in p space. The theorems are as follows:

$$\frac{d\bar{x}}{dt} = \frac{\partial E}{\partial \overline{p_x}}, \qquad \frac{d\bar{y}}{dt} = \frac{\partial E}{\partial \overline{p_y}}, \qquad \frac{d\bar{z}}{dt} = \frac{\partial E}{\partial \overline{p_z}}, \tag{12.1.3}$$

$$\frac{d\overline{p_x}}{dt} = -\frac{\partial V}{\partial \bar{x}}, \qquad \frac{d\overline{p_y}}{dt} = -\frac{\partial V}{\partial \bar{y}}, \qquad \frac{d\overline{p_z}}{dt} = -\frac{\partial V}{\partial \bar{z}}. \tag{12.1.4}$$

In these equations E is to be expressed as a function of $\overline{p_x}$, $\overline{p_y}$, $\overline{p_z}$, the values corresponding to the center of the packet, and similarly V is a function of $\bar{x}$, $\bar{y}$, $\bar{z}$. The reader familiar with Hamiltonian methods in mechanics will recognize at once that (12.1.3) and (12.1.4) are identical in form with the classical Hamiltonian equations, provided we set the Hamiltonian function equal to $E + V$. That is, the wave packet moves like a classical particle whose kinetic energy, as a function of momentum, was E, and whose potential energy was V. This interpretation will be useful to us in some of our applications of these equations.

Let us now consider why these equations seem reasonable. In the first place, (12.1.3) can be shown to be identical with the equations for group velocity encountered with any wave motion. With any type of wave whose velocity depends on the frequency, the velocity of the group, or wave packet, is different from the phase velocity of the wave. If ω is the angular frequency, k the propagation constant (equal to 2π divided by the wave length), the phase velocity is ω/k. We then can show, as in Appendix 4, that the group velocity is $d\omega/dk$. If we divide numerator and denominator of the right side of (12.1.3) by $h/2\pi$, we have $\partial(2\pi E/h)/\partial k_x$, which is just the correct form for the x component of group velocity, since $2\pi E/h$ is the angular frequency of the Schrödinger wave. Thus (12.1.3) is simply the vector form of this relation, giving the correct formula for the velocity of the wave packet. We shall find this relation very useful in computing the current carried by our solutions of Schrödinger's equation for the periodic potential, since the current is proportional to the velocity.

The other equations, (12.1.4), tell us that the time rate of change of the average momentum $\bar{p}$ of the wave packet equals the external force associated with the potential V. This, of course, would be obvious if p were really the momentum; but we remember that it is not, though it has certain analogies to a momentum. However, assuming that (12.1.3) is true, we can make it almost intuitive that (12.1.4) must be true also, by noting that $E + V$ is clearly the total energy of the system, E being the kinetic energy of the particle plus its potential energy in the periodic potential, V being the additional potential energy in the slowly varying potential, and that (12.1.3) and (12.1.4) together lead to conservation of energy. Thus, if we try to find the change of $(E + V)$ with time, we have

$$\frac{d(E + V)}{dt} = \frac{\partial(E + V)}{\partial \bar{x}} \frac{d\bar{x}}{dt} + \frac{\partial(E + V)}{\partial \bar{y}} \frac{d\bar{y}}{dt} + \frac{\partial(E + V)}{\partial \bar{z}} \frac{d\bar{z}}{dt}$$
$$+ \frac{\partial(E + V)}{\partial \overline{p_x}} \frac{d\overline{p_x}}{dt} + \frac{\partial(E + V)}{\partial \overline{p_y}} \frac{d\overline{p_y}}{dt} + \frac{\partial(E + V)}{\partial \overline{p_z}} \frac{d\overline{p_z}}{dt} = 0,$$

when we use (12.1.3) and (12.1.4). This conservation would not have resulted, assuming (12.1.3), unless (12.1.4) was also satisfied. Thus it is very plausible that Eqs. (12.1.3) and (12.1.4) should be correct.†

12.2 Consequences of the Solution for an Electron in an Electric Field. We shall state a number of the consequences of Eqs. (12.1.3) and

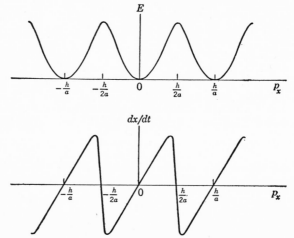

Fig. 12.2.1. Energy and velocity as functions of momentum; periodic potential problem.

(12.1.4) for the one-dimensional case and shall indicate the extension to three dimensions. In the first place, let us ask how the wave packet would move under the action of a constant electric field, so that $-\partial V/\partial \bar{x}$ was constant. Then (12.1.4) shows that $\overline{p_x}$ would increase with time at a constant rate. How then, we ask, would the velocity change? In Fig. 12.2.1 we give first the energy as a function of $\overline{p_x}$, as determined

† For more formal proof, see, for instance, J. C. Slater, *Phys. Rev.* **76**, 1592 (1949).

according to the principles of Chap. 10, and below it the velocity $d\bar{x}/dt$, which by (12.1.3) is simply the slope of the curve of energy vs. $\bar{p}_x$. We see that the velocity increases as the momentum increases from zero, and hence the velocity increases with time. As the momentum approaches $h/2a$, however, and we come to the maximum of the energy curve, the velocity goes to a maximum, decreases, and is zero just at $h/2a$. It then goes negative, to a large negative value, and gradually increases to zero, which it reaches when $\bar{p}_x$ equals h/a, just as it was zero when $\bar{p}_x$ was zero. How, we ask, can we physically explain this peculiar situation, by which a positive force, and a positive time rate of change of momentum, can sometimes be associated with a negative acceleration?

The explanation is tied up with the Bragg reflection, about which we spoke in Chap. 10. As the momentum of the electron approaches $h/2a$, its wave length approaches $2a$, the value for which Bragg reflection occurs. There is then a very great chance of reflection, or reversal of the velocity. This is the phenomenon which is occurring in the neighborhood of this value of $\bar{p}_x$. After the reflection, the electron will be traveling in the opposite direction, and further application of the force will gradually reverse its velocity, speed it up again, until again it reaches the correct momentum or velocity for Bragg reflection, and so on. It is in this way that the periodic dependence of velocity on $\bar{p}_x$ is to be understood.

It is interesting to ask not only how the wave packet moves under the action of a constant field, but also how it moves under the action of a force such that it never gets far from the minimum of energy. Near the minimum the energy is a quadratic function of $\bar{p}_x$; we may write it as $E = E_0 + \bar{p}_x^2/2m^*$, where E_0 is the value of energy at the minimum, and m^* is a quantity of the dimensions of a mass, but not, in general, equal to the electronic mass (unless it should happen to turn out that the curvature of the energy surface at its minimum was the same that we should get for a free electron). Then (12.1.3) tells us that $d\bar{x}/dt = \bar{p}_x/m^*$, and from (12.1.4) we have

$$m^* \frac{d^2\bar{x}}{dt^2} = -\frac{\partial V}{\partial \bar{x}} = F_x, \qquad (12.2.1)$$

where F_x is the x component of force associated with the potential V. This is the ordinary Newtonian equation of motion for a particle of mass m^*. On account of this behavior of the motion, m^* is called an effective mass. We recall that it has significance only so long as we are near enough the minimum of the energy curve so that it can be replaced by a parabola.

Similarly, near a maximum of the energy curve, which may come at $\bar{p}_x = h/2a$, we should have $E = E_1 - (\bar{p}_x - h/2a)^2/2m^{**}$, where E_1 is the value of energy at the maximum, and m^{**} is another constant.   In a similar way we have $d\bar{x}/dt = -(\overline{p_x} - h/2a)/m^{**}$, and

$$m^{**} \frac{d^2\bar{x}}{dt^2} = \frac{\partial V}{\partial \bar{x}} = -F_x. \qquad (12.2.2)$$

Near the top of the band, in other words, we have another effective mass; but more surprisingly, the force accelerates the particle in the opposite direction to what we should expect, as if the electron had the opposite charge to its real charge, so that it acted like a positive electron.   This is really, of course, nothing but an expression of the same thing which we saw when considering a steady force: it is in this neighborhood that we are meeting Bragg reflection, and the particle does, in fact, go in the opposite direction to what we should expect from the action of the external force alone.   In both the cases we have taken up, we note that the effective mass m^* or m^{**} can be quite different from the real electronic mass. Thus if the energy band is very narrow, so that there is small curvature at the bottom of the band, m^* will be large, sometimes very much larger than the electronic mass.   On the other hand, at the top of a band like that shown above, where the curvature is great, m^{**} will be very small. By looking back at Fig. 10.3.1, giving E as a function of p_x for an actual case, we see that we can often have cases in which the role of maximum and minimum are reversed, so that the maximum of the band comes at $p_x = 0$.   We also see that we can have many cases, particularly for the bands of higher energy, where both top and bottom of the bands have very large curvature, corresponding to very small effective masses.

Now let us consider the current carried by partly filled and by filled bands, and the way in which an external field affects this current.   In the first place, we observe that if the energy levels are filled up to a certain energy, the net current will be zero.   We remember from Sec. 10.4 that with a finite crystal there will be energy levels at equally spaced points along the p_x axis.   With a partly filled band these levels will be full on both sides of $p_x = 0$, out to equally great positive and negative values, and clearly there will be as many electrons with negative as with positive velocities.   In this calculation we are assuming that our wave packets are so extended in coordinate space that they can be sharply defined in momentum space, which is necessary in order to define precisely the maximum momentum, or maximum energy, in the distribution. But now let us assume that a constant external field acts on the distribution.   Then all wave packets move uniformly to the right along the p_x axis, so that after a lapse of time, there will be a net velocity, and hence a net current, proportional to the force and the time which has elapsed.

We shall take up the relation between this situation and the ordinary conductivity of a metal in a later section.

The situation is quite different, however, provided we have a filled band. In this case we have states uniformly filled for an interval h/a along the p_x axis. In such a case, by the periodicity of the function, the total current of all the electrons is always zero. We can see this analytically by a simple calculation: the average current, determined by the average velocity, must then be proportional to the integral of the velocity with respect to p_x, from one value of p_x to a value greater by h/a, because such integration with respect to p_x is equivalent to summing over all electrons or wave packets. But by (12.1.3) the velocity is the derivative of E with respect to p_x. Thus the integral of this quantity with respect to p_x is the difference of energies at the two ends of the interval of integration, and if this interval is h/a, the difference is zero on account of periodicity. Hence we have the justification of our earlier result, which we then stated rather intuitively: a substance in which all electrons are in filled energy bands, none in partly filled bands, is necessarily an insulator, whereas if we have partly filled bands, a current can be carried.

An interesting situation arises in case we have a band almost filled, with just a few empty levels near the top of the band, and then apply an external field. This situation is important particularly on account of its occurrence in some semiconductors, as well as in some metals. If all levels but one are filled, and a field is applied, it is clear that the p_x representing the empty level or hole will move along the p_x axis just as the p_x of a wave packet would move. Thus, from our result of (12.2.2), the hole will be accelerated as if it were a particle of positive charge. Let us next ask what the resulting contribution to the current will be. The current arising from the effect of the electric field is really carried by all the electrons filling the occupied energy levels. We have already seen that if all levels were filled, the current would be zero. Thus the current carried by all levels but the hole must be the negative of the current that would be carried by an electron occupying the empty level. That is, the current resulting from the acceleration of the hole is the negative of the current that would result from a single negative electron occupying the hole, or is the current that would result from a positive electron in that level. Both from the standpoint of acceleration and of current, then, the hole acts as if it were a positive electron with an effective mass m^{**}. This interpretation of a hole near the top of an energy band as acting like a positive electron is one which is of great usefulness in the discussion of conductivity.

Parenthetically, it is interesting to note the close resemblance of this mechanism to the theory of the positron. In the relativistic theory of the electron we treat the energy of the electron as being the sum of its ordinary kinetic energy and its rest energy m_0c^2, where m_0 is its rest mass, c the velocity of light. Thus the allowed energy levels of an electron start with the large positive value m_0c^2 and extend to all higher energies. However, the relativistic equations of motion permit also a set of energy levels of negative energy value, starting at $-m_0c^2$ and extending indefinitely downward from there to negative energies. This situation is like that of energy bands, with two allowed bands, the one for negative energies and the other for positive energies, with an energy gap of unallowed energies between $-m_0c^2$ and m_0c^2. Under ordinary circumstances, the lower band is assumed to be entirely filled and hence to contribute nothing to the flow of current; all ordinary electrons are those found in the upper band. However, under some circumstances, holes can appear in the lower band, and these holes will act like positive electrons according to the same arguments which we have just used in the theory of metals. These are the positrons, or positive electrons. And the creation of a positron-electron pair, by absorption of radiation, consists simply in raising one of the electrons from the lower, filled band to the upper, almost empty band, resulting in an electron of the ordinary sort in the upper band, leaving a hole acting like a positron in the lower band. The minimum quantum of energy permitting such pair formation is obviously given by $h\nu = 2m_0c^2$, the width of the gap; this is close to a million electron volts. In an entirely analogous way, if we have an insulator with all its lower bands filled, its upper bands empty, and absorb light whose quantum $h\nu$ is given by the gap width or more, it can raise an electron from the top of the lower band to the bottom of the upper one, creating essentially an electron and a positive electron, each of which can then carry current under the action of an external field. This is a simple model of the phenomenon of photoconductivity; and it shows us at once that there will be a low-frequency or long-wave limit of the effect, beyond which a photon is too small to be able to raise an electron through the width of the gap. In contrast to the relativistic case, however, the gaps here will be only a volt or two wide, so that the required radiation will be in the visible or neighboring parts of the spectrum, rather than in the gamma-ray range as with the problem of pair formation.

We have used the one-dimensional case in discussing our problem of the behavior of an electron in a periodic potential and an electric field; but our methods extend without trouble to the three-dimensional case. The general results are unaltered. One complication which can arise is worth mentioning. When we investigate the behavior of a wave packet near a minimum or maximum of the band, to get an effective mass, we find a more complicated situation. Near such a minimum, the energy will be a quadratic function of the momentum; in general this leads to an ellipsoidal sort of variation.   In such a case we can choose axes x, y, z along the principal axes of the ellipsoid, and then we find

$$E = E_0 + \frac{p_x^2}{2m_x^*} + \frac{p_y^2}{2m_y^*} + \frac{p_z^2}{2m_z^*},$$

where in general m_x^*, m_y^*, m_z^* will be different.   If we had not chosen the principal axes as coordinate axes, we should also have found cross terms, as for instance in $p_x p_y$, and should have found that the coefficients of this quadratic form, representing essentially the reciprocal of the effective mass, would have formed a tensor.   This tensor behavior of the effective mass, by which an electron or hole can be accelerated to quite different amounts, depending on the direction of the force, is of importance in some cases of crystals with unsymmetrical structure, but in cubic crystals, such as we generally meet in metals, of course it does not apply.   In those cases symmetry demands that the m^*'s in different directions be the same, so that the behavior is just like that of an electron with an ordinary scalar mass m^*, or a positive electron with mass m^{**}.

12.3. The Scattering of an Electron Wave.   If we had a perfect crystal, then according to the preceding section, a constant force acting on the electrons would accelerate them continuously, so that the current would keep on increasing.   It would not increase indefinitely in a metal on account of the Bragg reflection, which, as we have seen, limits it even though the momentum p increases without limit; but the increase would nevertheless be very great, and there would be nothing like Ohm's law. We must look for something which limits the increase of current, and results in a current proportional to the field, instead of having the time rate of increase of the current proportional to the field, as (12.2.1) would suggest.   This need of something to limit the increase of current was realized long before the application of the quantum theory to the problem of conduction; Drude, Lorentz, and others worked out a theory of conductivity in the early 1900's, which gave a simple classical explanation of the situation.   Let us first sketch this classical theory of conductivity, and then see how it must be modified to agree with the quantum theory.

The simplest way of describing the mechanism of Drude and Lorentz is to say that an electron traveling through matter will collide with the atoms it traverses, and this will be equivalent to a resistive force proportional to the velocity.   We then expect that an electron, of charge $-e$, mass m, subject to an electric field E, will be governed by an equation of motion

$$m \frac{d^2x}{dt^2} = -eE - a \frac{dx}{dt}, \tag{12.3.1}$$

where the term $-a\,dx/dt$ is the resistance proportional to the velocity. The solution of (12.3.1) consistent with the initial condition that the velocity starts from zero at $t = 0$ is

$$\frac{dx}{dt} = v = -\frac{eE}{a}\,(1 - e^{-t/t_0}), \qquad t_0 = \frac{m}{a}. \tag{12.3.2}$$

This indicates that after a time of the order of magnitude of t_0, the velocity v of the electron will have settled down to a value $-eE/a$, proportional to the electric field, obtained from (12.3.1) by setting the acceleration equal to zero. We shall see in a moment that this time t_0 is very small, so that for all practical purposes we can assume the steady state of constant velocity.

Now if we have N electrons per unit volume, the current density J will be given by $-Nev$. Hence we shall have

$$J = \frac{Ne^2}{a}\,E = \sigma E, \qquad \text{where } \sigma = \frac{Ne^2}{a}. \tag{12.3.3}$$

This is an expression of Ohm's law, σ being the electrical conductivity, or reciprocal of the specific resistance. We see that we can combine this with (12.3.2) to give an alternative formula for the conductivity,

$$\sigma = \frac{Ne^2 t_0}{m}. \tag{12.3.4}$$

From (12.3.4) we can estimate t_0, if we use the experimentally observed value of σ, assume that N is of the order of magnitude of one electron per atom, and use for m the electronic mass. When we carry out this calculation for a metal, we find an extremely small value of t_0, verifying our earlier statement that the state of constant velocity is reached almost immediately after application of the accelerating force.

The value of t_0 can be described in another way, if we ask for the solution of (12.3.1) for the case where the applied field E is zero, but where at $t = 0$ the velocity is a value v_0 different from zero. Then we find at once

$$v = v_0 e^{-t/t_0}, \tag{12.3.5}$$

showing that t_0 is the time required for an initial drift velocity of the electrons to fall to $1/e$ of its value. We shall use this interpretation of t_0 when we come to its quantum-theoretical interpretation in a later paragraph.

It is often convenient to write our expressions in a different form. We often define the mobility of an ion, under the action of an electric field, as the velocity which it acquires, per unit electric field. The terminal velocity, given by (12.3.2), is $-eE/a$, so that the mobility μ equals e/a. In terms of the mobility, (12.3.3) can be rewritten

$$\sigma = Ne\mu. \tag{12.3.6}$$

Experimental values of the mobility, assuming N to be of the order of magnitude of one electron per atom, or determining it as will be described later from the Hall effect, prove to be of the order of magnitude of hundreds of centimeters per second, per volt per centimeter of field.

We can easily go somewhat further than these simple formulas indicate, in looking for the mechanism behind the resistive force. As Lorentz assumed, we may assume that it is a result of collisions between the electron and the atoms it moves through. The simplest statistical approximation to this situation would then be to consider that the electron was accelerated during a mean free time t_1, and then collided, losing all evidence of its acceleration at the collision. The velocity of the electron at time t after a collision, using (12.3.1) without the resistive term, is $v = -(eE/m)t$, so that the average velocity during the mean free time will be $\bar{v} = -(eE/m)(t_1/2)$, the factor $\frac{1}{2}$ coming from averaging from the beginning of the mean free time, when the velocity is zero, to the time of collision. This value of velocity leads at once to

$$\sigma = \frac{Ne^2}{m}\frac{t_1}{2}. \tag{12.3.7}$$

From this we see that t_1 is closely associated with t_0, the time introduced before. In other words, the time taken to reach a constant velocity is essentially the same as the mean free time between collisions. Our simple calculation (12.3.7) is, of course, too crude to give numerically correct results. To improve it, we should take account of the three-dimensional nature of the motion, and of the fact that free times will not all have the same length, but will be statistically distributed. These refinements only have the effect, however, of changing the numerical coefficient in (12.3.7), not of changing the fundamental idea of the calculation.

Now let us try to interpret these same ideas in terms of wave mechanics. We are looking for a mechanism by which an electron, started through the crystal with a certain velocity, will gradually lose that velocity, adopting our solution (12.3.5) for the damping. By considering this process of exponential damping of an initial velocity of the particle, we can separate the two parts of our problem, the acceleration by the electric field and the damping. The first thing we notice is that our solution for an electron traveling through the periodic potential has no place in it for any mechanism of damping. In spite of the fact that the electron goes through atom after atom, the periodicity of the problem is such that we have our solutions of the problem in the form of regular electron waves, with no damping at all. This possibility, a result of wave mechanics, by which electrons can go through many atomic distances without finding obstacles, removes one puzzle in the classical theory of conductivity; it was hard to see how an electron could go even a single atomic distance without being stopped by a collision, and yet such a short mean free path would lead to much too small a conductivity.

To get damping of an electron wave according to wave mechanics, then, we must look for something besides propagation in a periodic potential; and we shall soon see that almost any disturbance of the periodic lattice will have the effect of damping the wave. The phenomenon which we must look for is the scattering of the electron waves by lattice irregularities. Scattering is familiar from optics. We know that as a plane wave of light enters a scattering medium, like a gas or liquid, wavelets will be scattered by each scattering center, such as a molecule or a dust particle, and these scattered wavelets will rob intensity from the incident wave. The scattered waves involve propagation of the wave in all directions from the scattering center. As light becomes more and more scattered, with multiple scattering, by which light which has already been scattered once is scattered again, it will be traveling uniformly in all directions. We see something of this effect in the atmosphere: the blue color of the sky is a result of scattered light (blue because the short waves scatter more than the long ones), and it reaches us from all directions because it has been scattered at various points in the atmosphere. On a clear day we still see the sun, though not as strongly as if there had been no scattering; the fraction of sunlight scattered on its way to us on a clear day is not very large. On a hazy day, however, there is more scattering, we do not see the sun at all, but we have a large amount of scattered light coming from all directions. All this can occur without any true absorption: by absorption we mean the real loss of the light, on account of a change of wave length or character, ending up as thermal motion, while with scattering the light is still there, but traveling in a different direction.

In a similar way the electron wave can be scattered, with the result that it is converted from a plane wave, having a definite momentum, to waves traveling in all directions, and thus not corresponding to a net momentum at all. This scattering obviously results in a loss of the net current flowing in the material; the random motion in the scattered wave can result in random currents, but not in any average current. Thus it is the type of phenomenon which can be described in terms of a mean free time for scattering, or in terms of a resisting force or a mobility: an electron, traversing such a scattering medium, will gradually lose its forward momentum, on account of the scattering, and this is equivalent

to a resisting force.   We even have an analogy between the way in which
our electron wave can traverse a regular crystal, and a somewhat similar
situation in the case of light.   A light wave passing through a regular
crystal is not scattered, even though the crystal contains a great many
atoms which individually produce scattered wavelets.   A careful treatment of the optical problem shows that the wavelets interfere destructively and produce no scattered wave, provided only that the atoms are
regularly arranged.   The only effect proves to be that of refraction, a
change in the phase velocity of the wave as it passes through the medium·
This holds even when the wave length gets comparable in dimensions
with the interatomic distances, as we find in the range of x-rays, except
in the single case when the wave satisfies the conditions for Bragg reflection; that is the only case in which the scattered wavelets from the various
atoms interfere constructively and produce a scattered beam.   And we
have already seen that the same thing is true of the electron waves.

The reason why a gas or liquid scatters light, while a transparent solid
does not, is that there are fluctuations of density in the gas or liquid,
which we do not have in the solid, and which result in imperfect destructive interference between the scattered wavelets.   The theory shows
that it is fluctuations of index of refraction which can produce scattering.
These fluctuations can be produced, in the first place, by impurities
distributed through the material.   They can also be produced by fluctuations of density arising from pressure differences.   In particular, a plane
wave of sound traversing a liquid causes scattering of a particular sort,
known as the Debye-Sears effect.   There are periodic planes of condensation and rarefaction as a result of the sound, and these lead to fluctuations
of the index of refraction, which depends on the density.   The fluctuations of density encountered in the sound wave, unlike those from random
fluctuations, are regularly arranged, and the scattered wavelets then can
interfere in a regular fashion.   We see at once that the mathematical
problem of studying their interference is just like that met in x-ray diffraction, where we have scattering from the variations of density in the
crystal planes.   It proves to be the case then that the Debye-Sears
reflection from the planes of condensation and rarefaction obeys the
Bragg law.   There is a modification, however.   The sound waves are
moving; thus the reflection is like reflection from a moving mirror, and
that results in a Doppler effect of the reflected light, a slight change of
frequency.   A characteristic of the Debye-Sears reflection is then a very
slight change in the frequency of the reflected light.

We have emphasized this Debye-Sears effect on account of its close
relationship to scattering of light, or of x-rays, by the thermal agitation of
the lattice.   We have seen in the preceding chapter that this thermal

agitation can be analyzed into a superposition of plane waves of an acoustical sort, which can have all wave lengths, down to limiting waves whose lengths are of the order of magnitude of interatomic dimensions. The scattering of light by the thermal agitation of the molecules can then be analyzed into scattering by the various plane waves, each behaving as in the Debye-Sears effect. Even x-ray scattering by the thermal agitation can be described in this way, since the shortest acoustical waves are short enough to scatter x-rays, according to the Bragg law. One can, as a matter of fact, give a complete theory of x-ray and optical scattering by the fluctuations of density arising from thermal agitation by such a method. The net results are not very different, however, from what we get by considering the scattering by the individual atoms, each in thermal agitation, assumed to scatter independently. That simple picture also leads to a fairly adequate understanding of this phase of scattering.

There is one feature of the scattering process which the Debye-Sears theory leads to in a very simple way: the change of frequency of the scattered light, which we have seen to arise from the Doppler effect. This change of frequency, in the x-ray range, is also known by another name: it is the Compton effect. Often the Compton effect is described in corpuscular language, rather than in this language of waves. A photon, striking an atom and being scattered, has a certain momentum. There is conservation of momentum in the scattering process. If, then, the photon after the collision travels off in some different direction, representing the scattered beam, the difference in momentum between its initial and final momentum must be made up by the atom, which then must have a certain momentum after the episode. If the atom has momentum, it must also have velocity, and kinetic energy, so that if it were originally at rest, it must have gained kinetic energy in the collision. Conservation of energy then requires that the photon must have lost a compensating energy; and since its energy is $h\nu$, its frequency must have been decreased by the scattering process. This is the Compton effect; the wave-mechanical theory of this effect operates with the waves of sound which we have been describing and the Doppler effect met on scattering from these moving waves, traveling as they do with the velocity of sound. The two pictures, the particle and wave pictures, lead to identical results.

We have gone into such a long description of the scattering of light, mainly to show that the scattering of electron waves does not introduce any new principles into the problem. We can treat scattering of electron waves, by methods like those of the preceding sections, if we remember that any distortion of the lattice, either produced by impurity atoms, or by thermal agitation, will result in variations of the electrical potential energy within the lattice. That is, we shall have a perturbing potential energy $V(x,y,z)$ fluctuating from point to point, and our problem of scattering can be handled by considering Schrödinger's equation for an electron in the periodic potential and such a fluctuating perturbation. In Sec. 12.1 we have seen how to handle the effect of such a fluctuation on the motion of a wave packet; it is also possible to go further and handle the effect of perturbations like this on the individual wave functions, showing that they will in fact be scattered much like light waves. Just as in the case of light, we shall find scattering by impurity atoms. We shall also find scattering by thermal agitation; and we shall find that this can be handled by the analogue to the Debye-Sears effect, scattering by the various acoustical waves, or alternatively, as scattering by the individual displaced atoms, treating an atom displaced from its equilibrium position by thermal agitation as something like an impurity atom.

This picture of scattering by the atoms as displaced by thermal agitation leads in a plausible way to one important result of the scattering theory which can be verified by more careful analysis. We naturally expect the amplitude of a scattered wavelet to be proportional to the displacement of the scattering atom from its equilibrium position, and hence the intensity of the scattered wavelet, being proportional to the square of its amplitude, to be proportional to the square of the displacement of the scattering atom. But the intensity of the scattered wavelet determines the probability of scattering of the particle. Furthermore, in the region of temperatures high enough for equipartition of energy to hold, the square of the displacement of the atom, which is proportional to its energy of oscillation, will be proportional to the temperature. We expect, then, that the probability of scattering of an electron by thermal agitation will be proportional to the absolute temperature. This fact proves to be of great importance in studying the temperature variation of the conductivity of a metal. At low temperatures, where equipartition does not hold and the amplitude of oscillation of the atoms is less than equipartition would suggest, we expect to find as well that the scattering of electron waves is less than indicated by the proportionality to temperature, and the more exact calculation, in fact, leads to this result.

The detailed theory of scattering of electrons by thermal agitation operates, as we might expect, by means of the plane acoustic waves, and the electron scattering by these waves, according to the Debye-Sears effect. One feature which that method brings in, and which is of importance in the general picture, is the analogue to the Compton effect, the way in which the kinetic energy of an electron will be slightly decreased when it is scattered by the plane waves of sound. This means that the electron has given a small kinetic energy to the atomic lattice, at each collision. We shall, of course, have to expect this to happen in any adequate theory of electrical resistance. An electric field, acting on electrons, and accelerating them, constantly does work on them. The momentum of the electrons is dissipated on collision with the atoms; but if the excess kinetic energy were not also dissipated, we should have a situation in which the random kinetic energy of the electrons continuously increased, without passing this energy on to the atoms. The recoil of the atoms, analogous to the Compton effect, furnishes the mechanism for energy interchange between the electrons and atoms by which effective thermal equilibrium is maintained between them. When an electric field continually acts on a conductor, we know that the work which it dissipates in the conductor appears as the Joulean heat, raising the temperature of the conductor. This increase of internal energy, of course, must, in equilibrium, be distributed between energy of the atoms and of the electrons. We shall shortly see, however, that the specific heat of the electrons is very small compared with that of the atoms, so that we must expect that almost all the Joulean heat appears as energy of the atoms. The mechanism which we have just described allows this energy, which in the first instance is delivered by the field to the electrons, to be immediately transferred to the atoms.

We have now seen that the electronic wave can be scattered, leading to a mean free time, mean free path, or mobility, by any irregularity in the lattice, including temperature agitation. Though scattering by temperature agitation is proportional to the temperature, at high temperatures, the scattering by other irregularities is approximately independent of temperature. As examples of other irregularities we may mention not only the obvious ones of impurities, but also irregularities resulting from cold work and other distortion of the crystal. Clearly, furthermore, in an alloy in which the atoms of different sorts are arranged somewhat randomly, we shall have irregularities for that reason, and consequent scattering. We can then use our simple expressions (12.3.4) or (12.3.7) for conductivity to draw some simple conclusions regarding the conductivity of a metal. In such a material the number N of free electrons is essentially independent of temperature. Then if we have no impurities or irregularities, so that all the scattering is produced by temperature agitation, we shall assume that the probability of scattering, given by the term $a\,dx/dt$ in (12.3.1), is proportional to the temperature, so that the conductivity will be inversely proportional to temperature, or the resistance proportional to temperature, as is known to be the case. On

the other hand, if there is additional scattering from irregularities, there
will be an additional term in (12.3.1), so that a will be the sum of two
terms, one proportional to temperature, the other independent of temperature.   The result will then be a specific resistance which is the sum
of two terms, one the thermal term proportional to the temperature, the
other a constant independent of temperature, generally called the residual
resistance, since it is present even at the absolute zero of temperature.
It is well known experimentally that such a residual resistance arises
from the presence of impurities, cold working, or alloying.   We note that
the proportionality of the thermal term in the resistance to temperature
does not hold at low enough temperatures, where it becomes much
smaller; more elaborate theory shows that this term, at low enough
temperatures, varies with the fifth power of the temperature.

We shall also be able to draw conclusions, from our elementary theory,
regarding the conductivity of semiconductors.   In these materials, as
we have already seen, there are no free electrons at the absolute zero of
temperature.   Thus the conductivity there goes to zero.   As the temperature rises, electrons become excited to the conduction band, and
holes appear in the lower, valence band.   Thus the number N of (12.3.4),
(12.3.6), or (12.3.7) increases rapidly with temperature.   This leads to
a very rapid rise of conductivity, or decrease of resistance, as the temperature rises.   This change in N, which is not met with metals, is the
principal reason for the rapid temperature variation of the conductivity
of semiconductors.   The mobility of the electrons, arising from electron
scattering, is of essentially the same form as found in a metal, and of
about the same order of magnitude, so that it tends to lead to an increase
of resistance at high temperatures, not nearly enough, however, to balance
the large decrease of resistance at high temperatures resulting from the
increase of N.   One feature of semiconductors is the possibility of conduction by both the electrons and the holes.   If both are simultaneously
effective, we simply add the currents and, consequently, the contributions
to the conductivity.   We notice, of course, that since the formulas for σ
involve e^2, the effect of an electron or a hole on the conductivity will be
identical, provided they have equal mobilities.   And the mobilities of
electrons and holes are not in fact very different, provided their effective
masses are the same; the theory of scattering of a hole is essentially that
of scattering of a positive electron, and its sign has no effect on its
behavior.

All this discussion has seemed very straightforward; but we have been
entirely forgetting that the electrons in a metal fill the conduction band
to a height of several volts in energy, that they obey the exclusion principle, and that, as a consequence, it is completely incorrect to suppose

that an electron has its velocity reduced to zero after each collision. This cannot happen: the energy level associated with zero kinetic energy is already filled. We may well expect, then, that the exclusion principle will have a profound effect on conductivity, which we have so far entirely missed. In the next section we shall consider this question. We shall, in fact, find that the effect is profound; but it turns out to work out in such a way that the results we have been stating, regarding the conductivity, effect of scattering, and so on, are still substantially correct. It is this fact which made it possible for a considerable period to use the classical theories of Drude and Lorentz, without serious trouble.

12.4. The Fermi Statistics and Metallic Electrons. The Pauli exclusion principle, stated in statistical language, furnishes the basis of the Fermi statistics. We may handle the derivation of this form of statistics either by the fundamental methods of statistical mechanics, basing our arguments on the antisymmetric wave functions which we know underlie the Pauli principle, or by kinetic methods, considering the probability of making various transitions between stationary states, and introducing the postulate that the probability of an electron making a transition to a stationary state which is already occupied by another electron is zero. We shall not carry through either type of argument, since they lie outside the province of the present treatment.† The results, however, are fortunately very simple, and we can easily state them and make use of them.

The results of Fermi statistics are stated in terms of a one-electron model, where we are assuming that each electron moves in a potential field dependent on position, without mutual interactions of the electrons; thus it is perfectly adapted to the method of molecular orbitals and of the self-consistent field, which are based on similar assumptions. A given electron, then, has a choice of many possible stationary states. We assume, as in our model of the metal, that we have a great many electrons to accommodate in these stationary states. The Fermi statistics then states that, at temperature T, the average number of electrons which will be found in a stationary state of energy E is given by

$$N(E) = \frac{2}{e^{(E-E_F)/kT} + 1}, \tag{12.4.1}$$

where E_F is a constant to be determined. This function has the form given in Fig. 12.4.1, showing that for E much less than E_F, $N(E)$ approaches 2, while for E much greater than E_F, $N(E)$ approaches zero. As we see

† Both methods are treated in J. C. Slater, "Introduction to Chemical Physics," McGraw-Hill Book Company, Inc., New York, 1939, Chaps. V and VI, and the application to the electron gas is taken up in Chaps. XXVIII and XXIX.

from the figure, the change from one situation to the other occurs more rapidly, the lower the temperature. At the absolute zero the change is infinitely rapid, all energies less than E_F having two electrons per energy level (one for each spin), while all energy levels above E_F are empty. The level E_F is called the Fermi level; it evidently corresponds, at the absolute zero, to the top of the occupied bands of energy. This is a perfectly definite energy in the case of a metal; though we shall see in a later section that the situation is not so simple in an insulator or semiconductor. At any temperature, E_F is to be determined from the condition that the

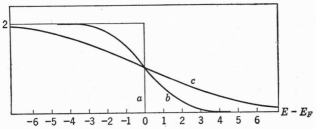

FIG. 12.4.1.   Fermi distribution function, as function of $E - E_F$, for several temperatures.   Curve a, $kT = 0$; b, $kT = 1$; c, $kT = 2.5$.

sum of $N(E)$ for all energy levels must come out to be the actual total number of electrons in the system:

$$\Sigma N(E) = N, \tag{12.4.2}$$

where the sum is over energy levels, N is the total number of electrons. Once we know the energies of the various stationary states, we can use this condition to determine E_F, though unfortunately the calculation is not easy to carry out, since we cannot analytically solve for E_F. What we actually have to do is to compute $\Sigma N(E)$, where $N(E)$ is given in (12.4.1), as a function of E_F, and choose that E_F for which the sum comes out equal to N.

When we actually carry out this calculation for the type of distribution of energy levels which we have already found to exist for the metal, we meet a rather simple situation. At the absolute zero of temperature, there is no problem; as we have seen in earlier chapters, the levels are filled up to a high enough level to accommodate all the electrons, and above that they are empty. It is clear, then, that the Fermi level at the absolute zero is simply the top of the occupied levels. As the temperature changes, it then proves to be the case that to a first approximation the Fermi level does not change. There is a sort of smearing out of the transition between full and empty levels, however; over a range of energies of the order of magnitude of kT (which, as we remember, is about $\frac{1}{40}$ volt at room temperature) the levels which were occupied at the absolute zero have lost some electrons, which have gone up into the levels which were empty at the absolute zero. This results in a slight increase of electronic energy and a slight contribution to an electronic specific heat; but calculation shows that the electronic specific heat, at any ordinary temperature, is small compared with the specific heat arising from lattice vibration. This removes one of the important difficulties with the Drude-Lorentz theory: if the electron gas were treated classically, there would be no reason why it should not have the specific heat of a classical monatomic gas; but the observed specific heats showed very clearly that it did not, but instead had practically no specific heat.

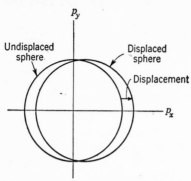

FIG. 12.4.2. Sphere corresponding to Fermi energy in momentum space, and displaced sphere under action of field along x axis for time t_1.

Now let us consider the influence of the Fermi statistics on electrical conduction in a metal. At an initial instant of time we assume the electrons to be in equilibrium. They will then fill up those energy levels below the Fermi level, with a rapid decrease of density in the neighborhood of the Fermi level, from the maximum of two electrons per level to zero. We may indicate this in a two-dimensional p space (this gives a little more information than the one-dimensional case we have considered earlier, and yet is easy to plot, which the real three-dimensional case is not). We can draw energy contours, lines of constant E, in this p space, and in particular, we can draw one corresponding to the Fermi energy. If the energy bands are not too far from those characteristic of free electrons, this Fermi energy will correspond to a circle (or sphere in three dimensions). It is shown in Fig. 12.4.2. Now let us consider what happens when the field is applied. If it is along the x axis, the wave packets representing the occupied levels, from what we have seen previously, will start to move along the p_x axis, in the way shown. This will correspond to the build-up of a current, which like the electronic velocities will increase proportionally to the time. However, the increase will not continue, on account of the scattering of the electron waves by the lattice irregularities.

To get a simple description, let us take that method of considering the scattering in which we assume that an electron moves for a time t_1, then is scattered. In the diagram above we have shown the displaced distribution of occupied levels after this time t_1. Now let us see what sort of collisions we shall have. The kinetic description of the Fermi statistics is very simple, as we indicated above: we calculate the probability of an electronic transition as if the Fermi statistics did not apply, but then arbitrarily exclude any transition into a state already occupied by an electron. Now in the process of scattering, as described by wave mechanics, without application of Fermi statistics, an electron would change its momentum, but with very small change in energy (the change is merely that resulting from the atomic recoil, as we have seen in the preceding section). In other words, its momentum will change from its original value to some other value corresponding to very slightly lower energy. A wave packet corresponding to a given p, in other words, will become dissipated by scattering into a distribution of intensity approximately on the surface of a sphere in p space (if we are dealing with the case above, in which the energy surfaces are approximately spherical). But now we see that if the wave packet we are considering is well below the Fermi energy in its energy, it cannot be scattered at all, on account of the exclusion principle. All the energy levels into which it could go are already filled. Thus its chance of scattering is zero. Only if it is very close to the Fermi level will it find empty states into which it can go, and only in that case will it be scattered. On the other hand, once it is up at the top of the Fermi level, its probability of being scattered will be just about the same as if the exclusion principle did not act; for it will have only a small chance of finding the level occupied into which it would be scattered.

We then build up the following picture of the process of scattering. Under the action of the impressed electric field, the wave packets representing the electrons move uniformly through momentum space, in the direction of the external force. This motion is not interfered with by scattering, until the regular motion, like a procession, has carried the wave packets up to the energy of the Fermi level, and perhaps slightly above. Then the probability of scattering will begin to operate, and after a time of the order of t_1 the electron will be scattered, its wave packet being spread somehow around the boundary of the occupied region in the momentum space, roughly on the surface of the Fermi energy level. This will lead to an equilibrium situation: the distribution will reach a steady state when it is displaced by the amount which it reaches in time t_1. But this is essentially equivalent to the situation which we met in classical statistics, as described in the previous section. If we are in a region where the energy of the electron is a quadratic function of the momentum, with an effective mass m^*, so that (12.2.1) holds, the velocity of each electron will have increased by the same amount in the time t_1, and the problem of finding the conductivity will be exactly as in (12.3.4), except that we are to use the effective mass m^* instead of the real mass. Thus we justify our statement that, though the situation is really very different from what it would be without the Fermi statistics or the Pauli exclusion principle, still the net result, as far as conductivity is concerned, is the same.

The situation is not changed in any important detail if the energy band is filled to a position such that we can no longer use (12.2.1) to indicate the acceleration of the wave packet. Our qualitative discussion, in terms of the displacement of the occupied levels in the momentum space, still holds. If, for instance, we are dealing with an almost filled band, we displace all the occupied levels, and the unoccupied levels may be pictured as being displaced along with them; it is as if we had positive electrons filling the levels which really are unoccupied. A little consideration shows that in this case we can use (12.2.2), just as we should otherwise use (12.2.1), and that we again have (12.3.4) as the correct formula for conductivity, only now using m^{**} instead of m^*. It makes no difference in the conductivity, in other words, whether we are dealing with electrons or holes.

As far as the formula (12.3.4) for the conductivity is concerned, we are dealing only with the ratio N/m^*, or N/m^{**}. Sometimes, instead of treating N as the real number of electrons, and m^* or m^{**} as an effective mass, as we have done, a different mode of description is used in which we write $N/m^* = N^*/m$, where m is the real electronic mass, and N^* is called an effective number of free electrons, the number of classical electrons which would be necessary to give the same conductivity. There is no objection to this description of the situation, though as we see from our derivation, it is somewhat more logical to use N for the real number of electrons and use an effective m^*. Further light on the actual number of free electrons, and also their sign, whether negative or positive, is given by the Hall effect, of which we now give an account.

12.5. The Hall Effect. Hall discovered many years ago that if a magnetic field is applied transverse to a conductor carrying a current, a difference of potential automatically appears across the conductor, transverse both to the direction of current flow and to the magnetic field, and proportional both to the current and to the magnetic field. Putting it in terms of quantities which do not involve the dimensions of the conductor, there is a transverse electric field which is automatically set up, proportional to the magnetic field and the current density. The Hall constant is defined as the transverse electric field per unit magnetic field and per

unit current density.   We can understand by a very simple argument why
the Hall effect should come about.

We recall that an electron in an electric and magnetic field is acted on
simultaneously by an electric force, proportional to the electronic charge
and the electric field, and in the direction of the field, and by a magnetic
force, proportional to the electronic charge, its velocity, and the magnetic
field, and in the direction at right angles to the plane determined by the
velocity and magnetic field.   Expressed in vector language, the force is

$$\mathbf{F} = q(\mathbf{E} + \mathbf{v} \times \mathbf{B}), \tag{12.5.1}$$

where q is the charge, $\mathbf{E}$ the electric field, and $\mathbf{v} \times \mathbf{B}$ the vector product of
velocity and magnetic field.   In the Hall effect, since the velocity $\mathbf{v}$ of
the electron is along the conductor, $\mathbf{B}$ transverse to it, the vector $\mathbf{v} \times \mathbf{B}$ is
also transverse.   In other words, if the electron traveled along the con-
ductor under the action of the magnetic field, there would be a transverse
force, tending to push it to one side of the conductor.   This, of course,
could not go on long, for the electron would strike the surface of the conductor, stop there, and remain as a surface charge.   This surface charge
would start establishing a transverse electric field inside the conductor,
and this process would go on until the transverse electric field was built
up to a large enough size so that the net transverse force, given by
(12.5.1), was zero, and the further electrons would travel straight down
the conductor without transverse acceleration.   For this to be the case,
it is clear from (12.5.1) that the magnitudes of the transverse E and the
product of v and B, must be equal, or

$$E = vB, \tag{12.5.2}$$

where now we are dealing only with the magnitudes of the quantities.
But we recall that the current density J is given by Nqv, where N is the
number of carriers per unit volume, q the charge.   Hence we have

$$E = \frac{JB}{Nq} = RJB, \qquad \text{where } R = \frac{1}{Nq}. \tag{12.5.3}$$

Here R is the Hall constant; we have demonstrated that the Hall effect
should occur as it is found experimentally.   If we are really dealing with
an electron, of course, q should be set equal to $-e$.   The sign convention
is so chosen that if the current is carried by electrons of negative sign,
the Hall constant is negative, whereas positive carriers would result in a
positive Hall coefficient.   Our simple derivation resulting in (12.5.3)
proves to give the correct result for the case of electrons with a Fermi
distribution, as we meet them in a metal.   For the classical Maxwellian

distribution, more careful study shows that (12.5.3) must be multiplied by a simple numerical coefficient.

In the early days of measurement of the Hall effect, Hall found that many metals showed negative Hall constants, as we should expect from electronic conductivity; but some metals showed positive Hall constants. This led Hall to an assumption of conduction by holes acting like positive electrons, which was in fact an anticipation of the picture to which we are led by the wave-mechanical theory of energy bands. We may now reasonably suppose that in those metals showing positive Hall constants, we are dealing with an almost filled band, so that the carriers of current appear to be positive electrons. To check this hypothesis, we must ask how the formula for Hall constant is worked out in quantum mechanics. We find that the derivation is very complicated, much too difficult to indicate here. But in the simple cases where (12.2.1) or (12.2.2) holds, the result is simple, and as we should guess: where (12.2.1) is applicable we have $R = -1/Ne$, and where (12.2.2) is applicable we have $R = 1/Ne$. In other words, the effective mass cancels out of the expression, just as the mass cancels out in the classical expression for the Hall constant, so that in such cases a measurement of Hall constant gives a valid measurement of the number of free electrons in the conduction band. Unfortunately, in intermediate cases the formula for Hall constant, which, of course, must go continuously from one of these limiting cases to the other, is extremely involved and is hard to correlate with other observable quantities. There is, however, one intermediate case in which the formula is rather simple and is particularly useful in cases of semiconductors. This is the case where we simultaneously have a rather small number of electrons in the bottom of one band, to which (12.2.1) applies, and a rather small number of holes at the top of another, governed by (12.2.2). Let there be n_1 electrons per atom, n_2 positive holes per atom, and let N be the number of atoms per unit volume. Then we have

$$R = \frac{1}{Ne} \frac{n_2/m^{**2} - n_1/m^{*2}}{(n_1/m^* + n_2/m^{**})^2}. \tag{12.5.4}$$

This formula reduces to the correct limiting values when either n_1 or n_2 is zero. It shows, moreover, that a suitable number of electrons and holes taken together can balance their contributions to the Hall constant, so that we can get intermediate cases between those of all positive and all negative carriers.

When we examine the Hall constants for the various metals, we find interesting results. For the alkali metals the constants come out rather close to $-1/Ne$, where N is the number of atoms per unit volume, indicating, therefore, that we are justified in treating these metals as having one free electron per atom, and satisfying the conditions for (12.2.1). For the metals Cu, Ag, and Au this is approximately true, though not as accurately as for the alkalies. For some other metals we get much poorer agreement with the expected number of electrons; we presumably are to explain this by assuming that the conditions of (12.2.1) or (12.2.2) are not fulfilled. Most interesting, perhaps, are the anomalous metals As, Sb, and Bi, which we have mentioned earlier. These materials have extraordinarily large Hall constants, and other magnetic effects associated with them are unusually large. This is usually interpreted in terms of the assumption that for these materials the electrons almost exactly fill one band, with very few electrons extending into another band. Thus we have the conditions for (12.5.4), with very small values of n_1 and n_2. The denominator will be very small compared with the numerator, unless we happen to have cancellation of the positive and negative terms in the numerator, which we do not seem to have in these cases; thus the Hall constant will be very large, as observed. The remarkable properties of these elements are assumed to be tied up with this situation, according to which the bands are very nearly completely filled or completely empty. Even in spite of this situation of very small effective numbers of free electrons, the conductivity is not as small as we might expect from (12.3.4); this must mean that the effective mass m^* or m^{**} is quite small. The Hall constant for Bi is negative, but that for Sb is positive, indicating that the numerator of (12.5.4) has opposite signs in the two cases, the negative electrons being more important current carriers for bismuth, but the positive holes for antimony.

From these remarks, it is clear that the Hall effect provides a piece of information about conductors which we cannot get in any other way: indication in a rather direct way about the number of current carriers and the sign of their charge, whereas conductivity gives information complicated by the effective mass, and complicated by the fact that the square of the charge, rather than its first power, enters, so that positive and negative carriers act alike. In the study of semiconductors, which we shall next consider, the Hall effect is even more important than with metals. Here we have very few carriers of current, and as a result, the Hall constant is very much larger than in the case of metals, and much easier to observe. With semiconductors, using (12.5.4) for the Hall constant and (12.3.6) for the conductivity, it has been possible in many cases to establish reliable values for the separate numbers of positive and negative carriers, and for the mobilities.

12.6. The Behavior of Semiconductors. Let us first consider an intrinsic semiconductor; that is, a substance which, like an insulator, has a lower, filled band, which we shall call the valence band, and an upper empty band, which we shall call the conduction band, with an energy gap between; but in which the gap is narrow enough so that appreciable numbers of electrons can be excited to the conduction band, leaving an equal number of holes in the valence band, by application of moderate temperatures. In such a material, following (12.3.6), the conductivity will be

$$\sigma = N_+ e\mu_+ + N_- e\mu_-, \qquad (12.6.1)$$

where N_+, N_- are the numbers of positive and negative carriers per unit volume, μ_+ and μ_- the corresponding mobilities. We have already mentioned that the mobilities are not very different in order of magnitude, and in temperature variation, in semiconductors from what they are in metals, so that the striking differences from the case of metals come in the N's. Let us now see what the Fermi statistics predicts about the dependence of these N's on temperature.

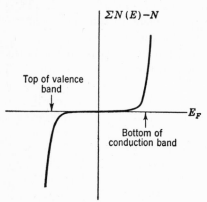

FIG. 12.6.1. Total number of electrons as function of Fermi energy; intrinsic semiconductor.

Let us assume that the distributions of energy levels in the empty and filled band are as given in the conditions for (12.2.1) and (12.2.2). Then it is a straightforward task, using (12.4.1) for the Fermi distribution, to compute the sum $\Sigma N(E)$ given in (12.4.2), which must be equal to N. When we make this calculation as a function of E_F, the result is as shown in Fig. 12.6.1, where we have assumed, for simplicity, that m^* for the conduction band equals m^{**} for the valence band. From this figure we see that when E_F is midway between the two energy bands, or in the middle of the gap, $\Sigma N(E)$ will be equal to the number N of electrons which must be accommodated. This then establishes the position of the Fermi level and shows that the situation is more complicated than the case of the metal, where the Fermi level is just at the top of the occupied bands.

Now that we know the position of the Fermi level, we can use (12.4.1) to find the number of electrons in the conduction band and the number of holes in the valence band. At ordinary temperatures, with ordinary semiconductors, the energy gap is very large compared with kT. If ΔE is the width of the energy gap, we then see that in the expression (12.4.1), where we have the exponential $e^{(E-E_F)/kT}$, this exponential is at least as great as $e^{\Delta E/2kT}$ for all energy levels in the conduction band, and unity can be neglected in comparison with it.   That is, if ε is the energy of a level in the conduction band, measured up from the bottom of that band, $N(E)$ for one of the levels in the conduction band will be given by

$$N(E) = 2e^{-\Delta E/2kT}e^{-\varepsilon/kT}. \tag{12.6.2}$$

If now we calculate the number of energy levels per unit range of energy, using the assumptions underlying (12.2.1), it is a simple matter of statistical theory to convert the sum of $N(E)$ into an integral, and carry out this integration over the levels of the conduction band.†   The calculation gives for the number of electrons per unit volume in the conduction band

$$\sum N(E) = \frac{2}{h^3}(2\pi m^*kT)^{3/2}e^{-\Delta E/2kT}. \tag{12.6.3}$$

It is easy to show that the number of holes in the valence band, obtained by summing $[2 - N(E)]$ over the levels of that band, has the same value as (12.6.3), where we remember that we are assuming that $m^* = m^{**}$; if we do not make that assumption, the formulas are slightly more complicated, but not different in essentials.   The number of electrons and holes must, of course, be equal, in order that the total sum of $N(E)$ over all levels may have the correct value.

As a result of (12.6.3), we now see that the number of both electrons and holes has the small factor $e^{-\Delta E/2kT}$, decreasing very rapidly to zero as the temperature goes to zero.   This factor will be the most important one in the expression (12.6.1) for conductivity.   It evidently has the general character of the expressions which we derived in the preceding chapter for processes governed by an activation energy.   As in such cases, it is convenient, experimentally, to plot the logarithm of the conductivity as a function of $1/T$.   In that case the result will be very nearly a straight line [the dependence of mobility on temperature, and the factor $T^{3/2}$ in (12.6.3), make a relatively small departure from the straight line arising from the exponential function].   Such straight lines are experimentally found for intrinsic semiconductors, and from the slope of the line we can find the gap width ΔE.   Intrinsic semiconductors seldom are found, however, on account of the great importance of impurities, which we shall next discuss.   It is almost impossible in most cases to prepare a semiconductor pure enough so that it behaves like an intrinsic semiconductor.   We have taken up this case mostly as a preparation for the more common case of the impurity semiconductor.

Let us now ask what effect we expect an impurity atom to have on a semiconductor.   To be specific, let us consider the semiconductors Si

† The method is given in J. C. Slater, "Introduction to Chemical Physics," McGraw-Hill Book Company, Inc., New York, 1939, Chap. IV.

and Ge, which have been most carefully investigated.   These substances, as we know, have four valence electrons per atom, and crystallize in the diamond structure, in which each atom has four nearest neighbors, so that the electrons are just sufficient to form covalent bonds with the neighbors, leading to the filled valence band and empty conduction band which are observed.   Let us now assume that one of the lattice sites is occupied, not by the Si or Ge atom which should be there, but by an impurity atom of N, P, As, or an element which normally has five electrons in its outer shell.   Let us assume, for the moment, that this impurity atom loses one of its electrons, so as to have just the four which would be required to fit into the covalent structure.   Then we still have just the right number of electrons to form all the covalent bonds and to fill the valence levels.   There will, however, be a disturbance in the lattice: the impurity atom is really a positive ion, and it will exert a perturbing force on its neighbors.   This perturbation can be described as a potential V, such as we introduced in Sec. 12.1.   Being the potential of a positive ion, it will be like a Coulomb potential, just as if we had a proton at the position of the impurity atom, but with one difference: the semiconductor will have a fairly high dielectric constant, and this means that instead of the factor $4\pi\epsilon_0$ in the denominator of the expression of Coulomb's law we must use $4\pi\epsilon$, where ϵ is the permittivity of the dielectric, greater than ϵ_0 by a factor equal to the dielectric constant.   Thus the Coulomb force will be a number of times smaller than the field of a proton.

In this perturbing field the energy levels of the electrons will no longer be as they would be in an unperturbed periodic potential.   In Sec. 12.1 we have shown how to handle a wave packet in the presence of such a perturbation as we have here; we see that it moves like a particle of mass m^* [if we are in the conditions where we can use (12.2.1)] in the presence of the potential V.   A similar derivation to that described in Sec. 12.1 shows that in a case like this, we can also set up a Schrödinger equation for a particle of mass m^* in the potential V and treat the perturbed wave functions according to wave mechanics; our earlier results on the motion of wave packets are really only the limiting case of this wave-mechanical method applied to the classical limit.   An electron in the field of our impurity atom will then obey a Schrödinger equation like that of a particle of mass m^* in a Coulomb field which is a number of times smaller than the field of a proton.   This Schrödinger equation is, of course, just like the hydrogen problem, except for the magnitudes of the charge and mass, and it will have corresponding solutions, corresponding to the wave functions and energy levels of hydrogen.   If we look back to Chap. 5, we find that the effect of the smaller Coulomb force is to decrease the magnitudes of the energies and increase the size of the orbits.   The same effect will also arise from the mass m^*, which is likely, in such a case, to be considerably less than the real electronic mass. The net effect, then, is to have in the neighborhood of the impurity atom wave functions for the electron, like hydrogen wave functions, only on such an extended scale that they spread over many atom diameters, with energy levels like the hydrogen spectrum, but on a much smaller energy scale, the $1s$ level corresponding, not to the 13.5 volts of the Rydberg energy, but perhaps to $\frac{1}{10}$ volt, if we use reasonable estimates of the constants involved. In addition to these discrete levels, there will be the continuum of levels associated with energies so high that the electron can

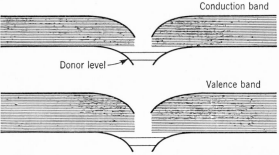

FIG. 12.6.2.   Valence and conduction bands near an n-type impurity atom, showing donor levels.

escape from the ion. This continuum of levels corresponds essentially to the conduction band.

When we look a little more closely into the relation between these levels and those which would be present in the absence of the impurity atom, we find that the following situation holds. We draw in Fig. 12.6.2 the top and bottom of the conduction band, as well as the top of the valence band, all modified by adding the V arising from the perturbing atom, as a function of position at points of a line drawn through the perturbing atom. The discrete impurity levels, arising as described in the preceding paragraph, are shown in the figure, below the conduction band. Their extension will be roughly in the region shown, where the classical kinetic energy is positive. The levels of the continuum are also shown, filling the energies of the unperturbed band. The wave functions of this continuum are modified, however, by the presence of the impurity atom. Our classical solution of Sec. 12.1, for the periodic potential plus the perturbing field, implies that the classical velocity is real, provided we are dealing with energies within an energy band, but goes to zero at either edge of the band and is imaginary in the gaps between bands. The corresponding solution of Schrödinger's equation falls off exponentially when the conditions are such that we are in a gap. Now in the figure above, we see that the higher energy levels of the continuum lead to a situation where the energy falls within the gap, at points near the impurity atom, on account of the distortion of the boundary of the band by the perturbing potential V. Hence the wave functions of these energy levels will fall off exponentially as we approach the impurity atom. By more elaborate means, we can show that not only do these levels of the continuum have a deficiency in their wave function near the impurity atom where the discrete wave functions have their intensity, so that the total charge density, if all levels are filled, is relatively unaffected by the impurity atom, but also the total number of levels in the band, including the discrete levels, is the same with the impurity present that it was without. The number of discrete levels introduced is just compensated by a decrease in the number of levels in the continuum, corresponding to the decrease in effective volume of the solid on account of the region cut out near the impurity atom by this exponential decrease in the continuum wave functions as they approach the impurity atom.

We may now consider the effect of these modifications of the wave functions and energy levels on the behavior of the substance. The valence band will be modified just as the conduction band is, as we see from Fig. 12.6.2. We recall that we have enough electrons to fill the valence band, and one besides. The valence band, as we have just seen, still has the same number of energy levels, in spite of its perturbation. Thus, when these levels are all filled, we shall have one electron left over. At the absolute zero, this will go into the next lower level available to it, the lowest discrete level surrounding the impurity atom. Thus it will be bound and not available for conduction. As the temperature increases, however, it needs only a small amount of thermal excitation to raise this electron to the continuous levels of the conduction band, so that it can take part in conduction. Thus a much smaller temperature will lead to appreciable conductivity than with an intrinsic semiconductor.

Of course, to have appreciable effect, we must have a good many of these impurity atoms, though the necessary number proves to be rather small compared with the total number of atoms; one impurity atom to a thousand is a large number for this purpose. Let us assume that we have impurity atoms of this sort distributed at random through the crystal. At each of these there will be discrete impurity levels, of the sort we have considered, the energy lying slightly below the bottom of the continuous conduction band, and the corresponding wave function localized in the neighborhood of the impurity atom. Such a situation is often symbolized as in Fig. 12.6.3, the dashes indicating impurity levels, the conduction and valence bands being drawn as they extend through the material. Let us now inquire how the existence of these impurity levels changes the statistical situation. We have a certain, rather small number of additional energy levels and an equivalent extra number of electrons. We must now make a new plot of $\Sigma N(E)$ as a function of E_F, in order to find the revised Fermi level. By comparison with the plot at the beginning of this section, Fig. 12.6.1, we find that $\Sigma N(E)$ is not changed to an appreciable extent by the presence of the impurity levels, on account of their small number. However, the significant change comes because this summation must now add to a larger total, on account of the electrons

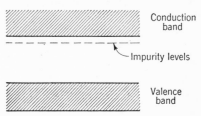

FIG. 12.6.3. Symbolic representation of impurity levels.

donated by the impurity atoms. We then find E_F a higher horizontal line, as shown in Fig. 12.6.4. This leads to a Fermi level much closer to the bottom of the conduction band than before. As a result of this, when we compute the number of electrons in the conduction band, getting a result analogous to (12.6.3), we find in the exponential not the energy difference $\Delta E/2$, which was the distance from the Fermi level to the bottom of the conduction band for the intrinsic semiconductor, but the much smaller value which we have just found. This results in a much increased number of electrons in the conduction band. On the other hand, in computing the number of holes, we have to use the energy difference between the new Fermi level and the top of the valence band, which is much larger than for the intrinsic case, and the result is that there are many fewer holes than before.

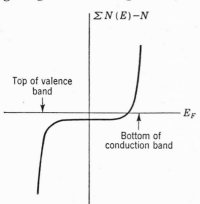

FIG. 12.6.4. Total number of electrons as function of Fermi energy; n-type semiconductor.

In this case it is obviously no longer necessary for the number of electrons to balance the number of holes; rather, the number of electrons, minus the number of holes, gives the number of electrons contributed by the impurity atoms.

The general behavior of the number of conduction electrons in this case is then as follows: At the absolute zero of temperature, there are **none**. We do not have to go to a very high temperature, however, to excite the electrons from the impurity atoms, so that we have a contribution to the number of conduction electrons, equal approximately to the number of impurity levels, which remains approximately independent of temperature up to high temperatures.   As the temperature is increased, the intrinsic conductivity starts, and at sufficiently high temperature it becomes greater than the conduction arising from impurities.   Thus if we plot the logarithm of the conductivity as a function of $1/T$, the result

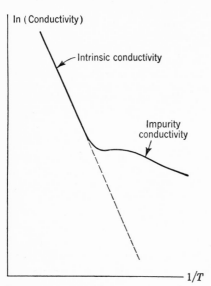

is as in Fig. 12.6.5.   The straight line represents the intrinsic conductivity, the slope being connected with the quantity $\Delta E/2$, as we have seen earlier.   However, at higher values of $1/T$ (that is, lower temperatures), the conductivity, instead of continuing to decrease as it would for an intrinsic semiconductor, becomes approximately constant.   At even lower temperatures it would start to decrease again, but in many actual cases it is not followed down to low enough temperatures to observe this phenomenon.

Fig. 12.6.5.   Logarithm of conductivity as function of $1/T$.

The type of semiconductor which we have been discussing is that in which there are impurities which can give up electrons to the conduction band; these are called n-type semiconductors, as we have mentioned before, and their impurities are of the donor type.   There also exist p-type semiconductors, with acceptor-type impurities, which result in conduction by holes, or positive carriers.   Impurities of this type are substituted atoms which have too few electrons to take their place properly in the band; thus, in Si or Ge, Al or Ga would be a p-type impurity.   Let us see how our picture is to be modified in this case.   The impurity atom replaces a Si or Ge atom in the lattice; let us assume, for the moment, that an extra electron is supplied, so that the energy band is filled.   This extra electron will be located on the impurity atom, converting it into a negative ion.   This will have the effect of raising the top of the valence and conduction bands, by the Coulomb potential energy term arising from a negative charge, as in Fig. 12.6.6.   We shall now have discrete levels at the top of band, coming from the holes, acting like positive electrons, executing hydrogenlike orbits about the negative ion. As in the other case, the modified band still has the same number of levels as in the unperturbed crystal. The extra electron which we added to fill the band then will be in the top level of the valence band, which is the discrete level. If this electron is now removed, to make the crystal electrically neutral, this level will be vacant. It is then a vacant impurity level slightly above the top of the valence band. As the temperature is raised, an electron can be excited from the continuum of the valence band to this impurity level, leaving a hole in this continuum, which will then lead to conduction by a positive carrier. The Fermi level, instead of being just below the conduction band, will be just above

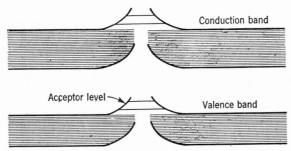

FIG. 12.6.6. Valence and conduction bands near a *p*-type impurity atom, showing acceptor levels.

the valence band, and if we have many such acceptor impurity atoms, there will be a corresponding number of positive carriers of current at ordinary temperatures, but very few electrons in the conduction band. The net result, as far as the relation between temperature and conductivity is concerned, will be as for the *n*-type semiconductor. One case can be distinguished from the other, however, by the Hall effect.

By careful analyses of conductivity and Hall effect as functions of temperature, it has been possible to understand the effects of impurities on the conductivity of semiconductors in a very complete way. The interest of these materials does not lie principally in their conductivity, however, but rather in other interesting properties which they have. When we make contacts between a semiconductor and a metal, we often find that the contact is rectifying, the resistance being different, depending on the direction in which the current is flowing. This effect is of great use in radio work, in which the early communication at ordinary radio frequencies used such rectifying crystals as detectors, and where now, though vacuum tubes furnish better rectifiers at ordinary radio frequencies, still the crystals are superior at microwave frequencies. Furthermore, there are interesting effects on illumination: illuminating a rectifying contact changes its apparent resistance, or produces photo-conductivity, resulting in a phenomenon which can be used to detect radiation. We shall now consider the explanation of these interesting effects. First, however, we must consider the general question of the boundary conditions at the surface between two conductors, whether they may be metals or semiconductors; until we understand these conditions, we cannot deal with such problems as rectifying contacts.

12.7. Boundary Conditions between Conducting Materials. As a first step in understanding the boundary conditions between different conductors, let us consider what goes on at the boundary of a finite crystal of a metal in empty space. The potential energy acting on the electron,

Fig. 12.7.1.   Potential energy at edge of a metal.

as indicated in Fig. 12.7.1, rises beyond the last atoms of the crystal, to a constant asymptotic value at large distances. This rise is made up of several things. At short distances, the electron is still inside the charge distributions of the atoms; thus the potential varies much as it does within an atom. At larger distances, the main effect is what is called the image force. An electron at a given distance from a conductor induces a surface charge at the surface of the conductor, which produces a field outside the conductor just as if there were a fictitious charge, of opposite sign to the charge outside the conductor, located as far behind the surface as the real charge is in front of it. This fictitious charge is called the electric image.† If the distance from plane to charge is d, there is then an attraction between the charge and its image, of amount $e^2/[4\pi\epsilon_0(2d)^2]$, since the charges, of amount e, are located at a distance $2d$ apart. The corresponding potential energy is $-e^2/16\pi\epsilon_0 d$. This, of course, would go to negative infinity as d went to zero; but for d smaller than the order of an interatomic distance, the image picture is inaccurate, since it is based on the assumption of a continuous conductor, and the image potential merges into the potential of the first layer of atoms. This process of merging is not the same on different crystal faces; it naturally depends on how many atoms there are per unit area on the face, and such matters

† See Slater and Frank, "Electromagnetism," McGraw-Hill Book Company, Inc., New York, 1947, Chap. I, for discussion of this problem.

as that.   Hence it can be that the limiting value which the potential would reach at infinity can be different for different faces of the same crystal.

This situation would involve us in a paradox; for clearly the potential must be single-valued and must go to a definite single value at infinity. The thing which happens is that, if we have a small crystal with some of its faces cut parallel to one crystal plane, some parallel to another, these crystal faces acquire surface charges, some positive, some negative, provided the crystal as a whole is uncharged.   If we place such surface charges on the various faces of a solid, and solve for the potential outside it by standard methods of electrostatics, we find that there are fields stretching out from it for distances comparable to the dimensions of the solid, which result in having a fixed potential at infinity, but different potentials outside the various faces.   The surface charges automatically adjust themselves in such a way that the potentials immediately outside the various faces, as determined by electrostatics, are the values which our study of the image forces indicated should be found at infinite distances from the various faces.   In interpreting this situation, we have to realize that there are three quite different scales of distances concerned in the problem.   First, there is the atomic scale, of the order of 10^{-8} cm; all the variation of potential inside the crystal has a scale of these dimensions.   Next, there is the image potential.   By the time we get something like 10^{-6} cm from the surface, this has practically reached its limiting value.   But this is still essentially at the surface, from the point of view of the really long-range forces arising from the surface charges. It is at points of the order of 10^{-6} cm from the various surfaces, then, that the potential, as viewed on the scale of the image fields, has reached its value characteristic of infinite distance, but that the potential of the surface charges has the value which it would attain just at the surface of the surface charge.

The result of our discussion, then, is that there is a potential difference between a point something like 10^{-6} cm outside one face of the crystal and a similar point outside another face.   This potential difference is characteristic of the two faces, not of the shape and size of the crystal, though the field outside the crystal, depending on the amount of surface charge on the faces, depends entirely on the nature of the sample.   This potential difference between the faces is called the contact difference of potential, or Volta difference of potential, between the faces; we see that we have such a potential difference between different faces of the same crystal.   Of course, however, symmetry will require that in some cases there be no such contact potential difference; to get a difference, the faces must really be oriented differently.

We get a contact difference of potential between two different metals in an even more obvious way than between two faces of the same crystal. Thus if we made up a composite sample, one half being made of one metal, the other half of the other, it is quite obvious from the type of argument we have just used that there will be a difference of potential between the faces of the two samples, and this is the contact potential difference. It is not necessary for the samples to be close together to set up this potential difference; all that is necessary is that they be in electrical contact. It is a fundamental feature of the Fermi statistics that, if we have a material of a composite sort in thermal equilibrium, the Fermi energy will be constant throughout the material. This can be proved in many ways;

FIG. 12.7.2.   Potential energy in region between two metals.

straightforwardly by statistics, or by kinetics, showing that it is only in this case that there will not be an unbalanced flow of electrons one way or the other. Suppose now that we take two samples of different metals, in the form of plates, like condenser plates, facing each other, and connect them electrically so that their Fermi levels will coincide. This will demand an electric field in the space between them, in order to produce the necessary difference of potential, as we see in Fig. 12.7.2. The difference of potential is fixed, independent of the distance between the plates; thus the field, and consequently the surface charge (which, as is shown in electrostatics, is proportional to it), must increase as the plates are brought closer together.

This is, in fact, used as the basis of a standard experimental method to measure contact difference of potential. The two plates are brought close together, until they almost touch (they can be separated, for instance, by a thin sheet of insulator). At this position they hold large surface charges of opposite sign. Then the electrical connection is broken, and in an insulated condition they are separated. The charges remain on them and, in the separated condition, lead to large potential differences between them, which can be measured with electrostatic voltmeters or other instruments, leading by a simple calculation to the contact potential difference.

The energy difference between the Fermi level and the energy at a distance from a crystal face, large enough so that the image potential has reached its limiting value, is called the thermionic work function (if we neglect certain small effects arising from temperature changes). It is this energy which enters into the formula for thermionic emission, the so-called Richardson formula, stating that the thermionic current is proportional to $T^2e^{-\Delta E/kT}$. Thus this energy difference ΔE plays the part of an activation energy for thermionic emission.† We now see that, since the Fermi level must be the same in two metals in contact, the difference of thermionic work function for two metals must be the same as the contact difference of potential between them. This furnishes a relation which can be tested experimentally, and the experiments check the theory satisfactorily. Many features of physical electronics, relating to thermionic and photoelectric emission from metals under the action of accelerating and retarding fields, are based on this general picture of the contact between two conductors, but it would carry us outside of our main subject to follow the question further.

If we carry the process of bringing the metallic surfaces together to the limit, and make them touch, the barrier between them will no longer have the form shown in Fig. 12.7.2, but clearly will practically disappear. It is impossible to get away from the surface of either, to set up the fields necessary to lead to the image potential. Nevertheless, we shall still have the equality of the Fermi levels in both metals. Also, since the surface charges of opposite sign on the surfaces of the two metals kept on building up as long as the metals were appreciably separated (that is, as long as the distance between them was large compared with the order of 10^{-6} cm), it seems likely that a rather large double layer (that is, a layer of dipoles, or a layer of positive charge and an adjacent equal layer of negative charge) automatically will form between the metals, to adjust their Fermi levels properly. This implies positive charge on one metal, negative on the other; that is, some of the atoms of one metal have lost electrons to the atoms of the other, forming dipoles on the surface layers. This is hardly surprising, since we know that in many cases of diatomic molecules composed of unlike atoms there is a tendency for one atom to gain charge, the other to lose it, forming polar molecules. This same tendency explains the dipole formation at the interface between two metals, and it is easily understandable that the exact amount of the dipole moment is something whose calculation would depend on elaborate applications of wave mechanics and certainly cannot be found from simple electrostatic considerations. We may expect, however, that the effect of the surface will not extend below the surface layer of atoms. Our

† This matter is discussed in detail in J. C. Slater, "Introduction to Chemical Physics," McGraw-Hill Book Company, Inc., New York, 1939, Chap. XXVIII.

knowledge of the electrical behavior of metals is enough to show us that we shall not have any net charge in the interior of the metal.

The situation at the surface of a semiconductor is quite different from that at the surface of a metal, and the whole problem of boundary conditions must be examined anew for the case where one of the materials is a semiconductor. The reason is that it is not nearly as easy to put a surface charge on the surface of a semiconductor or an insulator as it is on the surface of a metal. We must assume that the Fermi statistics applies to the surface layers of atoms of a metal or semiconductor, just as it does in the interior. In order to have the surface layer of atoms

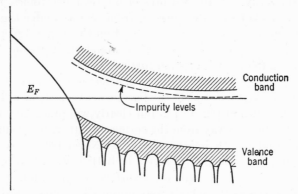

Fig. 12.7.3.   Modification of energy bands near charged surface of semiconductor.

charged, rather than uncharged as the Fermi statistics would ordinarily demand, the relative position of the Fermi level and the energy bands must be altered. Thus if all the energy bands are moved upward with respect to the Fermi level, this simply means that the levels will not be filled so high with electrons, so that there will be a net positive charge; if the energy bands are moved downward, we have the converse effect, of more electrons than normal, and a net negative charge. The number of levels per unit energy range in a metal is so great that the necessary modification of the energy bands is negligible, and we do not ordinarily have to consider it. With a semiconductor, on the contrary, a very large displacement of the energy bands with respect to the Fermi level must be made in order to change appreciably the charge on the atoms.

Thus let us consider an *n*-type semiconductor which must carry a positive surface charge, in order to produce a field at external points appropriate to match its boundary conditions to another conductor, say a metal, with a larger work function. Then we may produce arguments to show that the energy bands in the neighborhood of the surface must be modified as in Fig. 12.7.3. The argument is as follows. First, to have a positive charge, we have just seen that the energy bands must rise with respect to the Fermi level. When the bands rise as we have indicated, the Fermi level is depressed with respect to them, enough so that the impurity levels will lose their electrons, resulting in a positive volume charge of one electronic charge per impurity atom. However, unless the bands rise so high that the Fermi level gets close to the valence band, no appreciable number of electrons will be removed from the valence band, so that the maximum volume charge which can arise is that coming from

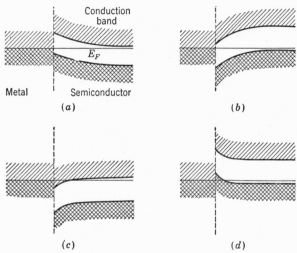

FIG. 12.7.4.   Contact between metal and semiconductor: (a) n-type semiconductor, metal with large work function; (b) p-type semiconductor, metal with small work function; (c) n-type semiconductor, metal with small work function; (d) p-type semiconductor, metal with large work function.

the impurity atoms. Now with this volume density of charge, a perturbing electrostatic field will be produced, according to Poisson's equation and the principles of electrostatics. It is just this perturbing field which raises the energy bands; this is an additional electrostatic field V, of the type which we have considered before in the present chapter, and Poisson's equation for a uniform positive density of charge tells us that V will rise parabolically with position. With volume charges of the size which we can actually have in a semiconductor, with the small number of impurity atoms ordinarily present, we have to go through a considerable layer of material to get enough charge to produce the required electric fields. We thus have a transition layer of positive charge density at the surface of the semiconductor which in some cases can be as great as 10^{-6} cm. Clearly the greater the required surface charge, the thicker the layer.

Now when we bring together a metal with a large work function and an n-type semiconductor with a smaller work function, we shall have a situation like that shown in (a) in Fig. 12.7.4. We have a negative surface charge on the surface of the metal and a compensating positive volume charge extending through a considerable surface layer of the semiconductor. Similarly (b) shows the case of a p-type semiconductor at a boundary with a metal which has a lower work function than the p-type semiconductor. The cases (c) and (d) are somewhat different. They are, respectively, an n-type semiconductor with a metal with lower work function than the semiconductor, and a p-type semiconductor with a metal with higher work function. In these cases the Fermi level dips into either the conduction or valence band of energy levels. In such a case there are so many levels per unit energy range that the necessary charge can be piled up in a very few atom layers, so that the surface charge in these cases is much more like that in a metal. Cases (a) and (b) are those which lead to rectifying properties; in the next section we shall explain how this comes about.

12.8. Rectification and Photoconductivity. Let us consider electrical conduction across the boundary between metal and semiconductor, in

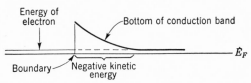

FIG. 12.8.1.   Region of negative kinetic energy near a rectifying barrier.

case (a) above. We remember that electrons have a negative kinetic energy, or their wave function is exponentially damped, when they fall inside an energy gap. Thus an electron at the bottom of the conduction band well within the semiconductor will find itself within the gap over a considerable distance near the boundary, as indicated in Fig. 12.8.1. It cannot, therefore, penetrate from semiconductor to metal, or an electron at the same energy in the metal cannot penetrate to the semiconductor, except by the tunnel effect; and the barrier is so high and wide that the tunnel effect is quite negligible. In other words, a barrier has been set up by the distribution of potentials near the surface, which must be surmounted by electrons passing in either direction. If ΔE is the height of this barrier above the Fermi level, only those electrons will be able to carry current which have energy at least as high as ΔE above the Fermi level; and we know that the number of such electrons has a Boltzmann factor $e^{-\Delta E/kT}$, arising from the Fermi statistics. Since this factor is small, the number of carriers is small, and even if the electrons have a normal mobility, the surface will appear to have a very high resistance.

This resistance is not the point of particular interest, however. The real question is the lack of symmetry between the two directions of current. When a current flows, we no longer have equilibrium, and the Fermi level no longer stays constant throughout the material. Rather, the Fermi level takes the place usually assigned to the electrical potential (or rather, $-e$ times the electrical potential, since we are considering the potential energy of an electron) in elementary electrical theory. Thus when we have current flowing in an ohmic resistor, the Fermi level will

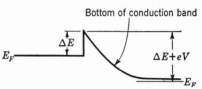

Fig. 12.8.2. Rectifying barrier with voltage in high-resistance direction.

have a slope, as given by the resistance and current from Ohm's law. The electrons will tend to roll downhill in the direction in which the Fermi level decreases. In a region of high resistance, the slope will be large, while in a low resistance region it will be small. In our case then, if a difference of potential is applied to the boundary between metal and semiconductor, almost the complete difference of potential will appear across the surface barrier, on account of the very low resistance of the metal and the comparatively low resistance of the bulk of the semiconductor. Suppose that the semiconductor has a positive potential V with respect to the metal. Then the potential energy of the electron in the semiconductor is lower by the amount eV than before, and the barrier becomes correspondingly higher, as shown in Fig. 12.8.2. The number of electrons per unit time traveling from left to right will still have the same factor $e^{-\Delta E/kT}$ as

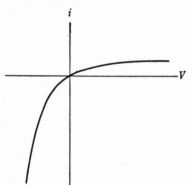

Fig. 12.8.3. Current-voltage characteristic of rectifying barrier.

before. But the number traveling from right to left will have a factor $e^{-(\Delta E+eV)/kT}$. Hence the net number traveling from left to right (or the current traveling from right to left, in the direction of decreasing potential, as it should) will be proportional to $e^{-\Delta E/kT}(1 - e^{-eV/kT})$. The factor $1 - e^{-eV/kT}$ is like those encountered in the preceding chapter, where we studied the kinetics of particles passing over potential barriers; only here we are dealing with electrons, rather than atoms. We show this factor, which is proportional to the current, in Fig. 12.8.3. We see that it is very unsymmetrical: for a positive voltage on the semiconductor the current very rapidly approaches a limiting value, whereas for a negative voltage on the semiconductor the current very rapidly increases in magnitude. This is the characteristic of a rectifier; and we note that the direction in which it passes large current is that in which electrons flow from the semiconductor into the metal. The function which we have given actually describes in a qualitative way the sort of rectifying characteristic found with such boundaries, though there are a good many refinements which must be applied to the theory to get agreement with experiment. For one thing, on account of the considerable distance between impurity atoms, it is not correct to assume a uniform charge distribution, and a barrier of constant height, all over the surface of separation between metal and semiconductor. There are great fluctuations, resulting in some parts which have higher barriers, other parts with lower barriers. When these are averaged together, the qualitative nature of the curve remains the same, but the quantitative details vary.

The case shown in (b) of Fig. 12.7.4 also leads to rectification. In this case the current inside the semiconductor is carried largely by the holes, which try to rise as close as possible to the top of the valence band, like bubbles of air in water below the surface of ice. To get from metal to semiconductor or vice versa, the holes must fall below the barrier which arises because the top of the valence band dips down near the metallic surface. The Boltzmann factor giving the number of holes as far below the Fermi level as that barrier is just the same in form that we have been dealing with in the case above; and we can carry through a practically identical argument, resulting in a similar formula for current vs. voltage. In this case the high current flows when the semiconductor is made positive; this is the case in which holes flow from the semiconductor into the metal. In cases (c) and (d), in contrast to these, there is no tendency toward rectification. Thus in case (c), where conduction in the semiconductor is by electrons, the electrons meet no barrier between metal and semiconductor, so that there is no high resistance barrier, and conduction is perfectly free, no matter which potential is applied to the semiconductor; the boundary between them behaves in an ohmic manner. The same thing is true of case (d). We should expect, then, that the behavior of the contact between a metal and a semiconductor would depend greatly on the relative work functions of metal and semiconductor. In some cases this is true. In others, however, such as Ge, the rectifying barrier seems to be almost independent of the work function of the metal. The interpretation which has been given to this is that there are certain "surface states" on the surface of the semiconductor, energy levels characteristic of the surface, and quite different from the bulk material, which have the same behavior that we should have if they consisted of a very thin layer of a metal like that shown in case (a). This surface behavior would be an inherent part of the semiconductor surface; there is good evidence for thinking that a free surface between Ge and a vacuum has a negative surface charge, and a compensating volume charge in the semiconductor, resulting in a barrier like that of case (a), quite independent of the metal. Any metal placed next to it then makes an ordinary metallic contact to the surface layer of the Ge. The origin of these surface states is not known, but their existence seems well demonstrated.

The photoconductive behavior of a rectifying barrier is easy to understand. Suppose we shine light on a barrier of the type shown in (a), whose quantum $h\nu$ is great enough so that an electron from the valence band can be raised to a point in the conduction band high enough so that it can surmount the barrier. It then adds to the very small number of electrons which already had that energy and could carry current. Since the resistance is so high, or the number of such electrons so small, a relatively small addition to the number of electrons, such as can be made by a relatively weak light source, will make a noticeable increase in the conductivity. The minimum value of $h\nu$ which can produce this effect is obviously the breadth of the energy gap between valence band and conduction band. A measurement of the long-wave limit of photoconductivity is then a method of estimating the gap width, quite independent of the measurement of intrinsic conductivity of the semiconductor as a function of T. Fortunately the two forms of measurement agree well in the cases where they have both been made accurately, demonstrating the essential correctness of this simple picture. The situation in case (b) is closely analogous, radiation raising an electron from the valence to the conduction band as before, but in this case the hole left by the removed electron being the carrier of current.

PROBLEMS

1. Assuming that copper has one electron per atom acting in metallic conduction, and taking the observed conductivity, find the mean time between collisions.

2. Assuming one electron per atom, and using conductivity at room temperature, find the mobility of the electrons in metallic copper; in sodium.

3. Compute a mean free path for an electron in copper at room temperature. To do this, find the mean free time by the use of Eq. (12.3.7), find a velocity by computing the maximum energy of the electrons in the Fermi distribution, assuming a free electron model with one electron per atom, and assume that the mean free path is the distance the electron travels in a mean free time, with the velocity from the top of the Fermi distribution.

4. Use the observed variation of conductivity of copper with temperature to find the variation of mean free path with temperature, proceeding as in the preceding problem.

5. Of all the electrons striking the surface of a metal, only those whose momentum normal to the surface is connected with a term in the kinetic energy greater than the work function can escape. Derive the expression for the number escaping per second. In doing this, note that the number striking 1 sq cm of the wall per second is the number contained in a cylinder of base 1 sq cm, slant height the vector velocity of the electron.

6. Show that if atoms and molecules obeyed Fermi statistics, the maximum kinetic energy at absolute zero, and consequent departure from the Maxwell-Boltzmann law at higher temperatures, would be so small that they would not ordinarily be observed. Actually molecules do not obey Fermi statistics, but another sort, called Bose statistics, which involves deviations from the Maxwell-Boltzmann law of about the same amount, though in the opposite direction, resulting in a reduction rather than an increase of mean kinetic energy and gas pressure.

7. Assume the distribution of energy levels for the electrons of a metal given by the theory of free electrons. Assume that the electrons obey the Fermi statistics. Show from the Fermi statistics that the electronic specific heat is proportional to the temperature, at low temperatures, and find the constant of proportionality.

8. Compute the electronic specific heat, from the problem above, for copper. Show that this contribution is negligible compared with the specific heat as given by the Dulong-Petit law, at all temperatures below the melting point of copper.

9. An intrinsic semiconductor has a gap width ΔE of 1 ev between filled and empty bands. The effective mass of the electrons and holes equals the actual electronic mass. Assume the mobility of both electrons and holes is 100 cm/sec per volt per cm. Compute the conductivity as a function of temperature, and plot the logarithm of the conductivity as a function of $1/T$.

10. The intrinsic semiconductor described in Prob. 9 is transformed into an n-type semiconductor by adding 10^{19} donor atoms per cu cm, with the donor level 0.05 ev below the conduction band. Find the Fermi level as a function of temperature, from the absolute zero to temperatures so high that the material acts like an intrinsic semiconductor.

11. Find the conductivity of the n-type semiconductor described in Prob. 10 as a function of temperature, assuming that the mobility of electrons and holes is still 100 cm/sec per volt per cm, independent of temperature. Plot the logarithm of the conductivity as a function of $1/T$, and compare with the result for the intrinsic semiconductor in Prob. 10.

12. The n-type semiconductor described in Prob. 11 is placed in an external field, so that the field at the surface of the semiconductor has the value of 5×10^6 volts/cm, pointing out of the semiconductor. Find the thickness of the surface layer of positive charge in the semiconductor. Plot the energy bands as a function of distance from the surface.

13. The n-type semiconductor in Prob. 12 is placed in contact with a metal. The double layer required by the boundary conditions is such as to produce a field of 5×10^6 volts/cm at the surface of the semiconductor, as in Prob. 12. Draw the energy bands in metal and semiconductor, and describe the resulting rectifying properties.

CHAPTER 13

THE NATURE OF DIELECTRICS

A dielectric, or insulator, put in an external electric field, acquires a polarization proportional to the field, and the constant of proportionality between polarization and field, called the polarizability, determines the dielectric constant. The polarizability and dielectric constant depend on the frequency of the external field; and when the field has a high enough frequency so that it can be considered as light, rather than an electric field, we find a close connection between the dielectric constant and refractive index. In turn, the refractive index goes through certain anomalies in the neighborhood of the absorption frequencies of the system, and these are determined by the quantum theory. Thus it comes about that the dielectric behavior of matter, though at first sight it seems a very classical sort of phenomenon, is in fact closely related to some of the fundamental principles of quantum mechanics.

There are three principal sorts of dielectric behavior. In the first place, any individual atom can be polarized by the field, the electronic structure being displaced with respect to the nucleus. The resonance frequencies associated with this type of polarization prove to be the frequencies at which the atom can absorb, as determined by the quantum theory; thus this type of polarization must be treated by quantum mechanics. Since these absorption frequencies are in the visible or ultraviolet part of the spectrum, the anomalies in refractive index associated with electronic polarization are in the visible or ultraviolet, and it is these anomalies that make transparent substances like glass dispersive in the visible spectrum, so that we can use them as prisms, and that make some materials colored. The contribution which electronic polarizability makes to the dielectric behavior is practically independent of frequency all through the range of frequencies which we usually regard as being electrical, down to wave lengths of a fraction of a millimeter, since all these frequencies are very small compared with the resonance frequency. In these low frequency ranges we can make simple approximate calculations of polarization, which, however, are only approximations to more accurate expressions furnished by the quantum theory.

The second type of polarization arises from the displacement of ions with positive charge, with respect to ions with negative charge. Such a polarization obviously will only occur in an ionic substance. In a crystal like an alkali halide, for instance, it is possible for the whole lattice of positive ions to shift with respect to the lattice of negative ions. Such a shift is opposed by elastic forces, and since it is concerned with the motion of atoms as a whole, it can be treated quite accurately by classical mechanics. The restoring force is approximately proportional to the displacement, so that the ions have the possibility of oscillating with respect to each other in a resonant manner. The resonant frequencies associated with this motion are in the infrared part of the spectrum; they are closely associated with the elastic vibrations concerned in the specific heat. In the visible spectrum the oscillations are so fast, compared with this resonance frequency, that the ionic displacement can hardly follow the field at all, and this part of the polarization is not active in the visible spectrum, whereas it is of great importance in the low-frequency range. Though its resonance frequency is considerably lower than those met in the visible spectrum, still it is so high, compared with ordinary electrical frequencies, that this effect, like the electronic polarization, gives a constant contribution to the low-frequency dielectric constant.

The third type of polarization arises from the rotation of molecules or parts of molecules which have permanent dipole moments. These dipoles are oriented by the electric field, the orientation being opposed by the thermal agitation. These orientations are free to take place in gases and, to some extent, in liquids; hardly at all in solids. Like the displacements of the ions, they can be handled by classical mechanics. Unlike those displacements, however, they do not have a restoring force and are not connected with any resonant frequency. They have a frictional force opposing the motion, and this results in a frequency dependence of polarizability, but of quite a different nature from that met with a resonance; the dielectric effect gradually decreases with increasing frequency, over quite a wide frequency range. This frequency range proves to be determined by the viscous or frictional force, which, like other viscous effects, can depend very strongly on temperature. Thus it comes about that the frequency dependence of this type of polarizability can be very striking, often occurring in the part of the spectrum treated by electrical methods, and can depend strongly on temperature.

The second and third of these three types of polarizability, as we have mentioned, can be handled by classical mechanics. We shall treat them, for the sake of completeness, even though quantum mechanics is not needed for them. When we handle the resonant type of effect met with ionic displacements, we meet a remarkable fact: that our formalism proves to fit very well the experimental facts on the electronic polarizability as well, if we put in proper values for the constants. This is a result of a remarkable formal similarity between the quantum theory of electronic polarization and classical models. It was on account of this similarity that theories of dielectric behavior and refraction, based on the classical electron theory of Drude and Lorentz, worked very accurately, and led physicists for a long time to suppose that optical properties of atoms could be explained by classical mechanics. In a later section we shall take up the quantum theory of electronic refractivity and see how this remarkable similarity arises.

13.1. The Classical Theory of Anomalous Dispersion. We shall start by reminding the reader of the classical theory of dielectric behavior and dispersion, based on the assumption that a dielectric contains many dipoles obeying classical mechanics, whose polarizations arise from the external field. This model, as we have seen, is very nearly literally true for the polarization arising from ionic displacement, and by coincidence proves to work also for electronic displacement.†

If E is the electric field strength, D the electric displacement, P the electric polarization, or total dipole moment per unit volume, the relations between these vectors, using the mks units, are

$$D = \kappa_e \epsilon_0 E = \epsilon_0 E + P, \qquad P = \chi_e \epsilon_0 E, \qquad \kappa_e = 1 + \chi_e. \quad (13.1.1)$$

Here κ_e is the dielectric constant, χ_e the susceptibility, and ϵ_0 the permittivity of free space. To translate the formulas to the Gaussian system of units, as usual we replace ϵ_0 by $1/4\pi$. The problem of setting up a theory of dielectric constant is that of finding the polarization set up by a given field. The simplest case is that in which we have N molecules per unit volume, each of which has a polarizability α, or each of which acquires a dipole moment αE in the presence of the field. Then we have $P = N\alpha E$, from which

$$\chi_e = \frac{N\alpha}{\epsilon_0}, \quad \kappa_e = 1 + \frac{N\alpha}{\epsilon_0}. \quad (13.1.2)$$

If we have more than one type of polarizable molecule, we need only add their contributions to susceptibility and dielectric constant.

Now let us suppose that each of these molecules contains a charged ion, of charge e, held to a position of equilibrium by an elastic restoring force proportional to the displacement, equal to $-ax$, if the displacement is x, with constant of proportionality a. The displacement is then $x = (e/a)E$, so that the induced dipole moment is $ex = (e^2/a)E$, and the polarizability α is equal to e^2/a, from which the dielectric constant follows at once from

† Further discussion of this classical theory of dielectrics is given in Slater and Frank, "Electromagnetism," McGraw-Hill Book Company, Inc., New York, 1947, Chaps. IV, IX.

(13.1.2). This holds only for the static case, however. If the external field varies sinusoidally with time, we must write a differential equation for the displacement of the particle, which will be

$$m \frac{d^2x}{dt^2} + mg \frac{dx}{dt} + m\omega_0^2 x = eE, \tag{13.1.3}$$

where the first term expresses the mass times the acceleration, the next term is a frictional resistance term proportional to the velocity, the next

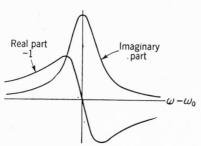

Fig. 13.1.1. Real and imaginary parts of dielectric constant, in region of anomalous dispersion.

the linear restoring force, and the term on the right the external force arising from the electric field. The restoring force term is expressed in this way, $m\omega_0^2$ being the previous constant a, since ω_0 proves to be the resonant angular frequency, the frequency with which the particle would oscillate in the absence of other forces. The resistive force must be put in to account for energy losses which always occur for one reason or another; we shall discuss their nature in the electronic case later.

If the external field is varying sinusoidally with time, being represented by the real part of the exponential $e^{i\omega t}$, we then find from (13.1.3)

$$ex = \frac{(e^2/m)E}{\omega_0^2 - \omega^2 + i\omega g}, \qquad \alpha = \frac{e^2/m}{\omega_0^2 - \omega^2 + i\omega g}. \tag{13.1.4}$$

This expression reduces to our value e^2/a at frequencies small compared with the resonant frequency; but at any frequency we may derive the dielectric constant from it according to (13.1.2), and we find a real and an imaginary component of dielectric constant, which have values as shown in Fig. 13.1.1. It is shown in optics that the real part of this dielectric constant is closely related to the index of refraction, the imaginary part to the absorption coefficient, of a material. The behavior of the index of refraction in the neighborhood of the resonant frequency, which we see in Fig. 13.1.1, is called anomalous dispersion; the dielectric constant and index of refraction increase with frequency in the range somewhat below the resonant frequency, pass through a maximum, and drop to low values just beyond the resonant frequency, the effect of the polarization being entirely lost at high enough frequencies, where, as we see from (13.1.4), the polarizability drops to very small values. The absorption goes to a peak at the resonance frequency, falling on both sides.

Behavior of the type described by (13.1.4) is found for the infrared resonances associated with the ionic displacements; but it is also found, as we have stated, for electronic displacement, though the electrons cannot be regarded as classical particles held to positions of equilibrium by linear restoring forces. A term in the polarizability proves experimentally to be present for each frequency corresponding to a possible transition from the ground state of an atom to an excited state, the frequency ω_0 being that given from the difference of energy levels by Bohr's frequency condition. The total electronic polarizability is the sum of these resonance terms; and the only difference between the observed behavior and formula (13.1.4) is that each of these terms has to be multiplied by a certain factor f, which generally is rather small compared with unity. That is, each atom acts as if it had a fraction of one electron connected with each of the transitions. To get the order of magnitude of the f's, we can state here that there is a sum rule stating that the sum of the f's for all possible transitions from the ground state to excited states is of the order of magnitude of unity, so that, since there are ordinarily an infinite number of possible transitions, corresponding to transitions to higher and higher members of optical series, the f's must go to zero as we go up in such a series. These f's are sometimes called oscillator strengths. We shall come back to the explanation of these facts, in terms of the quantum theory, in a later section.

The optical behavior of metals can also be described rather satisfactorily by polarizabilities like that of (13.1.4). One of the conduction electrons in a metal certainly does not behave in any way as if it were held to a position of equilibrium by a linear restoring force; but it does have an equation of motion much like that of (13.1.3) if we let $\omega_0 = 0$, having an inertial term and a resistance proportional to its velocity. We have used such an equation in (12.3.1) for discussing the conductivity of a metal. If we could handle the electron by classical mechanics, we should then conclude that its contribution to the polarizability was as given in (13.1.4), but with $\omega_0 = 0$. This gives a polarizability which formally becomes infinite at zero frequency, and at low frequencies, where only the last term in the denominator of (13.1.4) is appreciable, equals $-ie^2/m\omega g$. By methods of Sec. 12.3 we can get the relation between g and the conductivity, and this formula for polarizability, with the related expressions from (13.1.2), proves, in fact, to give fairly correct representations of the optical behavior of a metal.[†] We thus conclude that the treatment of electrical conductivity of a metal developed in Chap. 12 holds fairly well even at fairly high frequencies, as far as free

[†] See Slater and Frank, "Electromagnetism," McGraw-Hill Book Company, Inc., New York, 1947, Chap. IX, for further details.

electrons are concerned, and this can be justified by quantum-mechanical treatment of the problem.

There is one feature of the classical theory of anomalous dispersion in solids or liquids which must be considered to get satisfactory results, and which has no connection with the quantum theory. This is the so-called Lorentz correction. It is not correct to assume that the field acting on an ion in a solid or liquid is the same as the field E. That is the average field throughout the body; but an ion is not located at an average position, but rather is in a preferred position, since its neighbors must keep a certain distance away from it. The neighbors will have dipole moments, which exert a net field on the ion in question, and one can show in two important cases that this field is equal to $P/3\epsilon_0$. These cases are, first, that in which the ions are arranged on a simple cubic lattice, or some other forms of cubic lattices; second, that in which the ions are arranged in an isotropic way, as in a liquid. For other crystalline arrangements there is a similar situation, except that there will be a more complicated linear relationship between the field acting on an ion and the polarization.

If we have the field acting on an ion equal to $E + P/3\epsilon_0$, we have $P = N\alpha(E + P/3\epsilon_0)$, from which, using (13.1.1), we find

$$\frac{\kappa_e - 1}{\kappa_e + 2} = \frac{1}{3}\frac{N\alpha}{\epsilon_0}. \qquad (13.1.5)$$

This is the Clausius-Mossotti law, which proves experimentally to be rather well obeyed by many materials. In it, we are, of course, to write α as a sum of terms like (13.1.4), as before. We can also write (13.1.5) in the form

$$\kappa_e = 1 + \frac{N\alpha/\epsilon_0}{1 - N\alpha/3\epsilon_0}. \qquad (13.1.6)$$

This expression resembles (13.1.2) but shows that, on account of the denominator, which is less than unity, the effect of the Lorentz correction is generally to increase the dielectric constant. For many dielectrics, $N\alpha/3\epsilon_0$ has values in the neighborhood of one-half, so that the denominator is appreciably less than unity.

There are a few solids for which the term $N\alpha/3\epsilon_0$ is practically equal to unity, so that the denominator is practically zero, and the dielectric constant becomes practically infinite. The situation is really somewhat more complicated than this: the only materials of this sort that we know do not have the cubic symmetry necessary to apply the Lorentz correction in its elementary form, and the revised Lorentz correction leads to a term in the denominator, similar to $N\alpha/3\epsilon_0$, which is somewhat more complicated in form, but still practically equal to unity. This term further-

more proves to depend slightly on temperature.   This is a result of the
nonlinear terms in the forces acting on the ions, the same nonlinear terms
in the elastic restoring force which lead to the thermal expansion.   Thus
we can write $N\alpha/3\epsilon_0 = 1 - C(T - T_c)$, if C is a constant, T the absolute
temperature, T_c the particular temperature at which the quantity goes
through unity.   In the usual cases, C has the sign indicated.   Hence we
find

$$\kappa_e = \left(1 - \frac{3}{C}\right) + \frac{3/C}{T - T_c}. \tag{13.1.7}$$

The dielectric constant, in other words, becomes infinite at the critical
temperature T_c, decreasing as the temperature rises above this value.
At temperatures below the critical temperature, (13.1.7) is no longer
valid; but a more elaborate discussion shows that a permanent electric
polarization sets in below this temperature, the dipole moment increasing
as the temperature decreases.   A substance which has these properties is
called a ferroelectric, by analogy with the ferromagnetic material, which
shows a permanent magnetic moment below a critical temperature,
generally called the Curie temperature, and has a magnetic susceptibility
given by an expression similar to (13.1.7) at temperatures above the Curie
temperature.

13.2. The Classical Theory of Rotating Dipoles.   Let us assume that
a liquid or gas contains permanent dipoles of dipole moment μ, capable
of rotating freely.   The potential energy of such a dipole in a field E is
$-\mu E \cos \theta$, where θ is the angle between the direction of the dipole moment
and the field.   The average of $\cos \theta$ would be zero, if all orientations were
equally likely; but on account of the Boltzmann factor the orientations of
lower potential energy will be more likely, the Boltzmann factor being
$e^{(\mu E \cos \theta)/kT}$.   If we average the component of dipole moment in the
direction of the field, over all orientations of the molecule, taking account
of the Boltzmann factor, we find

$$\text{Mean dipole moment} = \mu L(y) = \mu \left(\coth y - \frac{1}{y}\right), \tag{13.2.1}$$

where $y = \mu E/kT$.   This function $L(y)$ is called the Langevin function,
the derivation having been first given by Langevin.†   It is shown in Fig.
13.2.1; we see that for small values of y it is proportional to y, whereas for
large y it approaches unity.   That is, for small values of $\mu E/kT$, or for
high temperatures or small electric fields, the mean dipole moment is proportional to the electric field, or there is a definite polarizability.   For

† A simple discussion is given in J. C. Slater, "Introduction to Chemical Physics,"
McGraw-Hill Book Company, Inc., New York, 1939, Chap. XXII, Sec. 3.

small values of y, the function $L(y)$ is approximately equal to $y/3$; thus in this limit we have the mean dipole moment equal to $\mu^2 E/3kT$. Hence we have a contribution of $\mu^2/3kT$ to add to the polarizability on account of the orientation of the dipoles. As a result of this, we have an additional term in (13.1.2). If we are dealing with dipole molecules, having a dipole moment as well as an ordinary polarizability, we have

$$\kappa_e = 1 + \frac{N}{\epsilon_0}\left(\alpha + \frac{\mu^2}{3kT}\right). \tag{13.2.2}$$

This formula has been much used by Debye, as well as others, and often goes by his name as well as that of Langevin.

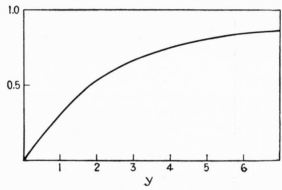

FIG. 13.2.1. Langevin function coth $y - 1/y$, giving mean dipole moment arising from rotation of dipole molecules, as function of $y = \mu E/kT$, where μ is the dipole moment, E the field strength.

Formula (13.2.2) shows that the two contributions to the dielectric constant, those coming from the polarizability and the orientation of the dipoles, differ in their dependence on temperature, the first being independent of temperature, the second inversely proportional to temperature. If κ_e is plotted as a function of $1/T$, we then should find a straight line; and this is found experimentally. It is then possible from the slope and intercept of this straight line to find both polarizability and dipole moment. This type of analysis of the dielectric constant of gases and liquids has proved very fruitful. The dipole moments found in this way are the basis of the remarks we have made in an earlier chapter about the polar or nonpolar properties of various molecules. In the hands of the chemists, such information has yielded much insight into molecular structure. As for the polarizabilities α, important results have been obtained from these as well. It is found that a simple additive rule works rather well for the electronic polarizabilities: the polarizability of the molecule is the sum of polarizabilities for the separate atoms or ions in it, these separate values being approximately the same for different molecules in which the same atoms or ions occur. We shall discuss the relation of these atomic values to quantum theory in a later section.

The behavior of the polarization arising from rotating dipoles, under the action of a high-frequency field, is entirely different from that of a polarizable dipole. We cannot properly treat the time variation of the polarization, except by a complicated application of kinetic theory, to study the way in which the thermal agitation affects the polarization. The result of this kinetic theory, however, is simple and easy to describe. In equilibrium under the action of a constant electric field, the polarization P, as we see from (13.2.2), equals $(N\mu^2/3\epsilon_0 kT)E$, where we are now disregarding the ionic polarization. Suppose now that we suddenly change the electric field E. We cannot assume that the polarization will instantly adjust to this changed field, for it takes time to readjust the orientations of the dipoles. Instead, we must assume that there will be a finite time, which we may call the relaxation time, which is required for the polarization to adjust itself, or for any incorrect polarizations to relax or disappear. We may express this situation in the form of a differential equation:

$$\frac{dP}{dt} = -\frac{1}{\tau}\left(P - \frac{N\mu^2}{3\epsilon_0 kT}\, E\right),\tag{13.2.3}$$

where τ is the relaxation time. If E is independent of time, the solution of this differential equation, which states merely that the time rate of change of polarization is proportional to the discrepancy between the existing polarization and the value which it should have under the field applied, is

$$P = \frac{N\mu^2}{3\epsilon_0 kT} + \left(P_0 - \frac{N\mu^2}{3\epsilon_0 kT}\right)e^{-t/\tau},\tag{13.2.4}$$

where P_0 is the initial polarization, and where the solution shows clearly the way in which the discrepancy between initial and final polarization falls to $1/e$ of its value in the relaxation time τ.

The kinetic treatment of the problem shows that (13.2.3) is a correct description of the polarization even in case E varies with time. We may rewrite it

$$\tau\frac{dP}{dt} + P = \frac{N\mu^2}{3\epsilon_0 kT}\, E.\tag{13.2.5}$$

If we then assume that E varies as $e^{i\omega t}$, so that P varies in the same way, we may at once solve for P in terms of E, and we find for the dielectric constant

$$\kappa_e = 1 + \frac{1}{1 + i\omega\tau}\frac{N\mu^2}{3\epsilon_0 kT}. \tag{13.2.6}$$

This indicates a complex dielectric constant, but without a resonance effect. The frequency dependence of real and imaginary parts of κ_e is

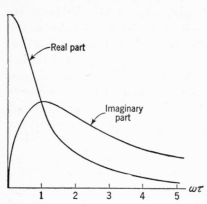

shown in Fig. 13.2.2. We see that the dielectric constant gradually drops from its static value to unity over a wide range of frequencies in the neighborhood of $1/\tau$, and that over a similarly wide range there is an imaginary component to the dielectric constant, leading to absorption.

The relaxation time τ arises because it takes a certain time to orient the dipoles, under the action of the field; and it is a viscous resistance which opposes the orientation. We shall then expect that the time τ will increase with increase of viscosity. Further study shows,

FIG. 13.2.2.   Real and imaginary part of dielectric constant minus one, as function of frequency, for dielectric containing rotating dipoles, from Eq. (13.2.6).

in fact, that this is the case. If we assume that the molecule can be regarded as a sphere of radius a, it can be shown that

$$\tau = \frac{4\pi\eta a^3}{kT}, \tag{13.2.7}$$

where η is the coefficient of viscosity. A demonstration of this formula by dimensional reasoning, giving everything but the constant 4π, is given in an elementary way in Appendix 19. Since different fluids can have very different viscosities, we expect that the relaxation times can vary over wide ranges, and this proves in fact to be the case. Many of them come in the high-frequency electrical or microwave range, so that many polar liquids have dielectric properties which depend strongly on frequency in the range which can be examined by electrical methods.

We have seen earlier that the coefficient of viscosity often varies very rapidly with temperature, being governed by an activation energy, as discussed in Sec. 11.5, and containing a factor $e^{E/kT}$. This leads to a rapid change of dielectric properties with temperature, at constant frequency. In fact, if we assume that η varies in this way with temperature, and that τ is given by (13.2.7), then (13.2.6) leads to a dielectric constant as a function of temperature, at constant frequency, such that the imaginary component, the absorption term, reaches a sharp peak at a given temperature, falling rapidly at both higher and lower temperatures. The whole temperature range over which absorption is appreciable can be surprisingly small. Such peaks of absorption at definite temperatures are characteristic of all sorts of relaxation phenomena, which are encountered whenever energy can be dissipated from a vibrating system by viscous action, without resonance. For instance, absorption of high-frequency sound shows similar relaxation effects and similar sharp peaks at definite temperatures.

In this discussion of the effects of rotating dipole molecules, we have disregarded the Lorentz correction, which we considered in Sec. 13.1 for the case of ionic polarization. If we modify (13.2.2) by making the Lorentz correction, so as to get formulas like (13.1.5) and (13.1.6), we shall obviously find a critical temperature in every case. If we disregard the ionic polarization, we have in place of (13.1.6)

$$\kappa_e = 1 + \frac{3T_c}{T - T_c}, \qquad T_c = \frac{N\mu^2}{9\epsilon_0 k}. \tag{13.2.8}$$

This is a result similar to (13.1.7), suggesting that all materials with rotating dipole molecules would be ferroelectric. It is interesting to put in observed values for N and μ, and find what sort of value (13.2.8) would predict for the critical temperature. When we do this, we are very much surprised. For water, for instance, a simple calculation shows that T_c should be in the neighborhood of 1200°K. In other words, at all observable temperatures water should be a dielectric analogous to a ferromagnetic material; and yet obviously it is not. We may then reasonably ask why it is not, and in what respects the theory we have sketched does not represent the facts.

Since we have mentioned the case of water, let us consider this material. Our theory shows that at any temperature below a quite high value, the dipoles of water should be oriented very definitely with respect to each other, provided it is in the liquid or solid state. But as a matter of fact, we already know that this is the case. We have mentioned that in water or in ice, the oxygen atom of a water molecule has close to it not only the two hydrogens associated with it in a molecule, but also two hydrogens coming from neighboring molecules. Now this is really just an example of the sort of relative orientation which our theory leads us to expect. The reason why it suggests an orientation of the dipoles at low temperatures is that the minimum energy of an array of dipoles will be secured if the positive end of one dipole is near the negative end of the next.   But the water molecules are really more complicated than dipoles; the description as dipoles is one which is only appropriate at considerable distances.   The water molecule is really triangular.   And the water, or ice, structure is one which achieves just what our theory has led us to expect: an arrangement of minimum potential energy.

This holds, for water, for all temperatures at which water is liquid or solid.   In other words, in the language of our simple theory, we are always below the Curie point, for the liquid or solid phases.   This does not mean, however, that the material has a permanent electric moment. The reason is the geometrical complication of the actual shapes of the molecules, and the structure of the crystal, or the behavior of the liquid. Different molecules can pack together in their positions of minimum energy, and yet with their dipole moments oriented in different directions, canceling any net dipole moment.†   Nevertheless, the qualitative features of our simple theory remain approximately applicable.   We cannot expect it to be exactly correct, since clearly the interactions of one molecule with another are more complicated than can be described by our simple picture.   At any rate, we can see that we can hardly expect to get a good description of the dielectric constant of liquid water from (13.2.2), which is based on the assumption that the dipoles can rotate freely, when we have now seen that they are really held rather firmly to definite orientations, so that an external applied field can only turn one molecule around by orienting its neighbors with it.   It is clear that any theory of the dielectric constant of such a liquid must take careful account of the molecular interactions.

It is for reasons similar to what we have just outlined that we do not, in fact, find the liquids composed of dipole molecules becoming ferro-electric, or having permanent polarizations at temperatures below a critical or Curie point.   The few solids which show ferroelectricity must be regarded as rather exceptional materials, in which the interactions which lead to spontaneous polarization have such symmetry behavior that the dipoles actually line up and produce spontaneous polarization. It would carry us too far into the structure of these rather complicated substances to describe them in detail.

13.3. The Quantum Theory of Electronic Polarization.   We have mentioned several times the fact that when electronic polarization is investigated by the quantum theory, the final result is very similar to that which we found in (13.1.4) to describe ionic polarization.   A really complete treatment of this problem is very complicated and involves the

---

† See J. C. Slater, "Introduction to Chemical Physics," McGraw-Hill Book Company, Inc., New York, 1939, p. 419, for a diagram of the ice structure, illustrating this fact.

Dirac radiation theory, which we have discussed in Appendix 11. A simplified form of the theory can be carried through very easily, however, and gives a good deal of the information which we need for a complete theory. We shall content ourselves with this simplified theory, together with some remarks as to the changes which more elaborate treatment brings about. The simple theory essentially treats the external electric field as a perturbative energy depending on time and treats its effect on the atom by the method of variation of constants, taken up in Sec. 4.5. This will give us the behavior in an external field of arbitrary frequency. An even simpler treatment is possible if the external field is constant, which we shall mention later.

Let an atom be placed in an external electric field, directed along the x axis, with x component equal to $E \cos \omega t$. For points near the origin (where we assume the atom to be located) we may consider that this field is derived from a potential $-Ex \cos \omega t$, so that the potential energy of the atom in the field is $eE \sum_i x_i \cos \omega t$, where the summation is over the electrons of the atom, x_i being the x coordinate of the ith electron. Let us assume that the Hamiltonian of the atom without the external field is H^0, and assume that the unperturbed problem can be solved exactly:

$$H^0 u_m^0 = E_m^0 u_m^0. \qquad (13.3.1)$$

Then we assume that our perturbed Hamiltonian H equals

$$H^0 + eE \sum_i x_i \cos \omega t.$$

We shall now try to expand the perturbed wave function in terms of these unperturbed functions u_m^0. We use Eq. (4.5.1), for the coefficients C_k in an expansion $\psi = \sum_m C_m(t) u_m^0(x)$. This equation is

$$\frac{dC_k}{dt} = -\frac{2\pi i}{h} \sum_m H_{km} C_m, \qquad (13.3.2)$$

where H_{km} is the matrix component of the energy between states k and m. This may be written

$$H_{km} = E_m^0 \delta_{km} - E \cos \omega t M_{km}, \qquad (13.3.3)$$

where $M_{km} = -\sum_i \int u_k^{0*} ex_i u_m^0 \, dv$, the matrix component of the electric moment between states k and m. If we let $C_k = c_k e^{-(2\pi i/h)E_k^0 t}$, and express $\cos \omega t$ in exponential form, (13.3.2) becomes

$$\frac{dc_k}{dt} = \frac{2\pi i}{h} \frac{E}{2} \sum_m M_{km} c_m \{ e^{i[\omega - (2\pi/h)(E_m{}^0 - E_k{}^0)]t} + e^{i[-\omega - (2\pi/h)(E_m{}^0 - E_k{}^0)]t} \}. \quad (13.3.4)$$

If the external field were not present, we plainly would have $dc_k/dt = 0$; if there is a small field, the time derivative will be small, or, in other words, the c's will be approximately constant. Putting it in other language, each c will be a constant plus a small time-varying quantity proportional to E, with, of course, still smaller terms in higher powers of E. Let us now assume that in the absence of the perturbing field, the atom is in one definite state, say that with subscript 1 (which we shall generally assume to be the ground state). That is, the terms independent of E will correspond to having $c_1 = 1$, all the other c's equal to zero. Now on the right side of (13.3.4) we may replace the c_k's which appear by their values in the absence of field, since this side of the equation contains the factor E, and any terms in the c's proportional to E would then become second-order terms, in E^2, which we shall neglect. Thus the right side of (13.3.4) degenerates to a single term, that for which $m = 1$, and we replace c_1 by unity. Let us simplify our notation by writing

$$E_k^0 - E_1^0 = \left(\frac{h}{2\pi} \right) \omega_k,$$

where ω_k is then the angular frequency associated with transition from the state 1 to the state k, according to Bohr's frequency condition, and is defined to be positive if the kth state is above the first state. We can now integrate (13.3.4) with respect to time, obtaining explicit formulas for the c_k's. We have such equations only for $k \neq 1$; the matrix component M_{11} is zero, since the electric moment has no diagonal components, so that (13.3.4) leads to the conclusion that $c_1 = 1$, up to terms in E^2. Then we find

$$c_k = \frac{2\pi}{h} \frac{E}{2} M_{k1} \left[\frac{e^{i(\omega + \omega_k)t}}{\omega + \omega_k} + \frac{e^{i(-\omega + \omega_k)t}}{-\omega + \omega_k} \right]. \quad (13.3.5)$$

In (13.3.5) we have not included a constant of integration. We know that there is no such constant of large size, since the c_k's by hypothesis contain terms only of the first or higher order in E; and any constant of integration proportional to E proves not to lead to any contributions to our polarization, though such constants are necessary in calculating transition probabilities, as in Appendix 11.

Now that we have found the c_k's, we can proceed with our task, which is to find the polarization produced by the external field. That is, we wish the average value of the electric moment, averaged over the wave function. By the fundamental principles of Chap. 3, this will be

$$\bar{M} = \sum_{m,n} C_m^* C_n M_{mn}. \tag{13.3.6}$$

We are interested only in terms linear in E; thus in the summation (13.3.6) we must either have $m = 1$ or $n = 1$, so that one of the C's will be C_1, independent of E. When we take account of the relation between the C's and the c's, and use (13.3.5), we find

$$\bar{M} = \frac{2\pi}{h} \frac{E}{2} \sum_k M_{k1}^2 \left(\frac{e^{i\omega t}}{\omega + \omega_k} + \frac{e^{-i\omega t}}{-\omega + \omega_k} + \frac{e^{-i\omega t}}{\omega + \omega_k} + \frac{e^{i\omega t}}{-\omega + \omega_k} \right)$$

$$= \frac{2\pi}{h} E \cos \omega t \sum_k \frac{2\omega_k M_{k1}^2}{\omega_k^2 - \omega^2}. \tag{13.3.7}$$

This result shows that there is a dipole moment per atom proportional to the external field; the constant of proportionality gives the polarizability of the atom. This may be written

$$\alpha = \sum_k \frac{f_k e^2/m}{\omega_k^2 - \omega^2}, \quad \text{where } f_k = \frac{4\pi m}{e^2 h} \omega_k M_{k1}^2. \tag{13.3.8}$$

We have written the result in this form, so as to make comparison easy with (13.1.4), which gave the polarizability arising from ionic displacement.

This important result (13.3.8) is generally called the Kramers-Heisenberg dispersion formula; it is an interesting historical fact that its derivation was one of the first steps in the development of quantum mechanics out of the earlier Bohr form of quantum theory. As we have pointed out before, the polarizability is like a sum of terms of the type (13.1.4), one associated with each transition which is possible from the state 1 in which the atom is located. Each of these terms is multiplied by a quantity f_k, which we have previously called the oscillator strength, and we have now found an explicit formula for these oscillator strengths. As we have mentioned earlier, there is a sum rule for these oscillator strengths, stating in a general way that the sum of the f_k's, for all possible transitions, equals unity; this sum rule is discussed in more detail, and its implications pointed out, in Appendix 20. It is interesting to note that we have terms in (13.3.8) corresponding to transitions to energy levels below the level in which the atom is located, provided this is an excited state, and that since the ω_k is negative for such transitions, they correspond to a sort of negative dispersion, the terms in the polarizability having the sign opposite to those found for an ionic oscillator. It is also interesting to note that there is a close relationship between the oscillator strength f_k given in (13.3.8) and the Einstein A and B coefficients, of which A is given in (4.7.1). Each of these involves the square of the matrix component of electric dipole moment between the states in question, so that we can immediately compute A and B from f, or vice versa. Measurement of anomalous dispersion is, in fact, often used as a method of finding the f's, and hence indirectly of finding the A's and B's.

Formula (13.3.8) agrees with (13.1.4), as we have seen, except that

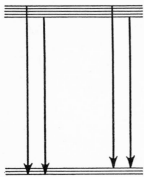

FIG. 13.3.1. Optical transitions between broadened upper and lower energy levels.

(13.3.8) does not have the frictional term $i\omega_g$ in the denominator and hence cannot lead to an explanation of absorption. The fault comes from our elementary method of derivation, and not from the fundamentals of the theory. If we proceed as in the Dirac radiation theory, as in Appendix 11, we can get a complete formula including the absorption term, simple enough so that we can easily describe it in qualitative language. In the first place, there is a general relation, called Kirchhoff's law, connecting the absorption coefficient and the emission of radiation by a body at a given wave length.[†] This states that the emission and absorption spectra of a given substance are closely related: at a frequency at which the substance emits strongly, it also absorbs strongly. A slight extension of this law shows that the detailed shape of the absorption spectrum must be the same as the shape of the emission spectrum, so that in particular the breadth of the emission line is the same as the breadth of the absorption line. Now the breadth of the absorption line is determined by the quantity g; in fact, we can show easily that it is just equal to g. Thus we can deduce the value of g by studying the shape of the emission line.

The best way to consider the breadth of an emission line is to assume that each of the two energy levels between which the emission occurs is really broadened, rather than being a perfectly sharp frequency. If this is the case, the emitted quantum can be connected with a transition from any part of the upper level to any part of the lower level, as indicated in Fig. 13.3.1. Then it is easy to show that the breadth of the spectrum line equals the sum of the breadths of the two energy levels, if

† See, for instance, J. C. Slater, "Introduction to Chemical Physics," McGraw-Hill Book Company, Inc., New York, 1939, Chap. XIX.

these breadths are properly defined.   Hence we must consider the causes of broadening of energy levels.   There are several causes; for instance, neighboring atoms may perturb each other, so that some atoms will have slightly different energy levels from others, and this will appear, on an average, to be a broadening of the level.   This is not the sort of effect we wish to consider here, however; we wish to think only of those effects which make an energy level, even of a single atom, inherently broad.   By the uncertainty principle, this is produced by a finite lifetime.   If an atom can exist in a stationary state only a time Δt, we have seen in Chap. 1, Eq. (1.6.2), that there will be an uncertainty in the energy given by $\Delta E = h/\Delta t$, so that the shorter the lifetime, the greater will be the broadening of the level.

This simple interpretation of the broadening of the levels proves to lead to correct formulas for the damping constants g of (13.1.4).   We naturally ask a further question, however.   The absorption of energy depends on g; why does this depend on the lifetime in the stationary states?   The qualitative reason is easy to understand.   Suppose, for instance, that we are dealing with an atom in its ground state, so that the lifetime of that ground state is essentially infinite, and the broadening comes only from the excited energy levels to which absorption can occur. Suppose there is some mechanism, such as collisions, responsible for shortening the lifetime in the excited state.   Such a collision is assumed to remove the excitation of the atom, transforming the excitation energy into some other sort, for example, kinetic energy of the particle which is colliding with the atom.   Then we have at the same time a mechanism of absorption: light is absorbed by the atom in its ground state, and instead of being reradiated or scattered as the atom returns to the ground state, the atom suffers a collision, which transforms the energy into some other form, so that it is lost as radiation.   There are many such mechanisms for absorption, but they all simultaneously broaden the lines.

13.4. Static Polarizability of Atoms.   In the preceding section we have taken up the polarization of atoms under the action of high-frequency electric fields.   We can get the static polarizability from (13.3.8) by setting the frequency equal to zero; it is

$$\alpha = \sum_k \frac{f_k e^2}{\omega_k^2 m}. \tag{13.4.1}$$

This formula can easily be found directly by second-order perturbation theory, without going through all the calculation we have made.   First we notice that the energy of a dipole of polarizability α, in a field E, is $-(\alpha/2)E^2$.   To prove this, we note that it requires no work to put the unpolarized dipole in the field.   When it is polarized, the internal energy of the dipole, connected with the restoring force, becomes $(\alpha/2)E^2$, or half the product of force eE and displacement $\alpha E/e$.   But at the same time, the potential energy in the external field becomes $-\alpha E^2$, equal to the force eE times the displacement $\alpha E/e$, with negative sign because the charge is being pulled in the direction of the field, and therefore to a lower potential.   Adding the two, the result is $-(\alpha/2)E^2$, as we have stated. We can now directly compute the same energy for the atom by perturbation theory, and by comparison derive the polarizability.

From second-order perturbation theory, Eq. (4.3.6), we know that the perturbed energy of a system is given by

$$E_i = H_{ii} + \sum_{j \neq i} \frac{H_{ij}H_{ji}}{H_{ii} - H_{jj}} + \cdots \qquad (13.4.2)$$

Let us apply this to our state 1 of the system.   The diagonal energy is just E_1^0, the unperturbed energy.   Thus the summation in (13.4.2) represents the added energy on account of the electric field.   The perturbative energy is $-eEx$ for each electron, so that the matrix component of this quantity is

$$H_{1k} = -EM_{1k},$$

where M is the matrix of electric moment, as before.   We thus have

$$E_1 = E_1^0 - \sum_k E^2 \frac{M_{1k}^2}{\omega_k} \frac{2\pi}{h}.$$

When we take account of the value of f_k from (13.3.8), we see that this is just $E_1^0 - (\alpha/2)E^2$, where α is given in (13.4.1), as it should be.

This gives us a fairly simple formula for polarizability; and yet, since we do not know all the necessary matrix components without a good deal of computation, it is not very much use for finding the order of magnitude of the quantity.   A very much simpler scheme, not based on the quantum theory at all, gives a correct idea of the order of magnitude of the electronic polarizability, proving to agree fairly well with the value of (13.4.1).   Suppose we have a perfectly conducting sphere of radius R and put it in an external field E.   Then it is a simple problem in electrostatics to prove that it acquires a dipole moment proportional to E and thus has a definite polarizability.   Furthermore, this polarizability proves to be proportional to the volume of the sphere and, in fact, proves to equal $4\pi\epsilon_0 R^3$.   If we compute this quantity for spheres of the order of magnitude of atomic dimensions, we find polarizabilities of the order of magnitude of those observed, or computed by the quantum theory. As this simple formula would suggest, we find that the largest atoms or ions show the largest electronic polarizabilities.   Thus in an ionic crystal the negative ions, which are quite large, show much larger polarizabilities than the small positive ions.   In many such substances the largest and most polarizable ions are those of oxygen, and often almost the whole polarizability comes from the oxygen ions.   In Table 13.4.1 we give cube roots of electronic polarizabilities divided by $4\pi\epsilon_0$, determined experimentally, for a number of ions; they are determined in such a way that the sum of these polarizabilities, for the ions constituting a crystal, shall agree as well as possible with the experimental value of the total polarizability of the substance.   We also give ionic radii, determined by the condition that the sum of radii equals the observed interionic distance in the crystal, for comparison; and we see that while there is nothing like quantitative agreement, still the orders of magnitude, and the general variation from one ion to another, are correct.

TABLE 13.4.1

Cube root of polarizability divided by $4\pi\epsilon_0$, for various ions, compared with ionic radii, as determined by crystal structure (angstroms).

Ion	$(\text{Pol}/4\pi\epsilon_0)^{1/3}$	Radius
$O^=$	1.11	1.32
F^-	1.02	1.33
Na^+	0.91	1.01
Mg^{++}	0.87	0.75
$S^=$	1.29	1.69
Cl^-	1.21	1.72
K^+	1.10	1.30
Ca^{++}	1.05	1.02

It is not by chance that these two ways of estimating polarizability show some agreement, as we can see by a simple calculation.   In the sum (13.4.1), one term, corresponding to the principal absorption from the ground state, generally makes by far the largest contribution.   That is, its oscillator strength f_k is somewhere near unity, the others all being much smaller.   Thus α must be of the order of magnitude of $e^2/\omega^2 m$, where ω is the angular frequency associated with this transition.   This angular frequency, multiplied by $h/2\pi$, will be the energy difference between the two states considered, which will not be very different from the term value of the ground state, since the excited level generally has a much smaller term value.   This energy, in turn, will not be very different from the potential energy $e^2/4\pi\epsilon_0 r$ of an electron at a distance r, which we may regard as the radius of the atom.   Thus, in order of magnitude, we have

$$\frac{e^2}{4\pi\epsilon_0 r} = \frac{h\omega}{2\pi}, \qquad \omega = \frac{e^2}{2\epsilon_0 rh}.$$

If we substitute this value in the expression $e^2/\omega^2 m$, we find

$$\frac{e^2}{\omega^2 m} = \frac{4\epsilon_0^2 r^2 h^2}{me^2} = 4\pi\epsilon_0 r^2 a_0, \tag{13.4.3}$$

where a_0 is the radius of the first Bohr orbit of hydrogen, given in (1.2.8). Since r will certainly be of the same order of magnitude as a_0, we see that (13.4.3) indicates a polarizability of the same order of magnitude as $4\pi\epsilon_0 R^3$, though perhaps increasing as the square, rather than the cube, of the radius.   Neither approximation is good enough to carry far.

13.5. Van der Waals' Force.   The Van der Waals force which we have discussed in Sec. 9.6 can be derived by second-order perturbation theory, in a way similar to that which we have just used in discussing polarizability.   In this case, instead of considering the perturbation of an atom by an external field, we consider its perturbation by another atom.   Let us imagine two atoms at distance R and investigate their mutual perturbations.   If the first forms instantaneously a dipole of moment μ, this will produce at the second a field proportional to $\mu/4\pi\epsilon_0 R^3$ times a function of the angle between μ and the line joining the atoms.   This will produce a perturbative energy proportional to the instantaneous dipole μ' of the second, times the field, or $\mu\mu'/4\pi\epsilon_0 R^3$ times functions of the angles of both dipoles.   This then is the perturbative energy which we must use in our perturbation problem.   As with the polarization by a constant field, the average value vanishes, and we must take second-order perturbations. For this, we need the non-diagonal matrix components of the quantity $\mu\mu'$, with the functions of angle.

If we consider the transition from the ground state to the state in which the first atom is in the kth state, the second the k'th state, the matrix component is the product of the $1k$ component of μ, where the index 1 stands for the ground state, and of the $1k'$ component of μ', together with the result of integrating the functions of angle.   On account of the spherical symmetry of each atom, the matrix component of μ can be determined from its x component, which we have called M_{1k}, and similarly that of μ' can be found from $M'_{1k'}$, the numerical factors coming from the angles.   The final result, then, of taking the matrix component and averaging over angles is to replace the matrix component of $\mu\mu'/R^3$ by a constant times $M_{1k}M'_{1k'}/R^3$, where the constant can be determined by carrying through the computation.   Next we need the diagonal elements of the total energy; these are simply the sums of the unperturbed energies of the two atoms.   We finally have for the perturbed energy then

$$\sum_{k,k'} \frac{\text{constant}}{(4\pi\epsilon_0)^2 R^6} \frac{M_{1k}^2 M_{1k'}^{'2}}{E_k^0 + E_{k'}^{'0} - E_1^0 - E_1^{'0}}. \tag{13.5.1}$$

When the whole computation is carried out the constant proves to be 6.

In most cases, as we have pointed out in the preceding section, one transition, or one group of transitions, proves to make the major contribution to the summations for either the polarizability or the Van der Waals force.   In this case the polarizability (13.4.1), using (13.3.7), can be written in the form

$$\alpha = \frac{2M_{1k}^2}{\Delta E}, \tag{13.5.2}$$

where ΔE is the energy difference between the ground state and the principal excited state.   This formula can be conveniently used to estimate atomic polarizabilities in cases where the matrix components M_{1k} are known, as from the Einstein A and B, or the observed oscillator strengths.   In this case, the Van der Waals potential from (13.5.1) is

$$-\frac{6}{(4\pi\epsilon_0)^2 R^6} \frac{\alpha\alpha' \, \Delta E \, \Delta E'}{4(\Delta E + \Delta E')} = -\frac{3}{2} \frac{1}{(4\pi\epsilon_0)^2 R^6} \frac{\Delta E \, \Delta E'}{\Delta E + \Delta E'} \alpha\alpha'. \tag{13.5.3}$$

This is a useful formula expressing the Van der Waals potential between any pair of atoms in terms of the principal energy differences of th   vo, which can be estimated from the spectrum, and the pola   , which can be observed or calculated.   In case the two a´ this reduces to

$$-\frac{3}{4} \frac{1}{R^6} \frac{\alpha^2 \, \Delta E}{(4\pi\epsilon_0)^2},$$

a useful expression which proves to be fairly accurate experi. We may rewrite this last formula in terms of expression (13.5.2), o.

$$-\frac{3}{2} \frac{1}{R^6} \frac{\alpha M_{1k}^2}{(4\pi\epsilon_0)^2}, \tag{1.}$$

a formula equivalent to the one proportional to $\mu^2\alpha/(4\pi\epsilon_0)^2 r^6$ of Sec. 9. We have, however, here stated the correct constant of proportionality in this expression.

PROBLEMS

1. Compute the index of refraction of sodium gas, assuming that it has one dispersion electron connected with the D line (5,890 A), six connected with the L absorption edge, and two with the K absorption edge.   Carry the calculation down to x-ray

wave lengths, and show that the index in the x-ray region differs only slightly from unity.

2. Show that a gas consisting entirely of excited atoms shows "negative dispersion" about the possible emission lines, a contribution to the index of refraction of the opposite sign to the normal contribution. Show that this may be of importance in a real gas in that the ordinary dispersion connected with a transition up from the normal state may be diminished by excited atoms. If the number of atoms in the ground and excited states is given by a Boltzmann factor, and if the two levels are close together compared with kT, show that the strength of the dispersion is proportional to $1/T$. This situation is observed in paramagnetic resonance experiments.

3. Assuming that the D line of sodium has one dispersion electron, compute the transition probabilities A and B, and find the mean life of an atom in the excited state before it radiates to the normal state.

4. The polarizability of the hydrogen atom is $4.5(4\pi\epsilon_0)a_0^3$. Using the formula for polarizability in terms of the number of dispersion electrons and energy levels, and remembering that hydrogen has one dispersion electron, find the range of $E_k - E_0$ making the important contribution to the sum, and find where E_k lies in the term system.

5. Helium has a polarizability $4\pi\epsilon_0 \times 0.20 \times 10^{-24}$ cu cm, and two dispersion electrons. Show that the most important terms in its dispersion come from the continuous spectrum beyond the series limit.

6. Using the polarizability and principal energy difference from Prob. 5, find the Van der Waals potential between two helium atoms.

7. Assume a dielectric constant for a substance containing permanent dipoles given by Eq. (13.2.6), where the relaxation time τ is given by (13.2.7), and the coefficient of viscosity η varies as $e^{E/kT}$. Find the absorption term from the dielectric constant as a function of temperature, plotting the result. Assume E is such a value as to give the absorption peak at a convenient temperature.

8. Write the Einstein A and B coefficients in terms of the oscillator strength f_k of Eq. (13.3.8).

9. Assume that both upper and lower energy levels concerned in an atomic transition are not perfectly sharp, but consist of broadened bands, as if each consisted of many stationary states close together (as in an energy band in a metal). Find the broadening of the resulting emitted radiation, and show that it is given by the sum of the breadths of the two levels. To make the problem precise, assume the distribution dN/dE of energy levels in each band to be given by a Gauss error curve with different half-widths for each band. Assume that any one of the levels of the upper band can combine with any level of the lower band, with equal probabilities. Find the total radiation emitted by all transitions from one of the levels of the upper band to one of the lower band, with a given energy difference, and hence given frequency. Show that the emitted radiation also has a Gaussian distribution of intensity, the breadth being the sum of the breadths of the two levels.

10. Discuss the situation of Prob. 9 when the distribution of energy levels in each band is given by a formula of type

$$\frac{1}{(E - E_0)^2 + \epsilon^2},$$

rather than a Gauss error curve.

CHAPTER 14

MAGNETISM

All types of matter have some magnetic properties, just as all types have dielectric or conducting properties, though only a few, the ferromagnetic materials, have such striking magnetic behavior that we think of them as being magnetic. Even though the magnetic properties of most materials are not spectacular, still they are very interesting and give a great deal of information about the structure of the materials. For this reason, they have been studied in a good deal of detail, and we shall go into their theory in the present chapter.

In a very superficial way, there is considerable analogy between the different types of magnetic materials and the different types of dielectric polarization. In the preceding chapter we have seen that dielectric action arises in two broad ways: in the production of induced dipoles, produced directly by the action of the field, either by displacing the electronic structure of atoms or by displacing ions as a whole; and in the orientation of already existing permanent dipoles by the external field. The first type of polarization is essentially independent of temperature, whereas the second type, being opposed by temperature agitation, decreases very rapidly with increase of temperature. In a similar way we have the diamagnetic effect, arising from the production of induced magnetic dipoles by action of the external field, and existing in all cases; and superposed on this, if we are dealing with materials having permanent magnetic dipole moments, we have the paramagnetic and ferromagnetic effects, coming from the orientation of these permanent dipoles, and decreasing with the temperature.

Diamagnetic behavior arises in a very simple way, from the same induced currents which we are familiar with in circuit theory. When a magnetic field is being established, its time rate of change induces electromotive forces in the atoms, and these electromotive forces build up circulating currents inside the atoms. Since there is nothing like resistance when we are dealing with currents within the atom, these currents persist so long as the magnetic field continues and do not die down until the field itself dies down, its decrease producing an electromotive force in the opposite direction. The circulating currents result in magnetic moments, which are proportional to the magnetic field. These moments are what are responsible for the diamagnetic behavior. By Lenz's law, the magnets are in a direction to oppose the external field; thus the diamagnetic effect results in a permeability less than unity. The theory of diamagnetism, which we shall set up in a simple way, proves to give a diamagnetic susceptibility which can be computed in a very simple way from the atomic wave function, and whose experimental value gives a rather sensitive test of the correctness of a theoretically determined wave function.

The currents which we consider in the theory of diamagnetism are ordinarily considered to circulate only within individual atoms. There are cases, however, where they appear to circulate throughout a rather complicated molecule. Thus in the benzene molecule, and some related substances, there is evidence that induced currents can be set up which circulate around the ring. Since we shall find the diamagnetic effect to increase with the square of the radius of the electronic current, such materials show unusually high diamagnetic susceptibility. If we consider metals, of course we know that current can circulate throughout the metal, so that in the process of building up a magnetic field we induce large-scale currents. These are the eddy currents, and naturally they die down on account of the electrical resistance, which we have in a metal, though not in an atom or molecule. Hence they do not result in a permanent magnetic moment proportional to the field and do not result in diamagnetism, though it can be proved, by methods more elaborate than we shall take up, that there is, in fact, a very small diamagnetism arising from the conduction electrons.

A superconductor, however, has quite a different situation. This is a metal, of particular properties, which becomes a perfect conductor below a transition temperature at a few degrees absolute. The exact reason, in terms of quantum mechanics, for this disappearance of resistance is still not clearly understood, though we can describe some features of it. But so long as we postulate the superconducting behavior, it is obvious that in a superconductor the large-scale eddy currents, extending through the whole conductor, will not die down after a magnetic field is established, so that a magnetic moment proportional to the field will remain, and the material will behave in a diamagnetic manner. This phenomenon, unlike ordinary diamagnetism, is very striking, and on a large scale: the effect is so large that the magnetic field is almost completely shielded from the inside of the superconductor. In a crude way, we shall find that superconductivity has approximately the same relation to diamagnetism that ferromagnetism has to paramagnetism: diamagnetism and paramagnetism are phenomena in which the individual atoms act independently of each other, whereas in superconductivity and ferromagnetism there is a cooperative action between atoms at a distance, so that the whole material can cooperate in a much greater effect than we could get from the isolated atoms. We see, from this description, that we shall find it appropriate to treat superconductivity along with diamagnetism.

The simplest examples of paramagnetism are found with isolated atoms, just as is the case with diamagnetism. We have seen in our discussion of atomic structure that an atom generally has a magnetic moment, arising from two sources: the orbital magnetic moment, coming from circulation of the electrons around the nucleus, as if they formed closed current loops, and the spin magnetic moment, an inherent property of the electron. In the absence of a magnetic field, these can be oriented in any arbitrary direction in space. In the presence of a field, we have space quantization: there are certain allowed orientations, characterized by having the angular momentum along the axis equal to an integral or half integral multiple of $h/2\pi$. Since the magnetic moment is proportional to the angular momentum, this gives definite components of magnetic moment along the axis, and hence definite energy levels, since the magnetic energy in the presence of the field equals the product of field strength and the component of magnetic moment along the field. At high temperature, all orientations would be equally likely; but at lower temperatures, the Boltzmann factor, indicating that the probability of finding an atom with energy E is proportional to $e^{-E/kT}$, indicates that those orientations with low energy, or with the magnetic moment oriented along the field, are more likely than those with high energy, or with opposite orientation. This leads us to the same sort of analysis as used in the preceding chapter in discussing the Langevin function, and here as there it leads to an average magnetic moment proportional to the magnetic field and inversely proportional to the absolute temperature. This is the origin of paramagnetic effects.

There are a good many solids which show paramagnetism. These must, as we see, be solids containing electrons in unfilled shells, for if we have electrons only in filled shells, there will be no magnetic moment. For instance, in an ionic crystal, like NaCl, all electrons are contained in rare-gas-like ions, whose orbital angular momenta and magnetic moments compensate to zero, and whose spins are likewise compensated. In a substance held by covalent bonds, the orbital magnetic moments generally cancel, and there are two electrons, with opposite spin, in each molecular orbital, so that here again there is no paramagnetism. We look for paramagnetism in substances containing ions of the iron group, the rare earths, or other elements containing incompleted inner shells. We find, as a matter of fact, that the salts of practically all these elements show paramagnetic behavior in their solid state, and often in solution as well.

The simplest paramagnetic salts are those of the rare-earth elements. In these substances the $4f$ electrons are so far within the atom that they behave almost identically, whether the atom is in chemical combination or not. It proves to be possible to explain the paramagnetism of rare-earth salts quite accurately by treating the $4f$ electrons as if they were in isolated atoms, finding their net magnetic moments from atomic multiplet theory, and applying the Langevin theory to these net magnetic moments. On the other hand, the salts of the iron-group elements behave quite differently. Their $3d$ electrons, which are responsible for the magnetic behavior, are not nearly as well shielded by the outer electrons as are the $4f$'s in the rare earths. In fact, the $3d$'s play a considerable role in the interatomic forces and the binding of the crystal. Thus the energy levels are perturbed to a considerable extent, and we cannot treat the $3d$ electrons as if they were in isolated atoms. We find that the orbital degeneracy which was concerned in the formation of the atomic multiplets is removed by the interactions of neighboring atoms, so that a single atomic multiplet is split up in the crystal into a number of energy levels, fairly closely spaced on a spectroscopic scale, but far apart compared with kT, so that only the lowest one is ordinarily excited at room temperatures. The spin degeneracy remains, however, and we find that the paramagnetism of the iron group is almost completely a result of the orientation of the spin magnetic moment, the orbital magnetic moment being completely removed by the crystalline perturbations.

Even though the iron-group ions are perturbed by their neighbors, still the paramagnetism of these salts can be explained by treating each ion as independent of its neighbors, and by using a Langevin type of theory. This holds, however, only as long as the ions are fairly far apart. The theory works best in salts containing a good deal of water of crystallization, for this has the effect of diluting the ions, forcing them further apart than in a crystal without water of crystallization. As we go to more concentrated salts, complications arising from interaction of neighboring ions appear, and these complications reach their climax in the ferromagnetic materials, consisting of the ferromagnetic metals Fe, Co, and Ni, some of their alloys with each other and with other elements, some oxides of ferromagnetic metals, and a few substances involving rare-earth metals. Here we meet phenomena which remind us at first sight of the ferroelectricity which we have described in the preceding chapter. The magnetic susceptibility, instead of being proportional to $1/T$ as in a paramagnetic material, is proportional to $1/(T - T_c)$, where T_c is a temperature often higher than room temperature, called the Curie temperature. The susceptibility goes infinite at this temperature, and below it there is a spontaneous magnetization, increasing as the temperature goes below the Curie point. It is this spontaneous magnetization which we observe in a permanent magnet, though the situation is greatly complicated by the fact that such a material magnetizes itself in separate small domains, of microscopic size, different domains having different directions of magnetization, so that most of the familiar magnetic phenomena, such as initial permeability, hysteresis, approach to saturation magnetization, and the amount of permanent magnetization, depend on the domain structure, rather than on the spontaneous magnetization on an atomic scale.

On account of the similarity of ferromagnetism to ferroelectricity, we might at first be tempted to think that it arose in the same way: that the correct field to assume to act on a magnetic dipole was not merely the external magnetic field, but that field corrected for the field of the other dipoles in the sample. We should, in other words, make a Lorentz correction here, as in the dielectric case, and then we should automatically be led to the correct temperature dependence of magnetization. When we try this, however, we find that the order of magnitude of the effect is altogether wrong to explain ferromagnetism. The magnetic interaction of the dipoles is so small that if a Curie point arose from this effect, it would come at a small fraction of a degree Kelvin, instead of at hundreds of degrees as the observed Curie points do. We could explain the observed effect if we assumed that there was an additional field acting on an individual dipole, proportional to the magnetization, but hundreds of times greater than the field predicted by the Lorentz correction. Such a field is called an inner field; it was postulated by Weiss, and the theory set up by postulating it, which runs closely parallel to the ferroelectric theory of the preceding chapter, is in moderately good agreement with experiment. But until wave mechanics was developed, there was no explanation as to the origin of Weiss's inner field.

The first application of quantum mechanics to this problem came from Heisenberg. He pointed out the analogy of the situation to the problem of multiplet structure, met in atomic theory. In our study of that subject, we have found the striking way in which the exclusion principle is tied up with the magnetic moment of atoms and molecules. Two multiplets, associated with different angular momentum and magnetic moment, can differ in energy by large amounts, on account of the indirect effect by which their wave functions must have different symmetry properties on account of the effect of the electron spin on the exclusion principle. These different wave functions result in different electrostatic energies, as calculated by various exchange integrals; the electrostatic energy differences between the multiplets are hundreds of times as great as would arise if the only interactions between the electrons were purely magnetic.   Heisenberg postulated that the same sort of thing goes on in ferromagnetics, the spin determining the orbital properties of the wave function, and hence the electrostatic energy, which then depends on the total magnetic moment.   In this way he was able to make it seem reasonable that, if the stable state of a crystal was a magnetic state, with spins parallel, it should require a great deal of energy, available only with a high Curie temperature, to destroy the magnetization.

This fundamental suggestion of Heisenberg is the basis of all subsequent theories of ferromagnetism, though the development of the theory has not in all cases followed Heisenberg's lead.   He proceeded by an analogy with the Heitler-London method, showing that the exchange integrals of that theory, if properly treated, could lead to a final result similar to that of the Weiss theory of internal fields.   He had to postulate exchange integrals of the opposite sign to those usually found, however: we remember that, for instance, in the H_2 molecule, the ground state is a singlet state, with no magnetic moment, and that is the usual situation with Heitler-London molecular models.   On the other hand, in an atom, the multiplet of highest multiplicity, or greatest magnetic moment, generally has the lowest energy, and this suggests that an approach which makes the interactions of the electrons in a single atom the most important ones is more likely to lead to a detailed description of ferromagnetism.   This is the case with treatments which have been given, using an energy-band, or molecular-orbital, approach.   Bloch first used this type of analysis, using free electrons, and showing that a free-electron gas, if treated properly, would behave in a ferromagnetic way if its density were low enough.   Later analysis, using more accurate energy-band wave functions, has shown substantially the same thing: that if the energy band is narrow enough, or the electrons are overlapping only slightly, so that they have small density in the region of overlapping, the exchange interactions are of such sign as to give ferromagnetism, whereas otherwise they are not.

Development of this type of investigation makes it clear why ferromagnetism is found only in the few cases where it occurs.   We should expect it only in elements with unfilled inner shells, like the iron group. Going through that group, the $3d$ orbits are gradually shrinking in size, from being essentially outer, excited orbits in the first elements of the group, Ca and Sc, to being really inside orbits at the end of the group, in Ni.   As long as the electronic orbits are too large, the bands are spread out, or the electrons overlap their neighbors too much to produce ferromagnetism.   As they get smaller, however, the situation changes, and we have ferromagnetism in Fe, Co, and Ni, the last three elements of the series.   In the preceding element, Mn, there is considerable tendency in compounds to have the opposite behavior, called antiferromagnetism, in which spins of neighboring atoms tend to line up strongly in an anti-parallel rather than a parallel relation to each other; this is a result of a considerable exchange interaction, but of opposite sign to that observed in the ferromagnetic elements.   There is considerable evidence that this effect changes sign as we approach Fe in the periodic table.

As the 3d electron gets further inside the atom, or as the atoms overlap less and less, as in some oxides, or even more in the paramagnetic salts, the tendency toward parallel orientation of neighboring spins remains, but gets weaker and weaker, as we should expect from the smaller interaction which the electrons can have if their wave functions do not overlap much. This shows itself in a decreasing Curie temperature, as is found in ferro-magnetic oxides; and in the ordinary paramagnetic salts the effect of overlapping or exchange is so small that it can be treated as a perturbation of the behavior which we should have with entirely isolated atoms.

There is one interesting type of experimentation which can be carried on with paramagnetic or ferromagnetic materials, and this relates to microwave resonance experiments.   We can look at these effects either from the basis of classical mechanics or of quantum theory.   We have seen in Chap. 6 that a magnetic atom in an external magnetic field has its axis precess around the field with a definite frequency, proportional to the field, equal to the Larmor frequency, or closely related to it. With the order of magnitude of magnetic field and magnetic behavior of atoms which we have, this frequency can easily lie in the microwave part of the spectrum.   If we now simultaneously impose a constant magnetic field, to induce precession, and an oscillating field of microwave fre-quency, we should expect that we could get resonance effects between the frequency of the imposed microwave radiation and the precession fre-quency.   As a matter of fact, such effects are easy to observe and give a good deal of information about the precessing dipoles which are responsi-ble for the paramagnetic or ferromagnetic behavior.   The corresponding quantum-theoretical way of looking at the same problem is to remember that the atom has energy levels in the external field, which we con-sidered in connection with the Zeeman effect, and that an external radi-ation field of suitable frequency can be absorbed by the atom, causing transitions from one of the Zeeman energy levels to another.   This method of description leads to the same results as the classical analysis.

Now that we have sketched the main types of magnetic behavior of matter, we shall proceed with more detailed discussion of the theory of the various effects, starting with the theory of diamagnetism.

14.1. Diamagnetism of Atoms.   Consider a spherically symmetrical atom, or an atom which, by being averaged over all orientations, has been rendered spherically symmetrical. Let the one-electron wave function of one of its electrons be $u(x,y,z)$. Let the magnetic field B be along the z axis, and consider a circular filament of charge, as in Fig. 14.1.1, with radius R, cross section da, in a plane perpendicular to the z axis, with the z axis (which passes through the nucleus of the atom) passing through its

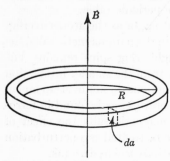

center. We shall now find the current induced in this filament when the magnetic field is built up from zero and hence find the magnetic moment of the filament; then we shall sum over all filaments to get the total magnetic moment contributed by this electron; and finally we shall sum over all electrons in unit volume to get the magnetization, or total magnetic moment per unit volume. We shall calculate using the rationalized mks units, but shall give the conversion to the nonrationalized Gaussian units.†

Fig. 14.1.1. Filament of current, for computing diamagnetism.

The Maxwell equation which expresses Faraday's induction law is curl $\mathbf{E} = -\dot{\mathbf{B}}$. Let us express this in integrated form, integrating over the circle spanning our filament. By Stokes' theorem, the surface integral of curl $\mathbf{E}$ may be written as the line integral of the tangential component of E around the circle. We can set up a solution of Maxwell's equations in which the lines of E are circles in the xy plane, of which our filament forms one, so that we may assume that E is already tangential to the circle. Then we have $2\pi R E = -\pi R^2 \dot{B}$, where now E, B are the magnitudes of the vectors. In other words, $E = -R\dot{B}/2$. This electric field will exert a force $-eE$ on an electron which happens to be in the filament and will hence give it an acceleration given by

$$\frac{m\,dv}{dt} = -eE = \left(\frac{eR}{2}\right)\frac{dB}{dt},$$

where the velocity v is around the circle. If we integrate this expression with respect to time, from a time at which B is zero, and if we assume that v refers merely to the additional velocity acquired as a result of the induction, we have

$$v = \frac{eR}{2m}\,B. \tag{14.1.1}$$

Now the charge density in our filament is $-eu^*u$. Thus the current

† The magnetic calculations are made as in Slater and Frank, "Electromagnetism," McGraw-Hill Book Company, Inc., New York, 1947, Chaps. V and VI.

density arising from the velocity (14.1.1) is the product of charge density and velocity, or is $-(e^2u^*uR/2m)B$. The current flowing in the filament is the product of current density and cross section da. The magnetic moment of a current flowing in a path of this sort equals the product of current and area of the path. Hence the magnetic moment contributed by the filament is

$$\text{Magnetic moment} = -\pi R^2 \, da \, \frac{e^2u^*uR}{2m} \, B$$

$$= 2\pi R u^* u \left(-\frac{e^2R^2}{4m}\right) B \, da. \qquad (14.1.2)$$

The latter form of (14.1.2) exhibits the magnetic moment of the filament as the product of the volume $2\pi R \, da$ of the filament, the intensity u^*u of the one-electron wave function, and the quantity $(-e^2R^2/4m)B$. To get the total magnetic moment, we need only integrate this over the whole wave function. This involves integrating R^2u^*u over the volume, or finding the average of R^2, by the methods of Chap. 3. But

$$R^2 = x^2 + y^2,$$

and with a spherically symmetrical atom $\overline{x^2} = \overline{y^2} = \overline{z^2} = \frac{1}{3}\overline{r^2}$, where r is the distance from the nucleus. Thus $\overline{R^2} = \frac{2}{3}\overline{r^2}$. When we take account of this, we find

$$\text{Magnetic moment of electron} = \frac{-e^2\overline{r^2}}{6m} \, B. \qquad (14.1.3)$$

To get the magnetization vector, or the total magnetic moment per unit volume, we sum expressions like (14.1.3) over all electrons in unit volume. That is, first we sum over the electrons of an atom, r being the distance from the nucleus of that atom; then, having found the moment of the atom, we sum the resulting quantity over all atoms in unit volume. Hence we have

$$M = \left(-\sum \frac{e^2\overline{r^2}}{6m}\right) \mu_0 H, \qquad (14.1.4)$$

where we have written B approximately as $\mu_0 H$, where μ_0 is the permittivity of free space; this is correct, since in a diamagnetic material the permeability is so nearly equal to unity. We recall that μ_0 is related to ϵ_0 and to c, the velocity of light, by the relation $\epsilon_0\mu_0 = 1/c^2$. Using this relation, we can rewrite (14.1.4) as

$$M = \left[-4\pi \sum \frac{e^2\overline{r^2}}{(4\pi\epsilon_0)6mc^2}\right] H. \qquad (14.1.5)$$

We are now ready to write the magnetic permeability κ_m, defined by the relation $\kappa_m = 1 + M/H$. We have

$$\kappa_m = 1 - 4\pi \sum \frac{e^2 \overline{r^2}}{(4\pi\epsilon_0)6mc^2},\qquad(14.1.6)$$

where we recall that the summation extends over all electrons in unit volume. We have written this expression in a form in which we can at once pass to the nonrationalized Gaussian units, as usual, by setting $4\pi\epsilon_0$ equal to unity. When we put numerical values into (14.1.6), we find that the resulting permeability is less than unity by a small quantity of the order of 10^{-6}, as is found experimentally. Not only this, but if we use theoretical wave functions to make calculations of $\overline{r^2}$, we come out with quite accurate agreement between the observed and the theoretical diamagnetism. This, in fact, is one of the rather sensitive tests of the correctness of an approximate theoretical wave function. It is clear that on account of the dependence of (14.1.6) on $\overline{r^2}$, it is the outermost electrons of an atom which make by far the greatest contributions to the diamagnetic susceptibility, and it is the outer part of their wave function which is important.

It is a simple matter, looking at formula (14.1.6), to see why the diamagnetic effect is so small. For the outer electrons of an atom, we may assume that $\overline{r^2}$ will be of the order of magnitude of a_0^2, where a_0 is the Bohr hydrogen radius. We may, as far as order of magnitude is concerned, assume that we have one such electron in a cube of volume a_0^3. Then, in (14.1.6), instead of summing, we can multiply the quantity we are summing by the number of particles per unit volume, which we are approximating as $1/a_0^3$. As far as order of magnitude is concerned then, the second term of (14.1.6) is given by $e^2/4\pi\epsilon_0 a_0 mc^2$. But when we put in the value of a_0, from Sec. 1.2, this is equal to $2Rhc/mc^2$, the ratio of twice the Rydberg energy to the constitutive energy of the electron, according to relativity. Alternatively, this is $(2\pi e^2/4\pi\epsilon_0 hc)^2$, which is the square of the so-called fine-structure constant, or very closely $1/(137)^2$. We see, then, that the diamagnetic susceptibility differs from unity by a very small quantity.

14.2. Superconductivity. The characteristic feature of diamagnetism is the way in which the induced current set up in an atom by the building up of the magnetic field is not subject to resistance and hence leads to a magnetic moment, proportional to the field, which persists as long as the field exists. If we wish to postulate that the current in a superconductor similarly is not subject to resistance, we can easily set up the equations giving the electromagnetic behavior of the superconductor. We shall first do this, showing the close resemblance to the problem of diamag-

netism.   Then we shall discuss the more difficult, and still not entirely
settled, question, why the resistance is absent in the superconductor.

We start, as in the case of diamagnetism, with the Faraday induction
equation, curl $\mathbf{E} = -\dot{\mathbf{B}}$, coupled with Newton's law for the acceleration
of electrons, $-eE = m\, dv/dt$, where now, if we are treating electrons in
the energy bands of a metal, we may have to use an effective mass for m,
in place of the real electronic mass.   If there are N electrons per unit
volume, there will be a current density $J = -Nev$.   Thus we can combine the equations above into the single equation

$$\text{curl}\left(\frac{m}{Ne^2}\dot{\mathbf{J}}\right) = -\dot{\mathbf{B}}. \tag{14.2.1}$$

As in the preceding section, we integrate this with respect to time and
include no constant of integration, assuming that J is zero when B is
zero; we return to this assumption, which might be questioned, a little
later.   We then have

$$\text{curl}\left(\frac{m\mathbf{J}}{Ne^2}\right) = -\mathbf{B}. \tag{14.2.2}$$

It has been suggested by F. London that Eq. (14.2.2) is the fundamental
electromagnetic equation of a superconductor, and the theory based on
this equation is generally called by his name.

We may now at once combine (14.2.2) with Maxwell's other equation,
which for a steady state is curl $\mathbf{H} = \mathbf{J}$.   If we assume that $\mathbf{B} = \mu_0\mathbf{H}$
(that is, that there is no magnetic material present, the only magnetic
effects coming from the current J, which we are explicitly considering), we
then find

$$\text{curl curl } \mathbf{H} = -\nabla^2\mathbf{H} = -\frac{Ne^2}{m}\mu_0\mathbf{H} = -\frac{4\pi Ne^2}{(4\pi\epsilon_0)mc^2}\mathbf{H}, \tag{14.2.3}$$

provided we are in a homogeneous medium in which Ne^2/m does not vary
from point to point.   Let us now consider the behavior of the magnetic
field H in the neighborhood of the surface of a superconductor.   Let
the surface be the surface $x = 0$, and assume that H varies only with
x.   Then (14.2.3) leads at once to a solution $H = H_0 e^{-x/\delta}$, where δ is
a so-called penetration depth, a distance in which the magnetic field falls
to $1/e$ of its value at the surface, given by

$$\delta^2 = \frac{4\pi\epsilon_0 mc^2}{4\pi Ne^2}. \tag{14.2.4}$$

Furthermore, since the current J can obviously only have components
tangential to the surface of the superconductor, it follows from Maxwell's

equations that H also has only tangential components, at right angles to the current J.

When we put in reasonable values for the constants in (14.2.4), using for N something like one electron per atom, for m the mass of an electron, the penetration depth comes out to be of the order of 10^{-6} cm. The picture which we get of the surface of a superconductor is then the following: In the interior, below a thin layer of the order of 10^{-6} cm thick, there is no magnetic field and no electric current. In this thin surface layer there is a surface current flowing, increasing in magnitude toward the surface. By a simple application of Ampere's law, there is a tangential magnetic field at the surface, at right angles to the surface current, the magnitude of the magnetic field equaling the magnitude of surface current, in amperes per meter of surface (if we use the mks units). This magnetic field, of course, is continuous with that imposed from outside sources on the superconductor, and in fact, as our method of derivation shows, it is the imposition of the magnetic field which has induced the surface currents which have shielded the inside of the material from the field.

Such a practically complete shielding of the interior of a material from magnetic lines of force bears a certain resemblance to what would go on in a magnetic medium with $\kappa_m = 0$; that is, in the most diamagnetic medium we could imagine. It is interesting to look at (14.1.6), and ask what conditions would have to be fulfilled, in order to have a real medium with this extreme diamagnetism. If we let the number of electrons per unit volume be N, we may rewrite (14.1.6) in the form

$$\kappa_m = 1 - \frac{4\pi N e^2 \overline{r^2}}{(4\pi\epsilon_0)6mc^2}.$$

If this were to equal zero, comparison with (14.2.4) shows that we should have to have $\overline{r^2} = 6\delta^2$. That is, if the atoms had dimensions of the order of 10^{-6}, or the penetration depth, they would have great enough diamagnetism to simulate a superconductor. However, there is no way to stretch (14.1.6) to this limit; it applies in this simple form only to real atoms, not to large aggregates of atoms, which must be handled quite differently. The currents induced in an atom, in the diamagnetic effect, shield the center of the atom very slightly from an external magnetic field; if the atom were as large as the penetration depth, this shielding layer would be thick enough to shield the field completely.

There is good evidence that superconductors really have an effect of penetration of field in good agreement with that predicted by (14.2.3). Experiments on thin wires and films of superconductors, whose dimensions are comparable with the penetration depth, show behavior which can be well explained by London's modification of Maxwell's equations. Furthermore, the equations can be used to predict time-varying phenomena as well as effects independent of time. At frequencies as high as those encountered with microwaves, ordinary electrodynamics would predict that an electromagnetic wave would penetrate a metal only a short distance, called the skin depth. This is ordinarily rather large compared with our penetration depth, but at low temperatures they can be comparable, and complicated interactions between these two effects occur, further complicated by the fact that the mean free path of the electrons becomes comparable to the penetration depth and skin depth, all of which can be explained to a fair approximation by London's equations, though these do not seem to be completely successful in all details. One gets the impression that (14.2.2) is at least a good approximation to the behavior of the electrons in a superconductor.

We have stated earlier that it is not completely obvious that we should not have a constant of integration in (14.2.2), since we have obtained it by integrating (14.2.1). If the current is set up by establishing a magnetic field, starting with an initial unmagnetized state in which there is no current, our procedure is certainly legitimate. However, there is an experiment, called the Meissner effect, which throws a somewhat different light on the problem. There is a transition temperature above which a metal ceases to be superconducting. Meissner took a superconductor above its transition temperature, established a magnetic field running through it in these conditions, and then cooled through the transition temperature, thinking that he would in that way "freeze in" a magnetic field in the inside. He expected, in other words, since there was no $\dot{B}$, and hence no electromotive force, in the problem, that no current density J would set up, and that the shielding effect would be absent. He found, however, that the shielding was just as if he had cooled the substance through the transition temperature in the absence of field and then imposed the field; the final result did not depend on the route by which the state was set up. This showed that (14.2.2) is correct, not merely (14.2.1), and that curl J goes to zero in the absence of a magnetic field. It is still not possible to give a completely convincing theoretical explanation of why this should be the case.

We have now stated something of the electromagnetic behavior of superconductors, but we have given no suggestion of why they show their peculiar properties. There have been many attempts to explain superconductivity, but none of them have yet been completely successful. However, the general outlines of the theory have become fairly clear. First let us ask what would be necessary in order not to have resistance.

We recall the mechanism of resistance in an ordinary metal. The electrons are accelerated in a body by the action of the external electric field, so that their representative points in a momentum space move uniformly in the direction of the field. This increases the energy of some of the electrons, so that they are able to fall into empty spaces in the Fermi distribution, having slightly lower energy and entirely different momentum. The change of momentum represents the stopping of the current, which we interpret as resistance, and the decrease of energy of the electrons is compensated by an increase of energy of the lattice, which we interpret as the Joulean heat. An essential part of this picture is that the electrons which rise to the top of the Fermi distribution have individual collisions with the lattice, just as if they were in the metal all by themselves; the Fermi statistics comes into play only in forbidding transitions to levels which are already occupied.

There must then be something which prevents the electrons which have risen to the top of the Fermi distribution from having such collisions, in a superconductor, so that once the displaced distribution of electrons is set up in the momentum space by the electric field which accompanies the building up of the magnetic field, this displacement can continue until the magnetic field dies down again, with accompanying electric field in the opposite direction, decelerating the electrons. Most of the suggestions for explaining superconductivity resolve themselves into some sort of modification of the electronic energy levels, either by interaction of the electrons with each other in a way not describable by the one-electron picture, or by interaction with the thermal vibrations of the lattice, in such a way as to make such transitions impossible. No such theory has gone far enough to be entirely convincing. The difference between the problem of the superconducting metal, which is very difficult, and that of the diamagnetic atom, which is simple, is that in the diamagnetic atom the electron which has been accelerated by the field has no other energy level to which it could go, since the atomic energy levels are spaced so far apart. On the other hand, in the metal, if the energy levels are arranged as in a normal metal, there are many levels into which the accelerated electron could go with decrease of energy, and the explanation of superconductivity must explain how either the probability of transition to such levels is removed, or more probably, how the levels themselves are modified, by interactions, so that the only lower levels to which the electrons would go would involve a cooperative motion of many electrons, a very unlikely occurrence.

While the general explanation of superconductivity is still one of the most puzzling unsolved problems of the structure of matter, there is one feature of it for which a simple theory can be given. If a superconductor is placed in an external magnetic field, the transition temperature is decreased, going to zero for a field of moderate size, called the critical field. This effect can be explained in a straightforward way from thermodynamics or statistical mechanics, and it is discussed in Appendix 21.

14.3. The Paramagnetism of Free Atoms. The paramagnetism of free atoms is obviously related closely to the Zeeman effect. In the Zeeman effect, an atom with resultant angular momentum $Jh/2\pi$, where J is the inner quantum number, can be oriented in the $(2J + 1)$ directions in which the component of angular momentum along the axis of the magnetic field is $Mh/2\pi$, where M goes from a maximum of J to a minimum of $-J$. But an atom has a magnetic moment proportional to its angular momentum; thus these orientations correspond to different components of magnetic moment along the axis, and hence to different magnetic energies in an external magnetic field. We are led, then, to the situation which we have described in the introductory section and which leads to the Langevin formula for the mean magnetic moment. By analogy with Eq. (13.2.2), we expect a contribution to the magnetic susceptibility proportional to the square of the magnetic moment of the atom and inversely proportional to kT. Let us now look a little more closely into the problem, to see if this is in fact the case.

Let us denote the magnetic moment of the Bohr magneton by β. Then the magnetic moment of an atom with inner quantum number J, g factor g, will be $g\beta J$. As we have seen in Sec. 7.1, its energy in a magnetic field B will be $-g\beta MB$, where the component of magnetic moment along the field is $g\beta M$. Then according to the Boltzmann factor, the probability of finding an atom with magnetic quantum number M, at temperature T, is proportional to $e^{g\beta MB/kT}$. The mean magnetic moment in the direction of the field is then

$$\text{Magnetic moment} = \frac{\displaystyle\sum_{-J}^{J} g\beta M e^{g\beta MB/kT}}{\displaystyle\sum_{-J}^{J} e^{g\beta MB/kT}}. \tag{14.3.1}$$

This summation can be carried out, leading to a complete formula for the magnetic moment.† To show the nature of the effect for small fields, we can proceed more simply, however. We expand the exponentials in power series and find, correct to the smallest terms in each case,

---

† For discussion, see J. H. Van Vleck, "Electric and Magnetic Susceptibilities," Oxford University Press, New York, 1932, p. 152.

$$\text{Magnetic moment} = \frac{\sum_{-J}^{J} g\beta M(1 + g\beta MB/kT + \cdots)}{\sum_{-J}^{J} (1 + \cdots)}.$$

In the numerator, since $\Sigma M = 0$, the first term vanishes, and we must take the second. We then have

$$\text{Magnetic moment} = \frac{g^2\beta^2 B/kT}{2J+1} \sum M^2. \tag{14.3.2}$$

It can be shown† that $\Sigma M^2 = (2J+1)J(J+1)/3$. Hence we have

$$\text{Magnetic moment} = \frac{g^2\beta^2 J(J+1)B}{3kT}. \tag{14.3.3}$$

This result is entirely analogous to the result of Sec. 13.2, for the electric case. There we found the mean electric dipole moment to be $\mu^2 E/3kT$, where μ was the permanent electric dipole moment. The corresponding permanent magnetic dipole moment in the present case is $g\beta J$, and in place of its square, we find from (14.3.3) that we must use the modification usually found in the quantum theory, according to which J^2 must be replaced by $J(J+1)$. This is the only way in which our result is affected by the quantum theory, which we must use in this case, since the energy levels are moderately widely separated.

We can now use the magnetic moment derived from (14.3.3) to set up the magnetic permeability κ_m, which as we remember equals

$$1 + \frac{\text{magnetic moment}}{H} = 1 + \frac{\text{magnetic moment} \times \mu_0}{B}.$$

We have

$$\kappa_m = 1 + N\mu_0 \frac{g^2\beta^2 J(J+1)}{3kT}, \tag{14.3.4}$$

where N is the number of dipoles per unit volume. To facilitate comparison of this formula, in the mks units, with Gaussian units, we may eliminate μ_0 by the relation $c^2 = 1/\epsilon_0\mu_0$ and may write out the value of β. Then we have

$$\kappa_m = 1 + \frac{4\pi N g^2}{4\pi\epsilon_0} \left(\frac{eh}{4\pi mc}\right)^2 \frac{J(J+1)}{3kT}. \tag{14.3.5}$$

Here, as usual, we omit the factor $4\pi\epsilon_0$ if we are using the Gaussian units.

The problem which we have now solved does not have many direct applications, for there are few paramagnetic monatomic gases on which

† For discussion, see J. H. Van Vleck, "Electric and Magnetic Susceptibilities," Oxford University Press, New York, 1932, p. 152.

magnetic experiments can be performed. There are some paramagnetic molecules, but the calculation of their permeability is more complicated, for in some cases there are other multiplet levels lying at such a low energy that they must be considered, as well as the Zeeman components of the ground state, in making the summation (14.3.1). The importance of (14.3.5) lies rather in the more complicated problems, such as permeability of paramagnetic salts, which show a close analogy to the case of free atoms. We shall proceed next to discuss these cases.

14.4. Paramagnetic Salts. The only paramagnetic salts to which the analysis of the preceding section applies with only minor modification are those of ions of the rare earths. As we see from Sec. 6.4, the rare-earth atoms consist entirely of closed shells, except for the $4f$ electrons, whose number varies from one rare earth to another, and for one $5d$ and two $6s$ electrons in each. In the ions these $5d$ and $6s$ electrons are removed, forming trivalent ions, so that the $4f$ electrons, far within the atom, are the only electrons not in closed shells, and the only ones which can take part in multiplet structure. Since they are so well shielded from neighboring atoms by the outer closed shells of the rare-earth ions, we should expect that these $4f$ electrons in the salts, either in crystalline form or in solution, would behave just about as in the corresponding free gaseous ions, and the evidence indicates that this is the case. Thus the rare-earth salts even show rather sharp absorption lines, like gases, and entirely unlike any other solids, and these lines can be correlated with lines in the spectrum of the gas.

Unfortunately, the rare-earth spectra have not been analyzed in enough detail for us to be sure in every case what is the ground state of the trivalent ion, and hence to determine its J value; but general principles allow us to find the value theoretically with fair certainty. When this is done, we can insert this value in (14.3.5) and hence predict the permeability. The results in most cases are in good agreement with experiment, and they justify us in thinking that the ions are relatively unaffected by their neighbors. The only cases where there are discrepancies are a few in which there are presumably other low-lying multiplet levels which complicate the situation. As progress is made in analyzing the spectra of the rare earths, both in gaseous form and in solids and liquids, the magnetic behavior will undoubtedly become entirely clear.

The other group of paramagnetic salts which have been investigated with a good deal of care are those of the iron group, in which the $3d$ shell is partly filled, and where it contributes the magnetic moment. Here, however, the situation is entirely different from the rare earths. If we take the J values of the lowest levels of the gaseous ions and try to insert these values in (14.3.5), the resulting permeabilities do not agree at all with those found in the salts in crystalline form or solution.   A clue to the difficulty is found from the determination of the so-called gyromagnetic ratio.   When a body such as a paramagnetic salt is magnetized, its magnetic moment in the direction of the field is established, and we have seen that this implies setting up an angular momentum in the direction of the field.   Since the total angular momentum of the body does not change when it is magnetized, assuming no torque acts on the body as a whole, the establishment of the orbital and spin angular momentum along the axis must be compensated by an equal and opposite change of angular momentum, and this acts like a torque, setting the whole body into rotation.   This torque, though very small, can be measured, and the ratio of magnetic moment to angular momentum, so determined, is called the gyromagnetic ratio.   Clearly, it should be proportional to the g factor, which measures the same thing in a dimensionless way, and the g factor itself is sometimes called the gyromagnetic ratio.   When the g factor is measured in this way for a rare-earth salt, it is found to agree substantially with the value expected from the gaseous spectrum; but when it is measured for a salt of the iron group, it is found to be approximately equal to 2, which is not the correct value according to the spectroscopic terms.

We recall that g for orbital angular momentum is unity, and for spin angular momentum is 2, whereas a mixture of the two types of angular momentum gives a value ordinarily intermediate between these values. Thus the simplest explanation of the gyromagnetic ratio of the iron-group salts is that the spin only is taking part in the magnetic behavior, and this is the assumption which seems to be correct.   The reason for this is found in the perturbative effect of neighboring ions on the rare-earth ion.   The $3d$ electron extends far enough out from the atom so that it can be considerably perturbed, unlike the $4f$ in the rare earths.   This perturbation can have the effect of what is called "quenching" the orbital angular momentum, so that the orbital wave function cannot freely orient in different directions but is tied down, so to speak, in the lattice.   In such a case the spin only is free to orient, and the ion acts, as far as its paramagnetic effect is concerned, like an ion with $g = 2$, and with J equal to S, the spin angular momentum.   If we determine S from proper analysis of the spectrum, substitute this value in (14.3.5), the resulting permeabilities agree well with the observations for the iron-group salts, though there is enough disagreement to indicate that the quenching of the orbital angular momentum is not always complete.

Let us investigate this quenching of orbital angular momentum a little more carefully, so as to understand what it is.   As a first step, we consider the five sublevels of a d electron, in their dependence on orientation, to see how they are affected by the sort of field met in a crystal. If the axis is along z, the five functions $e^{\pm 2i\varphi}P_2^2$ (cos θ), $e^{\pm i\varphi}P_2^1$ (cos θ), P_2^0 (cos θ), corresponding to $m_l = \pm 2$, ± 1, and 0, can be easily seen to be proportional to $(x \pm iy)^2/r^2$, $(x \pm iy)z/r^2$, $(2z^2 - x^2 - y^2)/r^2$. If we take real and imaginary parts of the first two, we have the five functions $(x^2 - y^2)/r^2$, xy/r^2, xz/r^2, yz/r^2, $(2z^2 - x^2 - y^2)/r^2$. Now the perturbing field acting on this d electron, in the crystal, can have many forms, but one of the simplest is a field of cubic symmetry, which may be assumed to have a potential energy of the form $A(x^4 + y^4 + z^4)$. It is clear by symmetry that the three wave functions xy/r^2, yz/r^2, zx/r^2 will have the same diagonal matrix component of the energy matrix. The remaining two functions will have a different diagonal component; it is easy to show that the two will have the same component. Thus a perturbing field of cubic symmetry will break up the states of the d wave function into two groups, one of three states, the other of two. Similar things occur with combinations of several d electrons, as has been shown by Bethe.

The resultant wave functions do not have a resultant magnetic moment. Thus when we consider the spin, which we have so far been neglecting, there will be no magnetic interaction between orbital and spin angular momentum. The orbital wave functions will act somewhat like s electrons, in this respect. Hence the spin alone will orient, and as we mentioned in a preceding paragraph, the ion will act as if it had only a spin magnetic moment. This is the simplest case, and it is not hard to set up more complicated cases which, in some crystals, agree better with experiment. Thus there could be a slight deviation from cubic symmetry, one axis being preferred with respect to the other two. This can result in still further splitting of the energy levels, and in some cases the levels can have some remaining orbital angular momentum, so that the g factor is somewhat less than 2.

These complications of detail should not cause us to lose sight, however, of the fundamental situation in the paramagnetism of salts of the iron group. Their behavior is based primarily on the atomic multiplets arising from a number of equivalent d electrons. In Table 7.3.4 we saw what these multiplets were. By Hund's rule that the multiplet of highest multiplicity has the lowest energy, we see that the multiplet of lowest energy is a doublet for one d electron, triplet for two, and so on up to five d electrons, for which we have a sextet. Thus for these states of lowest energy the spins set themselves parallel. The exclusion principle then comes into play, however: with five d electrons, all with parallel spin, we see that all five orbital d functions must be occupied, and the sixth d electron must then go into one of the orbital functions already occupied and hence must have an antiparallel spin, to avoid trouble with the exclusion principle.   Thus six d electrons have a quintet for the lowest state, and so on, finally ending with a singlet, or no spin at all, with a completed shell of ten d electrons.

This situation, by which the spin goes up to a maximum and down again to zero as we go through the shell of d electrons, or through the iron group, is the fundamental fact explaining the paramagnetism of the salts of this group; the orbital angular momentum, as we have stated, is quenched enough so that the quantum number L does not have a real meaning, but the situation acts more as if L were zero than any other way. And the reason why this multiplet of highest possible multiplicity lies lowest, resulting in a paramagnetic ground state, goes back to the exclusion principle, as we recall from our discussion of atomic multiplets.   If the electrons have their spins parallel, the exclusion principle demands that they be in different orbital wave functions, and in this case the electrostatic interaction energy between them is a minimum, so that the energy has its lowest possible value.   We see that this rule, then, has a direct application to paramagnetism, stating that an unfilled shell of electrons will, in general, result in a paramagnetic ion, the spin magnetic moment corresponding to a maximum possible number of spins being parallel to each other.

This general point of view is of great value in analyzing the ferromagnetic materials, to which we shall now turn.   The same elements which show paramagnetic ions in their salts tend to be ferromagnetic in their metallic forms, and we shall naturally look for close relations between the two phenomena.   This relationship is not brought out in Heisenberg's form of the theory of ferromagnetism, which we shall treat first, and for that reason we must consider that Heisenberg's theory, though suggestive, hardly is adequate to describe the actual facts.   We shall show, however, that by looking at the problem from the point of view of energy bands or molecular orbitals, rather than from the Heitler-London approach which Heisenberg used, we can get a proper understanding of ferromagnetic behavior.

14.5. Electronic Behavior in Ferromagnetism.   We have stated in our introductory section that many of the familiar properties of ferromagnetic materials arise in a rather secondary way, because they break up into ferromagnetic domains.   We shall postpone discussion of these domains until a later section but shall start by describing the behavior of a single domain, which is the part of the theory to which our study of electronic wave functions is most closely adapted.   A ferromagnetic material, as we have stated earlier, has a temperature of transition, called the Curie point, above which it is paramagnetic, with susceptibility approximately proportional to $1/(T - T_c)$, where T_c is the Curie temperature.   Below the Curie point, the material has a spontaneous polarization, increasing as the temperature goes down, behaving as a function of temperature roughly as shown in Fig. 14.5.1.   The spontaneous magnetic moment at the absolute zero presumably indicates the magnetic moment per atom: we may reasonably assume that this corresponds to a situation where all moments are parallel.   When we measure this moment, we find roughly that it corresponds to 0.6 Bohr magnetons per atom in Ni, 1.6 in Co, and about 2.3 in Fe, the three ordinary ferromagnetic elements.   The thermal dependence of magnetic moment and the interpretation of the Curie point in terms of statistical mechanics demand some study of the thermodynamics of magnetism; these subjects are discussed in Appendix 22, where we show that they can be understood in a straightforward way. We can say in a very qualitative way that as far as energy is concerned,

the lowest energy level of a ferromagnetic material is that where it is magnetized to saturation, but that this is a state of low entropy, since all the elementary magnets are required to be parallel under these conditions.   If the magnetic moment is decreased, the entropy is much greater, since there is much choice as to which elementary magnets have their moments reversed.   This increased entropy of the demagnetized state results in its being stable at higher temperatures, and the Curie temperature arises naturally from such a discussion.

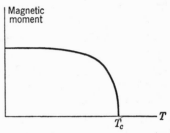

Fig. 14.5.1.   Spontaneous magnetization as function of temperature, for ferromagnetic material (schematic).

We have stated that a real ferromagnetic material below the Curie point consists of many domains, each magnetized in one definite direction, but on the whole canceling each other's magnetic effects on a macroscopic scale, since their directions of magnetization differ.   The ordinary process of magnetization consists in causing the domains whose magnetic moment points in the direction of the magnetizing field to grow, those in other directions to shrink, under action of an external field.   We come back to such questions in a later section.   For the moment, we may approach the question of ferromagnetism in a greatly simplified way: we simply ask, at the absolute zero of temperature, whether a given metal, corresponding to a single ferromagnetic domain, has a net magnetic moment or not.

At the outset, we may state that the gyromagnetic ratio for the ferromagnetic metals is such as to indicate quite accurately a g factor of 2. Thus we conclude that, just as for the paramagnetic salts of the iron group, the ferromagnetism arises from the electron spins, not from any orbital magnetic moment.   We then have to ask simply why the ground state of a ferromagnetic metal has a large resultant spin, or in the language of atomic multiplets, a high multiplicity.   We shall first state the arguments used by Heisenberg in discussing this problem.

Heisenberg's argument followed closely the lines of Heitler and London's discussion of the hydrogen molecule, which we have taken up in Chap. 8.   In that chapter we found that two hydrogen atoms could exist either in a singlet or a triplet state, with energies given by a constant plus or minus an exchange integral.   The plus sign was to be used for the singlet, the minus sign for the triplet.   The exchange integral proved to be negative; hence the singlet lay below the triplet and formed the ground state of the molecule.   Heisenberg postulated that the same sort of situation would hold in a solid, but that in a ferromagnetic solid the exchange integral would be positive, so that the multiplet with maximum spin would be the lowest, rather than the opposite situation as in H_2.   He assumed exchange integrals between an atom and each of its nearest neighbors and derived information about the temperature dependence of magnetization and other properties on the basis of these assumed exchange integrals.   He gave no reasons for assuming the exchange integrals to be positive in the particular case of the ferromagnetic elements.

Further work has made it clear that this simple argument, in the form suggested by Heisenberg, is not adequate.   In the first place, exchange integrals have been calculated, for a variety of wave functions, and in all cases except some very specialized ones the exchange integral has proved to be negative, so that it would not lead to ferromagnetism.   Furthermore, it certainly seems plausible that there should be a connection between the ferromagnetism of the metals of the iron group and the paramagnetism of their salts, and there is nothing in Heisenberg's theory to lead to such a relationship.   To avoid these difficulties, a different approach, based on the energy-band theory, has been used.   Like Heisenberg's original suggestion, its fundamental idea is that the energy associated with magnetic interactions is electrostatic, arising on account of the exclusion principle and the resulting relation between electron spin and orbital wave functions.   This is about as far as the similarity extends, however.

The first suggestion of this method was worked out by Bloch, for the case of really free electrons.   The details of Bloch's method are given in Appendix 22, but we can state the qualitative idea very simply.   Bloch considered two terms in the energy of a free-electron gas, the Fermi energy and the exchange energy.   The Fermi energy is simply the kinetic energy of all the electrons, according to Fermi statistics.   This is easily shown to be proportional to $(N/V)^{2/3}$, where N/V is the number of elec-

trons per unit volume.   The exchange energy is a little more complicated.
If we wish to calculate the electrostatic energy of a group of electrons and
nuclei, we must average Coulomb interaction terms between all pairs of
particles, averaged over the wave function.   By a well-known principle
of electrostatics, this can be replaced by an integral of one-half times the
charge density times the electrostatic potential, over all space.   In the
free-electron model, we must assume that there is a uniformly distributed
positive space charge, simulating the nuclei, just enough to cancel all the
negative charge of the electrons.   Thus the total charge density is zero,
and hence the electrostatic energy is zero, the repulsive energy between
like charges being just balanced by the attractive energy between unlike
charges.

This conclusion is not quite right, however.   The reason is that it
incorrectly includes an electrostatic interaction of each electron with
itself.   Each electron, of course, has a charge density represented by a
wave function, spread out through a certain volume.   What we really
want, for the electrostatic energy, is not $\frac{1}{2}\int \rho\varphi\, dv$, where ρ is the charge
density, φ the potential, but a slightly modified expression in which φ is
replaced by the potential exerted by all other electrons except the one
which we are considering.   We then must ask what is the distribution of
all other electrons in an electron gas, if we know that the electron we are
considering is at a given point x, y, z.   Certainly if the electrons obey the
exclusion principle, we shall automatically find that other electrons of the
same spin tend to avoid the point x, y, z where our electron is located.   It
can now be shown, as in Appendix 22, that we can evaluate exactly the
effect of the exclusion principle, or of exchange, on the distribution of
other electrons surrounding the given one.   We find that the distribution
of other electrons of the same spin as the one we are considering approaches
a constant density at large distances from x, y, z, but that as we approach
that point, the density decreases to zero.   The net deficiency in charge
amounts to just one electron; it is obvious that all other electrons must
add to just one less than all the electrons, since we know that the electron
we are considering is at x, y, z.   In a very crude way, we may say that
surrounding any electron, the other electrons of the same spin avoid a
hole with the electron in question at the center, large enough to include
one electron.   We can easily find the radius of this hole: if one electron is
to be included in it, and if the density of electrons is to be of the order of
magnitude of N/V electrons per unit volume, it is clear that we must
have, in order of magnitude, $1 = \frac{4}{3}\pi r^3(N/V)$, or r must be proportional
to $(N/V)^{-\frac{1}{3}}$.   This is the effect on the distribution of electrons of the
same spin; there will be no effect at all on the distribution of electrons of
the opposite spin, as long as we consider only the exclusion principle,

though, of course, electrostatic repulsion will tend to keep these electrons away as well.   This effect on electrons of opposite spin, called the correlation effect, is not as great as the exchange effect between electrons of the same spin, and to a first approximation we may neglect it.

Since we have made this correction to the charge distribution of all other electrons, acting on a given electron at x, y, z, there will be a corresponding correction to the potential at x, y, z.   This correction will be essentially the potential at the center of a sphere of radius r containing an electron, and this is, by the Coulomb law, inversely proportional to the radius, or proportional to $(N/V)^{1/3}$.   The total electrostatic potential energy will then have a negative term varying in this way: each electron is surrounded by a net positive charge, coming from subtracting off the electronic charge distribution, but leaving the positive charge simulating the nuclei.   Thus the total energy per electron, Fermi plus exchange, will be of the form $A(N/V)^{2/3} - B(N/V)^{1/3}$, where A, B are constants, evaluated in Appendix 22, and the energy per unit volume is proportional to N/V times this, or to $A(N/V)^{5/3} - B(N/V)^{4/3}$.

The situation now becomes more interesting when we consider the possibility that there are different numbers of electrons of the two possible spins.   It is clear that if we are to get a model for ferromagnetism, we must have all, or at any rate many, of the electrons having the same spin. Thus let there be N_1 electrons of positive spin, N_2 of negative spin, where in the ordinary gas N_1 will equal N_2, and each will equal $N/2$, where N is the total number of electrons, but where in a ferromagnetic substance N_1 will be larger than N_2 (or vice versa).   Then the total Fermi energy will be $A[(N_1/V)^{5/3} + (N_2/V)^{5/3}] - B[(N_1/V)^{4/3} + (N_2/V)^{4/3}]$.   Suppose we let $N_1 = (N + n)/2$, $N_2 = (N - n)/2$, so that $n = N_1 - N_2$, measuring the net spin.   Then we may expand the Fermi energy in power series in n, and we find without trouble

$$E = 2A\left(\frac{N}{2V}\right)^{5/3}\left[1 + \frac{10}{9}\left(\frac{n}{N}\right)^2 + \cdots\right]$$

$$- 2B\left(\frac{N}{2V}\right)^{4/3}\left[1 + \frac{4}{9}\left(\frac{n}{N}\right)^2 + \cdots\right]$$

$$= E_0 + \left(\frac{n}{N}\right)^2\left[\frac{20}{9}A\left(\frac{N}{2V}\right)^{5/3} - \frac{8}{9}B\left(\frac{N}{2V}\right)^{4/3}\right] + \cdots \qquad (14.5.1)$$

where E_0 is the energy when $n = 0$, or in the unmagnetized state.   If E is greater than E_0, it will require energy to magnetize the gas, and it will not magnetize spontaneously, or will not be ferromagnetic.   On the other hand, if E is less than E_0, the magnetized state will have lower energy than the unmagnetized, and the gas will be ferromagnetic.

The condition for ferromagnetism then, with this model, is

$$\frac{8}{9} B \left(\frac{N}{2V}\right)^{4/3} > \frac{20}{9} A \left(\frac{N}{2V}\right)^{5/3},$$

$$\frac{2}{5}\frac{B}{A} > \left(\frac{N}{2V}\right)^{1/3}. \tag{14.5.2}$$

That is, if the volume is great enough, according to this model, the gas will be ferromagnetic. When we put in the values of A and B, as found in Appendix 22, we find that the required volume is large enough, or the density small enough, so that no ordinary metal would be ferromagnetic, if it obeyed this model. All real metals have a larger density of conduction electrons. In other words, the simple picture of Bloch is not adequate to discuss ferromagnetism, but nevertheless it is of importance, for it leads to the correct understanding of the mechanism of ferromagnetism. We shall examine the physical features underlying it in the next section and shall show that these features remain in a more accurate theory. In particular, we shall find that, in a sense, the arguments can be applied to the d electrons only, rather than to all the electrons, and that they lead to a condition that the density of d electrons in the region between atoms must be small, or that the d shells of neighboring atoms must not overlap much, for ferromagnetism.

14.6. The Collective Electron Picture of Ferromagnetism. Let us examine in more detail the nature of the arguments involved in Bloch's calculation, as outlined in the preceding section. First, we have the Fermi energy. In Fig. 14.6.1 we show parabolas representing the density of states of each of the two spins, according to the Fermi statistics for free electrons, as outlined in Sec. 10.8. We first show the situation when there are equal numbers of electrons of each spin, then when there are more with positive spins than with negative spins. We see that to accomplish this change, we must take some electrons from the band corresponding to negative spin and raise them to higher energy in the band corresponding to positive spin, thus increasing the total Fermi energy. The fewer the levels per unit energy range, the greater this increase of energy will be. In fact, we can get an explicit formula for the increase of Fermi energy if we know only the number of energy bands per unit energy range dN/dE, as discussed in Sec. 10.8. Suppose we take $n/2$ electrons from the band of negative spin, transferring them to the band of positive spin. Let there be $\frac{1}{2} dN/dE$ levels per unit energy range corresponding to each spin. Then the average energy of the electrons which we remove must be less than the original Fermi level by the amount $(n/2)/(dN/dE)$, and the average energy of the levels to which we raise them is greater than the Fermi level by this same amount. Hence the increase of energy per electron, on the average, is $n/(dN/dE)$, and the total increase of Fermi energy is $(n^2/2)/(dN/dE)$. In other words, the fewer levels per unit energy range, the greater the increase in Fermi energy, as we mentioned above.

This calculation is appropriate for the free-electron gas, where we see at once that as the volume of the gas increases, so that the value of dN/dE increases, the increase in Fermi energy on magnetization will decrease. It is also appropriate, however, for any other energy-band calculation, since in any case we can find dN/dE. We see that to have a small increase of Fermi energy on magnetization, we wish to have large dN/dE, or a narrow band, with many levels in a small energy range. We

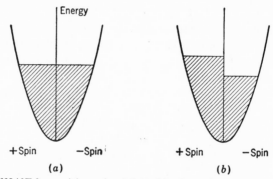

Fig. 14.6.1. dN/dE for positive spins (plotted horizontally to left), and for negative spins (horizontally to right).   Shaded regions indicate occupied energy levels.   Case (a) equal numbers of positive and negative spins; (b) more positive spins.

have already seen in Chap. 10 that this is characteristic of the 3d band of electrons in the iron group of elements.   This is one of the features of the iron group which renders it ferromagnetic.

The other term in the change of energy on magnetization is the exchange energy.   We have exchange energy only between pairs of electrons of the same spin.   We may say in a very crude way that there is an exchange integral between any pair of electrons of the same spin, and none between two electrons of opposite spin.   These integrals are negative, in the collective electron picture, for they represent the correction to the electrostatic potential energy arising when we take account of the interaction of the electron with itself.   To a very rough approximation we may take these integrals to be the same between any pair of electrons with the same spin.   If one of the integrals equals I, the total contribution of the exchange integrals will then be $(I/2)[(N + n)^2/4 + (N - n)^2/4]$, since the number of pairs of electrons with positive spin is approximately one-half times the square of the number of such electrons, and similarly with those with negative spin. In other words, the contribution of the exchange integrals to the total energy is $(I/4)(N^2 + n^2)$. The change in energy is $(I/4)n^2$, a negative quantity, since I is negative.

We have, then, two contributions to the energy proportional to n^2, where n is the number of spins not balanced by spins in the opposite direction, or is proportional to the magnetization. The first contribution comes from the Fermi energy, and is positive, being greater the broader the energy band, or the fewer the number of states per unit energy range. The second contribution comes from the exchange integral and is negative. We have ferromagnetism if the second, negative term outweighs the positive term, so as to make the magnetic state that of lowest energy.

These two terms clearly will appear quite generally, whether we use the simplified free-electron picture as Bloch did, or the more accurate picture of energy bands. Let us now see how the situation works out in the elements of the transition group. First we ask what is the exchange integral in the energy-band picture. In Appendix 22 we show that this is very similar to the exchange integral in an atom, which, as we have seen in a preceding section, is responsible for the ions of the transition group being paramagnetic. The reason for this is simple. The exchange integral is the electrostatic interaction between an electronic charge and another charge distribution, representing the exchange hole. This other charge distribution is very similar to that of the electron itself, and the result is that we get the electrostatic interaction between the charge distribution, which is just an atomic exchange integral. Since this is independent of interatomic distance, we see that the exchange energy is approximately a constant, not varying greatly from one atom to another.

The distinction between different materials then comes in the magnitude of the Fermi energy. If we compute this for a broad energy band, we find that the Fermi energy is much greater than the exchange energy, so that the substance is not ferromagnetic. The only way we can get ferromagnetism, then, is to have many electrons in a narrow band, such as we have in the iron group. And it is only when the band is quite narrow, even under these circumstances, that we find ferromagnetism. Thus as we go through the iron group, from the first elements to the last, we know that the $3d$ wave functions decrease in dimensions, as the orbit is drawn into the atom. With the first elements of the group, Sc, Ti, etc., the $3d$ wave functions of adjacent atoms will overlap so much that the energy band will be broadened a good deal, and there will be no ferromagnetism. As we go further, however, and the $3d$ band decreases in breadth on account of the shrinking of the $3d$ atomic wave function, we reach a point where the exchange energy more than balances the Fermi energy. Careful calculations have been made only for Ni, for which it is clear that we expect ferromagnetism; but extrapolation back from Ni to Co and Fe indicates that these elements should be ferromagnetic, and that just about at Mn the band should be broadened enough so that ferromagnetism should cease, just as is observed. From this argument, we see that the required condition for ferromagnetism is that there be an inner partly filled shell of electrons, whose radius is as small as possible compared with the interatomic distance. In Table 14.6.1 we give radii

TABLE 14.6.1

Observed interatomic distance in crystal, and sum of radii of $3d$ electrons (from Table 6.4.2), with ratio of distance to sum of radii, for elements of iron group, showing that this ratio is greatest for the ferromagnetic elements.

Element	Distance, angstroms	Sum of radii	Ratio
Ti	2.93	1.10	2.65
V	2.63	0.98	2.69
Cr	2.51	0.90	2.79
Mn	2.52	0.84	3.00
Fe	2.50	0.78	3.20
Co	2.51	0.72	3.50
Ni	2.50	0.68	3.69

of such inner shells for those atoms which might be expected to be ferromagnetic, the interatomic distance in the metal, and the ratio. We see that it is, in fact, just for the three elements Fe, Co, and Ni, which are the ones known to be ferromagnetic, that the ratio of interatomic distance to shell radius is greatest. There are also some alloys, the Heusler alloys, for instance, of Cu and Mn, in which one atom has a larger, another a smaller inner shell, which are ferromagnetic; the sum of the radii of the inner shells of the two adjacent atoms, in such a case, is about the same as for the ferromagnetic elements, so that the fundamental explanation of their behavior is the same.

The saturation magnetization, as we have seen, corresponds to about 0.6 electron spins per atom in Ni, 1.6 in Co, and 2.3 in Fe. The usual explanation of this fact is that in Ni the $3d$ band, which can hold 10 electrons per atom, and the $4s$, which can hold two, overlap, much as in Fig. 14.6.2. If these two bands are filled up to a common level, some of the 10 electrons per atom which must be accommodated will go into the $3d$ band, some into the $4s$. If we assume that about 0.6 electrons per atom go into the $4s$, then we have 9.4 remaining electrons for the $3d$ band. Half of these, or five, go into the orbitals corresponding to positive spin, leaving 4.4 for the orbitals with negative spin, or a net spin of 0.6 per atom. Similar explanations can be given for the other elements.

Pauling has advocated a somewhat different interpretation of the band structure in the 3d shell from this, in which the band is subdivided into two parts, a lower band in which the electrons only take part in metallic binding and do not act ferromagnetically, and an upper band in which they act ferromagnetically but not in metallic binding. This is proposed partly to explain why only Fe, Co, and Ni are ferromagnetic, whereas all the elements of the iron group are paramagnetic. It does not seem necessary to the writer to make such an assumption, which has not been supported by any detailed calculation of the nature of the 3d bands. If the width of the bands were constant all through the iron group, perhaps there would be some need for it, but the decreasing width, as we get to the

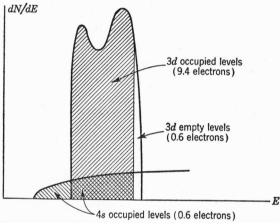

Fig. 14.6.2. Schematic representation of 3d and 4s energy bands for Ni, with 9.4 electrons per atom in 3d, 0.6 in 4s.

end of the iron group, which we have pointed out, will surely cause a change from nonferromagnetic elements in the early part of the group to ferromagnetic ones toward the end, as is observed.

It is interesting to think a little further about the close connection between the conditions for paramagnetism of the iron-group salts and for ferromagnetism of the metals. If the ferromagnetism of the metals results from the d electrons, as does the paramagnetism of the salts, and if rather small overlapping of the 3d orbits from neighboring atoms is a requirement for ferromagnetism, it follows that the structure of the 3d group in an individual ferromagnetic atom is similar to that in a paramagnetic salt: neighboring atoms perturb each other more in the metal, but not very much more. Thus each atom will certainly wish to arrange to have as large a spin magnetic moment as possible. The only question, then, is why the moments of neighboring atoms wish to set themselves parallel to each other, rather than, for instance, antiparallel.   The reason comes directly from the energy-band, or collective electron, point of view which we are using.   In the energy-band theory we know that there is a certain freedom for electrons to wander from one atom to a neighbor.   If an electron from one atom wanders into its neighboring atom, its energy will be lowest if its spin is parallel to the spin of the neighboring atom, just as if it were one of the electrons normally located in that atom.   The exchange integrals bringing this about are just those occurring in the paramagnetic theory.   It is just in these excursions from one atom to a neighbor then, that we meet the impetus to have all the electron spins line up, which results in neighboring atoms having parallel rather than anti-parallel magnetic moments.   And it is the energy-band theory which includes the possibility of these excursions, which are explicitly excluded by the Heitler-London calculation.   This is presumably the reason why the energy-band, or collective electron, picture of ferromagnetism is able to give a detailed explanation of the ferromagnetism of the iron group, whereas the Heisenberg theory, based on the Heitler-London method, is not successful.

14.7. The Domain Structure of Ferromagnetics.   The simple picture of ferromagnetism which we have described in the preceding sections fails to consider many important phenomena.   We shall do no more than describe them in a very brief qualitative manner in the present section. In the first place, there are complicated directional properties of magnet-ization, even in a cubic crystal.   One of these properties is magnetostric-tion.   If a single crystal could be magnetized in a single domain, we should find that the crystal deformed slightly, the direction of magnetiza-tion being a preferred direction: for instance, the crystal could stretch slightly along the direction of magnetization, shrink slightly in directions at right angles, or vice versa.   The reason for this must come from slight deviations from the ideal situation we have been considering, in which only the spin took part in magnetic phenomena.   If there is some trace of effect of orbital wave functions on magnetization, then when we shift the direction of magnetization, we shift the orbital electronic wave functions, and this has a slight effect on the elastic forces, setting up stresses which result in strains of the crystal.   When this is investigated experimentally, it is found that some directions of magnetization correspond to slightly lower energy than others; for instance, it could be that magnetization along the cubic 100 directions would correspond to lower energy than magnetization along the diagonal directions 110 or 111, on account of these elastic energy terms.   The directions corresponding to lower energy are then called directions of easy magnetization; the crystal, if it were a single domain, would spontaneously magnetize along these directions, whereas it would require a considerable effort, which could be supplied by an external magnetic field, to turn this magnetization along one of the directions of hard magnetization.

A single crystal will not normally magnetize itself, however, along one of the directions of easy magnetization. There are always a number of such directions: for instance, in the case we described above, there are six directions, which might be along the $\pm x$ axis, the $\pm y$ axis, and the $\pm z$ axis. We should expect that, on account of statistical fluctuations, part of the crystal would magnetize along each of these six directions. There would have to be boundaries between the regions magnetized in these various directions, which are called domains. In such a boundary, the direction of magnetization would have to shift from that appropriate to one domain to that appropriate to its neighboring domain. It will not shift suddenly, from one atom to the next; for then we should have neighboring atoms with spin in quite different direction, and this would correspond to a situation which certainly does not correspond to a minimum of energy. Closer examination of the theory of domain boundaries shows that the lowest value of the surface energy of the domain boundary will be attained if the direction of magnetization gradually rotates from the value characteristic of one domain to that of the other, the transition taking place over a number of atom layers. This involves a certain angle between spins of neighboring atoms, which is disadvantageous from an energy point of view, and also it involves some of the spins pointing along directions of hard magnetization; but neither of these involves as much surface energy as a sudden change of direction.

When this surface energy is required in order to form domain boundaries, we ask why the domains form at all, rather than having the whole crystal consist of a single domain. The reason is that if the crystal were a single domain, it would have free north and south poles on its two ends, like a little bar magnet. The magnetic field resulting from this would contain magnetic energy. If we have many domains, the poles are largely neutralized, and this magnetic energy is greatly diminished. This decreases the total energy and makes the state with many domains more stable.

Our picture of an unmagnetized single crystal, then, is that it consists of many domains, oriented along the various possible directions of easy magnetization in such a way as not to have an over-all magnetic moment. If now we apply a magnetic field, in a direction of easy magnetization, those domains whose magnetization points in the direction of the field will have their energy reduced, whereas those with magnetization in other directions will have their energy increased. The energy of the system can then decrease if the domains in the direction of the field increase, while the others shrink.   This is accomplished largely by a shifting of the domain boundaries.   The boundaries shift rather freely, but they are impeded by crystal imperfections, if there are any.   It sometimes requires a considerable magnetic field to make a boundary jump over such an imperfection; once it jumps over it, it tends to travel a considerable distance.   In this way the magnetization proceeds by finite jumps, and this is observed as the Barkhausen effect.   The field required to line up the domains rather completely, by this process of shifting of domain boundaries, is rather small, and once that field is reached, we have practically complete saturation.   If we reverse the field, the whole process reverses, only now, on account of the imperfections, we need a small field in the reverse direction before the magnetization entirely reverses.   We then have a curve of

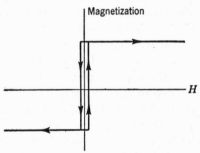

Fig. 14.7.1.   Schematic magnetization curve of single crystal, in direction of easy magnetization.

magnetization versus magnetizing field as in Fig. 14.7.1.   We recognize this as a hysteresis loop, but a very narrow one.

If we magnetize along a direction of hard magnetization, the situation is quite different.   There will ordinarily be several directions of easy magnetization which make equal angles with the magnetic field.   Thus if we have the field along the diagonal in the 111 direction, magnetization along the $+x$, $+y$, or $+z$ direction will be equally advantageous.   The first effect of the field, which requires only a very small field, as before, is to line up domains in one of these directions, causing domains which originally were oriented in one of the unsuitable directions, such as $-x$, $-y$, or $-z$, to shrink at the expense of one of the favorable domains. When this process has been carried to completion, however, we have not achieved saturation, since none of the spins are pointing along the field. We must then apply a much greater field, enough so that the magnetic energy overcomes the difference between the energy of magnetization in the directions of easy and hard magnetization, before we get complete saturation, by rotating the magnetization of each domain into the direc-

tion of the field.   We then have a curve of magnetization as in Fig.
14.7.2.

These complicated processes might be thought to be somewhat hypo-
thetical, but fortunately research of the last few years has made them the
subject of direct observation, and there is now no doubt about the
general behavior.   Bitter suggested a good many years ago that the
domains could be made visible, where they cut the surface of the sample,
by suspending a fine colloidal suspension of a ferromagnetic powder on
the surface; the powder particles cluster at the positions of strong north
or south poles, like the familiar iron filings on a magnet, and these con-
centrations of poles come where the domain boundaries cut the surfaces,
since there the spins are changing direction, and some of them must have

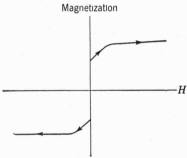

FIG. 14.7.2.   Schematic magnetization curve of single crystal, in direction of hard
magnetization.

components normal to the surface.   Shockley and Williams, by con-
tinuation of this technique, have rendered the domains visible during the
process of magnetization, so that one can clearly see the shifting of the
domain boundaries under the action of an external field, and the way in
which these boundaries are impeded by crystal imperfections.   The
domains are of a size conveniently visible in a microscope of fairly low
magnification.

So far, we have considered the magnetization of a single crystal.
Most ferromagnetic materials, however, are polycrystalline, with the
crystals oriented at random.   It is now clear that this will greatly complicate the situation, and our knowledge of the details of what happens is
not nearly as complete as it is with single crystals.   For one thing, the
external field will make different angles with the directions of easy
magnetization, in the various crystal grains.   Some of them will happen to
have a direction of easy magnetization nearly in the direction of the field,
and they will magnetize under application of a small field; while others

will have directions of hard magnetization along the field, and will magnetize slowly. It is this situation which results in the ordinary magnetization curve, in which quite a large magnetizing field is required to produce saturation. Further complications arise from the magnetostriction. As the different crystal grains are magnetized, they tend to deform differently, on account of their different orientation. Thus elastic strains will be set up in the crystal, reacting back on the behavior of the different grains, and greatly complicating the situation. It is hard to give a general account of the effect of these strains, but we can at least mention two quite different limiting cases, in which they lead to materials of importance for magnetic purposes.

For some purposes, one wishes a material of very high initial permeability, or one which magnetizes under action of a very small external field. To get this, we clearly want one in which the crystal shows practically no magnetostriction. Then there will be no directions of easy and hard magnetization; all directions will be directions of easy magnetization. It is then immaterial whether we are dealing with a single crystal or a polycrystalline sample: the magnetization curve will in any case resemble that of Fig. 14.7.1. Such a material is the alloy Permalloy. We note that the initial permeability, or magnetization per unit field, is very high, but that this does not imply that the saturation magnetization is any higher than in any other material. We merely reach saturation with much smaller magnetizing field.

An entirely different requirement is for a permanent magnet material. Here we wish the material to remain magnetized, even with a strong field tending to demagnetize it. It is hardly possible to give the complete set of requirements for a good permanent magnet material, but at least we can describe one feature which it has. One of the best materials for permanent magnets is Alnico 5, and it has a strong magnetostriction Part of the process of fabricating it is to make up the magnet in the shape in which it is to be used, put it in a magnetic field so as to magnetize it in the desired direction, and then give it a long annealing heat treatment at an elevated temperature. In this process the crystal grains will recrystallize in such a way that the direction of easy magnetization is along the direction in which the field is imposed, since this will correspond to a minimum energy in the presence of the field. When the magnet is then cooled down, this crystal orientation will be frozen in. Either of two directions of magnetization, that in which the magnet was treated or the opposite direction, will then be easy directions of magnetization, and any other direction will be a direction of hard magnetization for at least some of the grains. When we magnetize it at room temperature, then, there will be very small tendency for the direction of magnetization to shift, for this would involve its rotating into a direction of hard magnetization. Thus such a magnet can retain its magnetism for long periods of time.

14.8. Paramagnetic and Ferromagnetic Resonance. We mentioned in the introductory section that one way to investigate paramagnetism and ferromagnetism, aside from direct magnetic measurements, was to find the resonance between the Larmor rotation of the elementary magnets and an externally imposed radio-frequency field. We can understand this most easily for a single paramagnetic atom. From the study of precession which we gave in Sec. 7.1, we see that a paramagnetic atom in an external field will precess with a frequency equal to g times the Larmor frequency, where g is the Landé g factor. We naturally expect that if we impose an external field of this same frequency, there will be a resonance effect, and the atom can absorb energy, resulting in its shifting from one energy level to another (if we describe it according to quantum theory) or in its shifting its orientation in space, so as to have a different component of its angular momentum along the axis, and hence a different energy (if we describe it classically).

It is not hard to observe this effect, by a number of different experimental techniques, the most direct being a measurement of the frequency at which energy is absorbed for a given magnetic field, or more often, a magnetic field at which it is absorbed for a given frequency. The direct result of this measurement is the g factor. Such measurements have now been made for a good many paramagnetic salts, and the g factors have been found to be in the neighborhood of 2, as was to be expected. There are deviations, however, and these are to be explained in terms of incomplete quenching of the orbital angular momentum. The theory of this incomplete quenching is unfortunately quite complicated, and the details of the deviations of the g factors from 2 are still not worked out at all completely.

With a ferromagnetic material, we expect certain complications, on account of the magnetostriction and the directions of hard and easy magnetization. If the energy of the spin system is different when it points in different directions, on account of the hard and easy directions, there must be torques acting on the spin, given by the rate of change of energy with direction. Then the hypothesis underlying Larmor's theorem, that the torques come only from the external magnetic field, is not correct. We must rather take some sort of vector sum of the torque of the external field and that arising from the crystal orientation, to compute the frequency of precession. We expect, then, that this frequency will depend on the direction of the field in a rather complicated way in a single crystal. This is found to be the case, in experiments on single crystals. In a polycrystalline sample then, with different orientations of different crystal grains, we expect to find different resonances for different grains, so that the sample as a whole would show a very broad resonance, rather than a sharp one.   The only case in which we could expect a poly-crystalline sample to show a sharp resonance would be that in which there was no magnetostriction, and hence no anisotropic effect depending on crystal orientation.   Thus we should expect to find a sharp resonance in Permalloy; and, as a matter of fact, Yager has found just this situation to hold, for this and other similar materials.

PROBLEMS

1. Using the Langevin function, plot magnetic moment of a dipole in the direction of the field, for large fields, showing that it approaches a constant value, or saturation, at sufficiently large fields.   Prove that this corresponds to having all dipoles oriented along the field.

2. Compute the diamagnetic susceptibility of He gas at normal temperature and pressure, assuming each atom to have two electrons with wave functions as given by the shielding constants of Appendix 13.

3. For tin, the superconducting penetration depth is found experimentally to be about 10^{-6} cm.   Find how many conduction electrons per atom would be required to lead to this penetration depth.

4. Prove Eq. (14.3.2) for the special case where $J = \frac{1}{2}$.

5. Find the magnetic moment as a function of B, for $J = \frac{1}{2}$, from Eq. (14.3.1). Compare this result with a Langevin function.

6. A paramagnetic salt has one magnetic moment, with $J = \frac{1}{2}$, $g = 2$, per cube whose side is 4 A.   Find the paramagnetic susceptibility as a function of temperature, getting numerical values.

7. The sample of paramagnetic salt considered in Prob. 6 is magnetized in a field of 1,000 gauss.   Find the angular momentum which the magnetic moments must acquire in the process.   Since the total angular momentum of the sample remains constant, the mechanical angular momentum of atomic motion must change by a compensating amount.   Put in reasonable numbers for size of sample, and consider how hard it would be to determine the resulting motion experimentally.

8. Set up a theory for a ferromagnetic material, assuming an inner field as postulated by Weiss, and assuming that the magnetization is given by a Langevin function, in terms of the local field (inner plus external).   Derive the susceptibility above the Curie point from this model.

9. From the model of Prob. 8, find the permanent magnetization as a function of temperature, in the absence of external field, below the Curie point.

10. From the model of Prob. 9, find the susceptibility below the Curie point.   To do this, investigate the additional magnetization (in addition to the spontaneous magnetization) produced by a small external magnetic field, below the Curie point.

APPENDIX 1

BOHR THEORY FOR MOTION IN A CENTRAL FIELD

Let us carry out the quantization, according to Bohr's form of quantum theory, for a particle moving in an arbitrary central field; we shall later specialize for the case of the inverse-square field, to get the hydrogen atom. Thus we assume a particle of mass m, whose potential energy is $V(r)$, a function of r. We set up the problem in spherical polar coordinates. The Hamiltonian function for this problem† is

$$H = \frac{p_r^2}{2m} + \frac{p_\theta^2}{2mr^2} + \frac{p_\varphi^2}{2mr^2 \sin^2 \theta} + V(r).$$

Hamilton's equations are then

$$\frac{dp_r}{dt} = -\frac{\partial H}{\partial r} = \frac{p_\theta^2}{mr^3} + \frac{p_\varphi^2}{mr^3 \sin^2 \theta} - \frac{dV}{dr}$$

$$\frac{dp_\theta}{dt} = -\frac{\partial H}{\partial \theta} = \frac{p_\varphi^2 \cos \theta}{mr^2 \sin^3 \theta}$$

$$\frac{dp_\varphi}{dt} = -\frac{\partial H}{\partial \varphi} = 0,$$

$$\frac{dr}{dt} = \frac{\partial H}{\partial p_r} = \frac{p_r}{m}, \qquad \frac{d\theta}{dt} = \frac{\partial H}{\partial p_\theta} = \frac{p_\theta}{mr^2}, \qquad \frac{d\varphi}{dt} = \frac{\partial H}{\partial p_\varphi} = \frac{p_\varphi}{mr^2 \sin^2 \theta}.$$

From these equations we note first that p_φ is independent of time. This is easily seen to be the component of the angular momentum along the axis. The general quantum condition for an angular momentum which is constant is that the angular momentum equals an integer times $h/2\pi$. In this case we let the integer be m, so that we have $p_\varphi = mh/2\pi$. Next, from Hamilton's equations, we can show easily that

$$\frac{d}{dt}\left(p_\theta^2 + \frac{p_\varphi^2}{\sin^2 \theta}\right) = 0.$$

We can easily show that this quantity $p_\theta^2 + p_\varphi^2/\sin^2 \theta$ equals the square of the total angular momentum, which we shall abbreviate as p. Thus the magnitude of the angular momentum is constant, and hence p must be an integer times $h/2\pi$. We let this integer be k, so that we have $p = kh/2\pi$. Having quantized the total angular momentum, and its component along the axis, we see that the orientation of the normal to the orbit, which is in the direction of the total angular momentum vector, can have only certain discrete orientations with respect to the axis, and hence we arrive at the concept of space quantization.

If we replace $p_\theta^2 + p_\varphi^2/\sin^2 \theta$ by p^2, the Hamiltonian function can be replaced by

$$H = \frac{p_r^2}{2m} + \frac{p^2}{2mr^2} + V(r),$$

† See Slater and Frank, "Mechanics," McGraw-Hill Book Company, Inc., New York, 1947, Chap. IV.

just as if we started discussion of the problem in a set of polar coordinates in the plane of the orbit.   We can solve this expression for p_r as a function of r, and the radial quantum condition comes from integrating this expression from the minimum value of r consistent with a real value of p_r, to the maximum value of r. Twice this integral must equal an integer times h; if we let this integer be n_r, it is called the radial quantum number.   This gives us in the general case an algebraic equation for the total energy H as a function of n_r, in terms of p, which must equal $kh/2\pi$.   In other words, we show in the general case of the central field that the energy depends on n_r and k.

For the particular case of hydrogen, we let $V(r) = -Ze^2/4\pi\epsilon_0 r$, where Z is unity for hydrogen, but is equal to the atomic number if we are treating the hydrogenlike one-electron solution for an electron rotating around an arbitrary nucleus.   The Hamiltonian function then is as given in Eq. (6.5.2), except with k^2 substituted for $l(l+1)$.   The radial quantum condition is as in (6.5.3), except with $n_r h$ on the right, instead of $(n_r - \frac{1}{2})h$.   The integration is as carried out in (6.5.4), (6.5.5), and (6.5.6), the result being as in (6.5.6), only with k in place of $(l + \frac{1}{2})$, n_r in place of $(n_r - \frac{1}{2})$.   The final result for the energy is then just as in (6.5.7), the Rydberg formula, which is the same in Bohr theory as in Sec. 6.5, where we were handling the same problem by the quantum condition of wave mechanics.

In Slater and Frank, "Mechanics," Chap. III (as quoted previously), it is shown that the classical orbit for a particle moving according to the inverse-square law, such as we have here, is an ellipse.   In Eq. (5.4), Chap. III, of that text, it is shown that the major axis of the ellipse depends only on the energy, not on the angular momentum; thus, since we have seen that the energy depends only on the principal quantum number $n = n_r + k$, we see that all orbits of the same principal quantum number have the same major axis.   In Eq. (4.8) of that chapter we see that the square of the angular momentum is proportional to $1 - \epsilon^2$, where ϵ is the eccentricity, for different orbits with the same energy or major axis.   Furthermore, we see that the ratio b/a of minor to major axis equals $\sqrt{1 - \epsilon^2}$.   Thus the minor axis is proportional to the azimuthal quantum number.   It is easily shown that the maximum value of k consistent with any value of n is equal to n; this corresponds to the circular orbit.   Smaller values of k, down to the minimum of unity, correspond to more eccentric orbits.   For a given n, the orbits of smallest k value penetrate closest to the origin, or the nucleus.   In fact, it is not hard to show that the distance of closest approach of an orbit to a nucleus approaches a constant value for a given value of k, as the value of n increases without limit.

In Eq. (4.10) of the chapter just quoted, it is shown that the period T of rotation in one of the elliptical orbits equals $(2m/p)$ times the area A of the orbit. From this we can at once derive the magnetic moment of the orbit.   In the mks units, the magnetic moment of a current loop equals the current times the area enclosed by it.   In the electron's orbit, the charge e rotates once in time T, so that it is equivalent to a current e/T.   Then we have the magnetic moment equal to $(e/T)A = ep/2m$, or the magnetic moment is $(e/2m)$ times the angular momentum, as stated in Sec. 1.2.   In electromagnetic units, the same relation holds.   In Gaussian units, however, we are to measure e in electrostatic units. Since e in electrostatic units equals the value of e in electromagnetic units multiplied by c, we see that the magnetic moment in Gaussian units is $(e/2mc)$ times the angular momentum.

APPENDIX 2

THE MKS AND GAUSSIAN UNITS

The relation between mks and Gaussian units is discussed in considerable detail in Appendix II of Slater and Frank, "Electromagnetism," McGraw-Hill Book Company, Inc., New York, 1947, and we shall not repeat that discussion. We give here only enough information to make it easy for the reader familiar with one of the two systems to interpret formulas in the other. We consider only the types of formulas encountered in this book. In the mks units, the unit of length is the meter, and of mass the kilogram. The unit of charge is the coulomb, of potential difference the volt, of electric field strength the volt per meter, of current the ampere, of energy the joule, of rate of working the watt. The unit of electric displacement D is the coulomb per square meter, as for surface charge. The unit of magnetic induction B is the weber per square meter (1 weber/sq m = 10^4 gauss). The unit of magnetic field H is the ampere per meter, as for surface current. The unit of magnetic moment is the ampere $\times$ square meter. The quantity ϵ_0 equals 8.85×10^{-12} farads/m; it equals the capacity of a condenser with condenser plates 1 sq m in area, 1 m apart. The quantity μ_0 equals $4\pi \times 10^{-7}$ henry/m; it equals the inductance of a circuit consisting of two conductors in the form of parallel strips, 1 m wide, 1 m long, and 1 m apart. (In both these definitions, of course, the condenser and inductance must be provided with other conductors to act as guards, to obviate edge effects.) The quantities ϵ_0 and μ_0 are related by the equation $c = 1/\sqrt{\epsilon_0\mu_0}$, where c is the velocity of light, equal to 3×10^8 m/sec. The mks units are rationalized; Maxwell's equations in terms of them are curl $\mathbf{E} = -\partial\mathbf{B}/\partial t$, curl $\mathbf{H} = \partial\mathbf{D}/\partial t + \mathbf{J}$, div $\mathbf{D} = \rho$, div $\mathbf{B} = 0$. The force on a charge e moving with a velocity $\mathbf{v}$ is $e(\mathbf{E} + \mathbf{v} \times \mathbf{B})$.

In the Gaussian units, the unit of length is the centimeter, and of mass the gram. The units of charge, potential difference, electric current, and electric field are electrostatic units. The unit of D is the same as that of E. The units of B and H are the electromagnetic units. The units are nonrationalized; Maxwell's equations in terms of them are curl $\mathbf{E} = -(1/c)(\partial\mathbf{B}/\partial t)$,

$$\text{curl } \mathbf{H} = \frac{1}{c}\frac{\partial\mathbf{D}}{\partial t} + \frac{4\pi}{c}\mathbf{J},$$

div $\mathbf{D} = 4\pi\rho$, div $\mathbf{B} = 0$. The force on a charge e moving with a velocity $\mathbf{v}$ is $e[\mathbf{E} + (\mathbf{v} \times \mathbf{B})/c]$. Often, incorrectly, this law of force is stated to involve a term $\mathbf{v} \times \mathbf{H}$ instead of $\mathbf{v} \times \mathbf{B}$.

Electromagnetic formulas in this text are in practically all cases written in terms of mks units, but are expressed in a form in which we can immediately pass to the Gaussian units by omitting the factor $4\pi\epsilon_0$ wherever it appears, or by assuming that ϵ_0 equals $1/4\pi$. This is not a universal rule for passing from one set of units to the other, but in the simple cases encountered in this text it can be applied.

APPENDIX 3

THE PRINCIPLE OF LEAST ACTION

The principle of least action is a standard part of classical mechanics. It is treated, in a conventional way, for instance, in Whittaker, "Analytical Dynamics," Cambridge University Press or Dover Publications, Sec. 100. A similar treatment, but worked out in somewhat more detail, is given by H. Goldstein, "Classical Mechanics," Addison-Wesley Press, Inc., Cambridge, Mass. 1950, Sec. 7.5. E. C. Kemble, in "Fundamental Principles of Quantum Mechanics," McGraw-Hill Book Company, Inc., New York, 1937, gives a treatment intended particularly for its application to quantum mechanics, in his Appendix A. We shall follow essentially Kemble's treatment of a simplified problem of the motion of a single particle, in this appendix. It is worth mentioning that the first two chapters of Kemble's book contain treatments of many of the questions taken up in Chaps. 1 to 3 of the present book, in a more advanced form, but treated in the same general spirit; they would form useful supplementary reading for the student who wishes to follow the problems somewhat further than they are taken up in the present volume.

Consider a particle of mass m, moving under the action of a potential energy $V(x,y,z)$. The magnitude of its momentum at any point of space is then determined from the energy equation

$$\frac{p^2}{2m} + V = E, \qquad p = \sqrt{2m(E - V)}. \tag{1}$$

We now consider a path from a point A to a point B and compute S, the line integral of p along the path: $S = \int_A^B p \, ds$, where p is to be found as a function of x, y, z by (1). The principle of least action then states that if the path connecting A and B is the actual trajectory of a particle traveling from A to B with the energy E, the integral $\int p \, ds$ will be stationary, or its value along a neighboring path will differ from that along the trajectory by a small quantity of higher order.

As a first step, following Kemble, let us introduce a quantity u, increasing monotonically as we go along the path from A to B, in terms of which we can express the equation of the path parametrically by the relations $x = f_1(u)$, $y = f_2(u)$, $z = f_3(u)$. If dx/du is defined as x', dy/du as y', etc., we then have $ds = (x'^2 + y'^2 + z'^2)^{\frac{1}{2}} \, du$, so that the integral S becomes

$$S = \int_0^1 p(x'^2 + y'^2 + z'^2)^{\frac{1}{2}} \, du, \tag{2}$$

where we have arranged u in such a way that it takes on the value 0 at the point A, 1 at the point B.

Now we are to construct a slightly different path, such that it is given parametrically by $x = f_1(u) + \delta x(u)$, $y = f_2(u) + \delta y(u)$, etc., where δx, δy, δz are

438

functions of u, and where these new functions are again set up so that u will equal 0 at A, 1 at B. The derivative of this new x with respect to u will then be $x' + d(\delta x)/du$, where x' is as before. We can now construct the change in S, as given by (2), when we integrate along this slightly different path. In doing this, we are to take account of the fact that p is to be computed at a slightly different point for each value of u, and also that $(x'^2 + y'^2 + z'^2)^{\frac{1}{2}}$ is to be found using slightly different values of the derivatives. We then have

$$\delta S = \int_0^1 \left\{ \left(\frac{\partial p}{\partial x} \, \delta x + \frac{\partial p}{\partial y} \, \delta y + \frac{\partial p}{\partial z} \, \delta z \right) (x'^2 + y'^2 + z'^2)^{\frac{1}{2}} \right.$$
$$\left. + p \left[\frac{\partial}{\partial x'} (x'^2 + y'^2 + z'^2)^{\frac{1}{2}} \frac{d(\delta x)}{du} + \cdots \right] \right\} du. \quad (3)$$

The second part of the integral (3) can be integrated by parts. The integrated terms vanish, since δx, δy, δz are zero at $u = 0$ and 1, both paths passing through the points A and B. Thus the second part of (3) can be replaced by

$$- \int_0^1 \left\{ \frac{d}{du} \left[p \, \frac{\partial}{\partial x'} (x'^2 + y'^2 + z'^2)^{\frac{1}{2}} \right] \delta x + \cdots \right\} du. \quad (4)$$

We carry out the differentiation with respect to x' in (4) and remember that $ds = (x'^2 + y'^2 + z'^2)^{\frac{1}{2}} du$. Then (4) becomes

$$- \int_0^1 \left[\frac{d}{ds} \left(p \, \frac{dx}{ds} \right) \delta x + \cdots \right] (x'^2 + y'^2 + z'^2)^{\frac{1}{2}} du. \quad (5)$$

We now insert this modified term in (3), and have

$$\delta S = \int_0^1 \left\{ \left[\frac{\partial p}{\partial x} - \frac{d}{ds} \left(p \, \frac{dx}{ds} \right) \right] \delta x + \cdots \right\} (x'^2 + y'^2 + z'^2)^{\frac{1}{2}} du. \quad (6)$$

We now recall that the quantities $\delta x(u)$, $\delta y(u)$, $\delta z(u)$ were entirely independent and arbitrary functions of u, subject only to the condition that they reduced to zero when $u = 0$ or 1. We can then not have the integral in (6), representing δS, equal to zero, unless the coefficients of δx, δy, δz inside the integral sign are separately equal to zero. Hence we arrive at the differential equations

$$\frac{\partial p}{\partial x} - \frac{d}{ds} \left(p \, \frac{dx}{ds} \right) = 0, \qquad \text{etc.,} \quad (7)$$

representing the path of the particle. Any such problem as the present one, dealing with the variation of an integral, leads in the calculus of variations to such a differential equation, called the Euler equation, and it is in this way, by deriving differential equations, that we can arrive at the equations of motion of a mechanical problem from variation principles.

In the derivative $\partial p / \partial x$, we now use the form (1) for p, obtaining

$$\frac{\partial p}{\partial x} = - \left(\frac{m}{p} \right) \left(\frac{\partial V}{\partial x} \right).$$

In the derivative with respect to ds, we recall that $p/m = v = ds/dt$, so that $p/ds = m/dt$. Thus (7) becomes

$$-\frac{m}{p}\frac{\partial V}{\partial x} = \frac{m}{p}\frac{d}{dt}\left(m\frac{dx}{dt}\right), \qquad m\frac{d^2x}{dt^2} = -\frac{\partial V}{\partial x}, \qquad \text{etc.,}$$

or the ordinary Newtonian equations of motion for the particle. The path for which the integral S is stationary, as demanded by the principle of least action, is then the trajectory of a particle obeying Newton's laws, as we wished to prove.

APPENDIX 4

GROUP VELOCITY

A wave traveling along the x axis, with frequency ν and wave length $\lambda = 1/\beta$, can be expressed as a complex exponential function $e^{2\pi i(\nu t - \beta x)}$. Let us superpose two waves with slightly different frequencies and wave lengths and find the velocity with which the beats between them will travel. Thus let us add waves corresponding to $\nu + d\nu$, $\beta + d\beta$, and $\nu - d\nu$, $\beta - d\beta$. The sum of the two waves is

$$e^{2\pi i[(\nu+d\nu)t-(\beta+d\beta)x]} + e^{2\pi i[(\nu-d\nu)t-(\beta-d\beta)x]} = e^{2\pi i(\nu t-\beta x)}2\cos 2\pi[(d\nu)t - (d\beta)x].$$

The first term is a wave with the average frequency and propagation constant of the two superposed waves. It is multiplied by the cosine factor, which may be regarded as an amplitude, varying slowly with time and position. We note that the cosine function stays constant when $x = (d\nu/d\beta)t$, so that the beats travel forward with the velocity $d\nu/d\beta$, the value which we wished to show equal to the group velocity. We note that this velocity is independent of the differences between frequency and propagation constant of the two waves, so long as these differences are small enough so that $d\nu$ and $d\beta$ can be considered proportional to each other. We shall see in Appendix 5 that a wave packet can be built up as a superposition of many waves of approximately the same frequency and propagation constant. Hence the interference pattern between these waves, consisting of the beats between all of them, will travel forward at a constant velocity, the group velocity, and the wave packet will travel without change of form.

APPENDIX 5

FOURIER ANALYSIS OF A WAVE PACKET

Suppose we have a train of waves, represented by $\sin \omega_0 t$, which is confined to only a very short interval, so that the disturbance equals $\sin \omega_0 t$ from $t = -\Delta t/2$ to $t = \Delta t/2$, but is zero for all other times. We know by Fourier's integral theorem that such a disturbance can be decomposed in a spectrum, by the theorem

$$\varphi(t) = \frac{1}{\pi} \int_0^\infty d\omega \int_{-\infty}^\infty \varphi(T) \cos \omega(T - t) dT.$$

Here the integrand

$$\frac{1}{\pi} \int_{-\infty}^\infty \varphi(T) \cos \omega(T - t) dT = \frac{1}{\pi} \left[\cos \omega t \int_{-\infty}^\infty \varphi(T) \cos \omega T \, dT \right.$$
$$\left. + \sin \omega t \int_{-\infty}^\infty \varphi(T) \sin \omega T \, dT \right]$$

represents the oscillation of angular frequency ω in the spectrum. The quantities $(1/\pi) \int_{-\infty}^\infty \varphi(T) \cos \omega T \, dT$ and $(1/\pi) \int_{-\infty}^\infty \varphi(T) \sin \omega T \, dT$ are the amplitudes of terms in $\cos \omega t$ and $\sin \omega t$, so that the sum of their squares is proportional to the intensity of radiation at angular frequency ω. It is this quantity as a function of ω which we wish for investigating the spectrum.

Let us now assume that $\varphi(T) = \sin \omega_0 T$, for T between $-\Delta t/2$ and $\Delta t/2$, and $\varphi(T) = 0$ elsewhere. Then we can at once carry out the integrations. We find that the amplitude of the $\cos \omega t$ term is zero, and that the amplitude of the $\sin \omega t$ term is

$$\frac{1}{\pi} \left[\frac{\sin (\omega - \omega_0)\Delta t/2}{\omega - \omega_0} - \frac{\sin (\omega + \omega_0)\Delta t/2}{\omega + \omega_0} \right].$$

We shall find that the intensity drops to a low value when ω differs only slightly from ω_0, provided there are many waves in the train. Thus we are interested only in small values of $\omega - \omega_0$, and in this case the first term above is very large compared with the second. We then neglect the second term. When we square the resulting amplitude, to get the intensity, we see that it is proportional to $\sin^2 x/x^2$, where $x = (\omega - \omega_0)\Delta t/2$. The function $\sin^2 x/x^2$ equals unity when $x = 0$, then drops to zero when $x = \pi$, and has subsidiary maxima for larger values of x, which are so small that they can almost be neglected. In other words, practically all the intensity is included in frequencies which differ from ω_0 by no more than given by $\Delta\omega \, \Delta t = 2\pi$, $\Delta\nu \, \Delta t = 1$, which is the uncertainty relation stated in the text.

442

APPENDIX 6

THE WKB METHOD

In setting up the solution (2.3.1) of Schrödinger's equation according to the WKB method, it seems almost intuitive that the sinusoidal function should be as written there. Let us then assume that $u = f(x) \sin [(2\pi/h) \int p \, dx + \alpha]$, where $f(x)$ is an amplitude function to be determined, and substitute this into Schrödinger's equation (2.2.2), which we can write in the form

$$\frac{d^2u}{dx^2} + \frac{4\pi^2 p^2}{h^2} u = 0,$$

to see what differential equation f would have to satisfy. We remember, of course, that p is a function of x. When we carry out the differentiation and make the substitution, we find that the term $(4\pi^2 p^2/h^2)u$ is canceled, and the remaining part of the differential equation proves at once to be

$$\frac{d^2f}{dx^2} \sin \left(\frac{2\pi}{h} \int p \, dx + \alpha \right) + \left(2p \frac{df}{dx} + f \frac{dp}{dx} \right) \frac{2\pi}{h} \cos \left(\frac{2\pi}{h} \int p \, dx + \alpha \right) = 0.$$

We shall now show that the first term can be neglected compared with the second, provided p varies slowly enough with position. Consider the comparison of the quantity d^2f/dx^2, occurring in the first term, with the quantity $(2\pi p/h)df/dx$ occurring in the second. The ratio of the first to the second is

$$\frac{h}{2\pi p} \frac{d}{dx} \ln \frac{df}{dx}.$$

Since h/p is a wave length, this is the proportional change in df/dx in $1/2\pi$ wave lengths. If p varies by only a small fraction of itself in a wave length, we may reasonably assume that the same thing will be true of df/dx (and we can verify this as soon as we get a solution for f in terms of p). Thus the ratio of these two terms will be small, and the first can be neglected compared with the second.

We are then justified in setting only the second term equal to zero, which leads to the differential equation

$$2p \frac{df}{dx} + f \frac{dp}{dx} = 0, \qquad d \ln f = -\frac{1}{2} d \ln p,$$
$$\ln f = -\tfrac{1}{2} \ln p + \text{constant}, \qquad f = \text{constant} \times p^{-\frac{1}{2}},$$

agreeing with the solution (2.3.1). Once we see that this expresses the relation between f and p, we can find df/dx and its variation in a wave length and verify that this is in fact small if the fractional variation of p in a wave length is small. We also see that the term $f \, dp/dx$ is numerically equal to $2p \, df/dx$, but of opposite sign, so that in proving that the term in d^2f/dx^2 is small compared with the term in

$2p \, df/dx$, we have also shown that it is small compared with the term in $\int dp/dx$. We thus justify the correctness of our solution.

The WKB method can be used for many other problems than that of wave mechanics; any differential equation having the same general form as Schrödinger's equation can be solved approximately by similar methods. As another example, applied to the problem of a string with variable tension and density, see Slater and Frank, "Mechanics," McGraw-Hill Book Company, Inc., New York, 1947, Chap. X.

APPENDIX 7

EXPANSION IN ORTHOGONAL FUNCTIONS

There is a close relation between the orthogonality and normalization relations between two functions which are solutions of Schrödinger's equation,

$$\int u_i^* u_j \, dx = \delta_{ij},$$

and corresponding relations for two vectors. If we have two vectors U_i and U_j, each of unit magnitude (or normalized) and at right angles to each other, the scalar product $U_i \cdot U_j$ will be unity if $i = j$, zero if $i \neq j$, or will be δ_{ij}, so that the scalar product $U_i \cdot U_j$ and the integral $\int u_i^* u_j \, dx$ can be treated as being analogous. This analogy will guide us in all our treatment with orthogonal functions, and it is the reason why they are called orthogonal. To see a little more clearly why the analogy should hold, let us assume that u_i and u_j, instead of being functions of a continuous variable x, are defined only at discrete values of the variable, say at $x_1, x_2, \cdots, x_n$. The closest thing to the integral which we can define will then be something like the summation $\sum_k u_i^*(x_k) u_j(x_k)$. However,

this is a generalization of the scalar product, which can be written $\sum_k U_{ik} U_{jk}$,

where now k is to go over three indices, indicating the x, y, z coordinates in a three-dimensional space. If we go to an n-dimensional space, we get something which approaches the integral, as n becomes infinite. We begin to understand, then, the concept of an infinite-dimensional space, in which the first component of a vector represents the value of a function at x_1, the second component its value at x_2, etc., where x_1, x_2, etc., are values of the coordinate indefinitely close together. A vector in such a space, in other words, represents a whole function, and for this reason it is sometimes called a function space. And the orthogonality which we meet in wave mechanics, or in orthogonal function theory, may be interpreted as the orthogonality of vectors in this function space. The geometrical insight which we get in this way can be very valuable in interpreting the theorems which we shall meet. One feature of our wave-mechanical theory does not have a simple geometrical analogy: the way in which we must multiply the complex conjugate of a function by another function before integrating. We can still use the geometry, however, in spite of this added complication.

Let us use this concept first to discuss the orthogonality of solutions of Schrödinger's equation in a degenerate case, as met in Sec. 3.3. Suppose we have several solutions $u_1, \ldots, u_s$ of Schrödinger's equation, corresponding to the same energy. We can at once substitute an arbitrary linear combination $a_1 u_1 + \cdots + a_s u_s$ in Schrödinger's equation (3.1.4), and we find that this linear combination satisfies the equation. But now consider the s-dimensional subspace of the function space, determined by all linear combinations of this type. For instance, if s is three, to have a specific case in mind, all linear combinations of

445

u_1, u_2, u_3 will fill a three-dimensional space. We can then choose any three vectors of unit magnitude and at right angles to each other, in this space, just as if we were choosing the unit vectors of an ordinary coordinate system, and these three vectors, or functions, will have the property of satisfying Schrödinger's equation, at the same time being orthogonal and normalized. The choice can obviously be made in an infinite number of ways, just as we can set up an infinite number of sets of rectangular coordinates in space.

Next let us use our concept of orthogonal functions to discuss operators and matrix components, as in Eq. (3.6.5), $Fu_j = \sum_i F_{ij}u_i$. Here Fu_j represents a vector in our function space, produced by letting F operate on u_j. We are expressing it as a sum of scalar quantities F_{ij}, multiplied by the u_i's, which may be regarded as a set of unit vectors in function space. This is just like the procedure in three-dimensional vector analysis of writing a vector F as $iF_x + jF_y + kF_z$, where i, j, k are the unit vectors (analogous to the u_i's), and F_x, F_y, F_z are the components of F. Thus we see that F_{ij} represents the component of the vector Fu_j, along the axis given by the unit vector u_i. To find this component, of course, we wish to take the scalar product of Fu_j with the unit vector u_i, and the way to do this is to form the integral $\int u_i^* Fu_j \, dx$, which is just the formula given by (3.6.3).

In perturbation theory, the concept of function space is very useful. Thus in Eq. (4.1.1), we write the correct functions u_i of a problem as linear combinations $\sum_j S_{ji}u_j^0$ of the unperturbed functions u_j^0. The functions u_j^0 form one normalized and orthogonal set, and the u_j's form another. Thus this forms a direct analogue to the rotation of axes in ordinary three-dimensional space. In order that a linear transformation of this sort transform one set of normalized orthogonal vectors into another, it is well known from algebra that the S_{ji}'s have to satisfy certain conditions, generally called the orthogonality relations; we can easily prove that the S_{ji}'s in fact satisfy these conditions.

The general line of thought which we have described in the preceding paragraphs can be carried much further than we have done, and in fact forms the basis of much of the more advanced treatment of wave mechanics. We have given enough, however, to suggest to the student this line of approach. It is met in all branches of mathematical physics involving orthogonal functions. For instance, in the study of vibrating systems in mechanics, coupled particles, weighted strings, continuous strings and membranes, and so on, one can use very similar methods. Such problems are discussed from a very similar point of view in Slater and Frank, "Mechanics," McGraw-Hill Book Company, Inc., New York, 1947, Chaps. VII, VIII, X, and XI, and the reader familiar with those matters of normal vibrations will understand the present methods of wave mechanics much more completely.

APPENDIX 8

THE PHASE SPACE AND THE CORRESPONDENCE PRINCIPLE

Classical mechanics rests on the possibility of simultaneously measuring the coordinates $q_1, \ldots, q_n$ of a problem, and its momenta $p_1, \ldots, p_n$, whereas in quantum mechanics we cannot measure both coordinates and momenta simultaneously, unless we are satisfied with a certain degree of uncertainty. Thus in classical mechanics we can describe a system by using a $2n$-dimensional space, in which the q's and p's are used as coordinates, and in which a point gives complete information about the system. This space is the phase space, and a point in it is called a representative point. The phase space and the motion of representative points in it are the basis of most of advanced classical mechanics, and of classical statistical mechanics. On the other hand, in quantum mechanics we cannot use the phase space, on account of the uncertainty principle. In the present appendix, we shall first take up the classical phase space and some of its properties, and then shall take up the relationships of the phase space to wave mechanics and the quantum condition, which are very close. Part of this relationship comes through the correspondence principle, which was a guide in the early development of wave mechanics; but the relations permeate quantum statistics and many branches of quantum theory.

First we consider the phase space in classical mechanics. We base our discussion on Hamilton's equations,

$$\frac{dp_i}{dt} = -\frac{\partial H}{\partial q_i}, \qquad \frac{dq_i}{dt} = \frac{\partial H}{\partial p_i}, \tag{1}$$

which are taken up, for instance, in Slater and Frank, "Mechanics," McGraw-Hill Book Company, Inc., New York, 1947, Chap. IV. Here H is the Hamiltonian function, or energy of the system, expressed as a function of the q's and p's. The first set of Eqs. (1) are equivalent to Newton's equations of motion, while the second set express the relations between the momenta and the velocities. Equations (1) hold for any conservative mechanical system, the q's being the generalized coordinates, the p's their conjugate momenta. It is now clear that Hamilton's equations (1) give the $2n$ components of the $2n$-dimensional velocity of a representative point in the phase space. At any point in phase space (that is, for any given q's and p's), we know H and its derivatives with respect to the q's and p's; thus we set up a unique velocity of flow of the representative point, by (1). We may imagine the whole phase space filled with representative points, like the molecules of a fluid. Then (1) gives the velocity of flow at each point of the phase space, so that we have the same kind of information which we should have in a flowing fluid, if we knew the velocity of flow at every point of space. This hydrodynamic analogy is often useful in giving us increased insight into mechanical problems. It is particularly useful in classical statistical mechanics, where we can deal with an assembly, or ensemble, of systems which are identical as far as their Hamiltonian functions are concerned, but which have different

447

coordinates and momenta, or different energies and are in different phases of their motion (hence the name phase space). Statistical mechanics deals with averages over such assemblies. We may study the motion of a whole assembly as the flow of the representative points constituting it. These matters, and the applications to statistical mechanics, are taken up further in J. C. Slater, "Introduction to Chemical Physics," McGraw-Hill Book Company, Inc., New York, 1939, Chap. III; the present appendix will make close connection with that chapter.

There are two general theorems which we can easily prove about the flow of representative points in the phase space, aside from the obvious fact that, since H does not depend on time explicitly in the cases we are considering, the flow at a given point of phase space does not depend on time. The first of these theorems is a direct result of the conservation of energy: a point in phase space flows in such a way that the Hamiltonian function remains constant along the path of the point. We can set up what are called energy surfaces in the phase space: the $2n - 1$-dimensional regions for which H has a given value. They are called surfaces because, if the phase space had three dimensions, a single equation between them (like H = constant) would be the equation of a surface. Then, as a result of the conservation of energy, we see that the path of a representative point must lie entirely on a single energy surface.

The other simple general theorem is Liouville's theorem, which states that in an assembly of representative points moving according to Hamiltonian mechanics, the density of points will remain constant as we travel along with a given representative point. As a first part of the proof of Liouville's theorem, we note that the velocity of representative points, as defined by (1), has a divergence which is zero, in our $2n$-dimensional space. That is,

$$\text{div } \mathbf{v} = \frac{\partial}{\partial q_1} \frac{dq_1}{dt} + \frac{\partial}{\partial q_2} \frac{dq_2}{dt} + \cdots + \frac{\partial}{\partial p_1} \frac{dp_1}{dt} + \cdots$$

$$= \frac{\partial}{\partial q_1} \frac{\partial H}{\partial p_1} + \frac{\partial}{\partial q_2} \frac{\partial H}{\partial p_2} + \cdots + \frac{\partial}{\partial p_1} \left(-\frac{\partial H}{\partial q_1} \right) +$$

$$= 0.$$

Now a divergenceless flow has certain properties, which we can understand by analogy with divergenceless flow in three dimensions. To understand these properties, we consider the equation of continuity for a steady flow of a fluid of density ρ, velocity $\mathbf{v}$.

The equation of continuity is[†]

$$\frac{\partial \rho}{\partial t} + \text{div } (\rho \mathbf{v}) = 0, \qquad \text{or } \frac{\partial \rho}{\partial t} + \rho \text{ div } \mathbf{v} + \mathbf{v} \cdot \text{grad } \rho = 0,$$

expressing the fact that no fluid is manufactured or destroyed, so that the amount of fluid appearing within a volume is accounted for by what has flowed in over the surface of the volume. If div $\mathbf{v} = 0$, we then have $\partial \rho / \partial t + \mathbf{v} \cdot \text{grad } \rho = 0$. But this means essentially that the fluid is incompressible, or that the density following along with a particle remains fixed. For let us find $d\rho/dt$, the time rate

[†] See Slater and Frank, "Mechanics," McGraw-Hill Book Company, Inc., New York, 1947, Chap. XIII.

of change of density as we follow along with the particle. This is given by

$$\frac{d\rho}{dt} = \frac{\partial \rho}{\partial t} + \frac{\partial \rho}{\partial x}\frac{dx}{dt} + \frac{\partial \rho}{\partial y}\frac{dy}{dt} + \cdots = \frac{\partial \rho}{\partial t} + \mathbf{v}\cdot\text{grad }\rho,$$

so that we have shown that if div $\mathbf{v} = 0$, the fluid is incompressible. This result can be immediately generalized to $2n$ dimensions, proving Liouville's theorem. We notice that this does not imply that the density of fluid must be the same at all points of space. Let us imagine a fluid composed of large droplets of one sort of fluid suspended in another. If the fluids are chosen so that they do not mix, and the surfaces of separation remain sharp, then the density will change from point to point, as we go from the one fluid to the other. Further, if the whole fluid is moving, the density at any point of space will change with time, as first the one sort of fluid, then the other, will be carried past this point. But if the fluid is incompressible, the density of a particular part of the fluid, as we follow it in its motion, will be constant. That is, $\mathbf{v}\cdot\text{grad }\rho$ and $\partial\rho/\partial t$ are separately different from zero, but their sum vanishes.

We have now gone about as far as we can in the general case in describing the motion of representative points in the phase space, in classical mechanics. Next we inquire about various specialized types of motion, which have great importance. First, we note that any one-dimensional motion which does not go to infinity is periodic. The reason is that with a two-dimensional phase space the energy "surface" degenerates to a curve which is identical with the path of a representative point. These lines of constant energy, in the two-dimensional phase space, are like the contour lines on a map. For any ordinary kind of Hamiltonian, or of contours, the lines of constant energy will form closed lines, unless they go to infinity. A point moving around one of these closed lines will have its velocity prescribed at every point of its path; thus the time taken to go once around the path is definite, and after once traversing the path, the point will traverse it again and again, always taking the same time, and hence leading to a periodic orbit. An example of the path of a representative point in such a one-dimensional case has already been given, for the linear oscillator, in Sec. 1.2; other examples are given in "Introduction to Chemical Physics," Chap. III. In these examples we see the close relationship between the phase space and the quantum condition, to which we shall return shortly.

Once we have more than one coordinate in our problem, however, we no longer have any requirement that the motion be periodic. In some cases it is true that we have periodic motions, even in two or three dimensions. Thus the motion of a particle under the action of an inverse-square field is periodic. It is interesting to see why this is the case. In the general central field problem, treated as a two-dimensional motion, we know that we can separate variables, so that in polar coordinates we can handle the motion in r and in θ independently of each other.[†] The angular momentum stays constant, as well as the energy. The angular momentum, like the energy, is a function of the q's and p's; thus the representative point, instead of being able to reach every point of the three-dimensional $(2n - 1 = 3$, if $n = 2)$ energy surface, can reach only every point of a two-dimensional region determined simultaneously by the two equations: energy = constant, angular momentum = constant. We can go further than

† See Slater and Frank, "Mechanics," McGraw-Hill Book Company, Inc., New York, 1947, Chap. III.

this, however, as shown in the reference above. We can set up the problem of the motion of r, just as if it were a one-dimensional problem; hence the motion of r is periodic. Then we can expand r as a Fourier series in the time:

$$r = \sum_k A_k e^{ik\omega t},$$

where ω is the angular frequency. We can now use the relation that the angular momentum $mr^2 \, d\theta/dt$, which we may call p, is a constant. This means that $d\theta/dt$ equals p/mr^2, and since r is periodic with angular frequency ω, the same must be true of p/mr^2. We integrate with respect to time and find that θ similarly is periodic with the same angular frequency, aside from a term proportional to the time, coming from the integration of the constant term in $d\theta/dt$. If we denote this term proportional to time by $\omega_0 t$, we have then

$$\theta = \omega_0 t + \sum_k B_k e^{ik\omega t}.$$

We now investigate the x and y coordinates and their time dependence. We have $x + iy = re^{i\theta}$, and this is a convenient function to examine. We know that r is periodic with angular frequency ω, and so is the last term of θ. If we take $\exp(i \sum_k B_k e^{ik\omega t})$, since the quantity whose exponential is taken is periodic with this same frequency, the same must be true of the exponential. Thus finally we can expand $x + iy$ in the form

$$x + iy = e^{i\omega_0 t} \sum_k C_k e^{ik\omega t}.$$

But this is a summation of periodic terms, each having an angular frequency $\omega_0 + k\omega$. This is a special case of what is called a doubly periodic motion. Such a motion is one in which the coordinates can be expanded as a sum of periodic terms, having angular frequencies $k_1\omega_1 + k_2\omega_2$, where k_1, k_2 are integers, and ω_1, ω_2 fundamental angular frequencies. Our special case is that in which one of the k's takes on only the value unity. We see, then, that the general central field problem is a doubly periodic motion, of a rather special type.

In the special case of the inverse-square field, the angular frequency ω_0 is equal to ω. Thus every term of $x + iy$ has the form of a periodic term of angular frequency $k\omega$, and the whole motion is periodic. Let us see what are the implications of having a periodic, or a doubly periodic, motion when we interpret them in the phase space. If the motion is periodic, as with the inverse-square field, the representative point traces out a single closed curve in the phase space, just as it does in a periodic motion in a one-dimensional problem. This curve, a one-dimensional path, is determined by three separate equations between the q's and p's: the energy is constant, the angular momentum is constant, and the phase difference between the oscillations in r and in θ (when properly defined) is constant. On the other hand, in the doubly periodic motion, though the energy and angular momentum stay constant, the phase difference between these oscillations does not stay constant; the frequencies ω_0 and ω are different, and we assume incommensurable with each other. The representative point then, in the course of time, fills up the two-dimensional region determined by the constancy of the energy and angular momentum. The way in which a point, in the course of its travels, can fill up a surface is familiar from the well-known Lissajous figures in mechanics.

Finally, we can have motion in which the force is not central. Then not even the angular momentum stays constant, and the representative point, in the course of time, fills up the whole energy surface or comes arbitrarily close to any point of this energy surface. Such a motion is called quasi-ergodic. We can see that if we start with the inverse-square periodic motion and introduce a small perturbation in the form of a central field which does not follow the inverse-square law, the phase difference between the two oscillations, in r and θ, will gradually change, so that the representative point will gradually fill the two-dimensional region characteristic of the doubly periodic motion; the smaller the perturbation, the more slowly the point fills up the region. Similarly, if we introduce a small perturbation which is not central, the angular momentum will gradually change, and the representative point will eventually fill up the energy surface, but it will take longer to get around, the smaller the perturbation.

Situations similar to the ones we have described occur in many dimensions. There are a few problems in three dimensions in which we can separate variables, reducing the problem to three one-dimensional problems, and hence leading to triply periodic motions. The three-dimensional central field, the field of axial symmetry, and the field of two centers attracting according to the inverse-square law are three of the very limited number of such problems. In such a triply (or, more generally, a multiply) periodic problem, there are n quantities, including the energy, which stay constant during the motion; these quantities have the properties of angular momenta. There remain $(n - 1)$ phase differences between the oscillations of the various coordinates, and in very special cases some or all of these phase differences can also be constant; if they are all constant, we have a periodic problem. All of these multiply periodic cases are very exceptional, however; the general case is the quasi-ergodic motion, in which the representative point, in the course of time, comes arbitrarily close to every point of the energy surface. This quasi-ergodic motion is the basis of the ordinary treatment of statistical mechanics, and coupled with Liouville's theorem, it provides a justification of the methods of that subject.

The older quantum theory, in the form used by Bohr and Sommerfeld, could be applied only to cases in which the classical motion was multiply periodic. Each of the n quantities which stayed constant during the motion was quantized by an appropriate Sommerfeld quantum condition, so that it could take on only certain discrete values. The way of setting up these quantum conditions can be stated most generally by a change of variables, called a contact transformation, which can usefully be made in the case of a classical multiply periodic motion. These contact transformations are changes of coordinates of a particular type, so called because they transform two curves which are in contact with each other in the original space into curves in contact in the new space.

It is familiar from the theory of generalized coordinates that we can introduce any coordinates which are functions of the original coordinates, and Lagrange's or Hamilton's equations will still hold in terms of the new variables. Thus if we have set up a problem in terms of coordinates $q_1, \ldots, q_n$, and introduce new coordinates by the equations $q_i' = q_i'(q_1, \ldots, q_n)$, we can still use Lagrange's and Hamilton's equations in the new coordinates. The new Lagrangian and Hamiltonian functions are defined in terms of the old ones by simple rules, and the new momenta p_i' are functions of the old coordinates and momenta: $p_i' = p_i'(q_1, \ldots, q_n; p_1, \ldots, p_n)$. Such a transformation is called a point transformation. But in a contact transformation, the new coordinates as well as the new momenta are functions of both the old coordinates and momenta:

$$q_i' = q_i'(q_1, \ldots, q_n; p_1, \ldots, p_n)$$
$$p_i' = p_i'(q_1, \ldots, q_n; p_1, \ldots, p_n).$$

There must naturally be restrictions on the functions, just as in ordinary point transformations we require that the new momenta be derived from the new Lagrangian function.† When these restrictions are applied, however, it proves that Hamilton's equations are still satisfied in the new coordinates, though Lagrange's equations are not. Such contact transformations can often be very useful in complicated problems, reducing them to forms which can be handled mathematically.

A contact transformation can be most easily visualized simply as a change of variables in the phase space. For instance, suppose we have the phase space for a linear oscillator, as in Fig. 1.2.1. We can easily choose the scale so that the line of constant energy is a circle, rather than an ellipse. Then it is often useful to introduce polar coordinates in the phase space, so that the motion is represented by a constant value of r and a value of θ increasing uniformly with time. The angle θ, or rather $\theta/2\pi$, in this case, is often called the angle variable, and is used as the coordinate. This is from analogy with the rotation of a body acted on by no torques, where the angular momentum stays constant, and the angle increases linearly with the time. The momentum conjugate to the angle variable, which stays constant with time, is not simply the radius, as we should expect from the simple use of polar coordinates, but proves to be proportional to the square of r; in fact, it is just πr^2, or the area of the circle. This momentum is called the action variable, or phase integral, denoted by J, and the angle variable is denoted by w.

Since Hamilton's equations hold in the transformed coordinates, and since evidently the energy H depends only on J, beng independent of w, Hamilton's equations become

$$-\frac{\partial H}{\partial w} = 0 = \frac{dJ}{dt},$$

verifying the fact that J is a constant of the motion; and

$$\frac{\partial H}{\partial J} = \frac{dw}{dt},$$

a quantity independent of time, and of w, verifying the fact that w increases uniformly with time. Now since $w = \theta/2\pi$, it increases by unity in one period, so that dw/dt is just $1/T$, where T is the period, or is ν, the frequency of motion. Hence we have the important relation that

$$\nu = \frac{\partial H}{\partial J}, \tag{2}$$

† For further details about contact transformations, as well as more discussion of various matters taken up in this Appendix, see H. Goldstein, "Classical Mechanics," Addison-Wesley Press, Inc., Cambridge, Mass., 1950, Chaps. 8 and 9.

giving the frequency of motion in terms of the derivative of the energy with respect to the action variable J.

It can be shown in a similar way that action and angle variables can be introduced, in general, in one-dimensional periodic motions. In every case the w's increase uniformly with time, the frequency being given by Eq. (2). It also proves to be true, in general, that the action variable J is given by the area of the path of the representative point in phase space, which is the reason why it is called a phase integral. This area can be written $\oint p \, dq$, which proves to be equal to J. Connected with this is the criterion which a transformation of the p's and q's must satisfy if it is to be a contact transformation: it can be proved that it is a transformation in which areas in the phase space are preserved, or are not affected by the transformation, though the shape of an area in the new coordinates may be very different from what it was in the old. An immediate result of this is that the J's are the same no matter what coordinates we may use for computing them.

Angle variables can also be introduced in cases with several degrees of freedom, provided the motion is multiply periodic, by using a separate angle variable for each coordinate. It is evident that the method could not be used with motions which are not multiply periodic, for we have seen that it is only in the multiply periodic motions that there are quantities, as for example, angular momenta, which stay constant. Yet the action variables, or J's, must stay constant, and consequently cannot be introduced, for example, in quasi-ergodic motions, where by hypothesis constants of the motion of this sort do not exist.

Since the action variables J are equal to the integral $\oint p \, dq$, and this is the quantity concerned in Sommerfeld's quantum condition, it is clear that the quantum conditions can be stated in the form that each J must be an integral multiple of Planck's constant h; this is the most general form of quantum condition, in the older quantum theory of Bohr, which had to be restricted to multiply periodic systems in order to apply a quantum condition. We can now make a very interesting connection between Eq. (2) and Bohr's frequency condition. We first consider the case of only one degree of freedom. The emitted frequency, according to Bohr's condition, when a system jumps between states of energy E_2 and E_1 is $(E_2 - E_1)/h$. If we choose two states whose quantum numbers differ by unity, we have $\Delta H = E_2 - E_1$, $\Delta J = h$, so that the frequency given by Bohr's condition is

$$\nu = \frac{\Delta H}{\Delta J},$$

similar to (2), but with finite differences instead of derivatives. Hence we have the following relation: the derivative $\partial H/\partial J$ gives the classical frequency of motion of a system; the difference ratio $\Delta H/\Delta J$, where the difference of J is one unit, gives the frequency of emitted light according to the quantum theory. We shall consider later the significance of transitions of more than one unit in J.

For the oscillator, as one can immediately see from the fact that its energy in the nth state is $(n + \frac{1}{2})h\nu$, the classical and quantum frequencies are exactly equal, the derivative equaling the difference. This is plain from the fact that here $E = J\nu$, so that the curve of E against J is a straight line, and the ratio of a finite increment in ordinate to a finite increment in abscissa equals the slope or derivative. But for any other case the curve of E against J is really curved, so that the derivative and difference ratio are different, and classical and quantum frequencies do not agree. Thus in Fig. 1 we show an energy curve for an anharmonic oscillator, in which the tightness of binding decreases with increasing amplitude, the frequency decreases, and therefore the slope decreases with large quantum numbers. Here the classical frequency, as given by the slope of the curve, does not agree with the quantum frequency connected with the transition indicated. We may assume, however, that if we go to a very high quantum number, so that we are far out on the axis of abscissas, any ordinary energy curve will become asymptotically fairly smooth and straight, so that the chord and tangent to the curve will more and more nearly coincide. This certainly happens in the important physical applications. In these cases Bohr's correspondence principle states that in the limit of high quantum numbers, the classical and quantum frequencies become equal. This is essentially simply a special case of the general

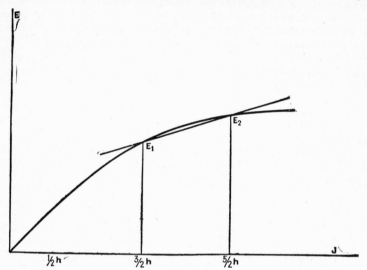

Fig. 1. Energy curve for anharmonic oscillator. Slope of curve gives classical frequency; slope of straight line connecting E_2 and E_1 gives quantum frequency.

result which we have stressed throughout, that in the limit of high quantum numbers the classical and quantum theories become essentially equivalent.

In classical mechanics certain problems, such as the central field motion, are separable, so that they can be broken up into several one-dimensional motions. Since each of these motions was periodic, the whole motion is multiply periodic in these cases. In these particular problems, separation of variables can also be carried out in the quantum theory. In phase space we can pick out the two-dimensional space representing one coordinate and its conjugate momentum, and the projection of the representative point on this plane will trace out a closed curve. There is a quantum condition associated with this coordinate, the area enclosed by the curved path in the two-dimensional space being an integer (or integer plus one-half) times h. Thus we have a quantum number associated with each degree of freedom in such a problem. Further, we can introduce angle and action variables connected with each of the coordinates, just as if each formed a problem of one degree of freedom. The various frequencies of the multiple periodicity can be found by differentiating the energy with respect to the various

J's, and the correspondence principle can be applied to connect these classical frequencies with the quantum frequencies associated with various possible transitions.

We have seen that a coordinate of, say, a doubly periodic motion can be analyzed in a series of harmonic terms, in which we have oscillations of angular frequency $k_1\omega_1 + k_2\omega_2$, or of frequency $k_1\nu_1 + k_2\nu_2$, where k_1, k_2 are arbitrary integers. Now we can carry out a general correspondence between any one of these overtone or combination frequencies and a corresponding transition. Thus let us consider the transition in which J_1 changes by k_1 units, J_2 by k_2 units, where J_1 and J_2 are the two action variables. The quantum frequency emitted will be

$$\frac{E(J_1, J_2) - E(J_1 - k_1h, J_2 - k_2h)}{h},$$

where E is the energy, written as function of the J's. But if we are allowed to replace differences by derivatives, as we assume we are in the correspondence principle, this becomes

$$\frac{1}{h}\left(\frac{\partial E}{\partial J_1} k_1h + \frac{\partial E}{\partial J_2} k_2h\right) = k_1\nu_1 + k_2\nu_2,$$

agreeing with the classical value, if $\nu_1 = \partial E/\partial J_1$, $\nu_2 = \partial E/\partial J_2$. Thus we have a one-to-one correspondence between all possible overtone vibrations of the classical motion and all possible quantum transitions.

We are now ready to see how it was that Bohr's correspondence principle could lead to predictions about the intensity of spectral lines. If we carry out the expansion of the electric dipole moment of the atom, as a series of sinusoidal terms in the time, we see that we shall have a sum of terms of frequencies $k_1\nu_1 + k_2\nu_2$ for a doubly periodic system, or a sum of such terms for a multiply periodic system, and we have just seen how each of these sinusoidal terms can be correlated with a quantum transition. Each such sinusoidal term will have a definite amplitude, and this amplitude will be the quantity whose square is proportional to the intensity of the corresponding radiation, if we assume classical mechanics. Bohr assumed that these amplitudes gave at least an indication of the radiated intensity, in the quantum theory. Now that we have the wave mechanics, we can see the exact nature of the correspondence: we find that in the limit of high quantum numbers the amplitudes of the classical sinusoidal terms approach the matrix components of the corresponding quantum transitions. For small quantum numbers, we expect the quantum matrix component to be in some sense an average of the classical amplitude, averaged between the initial and final state. We shall not go further into the details of this correspondence, but shall call attention to the case of selection principles. If a classical amplitude is zero, we can reasonably expect that the quantum amplitude, or the matrix component, of the corresponding transition will also be zero.

By use of this rule, many selection principles were proved before the availability of the wave mechanics. Thus with the linear oscillator, the classical motion is purely sinusoidal, without any harmonics. In other words, the amplitudes of all terms of frequency $k_1\nu$ are zero, except for $k_1 = 1$. We infer then that all transitions of the linear oscillator are forbidden, except those for which the quantum number changes by unity. This, of course, is the result found by wave mechanics. Again, in the central field motion in two dimensions, we found earlier in this appendix that in the analysis of the displacement in sinusoidal terms we had all integral multiples of the radial frequency ω, but the frequency ω_0 of angular motion appeared only with a coefficient of unity. This angular frequency can be shown to be that associated with the J leading to the azimuthal quantum number. Thus we see the proof, from the correspondence principle, that the azimuthal quantum number can change only by a single unit in a transition, a selection principle which also follows from the quantum theory.

APPENDIX 9

THE HERMITIAN CHARACTER OF MATRICES

We wish to prove that matrices involving the momentum as well as the coordinates are Hermitian. We shall not give a general proof; we shall consider only the energy and the momentum, and only for a one-dimensional problem, but it is not hard to generalize the results. Thus for the energy operator we wish to prove that $H_{12} = H_{21}^*$, or $\int u_1^* H u_2 \, dx = \int u_2 H u_1^* \, dx$. For the potential energy, depending only on the coordinates, this result is obvious, so that the only problem comes for the kinetic energy, or for the operator d^2/dx^2. Thus we wish to prove

$$\int u_1^* \frac{d^2 u_2}{dx^2} \, dx = \int u_2 \frac{d^2 u_1^*}{dx^2} \, dx.$$

This is an obvious case for using integration by parts. We integrate the expression on the left by parts, finding

$$\int u_1^* \frac{d^2 u_2}{dx^2} \, dx = u_1^* \frac{du_2}{dx} \bigg| - \int \frac{du_1^*}{dx} \frac{du_2}{dx} \, dx,$$

where the integrated terms are to be taken between limits at which we assume the wave functions to be zero, just as in the proof of orthogonality. Hence the integrated terms drop out. By another integration by parts, similar to the first one, the desired result is proved.

The similar proof for the momentum demands that we show

$$\int u_1^* \frac{h}{2\pi i} \frac{du_2}{dx} \, dx = \int u_2 \left(- \frac{h}{2\pi i} \right) \frac{du_1^*}{dx} \, dx,$$

which follows at once from a single integration by parts, similar to that used above.

APPENDIX 10

THE POWER-SERIES METHOD FOR PERTURBATIONS

Let us start with Eq. (4.3.4), the secular equation. We shall try to find the largest terms in the expansion of the determinant, the next largest terms, and so on. We shall look for the solution E_i, which must surely be not far from H_{ii}; since if the nondiagonal matrix components, which we are regarding as small, were zero, one of the solutions would be exactly H_{ii}. Then, of the diagonal elements $H_{11} - E_i$, $H_{22} - E_i$, . . . , $H_{nn} - E_i$, there is one, $H_{ii} - E_i$, which is small, but all the rest are large, if we assume the problem to be nondegenerate, so that no other diagonal element H_{jj} is close to H_{ii}. All the nondiagonal elements of the determinant are, by hypothesis, small.

In the expansion of the determinant, we take a product of elements, choosing one from each row, one from each column, of the determinant. We give it a coefficient ± 1, according as it requires an even or odd number of interchanges of rows or columns to bring this product into the principal diagonal. Then we add these products, with their appropriate coefficients. The largest term of the determinant is obviously the product of the elements along the principal diagonal, or $(H_{11} - E_i)(H_{22} - E_i) \cdots (H_{ii} - E_i) \cdots (H_{nn} - E_i)$, since this contains $(n - 1)$ large elements, only one small one. If we set this term alone equal to zero, we have an equation which is automatically factored, and to get the solution we desire, we set the factor $H_{ii} - E_i$ equal to zero, obtaining the first-order solution $E_i = H_{ii}$. To get further, we must take the terms of the next smaller order of small quantities. If we do not use all the elements along the principal diagonal, we see at once that we must omit two such elements, and to get the largest possible term, we omit the term $H_{ii} - E_i$ and one other, say $H_{jj} - E_i$. Thus instead of $(n - 1)$ large elements, we have $(n - 2)$ large elements, and, as we see at once, the two small elements H_{ij} and H_{ji}. Each such term will come in with a minus sign. We may then write the secular equation, complete to this order of magnitude, in the form

$$[(H_{11} - E_i)(H_{22} - E_i) \cdots (H_{ii} - E_i) \cdots (H_{nn} - E_i)] \left[1 - \sum_{j \neq i} \frac{H_{ij}H_{ji}}{(H_{ii} - E_i)(H_{jj} - E_i)} \right] = 0.$$

Now we set the last bracket equal to zero, and we have

$$E_i = H_{ii} + \sum_{j \neq i} \frac{H_{ij}H_{ji}}{E_i - H_{jj}}.$$

If we replace E_i in the denominators of the small correction terms in this expression by its approximate value H_{ii}, this agrees exactly with Eq. (4.3.6).

To get Eq. (4.3.7) for the u's in terms of the u^0's, we start with Eqs. (4.3.1).

We try to find the coefficients $S_{1i}, \ldots, S_{ni}$ by which we must multiply the unperturbed functions $u_1^0, \ldots, u_n^0$, to get the perturbed function u_i^0. Since the perturbations are small, we may assume that u_i will be not far from u_i^0, which means that S_{ii} will be approximately unity, all the other S_{ji}'s small. Let us then consider the jth equation of (4.3.1). The only large terms in it are

$$(H_{jj} - E_i)S_{ji} + H_{ji}S_{ii} = 0.$$

If we assume that S_{ii} can be replaced by its approximate value unity, we find

$$S_{ji} = \frac{H_{ji}}{H_{ii} - H_{jj}}, \qquad \text{if } j \neq i,$$

where we have again replaced E_i in the denominator by its approximate value H_{ii}. This leads at once to (4.3.7), which we wished to prove.

APPENDIX 11

QUANTUM THEORY OF THE ELECTROMAGNETIC FIELD

The first step in treating the electromagnetic field, and its interaction with matter, according to wave mechanics, is to set up a classical treatment of electromagnetic problems by Hamiltonian methods; for our rules for translating classical problems into wave mechanics hold only in case we can set up a Hamiltonian function. The first step in doing this is to show that the electromagnetic field can be divided into two parts, the electrostatic part, and the radiation field. It is a fundamental fact of vector analysis that any vector function of position can be written as the sum of two parts, one of which is solenoidal, or has no divergence, and the other of which is irrotational, or has no curl. Thus in Maxwell's equations $\text{curl } \mathbf{E} + \dot{\mathbf{B}} = 0$, $\text{div } \mathbf{B} = 0$, $\text{curl } \mathbf{H} - \dot{\mathbf{D}} = \mathbf{J}$, $\text{div } \mathbf{D} = \rho$, we can write $\mathbf{E} = \mathbf{E}_1 + \mathbf{E}_2$, $\mathbf{J} = \mathbf{J}_1 + \mathbf{J}_2$, where the part with subscript 1 is solenoidal, that with subscript 2 irrotational. We assume empty space, so that $\mathbf{D} = \epsilon_0\mathbf{E}$, $\mathbf{B} = \mu_0\mathbf{H}$; thus $\mathbf{D}$ similarly is equal to $\mathbf{D}_1 + \mathbf{D}_2$, where $\mathbf{D}_1 = \epsilon_0\mathbf{E}_1$, etc. The vectors $\mathbf{B}$ and $\mathbf{H}$ are automatically solenoidal. We may then separate the solenoidal and irrotational parts of Maxwell's equations. We have

$$\text{curl } \mathbf{E}_1 + \dot{\mathbf{B}} = 0, \qquad \text{div } \mathbf{B} = 0,$$
$$\text{curl } \mathbf{H} - \dot{\mathbf{D}}_1 = \mathbf{J}_1, \qquad \text{div } \mathbf{D}_1 = 0,$$
$$- \dot{\mathbf{D}}_2 = \mathbf{J}_2, \qquad \text{div } \mathbf{D}_2 = \rho.$$

The last two equations are equivalent, on account of the equation of continuity for electric charge and current. We remember that curl $\mathbf{E}_2 = 0$, so that we may write $\mathbf{E}_2 = -\text{grad } \varphi$, where φ is a scalar potential. Then we have at once $\nabla^2\varphi = -\rho/\epsilon_0$. That is, $\mathbf{E}_2$ is derivable from a scalar potential, which satisfies Poisson's equation. This is identical with the ordinary equations of electrostatics, so that $\mathbf{E}_2$ is determined by Coulomb's law from the charge distribution. The only difference between this problem and electrostatics is that ρ can change with time. Nevertheless, we are to find the field by Coulomb's law from the instantaneous charge, without taking account of retardation or the finite velocity of propagation of light. This field is the electrostatic field, and it can be handled in quantum mechanics just as a potential energy depending on position only.

The remaining field, which is solenoidal, can be derived from a vector potential $\mathbf{A}$, whose divergence is zero. Thus let $\mathbf{E}_1 = -\dot{\mathbf{A}}$, $\mathbf{B} = \text{curl } \mathbf{A}$. Maxwell's equations then at once lead to the wave equation for $\mathbf{A}$,

$$\nabla^2\mathbf{A} - \frac{1}{c^2}\frac{\partial^2\mathbf{A}}{\partial t^2} = -\mu_0\mathbf{J}_1. \tag{1}$$

This field, determined only from a vector potential, is the radiation field, and we see that it arises from the solenoidal part of the current only, the part which is not associated with electric charge specifically. It is this field which must be handled by quantum theory. We first show how to handle it in the case where the current is zero and then introduce the interaction with the current.

We get a suggestion as to how to handle the wave equation for **A** by Hamiltonian methods, by recalling the problem of the wave equation for mechanical oscillations of an elastic solid. We recall that there we introduce normal coordinates, representing the time-varying amplitudes of the various normal modes of oscillation, and can show that these normal coordinates obey the same differential equations as independent linear oscillators, so that the whole system can be regarded as a collection of linear oscillators, with a corresponding Hamiltonian function. Here, in a similar way, we can introduce normal modes of oscillation. One way to do this is to set up all the modes of oscillation possible in a large cavity bounded by perfectly reflecting walls. This is the problem of microwave oscillations. One can show that in such a cavity it is possible to set up a set of orthogonal vector functions $\mathbf{E}_a$ and $\mathbf{H}_a$, satisfying the equations $k_a\mathbf{E}_a = $ curl $\mathbf{H}_a$, $k_a\mathbf{H}_a = $ curl $\mathbf{E}_a$, where the k_a's are constants, satisfying at the same time the boundary conditions that the functions $\mathbf{E}_a$ are normal to the boundary, $\mathbf{H}_a$ tangential.† These functions are solenoidal, since each can be written as the curl of another vector, and by combining the equations above, we can show that they satisfy the wave equations $\nabla^2\mathbf{E}_a + k_a^2\mathbf{E}_a = 0$, $\nabla^2\mathbf{H}_a + k_a^2\mathbf{H}_a = 0$. Any two functions $\mathbf{E}_a$, or any two functions $\mathbf{H}_a$, are orthogonal to each other, in the sense that the scalar product of two of them integrates to zero over the volume of the resonant cavity. They can furthermore be simultaneously normalized, in such a way that the integral of an E_a^2, and simultaneously the integral of an H_a^2, over the cavity, is unity. Then we can expand any solenoidal function of position within the cavity in series of either the $\mathbf{E}_a$'s or the $\mathbf{H}_a$'s. Since the $\mathbf{E}_a$'s satisfy the same boundary condition at the surface of the cavity which the vector potential **A** must satisfy (for **A** must be normal to the surface conductor, since its time derivative, which is $-\mathbf{E}$, must be normal), it is natural to expand the vector potential in series in the $\mathbf{E}_a$'s.

We may then write

$$\mathbf{A} = \sum_a Q_a\mathbf{E}_a,$$

where the Q_a's are coefficients in the expansion, which must naturally be functions of time. In a case where there is no current, we then substitute this expression in (1) and find that it takes the form

$$\sum_a \left(-k_a^2 Q_a - \frac{1}{c^2}\frac{d^2Q_a}{dt^2} \right)\mathbf{E}_a = 0.$$

We may multiply by one of the $\mathbf{E}_a$'s, integrate over the volume, and at once show that each of the scalar quantities above must equal zero. That is, we have

$$\frac{d^2Q_a}{dt^2} = -k_a^2 c^2 Q_a, \tag{2}$$

† See J. C. Slater, "Microwave Electronics," D. Van Nostrand Company, Inc., New York, 1950, Chap. 4, for a discussion of the theory of resonant cavities along these lines.

the equation of a simple harmonic motion with angular frequency $\omega_a = k_a c$. From now on we shall generally use this natural frequency ω_a of the normal mode of the cavity in place of k_a. Q_a is then one of the normal coordinates expressing the field.

We may now find the equation of motion (2) in a Hamiltonian form. We wish to find the Hamiltonian function of the radiation field; we naturally expect that this will be the sum of the electric and magnetic energies within the cavity. The electric energy is the integral of $\epsilon_0 E^2/2$ over the resonant cavity, by fundamental principles of electrodynamics. This is the same as the integral of $\epsilon_0 \dot{A}^2/2$. When we express **A** as the expansion in terms of the $\mathbf{E}_a$'s and take account of the normalization and orthogonality properties of the $\mathbf{E}_a$'s we find at once that

$$\text{Electric energy} = \frac{\epsilon_0}{2} \sum_a \dot{Q}_a^2. \tag{3}$$

Similarly the magnetic energy is the integral of $B^2/2\mu_0$ over the cavity. We remember that $\mathbf{B} = \text{curl } \mathbf{A} = \sum_a Q_a \text{ curl } \mathbf{E}_a = \sum_a k_a Q_a \mathbf{H}_a$. When we square this and integrate, using the normalization and orthogonality properties of the $\mathbf{H}_a$'s, we then find

$$\text{Magnetic energy} = \frac{\epsilon_0}{2} \sum_a \omega_a^2 Q_a^2, \tag{4}$$

where we have used the expression for ω_a in terms of k_a and have used the relation $\epsilon_0 \mu_0 = 1/c^2$.

We thus see that, with this way of writing things, the electric energy has an analogy to a kinetic energy, the magnetic energy to a potential energy, provided we use the Q_a's as coordinates. To set up the Hamiltonian function, we must next find the momenta conjugate to the coordinates, and this demands setting up the Lagrangian function L = kinetic energy − potential energy = electric energy − magnetic energy, and defining a momentum P_a conjugate to Q_a by the relation $P_a = \partial L/\partial \dot{Q}_a$. We find at once that $P_a = \epsilon_0 \dot{Q}_a$. Then we can set up the Hamiltonian function, as the total energy expressed in terms of the momenta and coordinates, and have at once

$$H_1 = \sum_a \left(\frac{P_a^2}{2\epsilon_0} + \frac{\epsilon_0 \omega_a^2}{2} Q_a^2 \right). \tag{5}$$

This Hamiltonian is like that of a set of linear oscillators, as we have mentioned earlier, the ath oscillator having an angular frequency ω_a, and the quantity ϵ_0 taking the place of the mass. We verify at once that Hamilton's equations lead to the equation of motion (2).

Before we go on to treat the case where current is present, let us see how we should apply the wave mechanics to the radiation field in empty space in the cavity. The problem is exactly like a mechanical problem with the infinite set of coordinates Q_a. We should handle this by introducing a wave function varying sinusoidally with time, and with a space part equal to a function $u(Q_1, Q_2, \ldots)$.

This wave function would then satisfy the Schrödinger equation

$$\sum_a \left(-\frac{h^2}{8\pi^2\epsilon_0} \frac{\partial^2}{\partial Q_a^2} + \frac{\epsilon_0\omega_a^2}{2} Q_a^2 \right) u = Eu. \tag{6}$$

Since the Hamiltonian function is a sum of terms, one depending on each of the Q's, we can at once separate variables, writing $u = u_1(Q_1)u_2(Q_2) \cdots$, and find that u_a satisfies the equation

$$-\frac{h^2}{8\pi^2\epsilon_0} \frac{d^2 u_a}{d Q_a^2} + \frac{\epsilon_0\omega_a^2}{2} Q_a^2 u_a = E_a u_a, \tag{7}$$

where E_a is the energy of the ath normal mode, and where E is the sum of the E_a's. But (7) is just like the Schrödinger equation for a linear oscillator, which we have solved in Sec. 2.4, so that we know its wave functions and energy levels, and in particular, we know that

$$E_a = (n_a + \tfrac{1}{2})h\nu_a, \tag{8}$$

where $\nu_a = \omega_a/2\pi$. Thus we have verified that the energy of a normal mode of frequency ν can take on only certain discrete energies, differing by the amount $h\nu$. As we have stated in Chap. 4, this can be regarded as one of the bases for the photon hypothesis, according to which the energy of the radiation field can change only by an amount $h\nu$. We also have the justification for the remarks made in Sec. 4.7 about the limiting case of large electromagnetic energy, in which the quantum numbers n_a are all large, so that we can approach the case of classical electromagnetic theory, in which Q_a would be a definitely determined function of time, instead of being described only statistically by a wave function. By the same methods used to prove the correctness of Hamilton's equations for the motion of the center of mass of a wave packet, in Sec. 3.8, we can show that in the classical limit the Q_a's satisfy Eq. (2), which is equivalent to Maxwell's equations.

Now we are ready to return to the case where we have current $\mathbf{J}_1$, as in Eq. (1). We proceed as in the derivation of (2) but retain $\mathbf{J}_1$. We then find at once

$$\frac{d^2 Q_a}{dt^2} + \omega_a^2 Q_a = \frac{1}{\epsilon_0} \int \mathbf{J}_1 \cdot \mathbf{E}_a \, dv. \tag{9}$$

This is like the equation of a forced oscillator, in classical mechanics; the term on the right, being a function of time, plays the part of an external force. We can solve the problem classically by well known methods, and in this way we find the Q_a's, and hence the vector potential and field, set up by external currents. Equations (9), then, are essentially equivalent to Maxwell's equations. We can simplify the integral in the right side of the equations in several ways. First, it is easy to show that $\int \mathbf{J}_2 \cdot \mathbf{E}_a \, dv = 0$, where $\mathbf{J}_2$ is the irrotational part of the current density. This follows from a general theorem about the product of any irrotational function and an $\mathbf{E}_a$ vanishing when integrated over the complete volume. Thus we can replace $\mathbf{J}_1$, in the integral in (9), by $\mathbf{J}$, the total current density, which means that we can calculate it at once from the known motion of the charges. Secondly, if the current density consists of a number of point charges, of charge e_i, located at points with vector position $\mathbf{r}_i$, moving with velocities $\dot{\mathbf{r}}_i$, we can rewrite the right side of (9) in an explicit form.

To do this, we note that the integral in (9) will have contributions only from the places where the charges are.   The ith charge will have a current density which is infinite if it is really a point charge, or is very large, equal to the charge density times the velocity, if the charge density is large but not infinite.   If we integrate the current density of this electron over the volume, the result will be the charge e_i times the velocity vector $\dot{r}_i$.   The value of E_a will have to be computed at the position r_i of the charge.   Thus we may rewrite (9) in the form

$$\frac{d^2Q_a}{dt^2} + \omega_a^2 Q_a^2 = \frac{1}{\epsilon_0} \sum_i e_i \dot{\mathbf{r}}_i \cdot \mathbf{E}_a(r_i). \tag{10}$$

It is this equation which we now wish to derive from a Hamiltonian function.

It is clear that to get (10) from Hamilton's equations, these equations must somehow involve the coordinates of the point charges, as well as the electric field. Let us next, therefore, turn our attention to quite a different problem from that we have been considering so far, namely, the Hamiltonian formulation of the equations of motion of a set of point charges under the action of electric and magnetic fields.   Suppose we have a set of particles, the ith particle having a charge e_i, mass m_i, position r_i.   Let these particles move subject to their own Coulomb attractions and repulsions, and to the action of an external radiation field whose vector potential is A.   Then it is well known that their equations of motion are given by the Hamiltonian H_2, which is

$$H_2 = \sum_i \frac{[p_i - e_i A(r_i)]^2}{2m_i} + V(r_1, \ldots, r_n). \tag{11}$$

Here p_i is the vector momentum of the ith particle, the vector potential $A(r_i)$ is to be computed at the position of the ith particle, and V is the Coulomb inter-action energy, the sum of terms $e_i e_j/(4\pi\epsilon_0 r_{ij})$ for each pair of charges, where r_{ij} is the distance from the ith to the jth particle.   To verify the correctness of this Hamiltonian, we first consider the equation $\partial H_2/\partial p_i = \dot{r}_i$, r_i representing the vector form of the coordinates of the ith particle.   Really we must write a separate equation for each component of the momentum and velocity, and when we combine these into a vector equation, we have

$$\dot{\mathbf{r}}_i = \frac{\mathbf{p}_i - e_i \mathbf{A}(r_i)}{m_i}, \qquad \mathbf{p}_i = m_i \dot{\mathbf{r}}_i + e_i \mathbf{A}(r_i). \tag{12}$$

This equation shows the well-known fact that in the presence of a vector potential the momentum is no longer the mass times the velocity but contains an additional term derived from the vector potential.

Next we must consider the other Hamiltonian equation.   If we write the equation for the x component of the momentum of the ith particle, we have $dp_{ix}/dt = -\partial H_2/\partial x_i$.   On the left side of this equation we must use (12) for p_i, and note that it can change with time for three reasons: because $\dot{r}_i$ changes with time, because the r_i contained in $A_x(r_i)$ changes with time, and because $A_x(r_i)$ changes with time even at constant value of r_i.   Similarly, we note that the right side of the equation contains terms both on account of the dependence of $A(r_i)$ in H_2 on x_i, and on account of the dependence of V on x_i.   When we carry out the substitutions, the resulting equation is

$$m_i \ddot{x}_i + e_i \frac{\partial A_x}{\partial t}(r_i) + e_i \frac{\partial A_x}{\partial x_i}(r_i)\dot{x}_i + e_i \frac{\partial A_x}{\partial y_i}(r_i)\dot{y}_i + e_i \frac{\partial A_x}{\partial z_i}(r_i)z_i$$

$$= e_i \left[\frac{\partial A_x}{\partial x_i}(r_i)\dot{x}_i + \frac{\partial A_y}{\partial x_i}(r_i)\dot{y}_i + \frac{\partial Az}{\partial x_i}(r_i)\dot{z}_i \right] - \frac{\partial V}{\partial x_i}.$$

We combine terms, use the formulas for the E and B of the radiation field in terms of A, and find

$$m_i \ddot{x}_i = e_i [\mathbf{E} + (\dot{\mathbf{r}}_i \times \mathbf{B})]_x - \frac{\partial V}{\partial x_i}. \tag{13}$$

Here E and B are the electric and magnetic fields arising from A, computed at the position of the ith particle. We see therefore that the Hamiltonian (11) correctly describes the motion of the particles, under the action of the electric and magnetic forces of the radiation field, and their Coulomb interactions.

Since the vector potential A is to be written as an expansion in terms of the orthogonal functions E_a, we may now rewrite (11) in the form

$$H_2 = \sum_i \frac{\left[p_i - e_i \sum_a Q_a E_a(r_i) \right]^2}{2m_i} + V(r_1, \ldots, r_n). \tag{14}$$

This will lead to the same equations of motion of the particles which we have just found, since the only change is to express the radiation field in terms of our expansion. But now we observe that the term involving the Q_a's and $E_a(r_i)$ brings in at the same time the coordinates of the particles and of the radiation field; it is an interaction term between the two. It is now an important fact that we can add the Hamiltonian (5) of the radiation field and that (14) of the particles, and the resulting Hamiltonian function will lead to the correct equation (10) for the effect of the particles on the electromagnetic field; that is, it leads to Maxwell's equations including the effect of the currents. To show this, we need only apply Hamilton's equations for Q_a and P_a to the whole Hamiltonian $H_1 + H_2$, and the result follows immediately. We have thus found in H_1 and H_2 the complete formulation of the problem of interaction of particles and radiation field, in classical mechanics, so that we can proceed to transform this Hamiltonian function into a wave equation and formulate the problem according to wave mechanics.

Before we proceed with this quantum-mechanical formulation, it is well to qualify a little the statement of the preceding paragraph that we have formulated our problem completely according to classical mechanics. It is well known that if we try to set up a complete classical theory of a point electron, we find an infinite electrostatic self-energy, for there is an infinite amount of electrostatic energy in the field immediately around a given charge. We have avoided this term in our Hamiltonian H_2 by including in V only the interactions between pairs of particles, excluding the interaction of a charge with itself. This is legitimate here, but it does not entirely get rid of self-energy troubles. The reason is that, in addition, a moving point charge produces an infinite magnetic field in its neighborhood, which exerts infinite magnetic forces on it, and we have not eliminated these magnetic interactions in our formulation.   If we used (10) in a straightforward way to investigate the magnetic fields produced by a moving point charge, we should find just the infinite contributions to the field which we have just mentioned, and these, in turn, would produce infinite forces in (13).   Fortunately these terms will not concern us in the use which we shall make of the method, which is the study of the effect of radiation fields emitted by one atom in causing quantum transitions in another atom.   They should be enough to show the reader, however, that the subject of quantum electrodynamics is one with difficulties, in the way of infinite terms, which are fundamental, and not easy to avoid.   To go much further than we are doing in this elementary treatment, we have to treat the electron relativistically, involving us in the Dirac theory of the electron; and when this is done, various other infinite terms in the theory appear, which must all be handled together to get anything approaching a consistent theory.

The difficulties we have been mentioning fortunately do not come in in the problems we are considering in this appendix.   Let us then take our Hamiltonian $H_1 + H_2$ and set up the related Schrödinger equation.   We shall set it up in the form involving the time, for we wish to investigate nonstationary states by the method of variation of constants.   We then have a wave function ψ which is a function of the Q_a's and the r_i's.   And the Schrödinger equation is

$$\left[\sum_a \left(-\frac{h^2}{8\pi^2\epsilon_0}\frac{\partial^2}{\partial Q_a^2} + \frac{\epsilon_0\omega_a^2}{2}Q_a^2\right)\right.$$

$$+ \sum_i \left\{-\frac{h^2}{8\pi^2 m_i}\nabla_i^2 - \frac{e_i h}{2\pi i m_i}\nabla_i \cdot \sum_a Q_a E_a(r_i) + \frac{e_i^2}{2m_i}\left[\sum_a Q_a E_a(r_i)\right]^2\right\}$$

$$\left. + V(r_1, \ldots, r_n)\right]\psi = -\frac{h}{2\pi i}\frac{\partial\psi}{\partial t}. \quad (15)$$

It is worth while noting that in the term involving ∇_i, it is immaterial whether the Laplacian operator is written before or after the function $E_a(r_i)$.   The reason is that E_a is solenoidal, so that div $E_a \psi = E_a \cdot$ grad ψ.

Equation (15) is now the one which we must solve; but it is much too complicated to handle directly, even in the simplest cases.   Hence all discussions of it proceed by perturbation theory.   There are two terms involving both the coordinates of the radiation field and of the particles: those involving $\sum_a Q_a E_a(r_i)$, one

of the first power in the field, the other of the second power.   If these terms were omitted, the Hamiltonian would be a sum of terms depending only on the radiation field and terms depending only on the particles.   Then the problem could be separated, ψ being written as a product of a function of the field and a function of the particles.   The function of the field can be set up as described earlier, as a product of solutions of linear-oscillator-like problems, one for each normal mode of the cavity, each characterized by a quantum number n_a, indicating the number of photons in the corresponding mode of oscillation.   The function of the particles can be solved like all the problems of interaction of particles which we have considered in this volume, neglecting radiation.   Thus, at least in principle, we can set up a wave function of the particles corresponding to the quantum numbers of the particles.   The unperturbed problem then is that of separated radiation field and particles, and the energy is the sum of the energies of radiation field and particles.

We then introduce the remaining terms in the Hamiltonian as perturbations and proceed by perturbation theory.   In the ordinary case we use the method of variation of constants.   The essential quantity to compute in this method is the matrix component of energy between unperturbed wave functions.   We may denote an unperturbed wave function by giving the quantum numbers n_1, $n_2 \ldots$, of the various oscillators representing the radiation field, and the quantum numbers describing the atomic system, which we may symbolize by p (but which may include a number of quantum numbers).   We are then interested in the nondiagonal matrix component of energy between states with quantum numbers n_1, n_2, $\ldots$, p, and n_1', n_2', $\ldots$, p'.   The only terms of the Hamiltonian (15) which can lead to such nondiagonal terms are those involving the quantities $Q_a E_a(r_i)$; and a more careful examination, which we shall not give, shows that only the linear terms in these quantities need be retained for the present purposes. The quadratic terms, being of a smaller order of magnitude if the external fields are small, can be neglected.

We wish then to find the nondiagonal matrix component of the energy

$$\sum_i \sum_a \frac{(-e_i h)}{2\pi i m_i} Q_a E_a(r_i) \cdot \nabla_i \tag{16}$$

between two states of the system.   Let us find the component of one term of this summation, $(-e_i h/2\pi i m_i) Q_a E_{ax}(r_i)\partial/\partial x_i$.   Let us write the unperturbed wave function in the form $u_{n_1}(Q_1)u_{n_2}(Q_2) \cdots w_p(r_1, \ldots, r_n)$, where w represents the wave function of the particles.   The u's are the wave functions of the oscillators representing the field.   On account of their orthogonality, and the form of the energy operator, which involves the quantity Q_a, it is clear that the nondiagonal matrix component will be zero if any n'''s differ from the corresponding n's, except for n_a.   And on account of normalization of the u's, we have

$$\int u_{n_1}^*(Q_1) \cdots w_p^*(r_1, \ldots, r_n) Q_a E_{ax}(r_i) \frac{\partial}{\partial x_i} u_{n_1}(Q_1) \cdots$$

$$u_{n_a'}(Q_a) \cdots w_p'(r_1, \ldots, r_n)dQ_1 \cdots dr_1 \cdots$$

$$= \int u_{n_a}^*(Q_a) Q_a u_{n_a'}(Q_a)dQ_a \int w_p^*(r_1, \ldots, r_n) E_{ax}(r_i) \frac{\partial}{\partial x_i} w_p'(r_1, \ldots, r_n)dr_1. \tag{17}$$

The first factor in (17) above is the matrix component $\int u_{n_a}^*(Q_a) Q_a u_{n_a'}(Q_a)dQ_a$ of the coordinate Q_a, between two wave functions of a harmonic oscillator, characterized by quantum numbers n_a and n_a'.   The problem of finding the matrix component of the coordinate between two wave functions of a harmonic oscillator is a well known one, which we have already mentioned in Sec. 3.5.   There we stated that the matrix component is zero unless the quantum number increases or decreases by just one unit: n_a' must equal $n_a \pm 1$ in order to have a nonvanishing matrix component.   We shall see presently that this has a simple physical significance in our problem of radiation or absorption: in every such act only one photon is emitted or absorbed by the radiating system.   It is simple to get the actual values of the matrix components; this is easy enough so that it is handled in a problem (see Prob. 3, Chap. 3). From the result of that problem, we see that

$$\int u_{n_a}^*(Q_a) Q_a u_{n_a \pm 1}(Q_a) dQ_a = \sqrt{\frac{h(n_a + 1)}{8\pi^2 \epsilon_0 \nu_a}} \quad \text{for plus sign}$$

$$= \sqrt{\frac{h n_a}{8\pi^2 \epsilon_0 \nu_a}} \quad \text{for minus sign.} \quad (18)$$

Next we consider the remaining factor in (17), the matrix component

$$\int w_p^*(r_1, \ldots, r_n) E_{ax}(r_i) \frac{\partial}{\partial x_i} w_p'(r_1, \ldots, r_n) dr_1 \cdots dr_n.$$

In the most general case of an extended atomic system, this matrix component cannot be further simplified. However, we shall assume that our system is a single atom, whose dimensions are small compared with the wave length of the impinging radiation. In this case, first, $E_a(r_i)$ will remain approximately constant over the region where the wave function is appreciable, so that we may replace it by an average value $E_a(\overline{r_i})$ and take it outside the integral sign. This is legitimate if we are dealing with visible light but could not be done with x-rays; in that case, in fact, the factor $E_a(r_i)$ is the one which, in the closely related problem of x-ray scattering, leads to the atomic form factor. When now we take out this factor, the remaining integral $\int w_p^*(\partial/\partial x_i) w_p' \, dv$, where we have symbolized the variables of integration by dv, is clearly closely related to the matrix of the x component of momentum of the ith electron. In fact, if we include a factor $(h/2\pi i)$, it is just the matrix component in question. But now we can use Eq. (3.8.1), which states that the matrix component of the momentum equals the matrix component of the mass times velocity, to transform this to another form which is usually more convenient. Let us write out Eq. (3.8.1) explicitly, treating each wave function as an expansion of the form (3.2.2). We then have

$$\frac{d}{dt}(\bar{x}) = \sum_p \sum_{p'} c_p^* c_{p'} e^{-(2\pi i/h)(E_{p'} - E_p)t} \left(-\frac{2\pi i}{h} \right) (E_{p'} - E_p) x_{pp'}$$

$$= \frac{1}{m} \sum_p \sum_{p'} c_p^* c_{p'} e^{-(2\pi i/h)(E_{p'} - E_p)t} \int w_p^* \frac{h}{2\pi i} \frac{\partial}{\partial x} w_{p'} \, dv.$$

By comparing terms, we see at once that

$$\int w_p^* \frac{h}{2\pi i} \frac{\partial}{\partial x_i} w_{p'} \, dv = m_i \left(-\frac{2\pi i}{h} \right) (E_{p'} - E_p) x_{ipp'}. \quad (19)$$

That is, our integrals can be written in terms of matrix components of the electric displacement of the various particles. When we multiply by the ratios e_i/m_i involved in (16), these are converted into matrix components of the electric moments of the particles, and finally, when we sum over i, as in (16), we get the matrix components of the total electric moment of the atom, which we have denoted in Sec. 4.7 as $(ex)_{12}$, or in our case $(ex)_{pp'}$, and which we shall now denote as $M_{pp'}$.

We are now ready to put our information together and evaluate the nondiagonal matrix component of (16). We have a matrix component connected with each transition from the original state in which one particular oscillator has its quantum number change by ± 1 unit, and in which the atom has its quantum numbers change from p to p'. If it is the ath oscillator which has a transition, the matrix component is

$$H_{n_a, n_a \pm 1} = \sqrt{\frac{h(n_a + 1)}{8\pi^2 \epsilon_0 \nu_a}} \frac{2\pi i}{h} (E_{p'} - E_p) E_a(\bar{r}_i) M_{pp'} \quad \text{for plus sign,}$$

$$= \sqrt{\frac{h n_a}{8\pi^2 \epsilon_0 \nu_a}} \frac{2\pi i}{h} (E_{p'} - E_p) E_a(\bar{r}_i) M_{pp'} \quad \text{for minus sign.} \quad (20)$$

The energy will increase, in going from the first to the second state, by the amount $\pm h\nu_a + E_{p'} - E_p$. We shall see in a moment that, as in all perturbation problems, the important transitions are those in which the energy hardly changes at all. That is, for the important transitions, we have approximately

$$h\nu_a = E_p - E_{p'} \quad \text{for plus sign;}$$
$$= E_{p'} - E_p \quad \text{for minus sign.} \quad (21)$$

Since ν_a by its definition is positive, this means that the plus sign is associated with an atomic transition from one atomic state to a state of lower energy, or with an emission of radiation, the quantum number of the oscillator at the same time increasing, indicating the addition of a photon to the radiation field; similarly, the minus sign is associated with absorption of radiation. For the important terms, then, we may approximately replace ν_a in (20) by ν, the frequency associated with the atomic transition.

We are now ready to apply the method of variation of constants. Let us write the wave function of a perturbed problem as $\psi = \sum_m C_m(t) u_m^0(x)$, as in Sec. 4.5.

Let us assume that we start with an unperturbed problem, whose energy levels are the diagonal matrix components H_{mm} of the energy operator with respect to these unperturbed wave functions u_m^0; there are also nondiagonal matrix components, however, which do not vanish. It is then useful to write

$$C_m(t) = c_m(t) e^{-(2\pi i/h) H_{mm} t}, \quad (22)$$

where the exponential takes account of that part of the time variation of C_m arising from the diagonal matrix components of energy. When we substitute in Schrödinger's equation, and proceed as in the derivation of (4.5.1), we then find

$$\frac{dc_k}{dt} = -\frac{2\pi i}{h} \sum_{m \neq k} H_{km} c_m e^{(2\pi i/h)(H_{kk} - H_{mm})t}. \quad (23)$$

We shall now assume that at time $t = 0$ the system is entirely in a particular state, which we may denote by subscript zero. The time rates of change of the c_k's are small, for they depend only on the nondiagonal components H_{km}, which are zero if the perturbation is zero. Thus for some little time c_0 will be practically unity, the other c's practically zero. Let us use (23) for finding the rate of change of one of the c_k's corresponding to a state for which $k \neq 0$; that is, the rate at which a state builds up. On the right side of (23) we can then approximately replace the values c_m which appear inside the summation by their values at $t = 0$; that is, we can replace c_0 by unity, the other c's by zero. When we do this, (23) reduces to a single term,

$$\frac{dc_k}{dt} = -\frac{2\pi i}{h} H_{k0} e^{(2\pi i/h)(H_{kk}-H_{00})t}.$$

This can be at once integrated; its integral, corresponding to the initial condition that c_k be zero when $t = 0$, is

$$c_k = H_{k0} \frac{e^{(2\pi i/h)(H_{kk}-H_{00})t} - 1}{H_{00} - H_{kk}}.$$

We are interested in the value $c_k^* c_k$, representing the probability of finding the system in the kth state at time t. From the expression above we find

$$c_k^* c_k = \frac{4|H_{k0}|^2}{(H_{00} - H_{kk})^2} \sin^2 \frac{\pi}{h}(H_{kk} - H_{00})t. \qquad (24)$$

That is, the probability of finding the system in one particular state goes sinusoidally with the time. However, in our problem, and in many important problems of transitions from one state to another, we have many possible states into which the system can go. The reason is that we have available photons of all possible energies, so that the total change of energy of the system, made up of the change of energy of the atom, and the almost exactly compensating change of energy of the radiation field, can take on any desired value. It is this total change of energy which we shall identify with the $H_{kk} - H_{00}$ of Eq. (24); the very small changes of energy, corresponding to almost exact conservation of energy between atomic system and field, are important because of the term in the denominator of (24).

What we are really interested in is the sum of the $c_k^* c_k$'s over all states k corresponding to the same transition of the atomic system, but to the different possible transitions of the oscillators representing the field. In other words, we lump together many transitions resulting in the emission or absorption of photons whose energies are almost right to result in conservation. Though we shall not do it, it is rather obvious that we could investigate the breadth of the emitted or absorbed spectral line by studying the amount of energy emitted or absorbed in oscillators or photons of various frequencies close to that for which conservation is satisfied. Now let us carry out a summation of the quantity in (24). Let us suppose that there are energy levels of the oscillators distributed in a uniform way over energies in the neighborhood of those leading to conservation, the number of energy levels per unit energy range being dN/dE. We can convert the summation into an integration by introducing a quantity $u = (\pi/h)(H_{kk} - H_{00})t$ and integrating with respect to u. The matrix component H_{k0} will be approximately independent of u, so that it can be taken outside the integral sign. We then have

$$\sum_k c_k^* c_k = 4|H_{k0}|^2 \frac{dN}{dE} \frac{\pi t}{h} \int_{-\infty}^{\infty} \frac{\sin^2 u}{u^2} \, du$$

$$= \frac{4\pi^2}{h} |H_{k0}|^2 \frac{dN}{dE} t. \qquad (25)$$

Here we have integrated from $-\infty$ to ∞; but the essential contributions to the integral all come from small values of u.

In (25) we see that when we take account of the continuum of levels into which transitions are possible, the number of systems in the state resulting from an atomic transition increases proportionally to the time, unlike the situation in (24), where it varied sinusoidally. Thus we can take the time rate of change of (25), or the factor multiplying t, as the probability of a transition per unit time. We are now ready to use the matrix components (20) to work out the quantity (25) quantitatively. In doing this, we must consider the quantity $E_a(\overline{r_i})$ appearing in (20). Different oscillators will have different values of this quantity, as the phase of the different normal vibrations happens to differ at the location of the atom. We really should take an average value in evaluating the square of the matrix component in (25). The mean square of E_a, averaged over the volume V of the container, is easily found, for we know that E_a^2 integrates to unity; hence the mean-square value is $1/V$. We also have the mean-square value of the cosine of the angle between E_a and $M_{pp'}$; since there will be normal modes with their electric fields in all sorts of directions, oriented at random, the mean-square value of the cosine will be one-third. Hence the square of $E_a(\overline{r_i}) \cdot M_{pp'}$ in (20) is to be replaced by $|M_{pp'}|^2/3V$. We note also that we are to use (21) and replace the frequencies concerned by ν, the frequency associated with the transition $p \to p'$ by Bohr's frequency condition.

When we make these changes, we find that in place of (25) we have

$$\sum_k c_k^* c_k = \frac{8\pi^3}{(4\pi\epsilon_0)h^2} \frac{|M_{pp'}|^2}{3} h \frac{dN}{dE} \frac{h\nu}{V} t \quad \begin{cases} (\overline{n_a} + 1) \text{ for emission} \\ (\overline{n_a}) \text{ for absorption} \end{cases} \quad (26)$$

where $\overline{n_a}$ represents the average value of the n_a for those oscillators for which conservation is approximately satisfied. We can now interpret expression (26) in terms of the language used in Sec. 4.6, and in particular in terms of Eq. (4.6.5). The quantity $h\, dN/dE$ is the same as $dN/d\nu$, the number of electromagnetic oscillations per unit frequency range; we have seen in Sec. 4.6 that this is $8\pi\nu^2/c^3$ per unit volume, or is $8\pi\nu^2 V/c^3$ for the volume V. The upper equation of (26) then tells us that the probability that an atom in state p [equivalent to state 2 in Eq. (4.6.5)] will emit radiation and have a transition per unit time to state p' [equivalent to state 1 in (4.6.5)] is

$$\frac{8\pi^3}{(4\pi\epsilon_0)h^2} \frac{|M_{pp'}|^2}{3} \frac{8\pi h\nu^3}{c^3} (\overline{n_a} + 1). \quad (27)$$

Here $\overline{n_a}$ is equivalent to N_ν of (4.6.5). We thus see by comparison that we have agreement between (27) and (4.6.5), provided

$$B = \frac{8\pi^3 |M_{pp'}|^2}{(4\pi\epsilon_0)3h^2}, \qquad A = \frac{64\pi^4 |M_{pp'}|^2 \nu^3}{(4\pi\epsilon_0)3c^3 h}. \quad (28)$$

This value agrees with the value (4.7.1) given in the text. The case of absorption likewise agrees with Sec. 4.6.

By this calculation then, we have justified Einstein's picture of the emission and absorption of radiation and have derived values for his probability coefficients A and B. This is one of the simplest calculations in the quantum theory of radiation, and we shall not give any others, though the general theory is interesting and important. It is treated in great detail in W. Heitler, "The Quantum Theory of Radiation," Oxford University Press, New York, where references to the original work are also given. Heitler shows how we can obtain details not only about emission and absorption, but about scattering, dispersion, and other optical problems, about frequency distribution, polarization, and all the features of interest in physical optics. These problems, though diverse, still all use essentially the same principles which we have worked out in this appendix. Heitler also goes deeply into the relativistic case, where the energy of the electrons or photons can become much greater than we have assumed in our treatment. In that case, many new phenomena come in, most of them arising from the possibility of creation of positron-electron pairs, which do not concern us at the low energies considered in the present volume, but which are of great importance in nuclear physics.

APPENDIX 12

SCHRÖDINGER'S EQUATION FOR THE CENTRAL FIELD PROBLEM

Schrödinger's equation for the central field problem is $(-\nabla^2 + V)u = Eu$, where V, the potential energy, is a function of r, which is equal to $-2Z/r$ in atomic units for the Coulomb field, as given in Eq. (5.1.2). We express this equation in spherical polar coordinates, in which it is well known that the equation becomes

$$\frac{1}{r^2}\frac{\partial}{\partial r}\left(r^2\frac{\partial u}{\partial r}\right) + \frac{1}{r^2 \sin\theta}\frac{\partial}{\partial\theta}\left(\sin\theta\frac{\partial u}{\partial\theta}\right) + \frac{1}{r^2 \sin^2\theta}\frac{\partial^2 u}{\partial\varphi^2} = (V - E)u. \quad (1)$$

The expression for the Laplacian in spherical coordinates is given, for instance, in Slater and Frank, "Mechanics," McGraw-Hill Book Company, Inc., New York, 1947, Appendix VII, or Slater and Frank, "Electromagnetism," Appendix IV. We now assume, as in Sec. 5.1, that u can be written as a product of functions R, Θ, Φ, which are functions respectively of r, θ, and φ. We substitute this expression for u into (1) and divide by the product $R\Theta\Phi$. We multiply by r^2; and then, rearranging terms, we can rewrite (1) in the form

$$\frac{1}{R}\frac{d}{dr}\left(r^2\frac{dR}{dr}\right) - r^2(V - E) = -\frac{1}{\Theta}\frac{1}{\sin\theta}\frac{d}{d\theta}\left(\sin\theta\frac{d\Theta}{d\theta}\right) - \frac{1}{\Phi}\frac{1}{\sin^2\theta}\frac{d^2\Phi}{d\varphi^2}. \quad (2)$$

In this equation the left side is a function of r alone, the right side a function of the angles alone. These quantities cannot be equal, for all values of r, θ, and φ, unless each side is a constant. Let this constant be called $l(l + 1)$. Setting the left side of (2) equal to this constant, we arrive at the first equation of (5.1.3). Setting the right side of (2) equal to the constant, we may then multiply by $\sin^2\theta$, rearrange terms, and we find

$$\frac{1}{\Phi}\frac{d^2\Phi}{d\varphi^2} = \left[-\frac{1}{\Theta}\frac{1}{\sin\theta}\frac{d}{d\theta}\left(\sin\theta\frac{d\Theta}{d\theta}\right) - l(l + 1)\right]\sin^2\theta. \quad (3)$$

Here the left side is a function of φ alone, the right side a function of θ alone; by the same argument used above, each side must then be a constant, and we let this constant be called $-m^2$. When we set the left side of (3) equal to this constant, we arrive at the third equation of (5.1.3); when we set the right side equal to the same constant, we find the second equation of (5.1.3).

We now proceed to solve Eqs. (5.1.3) as described in the text. The spherical harmonics which we meet are taken up in somewhat more detail in Appendix V of Slater and Frank, "Electromagnetism." They are taken up in a good deal more detail, and the wave functions for hydrogen are set up in a convenient form for practical use, in Chap. V of Pauling and Wilson, "Introduction to Quantum

Mechanics," McGraw-Hill Book Company, Inc., New York, 1935. That reference is a good one for supplementing the present work in a good many cases where more detailed presentation of results is desired.

The Laplacian operator on the left side of (1) has to be multiplied by $-h^2/8\pi^2 m$ to convert it into the kinetic energy operator, in ordinary rather than atomic units. It then becomes the operator which we have used in our discussion of the angular momentum in Sec. 5.3.

APPENDIX 13

APPROXIMATE ATOMIC WAVE FUNCTIONS AND ENERGY LEVELS

In Sec. 6.3 we have seen that it is not a bad approximation to use hydrogenlike wave functions to represent the various wave functions of an atom; but the effective nuclear charge must be different from the actual nuclear charge, on account of the effects of inner and outer shielding. For estimating the size of the wave function, we have seen that only inner shielding needs to be taken into account, but for the energy we must consider outer shielding as well. In the present appendix we shall take up the question of approximate hydrogenlike wave functions in more detail and shall use them to investigate the energy relationships in the atom.

The first thing which we shall do is to give some rules, empirically determined, which lead to fairly good effective nuclear charges, or shielding constants, for the lighter elements. We have seen that the field acting on an electron at distance r is $Z(r)e/4\pi\epsilon_0 r^2$, where $Z(r)$ is the total number of electronic charges contained within a sphere of radius r, including both the nuclear charge and the electrons within the sphere. If we were to choose a value of $Z(r)$ corresponding to the radius of maximum density, for a given wave function, we should not make a very bad error by using this value as a constant value for that whole wave function; in other words, it would be an effective nuclear charge for a hydrogenlike problem whose wave function would be a good approximation to the correct wave function. It is convenient to write this value of $Z(r)$ in the form $Z - S_i$, where Z is the nuclear charge, S_i an inner shielding constant. To get S_i, we should add up the total number of electrons within a sphere whose radius is the effective radius of the ith electron's wave function.

It is easier to figure not by means of the radius, but from the quantum number, since to a rough approximation the radius of an orbit is $n_i^2/(Z - S_i)$, where n_i is the principal quantum number, so that electrons inside a given one are those of smaller principal quantum number. Table 1 proves to give roughly the contribution to the shielding constant of a given electron from each other type of electron, valid for the electrons found in the light atoms. We see that the shielding of one electron by a second does not go suddenly from unity to zero as the shielding electron's quantum number becomes greater than that of the shielded electron, but instead changes gradually, in accordance with the fact that each electron really has charge distributed over all distances, and it is possible for part of the charge to be inside, part outside, a given radius.

To illustrate the use of this table, let us take the case of Na, $Z = 11$, in its ground state $1s^2 2s^2 2p^6 3s$. Evidently we have three shells, corresponding to the three values of n. Then we have

$n = 1: S = 0.35,$ radius $= n^2/(Z - S) = 1/10.65 = 0.09$
$n = 2: S = 2(0.85) + 7(0.35) = 4.15,$ radius $= 4/6.85 = 0.58$
$n = 3: S = 2 + 8(0.85) = 8.80,$ radius $= 9/2.20 = 4.09.$

In angstrom units these values are 0.048, 0.31, 2.16. They can be compared with the more accurate values given in Table 6.4.2, or 0.050 for the 1s shell, 0.32 for the 2s, 0.28 for the 2p, 1.55 for the 3s. Our values are quite good for the inner electrons, rather inaccurate for the valence electron; and this is characteristic of the wave functions determined by our simple rules. Though they are not very accurate, still they are good enough to provide a valuable guide in examining atomic magnitudes.

TABLE 1. CONTRIBUTION OF ONE SHIELDING ELECTRON OF GIVEN QUANTUM NUMBER TO SHIELDING CONSTANT OF SHIELDED ELECTRON

Shielded electron	Shielding electron				
	1s	2s	2p	3s	3p
1s	0.35	0	0	0	0
2s	0.85	0.35	0.35	0	0
2p	0.85	0.35	0.35	0	0
3s	1.00	0.85	0.85	0.35	0.35
3p	1.00	0.85	0.85	0.35	0.35

The calculations we have given so far refer to wave functions rather than energy levels. To examine energy values, we shall proceed in a straightforward manner. First we shall apply the Hamiltonian operator to the wave function of the whole atom and try, in this way, to get a value for the energy of the whole atom. We shall show that this can be done as well for an ion, shall subtract energies, and shall find that this gives in fact a fairly good value for the corresponding ionization potential. Proceeding further, we shall look into the values of the one-electron energies of the problem and shall show that these form good approximations to the ionization potentials, as indicated in Sec. 6.3.

The result of the approximate calculation we have made has been a set of one-electron hydrogenlike wave functions, one for each electron of the atom. These satisfy equations which, in atomic units, are

$$\left[-\nabla_i^2 - \frac{2(Z - S_i)}{r_i} \right] u_i = - \frac{(Z - S_i)^2}{n_i^2} u_i. \tag{1}$$

Now the potential energy of the whole atom, in atomic units, is

$$- \sum_i \frac{2Z}{r_i} + \sum_{\text{all pairs}} \frac{2}{r_{ij}},$$

if r_{ij} is the distance between the ith and jth electrons. Thus the Hamiltonian is

$$H = \sum_i \left(-\nabla_i^2 - \frac{2Z}{r_i} + \sum_{j \text{ inside } i} \frac{2}{r_{ij}} + \sum_{j \text{ in same shell as } i} \frac{1}{r_{ij}} \right),$$

where the two summations are the same thing as the sum over all pairs. If now we assume that $u = u_1, \ldots, u_n$, where the u's are as we have found, and try to see how good an approximation this forms, we have, substituting for the Laplacians, from Eq. (1),

$$Hu = \left[- \sum_i \frac{(Z - S_i)^2}{n_i^2} \right] u + \sum_i \left(- \frac{2S_i}{r_i} + \sum_{j \text{ inside } i} \frac{2}{r_{ij}} + \sum_{j \text{ in same shell as } i} \frac{1}{r_{ij}} \right) u.$$

If Schrödinger's equation were satisfied, this would be Eu, where E is a constant. This is not true; the first term is a constant times u, but the second is a variable function of the r's times u. The average value of the last term, however, is approximately zero. For $2/r_{ij}$ is the potential, at the ith electron, of the jth electron. If the latter is inside, and we average over its position, and average to make it spherically symmetrical, the potential will be the same as if it were concentrated at the center, or will be $2/r_i$. For an electron in the same shell, it turns out that the average of $1/r_{ij}$ is about $2(0.35)/r_i$. The summation, for all electrons inside or in the same shell as i, is then essentially $2S_i/r_i$, just canceling the first term, leaving the result, using this approximate method of averaging, of

$$Hu = - \sum_i \frac{(Z - S_i)^2}{n_i^2} u,$$

showing that we have an approximate solution, and that the energy of the atom is $- \sum_i \dfrac{(Z - S_i)^2}{n_i^2}$. This represents the negative of the energy required to remove all the electrons from the atom. If we wish to find the energy of the atom by first-order perturbation theory, we recall that we must find the diagonal term of the energy matrix, or $\int u^* Hu \, dv$. This means averaging the energy over the wave function, or over the motions of the electrons; and to the same approximation we have just used, the summations average to zero, leaving the same energy we just found.

As an example of the calculation of energy, we can again take the case of Na. The energy of normal Na is, using the shielding constants found above, $-[2(10.65/1)^2 + 8(6.85/2)^2 + (2.20/3)^2] = -321.4$ Rydbergs. With one $1s$ electron removed, making the appropriate changes in shielding constants, the energy is $-[(11.00/1)^2 + 8(7.20/2)^2 + (3.05/3)^2] = -240.6$ Rydbergs. The difference is 80.8 Rydbergs, representing the ionization potential, to be compared with the correct value 80.9 from Table 6.4.1. Similarly with the $2s$ or $2p$ removed, the energy is $-[2(10.65/1)^2 + 7(7.20/2)^2 + (3.05/3)^2] = -318.6$, leaving an ionization potential of 2.8 Rydbergs, in almost exact agreement with the experimental value 2.79 for the $2p$, though the $2s$, with 5.10, is quite different; it is obvious that our simplified rules, which treat s and p electrons as being identical, cannot take account of the experimental differences between these levels, which get less and less important as we go to heavier atoms. Finally the ionization potential of the $3s$, as we immediately see, is simply $(2.20/3)^2 = 0.54$ Rydbergs, compared with the experimental value of 0.38.

The method of computing energies of the whole atom or ion, which we have outlined in the preceding paragraphs, is fairly accurate. We have pointed out in the text, however, that it involves subtracting one large quantity from another, and we have mentioned that the one-electron energy levels in the method of the self-consistent field prove in fact to form fairly accurate approximations to the ionization potentials.   Our method of effective nuclear charges, being an approximation to the method of self-consistent fields, should show the same property, and we can give a simple though not entirely satisfactory proof.   The negative of the ionization potential is the energy of the atom minus the energy of the ion. If the ith electron is to be removed, and if S_i represents a shielding constant in the atom, S_i' for the ion, then the energy of the atom minus the energy of the ion is

$$-\sum_j \frac{(Z-S_j)^2}{n_j^2} + \sum_{j \neq i} \frac{(Z-S_j')^2}{n_j^2}.$$

If we set $S_j' = S_j - (S_j - S_j')$, and expand, this is

$$-\frac{(Z-S_i)^2}{n_i^2} + \sum_{j \neq i} \frac{1}{n_j^2}[(Z-S_j)^2 + 2(Z-S_j)(S_j - S_j') + (S_j - S_j')^2$$
$$- (Z-S_j)^2].$$

Our simple proof holds only in case there is no other electron in the same shell as the ith, and if we assume that each electron shields by either 1 or 0.   Then we have $S_j - S_j' = 0$ if the jth electron is inside the ith, 1 if the jth is outside the ith. Thus for the ionization energy we have

$$-\frac{(Z-S_i)^2}{n_i^2} + \sum_{j \text{ outside } i} \frac{2(Z-S_i + \frac{1}{2})}{n_j^2}. \tag{2}$$

If we disregard the small correction $\frac{1}{2}$ in the last term of (2), we see that this last term can be rewritten as

$$\sum_{j \text{ outside } i} \frac{2}{r_j},$$

where r_j is the radius of the jth shell, using the simple method of computation which we are employing.   But this is then just the correction for outer shielding, discussed in Sec. 6.3.   Thus we find that the ionization energy (2), as found from the difference of the energy of atom and ion, equals the energy of the hydrogenlike orbit, determined by use of the inner shielding constant S_i for the ith electron, with a correction on account of outer shielding, which in this method of calculation comes from the rearrangement of shielding constants of the outer electrons when an inner electron is removed.   But the discussion of Sec. 6.3 shows that the one-electron energy is determined in just the same way from inner and outer shielding.   Hence, to the rather crude order of approximation which we are using at the moment, we verify our earlier statement that the energy of the one-electron problem equals the ionization potential of the corresponding electron.

Fortunately we do not have to rely on such inaccurate arguments to verify this important theorem.   By use of proper self-consistent wave functions, we can carry through an argument following the same steps as the one we have just given, but expressing the energy properly in terms of average values of the various potential energy terms.   When this argument is properly carried out, we verify the correctness of our statement, to a much better order of accuracy than we have been using in this appendix.

APPENDIX 14

THE LANDÉ FORMULA

In this appendix we wish to investigate the interaction of two angular momentum vectors, which have an interaction energy proportional to the cosine of the angle between the vectors, according to wave mechanics, and to prove the Landé formula (7.2.2), giving the energy levels of this system. We could carry out this calculation using Schrödinger's equation, leading to a solution involving spherical harmonics of the angles; the theorems which we shall prove are essentially theorems concerning these spherical harmonics. However, we can give our results in a more simple and elegant way by using matrix methods. It is in this way, before the development of wave mechanics but after matrix mechanics had been worked out, that these theorems were first proved, and though the matrix methods are more involved than wave mechanics for many problems, this particular one is best handled by matrices. We shall start by deducing the properties of a single angular momentum vector, arriving at space quantization directly from matrix mechanics. Then we shall investigate the coupling of two such vectors.

The angular momentum $\mathbf{M}$ of a particle of mass m, at a position with vector displacement $\mathbf{r}$, moving with velocity $\mathbf{v}$, according to the classical mechanics, is equal to $m(\mathbf{r} \times \mathbf{v})$. Thus its x component is $M_x = yp_z - zp_y$, where p is the classical linear momentum vector, equal to mv. Corresponding to this, we can at once set up the quantum-mechanical operator corresponding to M_x: it is

$$M_x = \frac{h}{2\pi i}\left(y\,\frac{\partial}{\partial z} - z\,\frac{\partial}{\partial y} \right), \tag{1}$$

with corresponding formulas for the other components. We can now use the operator expression (1), or the commutation rules for coordinates and momenta, given in (3.7.1), to prove that if the Hamiltonian operator is the sum of the kinetic energy operator and a potential energy function which depends only on the distance r from a point, all three components of the angular momentum commute with the energy operator. This means, according to Sec. 3.7, that the three components of angular momentum are constant, in a central field, as we should expect from the analogy to classical mechanics. Similarly, we can prove that the operator $M_x^2 + M_y^2 + M_z^2$, representing the square of the magnitude of the angular momentum, commutes with a spherically symmetrical Hamiltonian, so that the total angular momentum remains constant in the absence of torques. We can go even further than this statement. If we have an atom consisting of a number of electrons, moving in the central field of the nucleus, but subject to Coulomb forces between electrons, we can set up angular momentum operators for the whole electronic system, consisting of sums of operators like (1) extended over all electrons. We can still prove that this total angular momentum commutes with the Hamiltonian, so that the angular momentum of the whole system of electrons is conserved, so long as the only torques are internal.

If there is an external field involving torques perpendicular to the z axis, the simplest way of describing the situation is that there is an additional term in the potential energy depending on the two quantities $x^2 + y^2$ and z; the dependence on x and y only in the combination $x^2 + y^2$ insures that there should be no component of torque along the z direction. (The proper way of handling a magnetic field is more complicated, involving the introduction of vector potentials, but it leads to the same final result in such a case as this.) When we introduce such an additional term into the Hamiltonian function, we find that the Hamiltonian still commutes with M_z, so that the z component of angular momentum still stays constant; but it no longer commutes with M_x, M_y, or M^2, so that these quantities vary with the time.

We may now use these simple facts regarding the angular momentum operator, together with other theorems which we shall prove, to derive a great deal of information about the behavior of the angular momentum vector. First, we can prove directly from (1) that the following commutation rules hold for the M's:

$$M_y M_z - M_z M_y = -\frac{h}{2\pi i} M_x,$$

$$M_z M_x - M_x M_z = -\frac{h}{2\pi i} M_y,$$

$$M_x M_y - M_y M_x = -\frac{h}{2\pi i} M_z, \tag{2}$$

and also

$$M_x(M_x^2 + M_y^2 + M_z^2) - (M_x^2 + M_y^2 + M_z^2)M_x = 0, \tag{3}$$

and similarly with M_y and M_z. These hold even if the M's are sums of operators over all electrons of an atom.

We recall from Sec. 3.7 that if two operators both have diagonal matrices, their operators must commute with each other. But from (2) no two components of the angular momentum commute with each other. Thus no two components can simultaneously have diagonal matrices. It is a little puzzling at this point that all three components of M do not simultaneously have diagonal matrices, for we have just seen that if the electrons move in a central field, all three components of M commute with the energy, and hence are independent of time, and we are used to thinking that the matrix of any quantity independent of time must be diagonal. This is not the case here, and we shall see later how the situation is to be explained. But, at least, (2) and (3) lead to a justification of the possibility of assuming that one component of $\mathbf{M}$, say M_z, which, as we have seen, remains constant even in the presence of a torque perpendicular to z, has a diagonal matrix, and that simultaneously $M_x^2 + M_y^2 + M_z^2$ has a diagonal matrix, provided there is no external torque. We shall assume this, being prepared to find that M_x and M_y do not have diagonal matrices.

Let the quantum number which characterizes the various values of M_z be called m. Then let us write the (m,m') component of the first and second equations of (2) in matrix form. We have

$$M_y(m,m')M_z(m',m') - M_z(m,m)M_y(m,m')$$

$$= M_y(m,m')[M_z(m',m') - M_z(m,m)] = -\frac{h}{2\pi i} M_x(m,m'), \tag{4}$$

where we denote the (m,m') component of M_y by $M_y(m,m')$, etc.; and

$$[M_z(m,m) - M_z(m',m')]M_x(m,m') = -\frac{h}{2\pi i} M_y(m,m'). \tag{5}$$

Both (4) and (5) give values for the ratio $M_x(m,m')/M_y(m,m')$. If we equate these values, we have an equation for M_z; it is

$$[M_z(m',m') - M_z(m,m)]^2 = \left(\frac{h}{2\pi}\right)^2. \tag{6}$$

This equation seems to imply that the M_z for any quantum number m' differs from that for the quantum number m by the amount $h/2\pi$. This obviously cannot be true in general; but in deriving (6) we have overlooked the possibility that $M_x(m,m')$ and $M_y(m,m')$ should both be zero, in which case (4) and (5) would be satisfied by any arbitrary value of $M_z(m',m')$. What we have really derived in (6) is the statement that $M_z(m',m')$ differs from $M_z(m,m)$ by $h/2\pi$, provided there are nonvanishing matrix components $M_x(m,m')$ and $M_y(m,m')$ between the two states.

These statements are consistent with the following simple situation. $M_x(m,m')$ and $M_y(m,m')$ have nonvanishing matrix components only for the case where $m' = m \pm 1$; and (6) applies just in these cases, showing that the value of M_z increases by $h/2\pi$ when m increases by unity. We may then set $M_z = mh/2\pi$, establishing the quantized value of the component of angular momentum, which we have already derived in Chap. 5 for Schrödinger's equation. To get the symmetry between positive and negative values of M_z which we should obviously have, we must either have m an integer or have it equal to an integer $+ \frac{1}{2}$. The first case is that which we have with orbital angular momentum; the second is the case with electron spins.

Now that we have established the value of M_z, we can use either (4) or (5) to show that

$$\frac{M_x(m, m \pm 1)}{M_y(m, m \pm 1)} = \mp i, \tag{7}$$

where the upper or lower signs are to be used together, respectively. This shows that if, for instance, the matrix components of M_x are real, those of M_y are imaginary. We shall choose this case; if we made the opposite choice, the eventual results would be the same. We may assume that the matrices of M_x and M_y are Hermitian; thus we can conclude that

$$M_x(m + 1, m) = M_x(m, m + 1), \qquad M_y(m + 1, m) = -M_y(m, m + 1), \qquad \text{etc.}$$

Putting these results together, we can then use the third equation of (2) to fix the values of these components of M_x and M_y. We use the formulas for a matrix product and set up this equation for the (m,m) component. We have

$$M_x(m, m + 1)M_y(m + 1, m) + M_x(m, m - 1)M_y(m - 1, m)$$

$$- M_y(m, m + 1)M_x(m + 1, m) - M_y(m, m - 1)M_x(m - 1, m) = -m\left(\frac{h}{2\pi}\right)^2.$$

This leads at once to

$$M_x^2(m - 1, m) = M_x^2(m, m + 1) + \frac{1}{2} m \left(\frac{h}{2\pi}\right)^2. \tag{8}$$

This equation can be satisfied only if there is an upper bound to m; if it were not the case, there would be negative values for some of the components M_z^2. Let us then assume that the maximum value of m is called l. We then have in (8) complete information for finding all the M_x's. We find easily

$$M_x(m, m+1) = M_x(m+1, m) = \sqrt{(l-m)(l+m+1)}\, \frac{h}{4\pi}$$

$$M_y(m, m+1) = -M_y(m+1, m) = i\sqrt{(l-m)(l+m+1)}\, \frac{h}{4\pi}$$

$$M_z(m,m) = \frac{mh}{2\pi}. \tag{9}$$

With these values for the matrix components of the M's, we can at once find the matrix components of $M_x^2 + M_y^2 + M_z^2$. We find, as we should expect, that this quantity has a diagonal matrix; and we find by elementary matrix multiplication that its diagonal components are all equal to $l(l+1)(h/2\pi)^2$, independent of m. In other words, we have established this as the average value of the square of the magnitude of the angular momentum, in agreement with the results of wave mechanics.

What we have done so far might seem to be a rather roundabout way of proving the same results we have already found from Schrödinger's equation. Really we are in position to get a good deal more, however. For if we write M_x, M_y, M_z as sums of terms like (1), summed over all electrons, rather than as single terms, we can still prove the commutation rules (2) and (3). But these rules are all that we have used for our subsequent calculation. Thus our present method allows us to prove that the sum of a number of angular momentum vectors, such as the orbital angular momentum vectors of the electrons of an atom, has the same quantized component of angular momentum along a fixed direction, and the same quantized magnitude of angular momentum, which we have found for a single particle. It verifies, in other words, the rules which we have tacitly assumed in the text, that the vector sum of a number of angular momentum vectors is itself quantized.

Our rules can easily be adapted to the case of an electron spin, or a vector combination of electron spins. An electron spin acts like an angular momentum vector with $l = \frac{1}{2}$, so that m can take on only two values, $\pm \frac{1}{2}$. From (9) we then have $M_z(-\frac{1}{2}, \frac{1}{2}) = M_z(\frac{1}{2}, -\frac{1}{2}) = h/4\pi$, with corresponding values for M_y. Spins also have the same properties as orbital angular momenta; they combine vectorially to give a quantized resultant. Thus it is immaterial, as far as our rules of manipulation are concerned, whether we are dealing with orbital or spin angular momentum.

So far we have been tacitly assuming that there is no torque acting on our angular momentum vector. However, if there is a torque perpendicular to the z axis, we expect that the z component of angular momentum will still remain fixed, though the x and y components will not. In this case the energy will depend on the z component of angular momentum, or on m. If the torque is zero, however, the problem will be degenerate, states of different m values corresponding to the same energy. We can now use these facts to understand the existence of nondiagonal matrix components for M_x and M_y, as we have found in (9). If we take the average value of angular momentum, using the ordinary rules of quantum mechanics, the component $M_x(m, m+1)$, for instance, will be multiplied by an exponential function of time, $e^{(2\pi i/h)(E_{m+1}-E_m)t}$, and the other components will be multiplied by similar exponentials.   In the simplest case where the energy is proportional to the component of angular momentum along the z axis, or to m, as in the magnetic case where the energy is $-mh\nu_L$, ν_L being the Larmor frequency, this will give an exponential $e^{-2\pi i\nu_L t}$, so that M_x and M_y will oscillate with the Larmor frequency.   It is easy to get a complete interpretation of the motions, including the factor i in front of the formula for M_y in (9), which indicates a phase difference of 90° between M_x and M_y, and to show that in quantum theory as in classical theory we can interpret the result as being a precession of the total angular momentum vector about the z axis, with the Larmor frequency.

We now see how it is that, in the absence of a torque, the x and y components of angular momentum stay constant, even though they are not represented by diagonal matrices.   These components oscillate with the Larmor frequency ν, or corresponding frequencies in case the problem is not a magnetic one; and these frequencies go to zero if there is no torque.   In other words, we note that there are two ways in which a matrix can represent a constant quantity: either it can be a diagonal matrix, or it can have nondiagonal components only between degenerate states, states with the same energy. M_z is of the first type, M_x and M_y of the second.   The difference is that when the degeneracy is removed by imposing a torque perpendicular to the z direction, M_x and M_y start to vary sinusoidally with time with a frequency proportional to the torque, while M_z still stays constant. Of course, the choice of axis along which the component of angular momentum has a diagonal matrix is at our disposal.   We naturally choose it to be that direction along which we are going to impose a magnetic field, so that the choice of matrix components will still be correct even when there is a torque.

We now have secured a good understanding of the behavior of a single angular momentum vector, both in the absence of a field and in the presence of a torque such as is produced by a magnetic field.   Next we go on to our main problem, the coupling of two such vectors, say L and S, by an energy proportional to the cosine of the angle between the vectors.   The cosine of this angle is, of course, the scalar product of the angular momenta of the vectors, divided by the magnitudes of the angular momenta.   Let the angular momentum operators of the two vectors be $\mathbf{M}_1$ and $\mathbf{M}_2$; then the energy can be written in the form

$$\frac{\alpha \, (\mathbf{M}_1 \cdot \mathbf{M}_2)}{LS(h/2\pi)^2},$$

where α is a constant.   In the presence of this interaction, of course, the components of the two vectors L and S along the z axis will no longer be constant.   That is, M_L and M_S, representing the components of L and S along the z axis, will no longer be quantum numbers, and M_{z1} and M_{z2} will no longer be diagonal matrices with respect to the new quantum numbers which we must introduce to represent the system.   By the principles which we have been discussing, however, the total angular momentum, and its projection along the z axis, will still be constant, so long as there are no torques acting on the system as a whole.   As in Sec. 7.2, we may denote this total angular momentum by the quantum number J, and its projection along the z axis by M, (not to be confused with the angular momentum operator $\mathbf{M}$), and we may set up a table, like Table 7.2.1, to show how the values of M_L and M_S for the unperturbed levels correlate with the values of J and M for the perturbed levels.   To justify the general method of discussion used in Sec. 7.2, we then need two theorems, which we shall now prove.   First, there are no components of energy between states with different values of the total angular momentum along the z axis, symbolized by $M_L + M_S$ or M. Second, for each problem corresponding to a given M, we shall find perturbed energies which depend only on the J value of the resulting term, not on M. Once we have proved these theorems, we may then find the diagonal matrix components of energy and proceed to use the diagonal sum rule as in Sec. 7.2.

To prove our theorem that there are no nondiagonal matrix components of energy between states of different M value, we can use the theorem, which we have already quoted, that the total z component of angular momentum of all electrons commutes with the Hamiltonian operator H. Thus, if M represents the quantum number describing the total z component of angular momentum, or $M_L + M_S$, we have $HM_z - M_zH = 0$ as an operator equation, or the corresponding matrix equation

$$H(M,M')M_z(M',M') - M_z(M,M)H(M,M') = 0,$$
$$H(M,M')[M_z(M',M') - M_z(M,M)] = 0,$$

from which at once $H(M,M')$ must be zero if M' is different from M. This fact, that an energy operator involving only internal forces has no matrix components between two states of different component of angular momentum along the z axis, is often of great value.

The other theorem, that the perturbed energy levels corresponding to the same J value but different M values must be the same, is proved in a somewhat similar way. We know that $HM_z - M_zH = 0$, and yet that M_z has nondiagonal matrix components between states of different M value but the same J value. Let us then set up the matrix component of this equation between two such states, corresponding to the same J, but to values of M differing by 1 or -1 (so that M_z will have matrix components different from zero). For instance, we have

$$H(M,M)M_z(M, M + 1) - M_z(M, M + 1)H(M + 1, M + 1) = 0,$$
$$M_z(M, M + 1)[H(M,M) - H(M + 1, M + 1)] = 0.$$

Since $M_z(M, M + 1)$ is different from zero, we see that $H(M,M)$ must equal $H(M + 1, M + 1)$, or the energy values associated with the two M values must be the same, after we have carried out the perturbation calculation to get wave functions in which J and M are the suitable quantum numbers.

Now that we have justified our use of the diagonal sum rule, we may proceed to use it to calculate the energy levels associated with different J values, and so to verify the Landé formula (7.2.2). We find at once that the diagonal matrix component of energy, in the unperturbed system, associated with quantum numbers M_L and M_S, is

$$H(M_LM_S,M_LM_S) = \frac{\alpha M_L M_S}{LS}. \tag{10}$$

This arises simply from the z components of $\mathbf{M}_1$ and $\mathbf{M}_2$, for the x and y components have no diagonal matrix components. Before taking up the general case, let us apply these diagonal matrix components, and the diagonal sum rule, to the case of two vectors, with $L = 1$, $S = 2$, taken up in Table 7.2.1 (here L stands for l_1 of the table, S stands for l_2, J for L, etc.). For the state with $J = 3$, we have $M_L = 1$, $M_S = 2$, so that we see from (10) that the energy is simply α. Similarly, for $M = 2$, we have two states, with $M_L = 1$, $M_S = 1$, and $M_L = 0$, $M_S = 2$. The first of these has an unperturbed energy of $\alpha/2$, from (10), and the second of zero.   The sum of these is $\alpha/2$; this, by the sum rule, must be the sum of the energies of the states with $J = 3$ and $J = 2$.   Since we have already found that the state with $J = 3$ has energy α, this means that the state with $J = 2$ has energy $-\alpha/2$.   Next, the three states with $M = 1$ have $M_L = 1$, $M_S = 0$; $M_L = 0$, $M_S = 1$; and $M_L = -1$, $M_S = 2$.   The unperturbed energies are 0, 0, $-\alpha$, so that the sum of the energies is $-\alpha$.   This must be the sum of the energies of states with $J = 3, 2, 1$, which leaves $-3\alpha/2$ for the energy of the state with $J = 1$.   We readily verify that the other states, with $M = 0, -1, -2, -3$, are consistent with the energies which we have already found and give no new information.   We now note that substitution in the Landé formula (7.2.2) gives the same energies which we have found, so that we have proved the Landé formula for this simple case.

We can now use the same method for proving the Landé formula in the general case.   In every case there will be just one level with the maximum value of M, two with the next lower value, and so on, so that the sum rule will allow us to fix all the energies uniquely, as in our simple case.   The state of highest J value, with $J = L + S$, will correspond to the case $M_L = L$, $M_S = S$, so that by (10) its energy will be α; this is what the Landé formula (7.2.2) predicts in this case. It is then easier not to verify each energy level corresponding to each J value according to the Landé formula, but to find the values of the differences between the level corresponding to J and to $J - 1$.   The difference of the cosines, as computed by (7.2.2), is $[J(J + 1) - (J - 1)J]/2LS = J/2LS$, so that the difference of energies is α times this.   This rule, according to which the interval between levels with values J and $J - 1$ is proportional to J, is often called the Landé interval rule.   Let us see how to prove this in the general case.

We shall consider those two M values for which there are respectively p and $p + 1$ sublevels; that is, these M values are $L + S - p + 1$ and $L + S - p$. The sums of $M_L M_S$ for these two M values are

$$L(S - p + 1) + (L - 1)(S - p + 2) + \cdots + (L - p + 1)S$$

and

$$L(S - p) + (L - 1)(S - p + 1) + \cdots + (L - p)S.$$

We have only to multiply these by α/LS to get the corresponding sums of energies, in the first case of all states from $J = L + S$ down to $J = L + S - p + 1$, and in the second case down to $L + S - p$.   The difference, in other words, is the energy of the state with $J = L + S - p$.   But if we take the difference of the two sums above, it can be easily rewritten in the form

$$LS - (L + S) - (L + S - 1) - \cdots - (L + S - p + 1).$$

This equals the value LS minus the J values of all terms down to that with $J = L + S - p$.   According to the Landé interval rule, this quantity, divided by LS, is just the value of the cosine to be associated with the state $J = L + S - p$, so that we have verified formula (7.2.2) in the general case.

APPENDIX 15

THE ENERGIES OF ATOMIC MULTIPLETS

To solve atomic multiplet problems by the use of the diagonal sum rule, we must find diagonal matrix components of the energy with respect to the unperturbed wave functions, and this involves, according to (7.7.7), finding the quantities $(i/f/i)$, $(ij/g/ij)$, and $(ij/g/ji)$, defined in (7.7.5) and (7.7.6). We must assume that the one-electron functions u involved in these integrals are solutions of the central field problem, so that they have the form $R(r)\Theta(\theta)\Phi(\varphi)$, as in Chap. 5. The function R depends on n, the principal quantum number, and l, the azimuthal quantum number; the function of angles depends on l and on m_l, its component along z. In the definition of $(ij/g/ij)$ and $(ij/g/ji)$ we can now expand $1/r_{12}$ in terms of spherical harmonics of angles and powers of the distances r_1 and r_2. Then we can explicitly carry out the integrations with respect to angles and reduce the definitions of $(ij/g/ij)$ and $(ij/g/ji)$ to integrals over the radii. We shall not give the details of this integration but shall merely give the results.† The quantity $(ij/g/ij)$ really depends on the quantum numbers n, l, and m_l of the two wave functions; we may call it $J(n, l, m_l; n', l', m_{l'})$. Similarly we can call $(ij/g/ji)$ by the symbol $K(n, l, m_l; n', l', m_{l'})$. We find that we do not need the quantities $(i/f/i)$, provided we are interested only in the separation of the various levels of the multiplets, for it can be shown that they affect only the position of the center of gravity of a multiplet, not the separation.

Now in the reference above it is shown that

$$J(n, l, m_l; n', l', m_{l'}) = \sum_k a^k(l, m_l; l', m_{l'}) F^k(n, l; n', l'), \tag{1}$$

where

$$F^k(n, l; n', l') = 2(4\pi)^2 \int_0^\infty \int_0^\infty R_{nl}^2(r) R_{n'l'}^2(r') \frac{r(a)^k}{r(b)^{k+1}} r^2 r'^2 \, dr \, dr',$$

where by definition $r(a)$ is the smaller, $r(b)$ the larger, of r and r'. The coefficients a^k are given in Table 1. Similarly we have

$$K(n, l, m_l; n', l', m_{l'}) = \sum_k b^k(l, m_l; l', m_{l'}) G^k(n, l; n', l') \tag{2}$$

where

$$G^k(n, l; n', l') = 2(4\pi)^2 \int_0^\infty \int_0^\infty R_{nl}(r) R_{n'l'}(r) R_{nl}(r') R_{n'l'}(r') \frac{r(a)^k}{r(b)^{k+1}} r^2 r'^2 \, dr \, dr',$$

and the b^k's are also given in Table 1.

† The calculation is given in J. C. Slater, *Phys. Rev.* **34**, 1293 (1929)

Now that we have found the diagonal matrix components of the energy for the unperturbed wave functions, we are ready to use the diagonal sum rule to find the energies of the multiplets. The results will be different in each case, and we merely give an example to illustrate the method. We shall take as an example that of two equivalent p electrons, as discussed in Sec. 7.3 and Fig. 7.3.4. There are many ways to use the sum rule to get the result, in such a simple case as this. For instance, we have one unperturbed state with $M_L = 2$, $M_S = 0$, coming from the state with $m_{l_1} = m_{l_2} = 1$, with the two spins opposite to each other. This state, as we see from Fig. 7.3.4, must give the energy of the ^1D level. Using our rules, and omitting the I integrals, which are the same for all multiplets, the energy is $J(n, 1, 1; n, 1, 1)$, which is seen by use of the table to be $F^0(n1,n1) + \frac{1}{25}F^2(n1,n1)$. Next we may consider the two states with $M_L = 1$, $M_S = 0$, arising from $m_{l_1} = 1$, $m_{l_2} = 0$, with opposite spins, one state having $m_{s_1} = \frac{1}{2}$, $m_{s_2} = -\frac{1}{2}$, and the other having the reversed signs. The diagonal energy of each of these unperturbed states is seen from the table to be $F^0(n1,n1) - \frac{2}{25}F^2(n1,n1)$. Since this must be the sum of the ^1D and ^3P energies, we see that the energy of the ^3P is $F^0(n1,n1) - \frac{5}{25}F^2(n1,n1)$. Finally, we may use the state with $M_L = 0$, $M_S = 0$. There are three such states, two arising from $m_{l_1} = 1$, $m_{l_2} = -1$, with the two possible arrangements of opposed spins, and the third from $m_{l_1} = m_{l_2} = 0$, with opposed spins. The first two have energy $F^0(n1,n1) + \frac{1}{25}F^2(n1,n1)$, the third has $F^0(n1,n1) + \frac{4}{25}F^2(n1,n1)$. If we add these three, subtract from them the energies of ^1D and ^3P which we have already found, the remainder must be the energy of the ^1S. This is then found to be $F^0(n1,n1) + \frac{10}{25}F^2(n1,n1)$.

It is interesting to look at the energies of the three multiplets found in the preceding paragraph. We note by the definition that $F^2(n1,n1)$ is necessarily positive. Then the highest multiplet is the ^1S, with a contribution $\frac{10}{25}F^2$ in its energy. The next lower is ^1D, with $\frac{1}{25}F^2$, and the lowest is ^3P, with $-\frac{5}{25}F^2$. This is interesting for two particular reasons. First, the separations between multiplets depend only on one parameter, $F^2(n1,n1)$, so that the intervals between multiplets are in simple arithmetic relation to each other, the interval between ^1S and ^1D being three-halves as great as that between ^1D and ^3P. Such simple relationships are found in a few cases of multiplets, but more often the intervals depend on more than one integral, and since these have no simple relationship to each other, the intervals do not have simple ratios. Second, the ^3P, the multiplet of highest multiplicity, has the lowest energy. This is an example of a general rule, stated empirically by Hund before the theory was worked out, and the theory in most cases leads to this same situation. The reason for it is qualitatively simple. In the multiplet of highest multiplicity as many spins as possible are parallel to each other, so that the exclusion principle requires the orbital wave functions to be different, the charge distributions are separated from each other, and the repulsive Coulomb electrostatic interaction between electrons is minimized, leading to a low energy. By examining the meaning of our various integrals, in particular F^2, we could get detailed information as to how this works out in each particular case.

We have used one particular set of sum rules to get the energy levels of our problem of two equivalent p electrons; but there are a number of other unperturbed states which we could have used equally well. The reader can easily convince himself by trial that the same answers are obtained for the energies of the multiplets, no matter which states are used. In more complicated multiplet structures there will ordinarily not be as much choice, and there are plenty of fairly complicated cases where the diagonal sum rule does not suffice to determine the energies of all multiplets. In such a case, we must compute nondiagonal matrix components of energy as well, and use the conventional methods of perturbation theory. Even when this is necessary, however, the problem of finding the multiplets is not very difficult. The nondiagonal matrix components involve the same F and G integrals which we have been using, and rules for setting them up are easily stated, though we shall not give them here.

TABLE 1

$a^k(l,\ m_l;\ l',\ m_{l'})$

(*Note:* In cases with two $\pm$ signs, the signs can be combined in any of the four possible ways.)

Electrons	l	m_l	l'	$m_{l'}$	$k = 0$	2	4
ss	0	0	0	0	1	0	0
sp	0	0	1	± 1	1	0	0
	0	0	1	0	1	0	0
pp	1	± 1	1	± 1	1	$\frac{1}{25}$	0
	1	± 1	1	0	1	$-\frac{2}{25}$	0
	1	0	1	0	1	$\frac{4}{25}$	0
sd	0	0	2	± 2	1	0	0
	0	0	2	± 1	1	0	0
	0	0	2	0	1	0	0
pd	1	± 1	2	± 2	1	$\frac{2}{35}$	0
	1	± 1	2	± 1	1	$-\frac{1}{35}$	0
	1	± 1	2	0	1	$-\frac{2}{35}$	0
	1	0	2	± 2	1	$-\frac{4}{35}$	0
	1	0	2	± 1	1	$\frac{2}{35}$	0
	1	0	2	0	1	$\frac{4}{35}$	0
dd	2	± 2	2	± 2	1	$\frac{4}{49}$	$\frac{1}{441}$
	2	± 2	2	± 1	1	$-\frac{2}{49}$	$-\frac{4}{441}$
	2	± 2	2	0	1	$-\frac{4}{49}$	$\frac{6}{441}$
	2	± 1	2	± 1	1	$\frac{1}{49}$	$\frac{16}{441}$
	2	± 1	2	0	1	$\frac{2}{49}$	$-\frac{24}{441}$
	2	0	2	0	1	$\frac{4}{49}$	$\frac{36}{441}$

Table 1.—*Continued*

$$b^k(l, m_l; l', m_{l'})$$

(*Note:* In cases where there are two ± signs, the two upper, or the two lower, signs must be taken together.)

Electrons	l	m_l	l'	$m_{l'}$	$k = 0$	1	2	3	4
ss	0	0	0	0	1	0	0	0	0
sp	0	0	1	±1	0	$\frac{1}{3}$	0	0	0
	0	0	1	0	0	$\frac{1}{3}$	0	0	0
pp	1	±1	1	±1	1	0	$\frac{1}{25}$	0	0
	1	±1	1	0	0	0	$\frac{3}{25}$	0	0
	1	±1	1	∓1	0	0	$\frac{6}{25}$	0	0
	1	0	1	0	1	0	$\frac{4}{25}$	0	0
sd	0	0	2	±2	0	0	$\frac{1}{5}$	0	0
	0	0	2	±1	0	0	$\frac{1}{5}$	0	0
	0	0	2	0	0	0	$\frac{1}{5}$	0	0
pd	1	±1	2	±2	0	$\frac{2}{5}$	0	$\frac{3}{245}$	0
	1	±1	2	±1	0	$\frac{1}{5}$	0	$\frac{9}{245}$	0
	1	±1	2	0	0	$\frac{1}{15}$	0	$\frac{18}{245}$	0
	1	±1	2	∓1	0	0	0	$\frac{30}{245}$	0
	1	±1	2	∓2	0	0	0	$\frac{45}{245}$	0
	1	0	2	±2	0	0	0	$\frac{15}{245}$	0
	1	0	2	±1	0	$\frac{1}{5}$	0	$\frac{24}{245}$	0
	1	0	2	0	0	$\frac{4}{15}$	0	$\frac{27}{245}$	0
dd	2	±2	2	±2	1	0	$\frac{4}{49}$	0	$\frac{1}{441}$
	2	±2	2	±1	0	0	$\frac{6}{49}$	0	$\frac{5}{441}$
	2	±2	2	0	0	0	$\frac{4}{49}$	0	$\frac{15}{441}$
	2	±2	2	∓1	0	0	0	0	$\frac{35}{441}$
	2	±2	2	∓2	0	0	0	0	$\frac{70}{441}$
	2	±1	2	±1	1	0	$\frac{1}{49}$	0	$\frac{16}{441}$
	2	±1	2	0	0	0	$\frac{1}{49}$	0	$\frac{30}{441}$
	2	±1	2	∓1	0	0	$\frac{6}{49}$	0	$\frac{40}{441}$
	2	0	2	0	1	0	$\frac{4}{49}$	0	$\frac{36}{441}$

APPENDIX 16

THE THEORY OF MOLECULAR BINDING

All the theories of molecular binding, whether based on atomic orbitals, molecular orbitals, or other starting points, have a common mathematical background, which is very similar to what we have already encountered in the theory of atomic structure. We start with a set of one-electron wave functions, or orbitals, functions of coordinates and spin, one for each of the electrons which must be considered. We build up an antisymmetric wave function for all the electrons, corresponding to one electron being in each of these orbitals, using the determinantal method to set up this wave function. We ordinarily must use a linear combination of a number of such antisymmetric wave functions, to get a reasonable approximation to the real function. First, we need to take into account the spin degeneracy, which is treated just as in the atomic case. The problem is somewhat different from the atomic case, however, in that we are usually interested in the ground state of the electronic system for molecular binding, and generally this is one of very low multiplicity, usually a singlet, rather than having high multiplicity as with atoms. Next, we consider the equivalent to the orbital degeneracy in the atomic case: we make linear combinations of wave functions with different orbitals. Since we do not have the spherical symmetry of the single atom, these different orbitals do not ordinarily consist just of different spherical harmonics, corresponding to different orientations of an angular momentum vector in space; nevertheless, we usually have a number of orbitals which must be considered. They may correspond to different ways of drawing molecular bonds between atoms, for instance, and the process of combining such functions is in that case called resonance. In any case, however, we are left with a number of determinantal wave functions between which we make linear combinations, and this leads to a secular equation, which is generally too complicated to solve directly, but which we can simplify by such devices as the diagonal sum rule, and others which we shall investigate, so that the final result is a linear combination of antisymmetric wave functions, forming a fairly good approximation to the correct wave function. We find its energy as a function of internuclear distances, and that energy, and the related wave function, are the subject of our calculation.

There is just one respect in which the problem is often more complicated than the atomic problem: we often, as in the Heitler-London method, must deal with atomic orbitals which are not orthogonal to each other, and the lack of orthogonality can be of decisive importance, so that it cannot be neglected. To handle these cases, we shall first reformulate our perturbation method so as to allow nonorthogonal wave functions; we shall see that the modifications of the previous method are not great. Once we have got this more general formulation, we can fit all the various approaches to molecular problems into a single framework, and we shall give a number of examples to indicate how things work.

In Sec. 4.1 we set up the perturbation theory. The assumption that the unperturbed wave functions were orthogonal to each other came in Eq. (4.1.2), where we replaced the integral $\int u_k^{0*} u_j^0 \, dv$ by δ_{kj}, where the u^0's were the unperturbed wave functions. The only difference which comes in with nonorthogonal wave functions is to write

$$\int u_k^{0*} u_j^0 \, dv = d_{kj}, \tag{1}$$

where Eq. (1) serves as a definition of d_{kj}, and where if the u^0's are not orthogonal, the nondiagonal terms of d_{kj} do not vanish. When we come to the equivalent of Eq. (4.1.3) for the coefficients S_{ji} for transforming the unperturbed into the perturbed wave functions, we must then substitute d_{kj} for δ_{kj}, and the secular equation (4.3.4) becomes

$$\begin{vmatrix} H_{11} - d_{11}E & H_{12} - d_{12}E & \cdots & H_{1n} - d_{1n}E \\ H_{21} - d_{21}E & \cdots & \cdots & H_{2n} - d_{2n}E \\ \cdots\cdots\cdots\cdots\cdots\cdots\cdots\cdots\cdots\cdots \\ H_{n1} - d_{n1}E & \cdots & \cdots & H_{nn} - d_{nn}E \end{vmatrix} = 0. \tag{2}$$

The qualitative results of the solution of the perturbation problem are not altered by the terms in d_{ij} in this secular equation. Some quantitative results are changed, however, such as, for instance, the diagonal sum rule. The equations become somewhat more difficult to solve, but not seriously different.

Now let us apply our general method to the first problem discussed in the text, the hydrogen molecule. We first consider the Heitler-London method. If $u_a(x)$ and $u_b(x)$ represent normalized hydrogen functions surrounding atoms a and b, as in Sec. 8.3, then we consider a problem of spin degeneracy, in which the spins of the two electrons can be arranged in any of the four possible ways, but in which one electron is always in the orbital function u_a, the other always in u_b. The problem then has a close resemblance to that of two s electrons taken up in Sec. 7.8. We set up the same four determinantal wave functions I to IV as in that section, where for instance the function I is given by

$$\frac{1}{\sqrt{2}} \begin{vmatrix} u_a(x_1)\alpha(s_1) & u_a(x_2)\alpha(s_2) \\ u_b(x_1)\alpha(s_1) & u_b(x_2)\alpha(s_2) \end{vmatrix},$$

and where the other functions differ only in the assignment of spins to the orbital functions u_a and u_b. We then can start from first principles and compute the matrix components of energy and of unity between these various functions, so as not to make any mistakes on account of the lack of orthogonality of the functions u_a and u_b. We readily find, using some of the results of Sec. 8.3,

$$\begin{aligned} H_{\mathrm{I,I}} &= H_{\mathrm{IV,IV}} = (ab/H/ab) - (ab/H/ba), \\ H_{\mathrm{II,II}} &= H_{\mathrm{III,III}} = (ab/H/ab) \\ H_{\mathrm{II,III}} &= -(ab/H/ba) \\ d_{\mathrm{I,I}} &= d_{\mathrm{IV,IV}} = 1 - \alpha^2, \\ d_{\mathrm{II,II}} &= d_{\mathrm{III,III}} = 1 \\ d_{\mathrm{II,III}} &= -\alpha^2, \end{aligned} \tag{3}$$

where the quantities like $(ab/H/ab)$ are defined in (8.3.6), and α (not to be confused with the spin function α in the determinant above) is defined in (8.3.2). As in Sec. 7.8, there are no matrix components either of H or of unity between states with different M_S; that is, state I, with $M_S = 1$, states II and III with $M_S = 0$, and state IV, with $M_S = 0$, form three separate problems.

The energy of the triplet can then be found from state I; we have

$$H_{I,I} - d_{I,I}E = 0,$$

from which

$$E = \frac{(ab/H/ab) - (ab/H/ba)}{1 - \alpha^2}, \tag{4}$$

in agreement with (8.3.5). To get the singlet, we must solve the secular problem between states II and III. We have

$$\begin{vmatrix} H_{II,II} - d_{II,II}E & H_{II,III} - d_{II,III}E \\ H_{III,II} - d_{III,II}E & H_{III,III} - d_{III,III}E \end{vmatrix} = 0.$$

When we substitute the values of matrix components from (3), we find that this secular equation at once factors, giving

$$[(ab/H/ab) - (ab/H/ba) - (1 - \alpha^2)E][(ab/H/ab) + (ab/H/ba) - (1 + \alpha^2)E] = 0.$$

If we set the first factor equal to zero, we get the triplet solution found above in (4). From the other factor we have

$$E = \frac{(ab/H/ab) + (ab/H/ba)}{1 + \alpha^2} \tag{5}$$

as the energy of the singlet, again in agreement with (8.3.5). Now that we have found the energies, we can solve for the wave functions; and when we do it, we find that they are as given in (7.8.3), except for the normalization indicated in (8.3.3), so that our treatment of Sec. 8.3, which began by postulating the orbital part of the wave functions, is justified by a straightforward perturbation calculation.

Instead of using the Heitler-London method, we may prefer the molecular orbital method, or may prefer to find the relationship between the two, as in Sec. 8.4. We notice that in that section we did not really use accurate molecular orbital functions, which were really solutions of a two-center problem. We used, instead, combinations $u_a \pm u_b$ of atomic orbitals, suitably normalized. This method, which has been denoted by Mulliken the method of linear combinations of atomic orbitals, and abbreviated by him LCAO, is what is usually meant when we speak of the use of molecular orbitals, though clearly it is less satisfactory than a real use of molecular orbitals would be. We now set up, as in Sec. 8.4, the normalized functions

$$\frac{u_a(x) \pm u_b(x)}{\sqrt{2(1 \pm \alpha)}},$$

which we may denote by u_s and u_a, signifying symmetric and antisymmetric, respectively. We may now combine these molecular orbitals with spin functions and make up determinantal wave functions from them, compute the matrix components of energy, and carry out a perturbation calculation between various unperturbed states. In using the LCAO method, since the orbitals are orthogonal, we have the same rules for finding matrix components of energy which were given in Eqs. (7.7.5) and (7.7.6); but we must remember that in the operators f of that section we must include electrostatic attractions between each electron and each nucleus, and repulsions between the various nuclei.

There are now various ways in which we can proceed, depending on how many unperturbed states we consider in our perturbation problem. In the Heitler-London method we get nowhere at all unless we consider at least the four states leading to the problem of spin degeneracy, as we have just seen; but in the molecular orbital method this is not the case, and ordinarily we think of this method just from the point of view of taking one wave function and considering its diagonal energy as the energy of the system. This wave function is that corresponding to each of the electrons being in the symmetrical orbital u_s, with opposite spins. The diagonal energy of this state is then $(ss/H/ss)$, in a notation similar to what we have been using. In other words, it is

$$\frac{1}{4(1+\alpha)^2} \int [u_a(x_1) + u_b(x_1)][u_a(x_2) + u_b(x_2)]H[u_a(x_1) + u_b(x_1)][u_a(x_2) + u_b(x_2)]dx_1\,dx_2.$$

Multiplying out, we can rewrite this in the form

$$\frac{1}{2(1+\alpha)^2}[(ab/H/ab) + (ab/H/ba) + (aa/H/aa) + (aa/H/bb) + 4(aa/H/ab)],$$

where $(ab/H/ab)$ and $(ab/H/ba)$ are as defined in (8.3.6), and the other quantities are defined similarly. This is a complicated quantity, which cannot be interpreted properly without actually carrying out the integrations symbolized by these quantities and plotting the resulting energy as a function of distance. We observe that the integrals are of the same general nature as those occurring in the Heitler-London method, though some of them are more complicated. This is one of the features of the LCAO method: its integrals reduce to integrals over various atomic orbitals times quantities like $1/r_{a1}$ or $1/r_{12}$. Such integrals can be carried out in practical cases, though the mathematical steps are difficult. If the atomic orbitals can be approximated in an analytic form, analytic results can be obtained for the integrals. It is by these general methods that the results plotted in Fig. 8.2.2 were obtained.

If we wish to carry the molecular orbital method further, as in Sec. 8.2, we set up several unperturbed functions and investigate the perturbation problem between them. In that section we really were considering six unperturbed functions: that in which both electrons were in the symmetric state, with opposite spins; that in which both were in the antisymmetric, with opposite spins; and the four states corresponding to spin degeneracy, in which one electron is in the symmetric orbital, one in the antisymmetric, and the spins take up their four possible arrangements, leading to a singlet and triplet. As we stated in the text, when we write down the diagonal and nondiagonal matrix components of energy, following the methods which by now are becoming clear, we find that there are no matrix components of energy between the first two states and the last four. Thus the problem of spin degeneracy can be handled by itself, and the problem of two electrons in symmetric orbitals, and two in antisymmetric, becomes a perturbation problem with two unperturbed wave functions, which must be solved in the conventional way without any simplifications, and which leads to a solution in the form of a solution of a quadratic equation, as in (4.2.4). The resulting energy levels, coming from application of this perturbation calculation, are shown in Fig. 8.2.2.

Now we shall take up a more difficult problem, mentioned only qualitatively in the text, that of three hydrogen atoms, with atomic orbitals u_a, u_b, u_c, and three electrons. The spin-degeneracy problem here, as we mentioned in Sec. 7.3 and Table 7.3.5, leads to a quartet and two doublets, and the energies of the doublets are given by the solutions of a quadratic. The problem is that discussed in Sec. 9.3 of the text. Its solution gives a good deal of insight into more complicated problems of molecular structure. There are eight unperturbed wave functions, the four given in Table 7.3.5 (which we shall label I, II, III, IV), and four similar ones corresponding to negative values of M_S. We have stated in the text that state I by itself gives the quartet energy, and II, III, and IV give a cubic, one of whose roots gives the quartet energy, and the other two roots give the two doublets.

For the matrix components with respect to state I we then find

$$H_{I,I} = (abc/H/abc) - (abc/H/bac) - (abc/H/acb) - (abc/H/cba)$$
$$+ (abc/H/bca) + (abc/H/cab),$$
$$d_{I,I} = (abc/1/abc) - (abc/1/bac) - (abc/1/acb) - (abc/1/cba)$$
$$+ (abc/1/bca) + (abc/1/cab), \quad (6)$$

where by definition, for instance,

$$(abc/H/bac) = \int u_a^*(x_1)u_b^*(x_2)u_c^*(x_3)Hu_b(x_1)u_a(x_2)u_c(x_3) \; dx_1 \, dx_2 \, dx_3, \quad (7)$$

and where $(abc/1/bac)$ is the same expression with H omitted. We get at the formulas (6) by direct expansion of the determinantal wave functions, and since the functions u_a, u_b, u_c are not orthogonal, we have none of the simplifications found in Sec. 7.7. The energy of the quartet is then $H_{I,I}/d_{I,I}$, where the quantities are given in (6). It is worth noting that if the functions u_a, u_b, u_c are nearly orthogonal, the last two terms in numerator and denominator will be small compared with the others, since they correspond to interchange of three electrons. Thus to an approximation we may write the formula without these terms. The numerator is then the first term, minus three exchange integrals corresponding to the three possible interchanges of two electrons. Each of these exchange integrals will be somewhat similar to the exchange integral in the Heitler-London theory of hydrogen and, hence, will be negative. Thus the quartet term will have positive exchange contributions, as the triplet does in the Heitler-London theory of hydrogen, which shows that this quartet term will represent an excited level.

To investigate the doublet terms, we must consider the secular equation between II, III, and IV. We have

$$H_{II,II} = (abc/H/abc) - (abc/H/bac)$$
$$H_{III,III} = (abc/H/abc) - (abc/H/cba)$$
$$H_{IV,IV} = (abc/H/abc) - (abc/H/acb)$$
$$H_{II,III} = (abc/H/cab) - (abc/H/acb)$$
$$H_{III,IV} = (abc/H/cab) - (abc/H/bac)$$
$$H_{II,IV} = (abc/H/cab) - (abc/H/cba).$$

The matrices of unity are just the same, with 1 substituted for H. Instead of trying to solve the cubic equation between II, III, and IV, we adopt a method which often proves to be useful in molecular problems. We introduce four linear combinations of the three functions, which we shall call A, B, C, D, by the equations

$$A = \frac{1}{\sqrt{2}} \, (\text{II} - \text{III})$$

$$B = \frac{1}{\sqrt{2}} \, (\text{III} - \text{IV})$$

$$C = \frac{1}{\sqrt{2}} \, (\text{IV} - \text{II})$$

$$D = \tfrac{1}{2}(\text{II} + \text{III} + \text{IV}).$$

These four functions cannot, of course, be linearly independent, since obviously $A + B + C = 0$. Thus one can use three independent ones, as A, B, and D, for setting up a new secular equation. When we compute matrices of H and of unity with respect to these functions, we discover immediately that all matrices between D and any one of the other three functions are zero. That means that our secular equation is already factored: one energy level is that obtained directly from D, or $H_{D,D}/d_{D,D}$, and the other two are roots of a quadratic obtained, say, from the functions A and B. Now the first energy value proves to be just the energy of the quartet, so that we see that D is the wave function of the quartet. The wave functions for the doublets are then two orthogonal linear combinations of A and B (or A and B and C, which comes to the same thing).

Let us inquire what is the physical significance of the functions A, B, and C which we have introduced. Function A is essentially $\text{II} - \text{III}$. If we look back to Table 7.3.5, we see that in both of these functions II and III the spin of orbital u_a is $\tfrac{1}{2}$, while in II that of u_b is $\tfrac{1}{2}$, and of u_c, $-\tfrac{1}{2}$, whereas in III these two orbitals have their spins reversed. If it were not for orbital u_a, this situation would be just as in the singlet state of a hydrogen molecule containing orbitals u_b and u_c; the process of taking the difference $\text{II} - \text{III}$ is just equivalent to what we did to set up the singlet state for that molecule in (7.8.3). In other words, the function A is set up as if we were forming a covalent bond between orbitals u_b and u_c, disregarding u_a. Similarly, function B corresponds to a bond between u_a and u_b, and C between u_a and u_c. Now if the atom a were far from b and c, which were close to each other, function A would depend on the orbitals u_b and u_c, just as it would if the electrons represented by these orbitals formed a covalent bond between the corresponding atoms. In other words, A would represent the correct wave function for the singlet state under these circumstances. Similarly, if atom c is far from a and b, function B is the correct wave function, and if b is far away, C is correct. When all atoms are near together, we must use a correct linear combination of the three functions, to be determined by perturbation theory. We shall not, as a matter of fact, carry out the perturbation calculation,[†] but it is not difficult, and the resulting quadratic equation can be set up and solved immediately. It is this solution which is used in Sec. 9.3.

Functions like A, B, and C, which we have just been discussing, are sometimes called bond functions, for each assumes a particular way of drawing a covalent bond between a pair of atoms and sets up wave functions accordingly. The use of such bond functions is one standard way of attacking molecular problems. If only one way of drawing the covalent bonds corresponds to a low energy value, the bond function connected with this bond will itself form a good approximation to the wave function, and its diagonal energy value will be a good approximation

† For this, and other similar cases, see J. C. Slater, *Phys. Rev.* **38**, 1109 (1931).

to the energy.   If, on the contrary, several ways of drawing the bonds are approximately equally reasonable, the correct wave function will be a linear combination of the appropriate bond functions.   We find this linear combination by finding diagonal and nondiagonal matrix components between the various functions, and solving a secular equation between them.   This is the situation in which we speak of the system resonating between various types of covalent binding.   In any such perturbation problem, the effect of applying the perturbations, as we know, is always to push the energy levels apart, so that the resulting ground state will have a lower energy than the diagonal energy of any of the bond functions.   This is the origin of the extra binding resulting from resonance.

If we have a bond function like A, implying covalent binding between atoms b and c, we then are interested in the way the energy depends on the position of atom a.   From our discussion of saturation of valence, we may expect that atom a will be repelled by either b or c under these circumstances.   To check this, we may find the diagonal energy corresponding to function A, which is a correct value of the energy in the case where atoms b and c are close together, while a is far off.   We easily find that the diagonal matrix component is

$$H_{A,A} = (abc/H/abc) + (abc/H/acb) - \tfrac{1}{2}[(abc/H/bac) + (abc/H/cba)]$$
$$- (abc/H/cab).$$

The component $d_{A,A}$ is the same, with 1 substituted for H.   This formula is very significant.   If atom a is far enough away, only the first two terms will remain, and they represent just the terms which we should get in an ordinary Heitler-London theory of the molecule formed from atoms b and c, the exchange integral $(abc/H/acb)$, which is negative, coming in with positive coefficient, resulting in binding.   The next two terms correspond to similar Heitler-London exchange integrals between a and b, and between a and c, respectively.   These exchange integrals become greater numerically as atom a approaches b and c.   Since they are negative and come in with a negative coefficient, they represent positive contributions to the energy, or repulsion, as indicated in Sec. 9.3.   The coefficient in front of the integral, however, is only one-half as great as if atoms b and c were not bound into a molecule, and as if a were approaching b or c in the repulsive, triplet state of the diatomic molecule.   This weakening of the repulsion was also mentioned in Sec. 9.3.   Finally, we have the term $-(abc/H/cab)$, representing' a cyclic permutation of all three electrons.   This term, like many similar ones which appear in more complicated problems, is small, and does not affect the result decisively.   These results, though shown only for the simple case of three hydrogens, are typical of those which are obtained in much more general cases by the same methods.

So far we have been speaking of the interactions of hydrogen atoms, with their $1s$ electrons, spherically symmetrical, so that we have no directional properties connected with the valence bonds.   Next we take up the directional properties associated with p valences, as discussed in Secs. 9.4 and 9.5.   It is clear from the Heitler-London method that the tightest binding will come for maximum overlapping of the wave functions; we saw in Sec. 8.3 that the binding was a result of the existence of the exchange charge in the region between the atoms.   The same situation will hold if we use the molecular orbital method; we have seen in our discussion that if we use the LCAO method, we come to much the same exchange integrals, and qualitatively it is the overlapping of wave functions which is responsible for binding, as in the Heitler-London method.   Thus we justify the statements in the text regarding the strong binding of a p electron and another atom located along the axis along which it points. These statements can be justified quantitatively by setting up the whole energy of molecules like H_2O, NH_3, mentioned in the text, and computing the necessary exchange integrals. Such calculations are difficult but do not involve any essentially different principles from those which we have already discussed.

We can also justify the use of the hybrid orbitals discussed in the text: we can set up these hybrid orbitals in such a case as CH_4, compute the binding energy of the molecule when we use them, and compare with the energy when ordinary orbitals are used. The result is that the use of the hybrid orbitals gives a greater binding energy and, hence, is nearer the truth. As for the definition of the hybrid orbitals, it is very simple. Let us denote our four wave functions as p_x, p_y, p_z, s. Then a linear combination of them may be written

$$a_{i1}p_x + a_{i2}p_y + a_{i3}p_z + a_{i4}s,$$

and if we have four linear combinations we may let the index i run from 1 to 4 to give these functions. We wish these hybrid functions to be normalized and orthogonal; and when we remember the normalization and orthogonality of the original functions, this leads at once to the condition

$$\sum_k a_{ik}a_{jk} = \delta_{ij}.$$

Furthermore, since p_x, p_y, p_z are proportional to x, y, and z, we see that the vector of components a_{i1}, a_{i2}, a_{i3} points in the direction in which the ith wave function has maximum intensity. If then we wish to set up hybrid functions with maximum intensity in given directions, such as the tetrahedral or trigonal directions, we need only choose the relative magnitudes of the a_{i1}, a_{i2}, a_{i3} components, and choose the other quantities to secure normalization and orthogonality of the resulting functions. When we proceed in this way, we find that the wave functions may be written in the following way:

$$
\begin{aligned}
\textit{Tetrahedral:} \quad & \tfrac{1}{2}(p_x + p_y + p_z + s) \\
& \tfrac{1}{2}(-p_x - p_y + p_z + s) \\
& \tfrac{1}{2}(p_x - p_y - p_z + s) \\
& \tfrac{1}{2}(-p_x + p_y - p_z + s)
\end{aligned}
$$

$$
\begin{aligned}
\textit{Trigonal:} \quad & \sqrt{\tfrac{2}{3}}\, p_x + \sqrt{\tfrac{1}{3}}\, s \\
& -\sqrt{\tfrac{1}{6}}\, p_x + \sqrt{\tfrac{1}{2}}\, p_y + \sqrt{\tfrac{1}{3}}\, s \\
& -\sqrt{\tfrac{1}{6}}\, p_x - \sqrt{\tfrac{1}{2}}\, p_y + \sqrt{\tfrac{1}{3}}\, s \\
& p_z.
\end{aligned}
$$

APPENDIX 17

THE ENERGY OF A CRYSTAL LATTICE

The energy operator for a whole crystal, or other piece of matter, is made up of the following four types of terms: the kinetic energy of all electrons; the potential energy of interaction of pairs of nuclei; the potential energy of interactions of pairs of electrons; and the potential energy of interactions of pairs of nuclei and electrons. This disregards the fifth type of term, the kinetic energy of all nuclei, which we neglect when we assume the nuclei to be at rest. The whole energy of the lattice is the average of this operator, averaged over the electronic wave function.

Similarly, the one-electron energy operator, for an electron in the field of the nuclei and the averaged-out charge of the other electrons, is the sum of the kinetic energy of the electron, its energy of interaction with the nuclei, and with the other electrons. The one-electron energy is the average of this operator over the one-electron wave function, which is essentially the same as the average over the many-electron wave function of the kinetic energy, the interaction energy of this electron with the nuclei, and the average, over all electrons, of the interaction energy between this electron and all others. Let us now compare the sum of these one-electron energies with the total energy of the crystal.

If we add the one-electron energy operators, we correctly reproduce two of the terms in the total energy: the sum of all kinetic energies of electrons and the sum of the interaction energies between nuclei and electrons. We have twice the interaction energies between pairs of electrons, however; for if we write the inter-action energies between electrons concerned in the one-electron energy of the ith electron, we have $\sum_{j \neq i} 2/r_{ij}$, in atomic units, and if we then sum over i, we have twice the sum over pairs of electrons, since each pair is counted twice. As compensation for this, we lack the sum of electrostatic energies between pairs of nuclei.

If both the electronic and the nuclear charge were uniformly distributed over the volume, the electrostatic interaction energy between pairs of electrons would equal the interaction between pairs of nuclei, because each could be converted into an integral of the form $\frac{1}{2} \int \rho\varphi \, dv$, where ρ is a charge density, φ the electrostatic potential of the corresponding charge density, and the charge densities and potentials of positive and negative charge would be equal and opposite. Thus in this simple case the sum of one-electron energies would equal the total energy. This is rather far from the case, however, in the actual crystal. The reason, in simple language, is that since the nuclear charge is actually concentrated in the various nuclei, and since we do not include electrostatic interactions between the various protons of a single nucleus in our total energy, the actual sum of inter-action energies between pairs of nuclei is considerably smaller numerically than what we should find for a uniform positive charge density. Thus the sum of one-electron energies is considerably greater than the total energy of the crystal. This

498

becomes most clear in the case of a single atom, as taken up in Appendix 13, where the total energy of the atom is considerably more negative than the sum of one-electron energies. To see the reason physically, we note that the total energy of the atom is the negative of the work done in removing each electron in succession. This is the negative of the sum of one-electron energies of the outermost electrons of a series of ions of greater and greater positive charge, each representing the state of the atom when the corresponding electron is to be removed. These ionization energies of positive ions are greater than for neutral atoms, so that the work required to remove all electrons from the atom is greater than the sum of the energies required to remove each separate electron from a neutral atom.

In spite of this difference between the sum of one-electron energies and the energy of the whole crystal, still the two quantities are sufficiently alike so that qualitatively we can derive results about the whole energy from the sum of one-electron energies. To investigate the total energy quantitatively, we must take up the average of the energy operator over the wave function in much more careful manner than we have sketched here.

APPENDIX 18

THE SEPARATION OF ELECTRONIC AND NUCLEAR MOTION

We shall follow the argument described in Sec. 11.1, leading to an approximate separation of variables between electronic and nuclear motion. Let the electronic coordinates be symbolized by x_i, the nuclear ones by X_j, the mass of an electron being m, and of the jth nucleus M_j. Then Schrödinger's equation may be written

$$\left[\sum_i - \frac{h^2}{8\pi^2 m} \frac{\partial^2}{\partial x_i^2} + \sum_j - \frac{h^2}{8\pi^2 M_j} \frac{\partial^2}{\partial X_j^2} + V(x_i, X_j) \right] \psi = - \frac{h}{2\pi i} \frac{\partial \psi}{\partial t}.$$

Now assume that $\psi = e^{-(2\pi i/h)Et} u(x_i, X_j) v(X_j)$, where $u(x_i, X_j)$ is the wave function for the electrons, assuming the nuclei fixed, and containing therefore the X_j's as parameters, and where $v(X_j)$ is the wave function for the nuclei, under the action of the potential arising from the electrons. That is, u is the solution of the equation

$$\left[\sum_i - \frac{h^2}{8\pi^2 m} \frac{\partial^2}{\partial x_i^2} + V(x_i, X_j) \right] u(x_i, X_j) = \epsilon(X_j) u(x_i, X_j).$$

The Hamiltonian on the left is what we get by assuming that the masses of the nuclei are infinite, so that they stay at rest. Since the potential function V depends on the X_j's as parameters, the energy ϵ must also show this dependence. Now we take $\epsilon(X_j)$ as the potential for the nuclei; that is, v satisfies the equation

$$\left[\sum_j - \frac{h^2}{8\pi^2 M_j} \frac{\partial^2}{\partial X_j^2} + \epsilon(X_j) \right] v(X_j) = Ev(X_j),$$

where E is the whole energy of the system. For example, with a diatomic molecule, $\epsilon(X_j)$, the electronic energy as a function of the nuclear position, is the potential curve we have often used, and E is the vibrational energy level, measuring actually the total energy, electronic and vibrational, and staying constant during the motion, the electronic energy decreasing when vibrational energy increases, and vice versa.

Let us now see what differential equation uv satisfies; it proves to be this product which approximates a wave function for the whole system. We have easily

$$\left[\sum_i - \frac{h^2}{8\pi^2 m} \frac{\partial^2}{\partial x_i^2} + \sum_j - \frac{h^2}{8\pi^2 M_j} \frac{\partial^2}{\partial X_j^2} + V(x_i, X_j) \right] u(x_i, X_j) v(X_j)$$

$$= Eu(x_i, X_j) v(X_j) + \sum_j - \frac{h^2}{8\pi^2 M_j} \left(2 \frac{\partial u}{\partial X_j} \frac{\partial v}{\partial X_j} + \frac{\partial^2 u}{\partial X_j^2} v \right).$$

If it were not for the last summation, this would be exactly the equation we wish ψ to satisfy. But it is not difficult to show that these terms are small. Thus, for example, with the last one, u depends on the X_j's in very much the same way in which it depends on x_i, since it depends largely on the differences $(x_i - X_j)$, representing the coordinates of electrons with respect to the various nuclei, which are the essential things in the electronic motion. Hence $\partial^2 u/\partial X_j^2$ is of the same order of magnitude as $\partial^2 u/\partial x_i^2$. But this quantity, multiplied by $h^2/8\pi^2 m$, is of the order of magnitude of the energy of one of the electrons, an appreciable fraction of the energy of the system. The term appears here, however, multiplied by $h^2/8\pi^2 M_j$, smaller in the ratio of m/M_j, and since M_j is thousands of times m, this means that these terms are much smaller than the others and can be neglected. Thus, approximately, uv forms a solution of the problem, and we are justified in using the electronic energy as a potential function for the nuclei. But, to a higher approximation, we cannot neglect these small terms. We can find their matrix components between the state we are interested in, and all other states, differing in electronic and nuclear motions, and these components, though small, will be different from zero. It is these components, of the term

$$\sum_j - \frac{h^2}{8\pi^2 M_j}\left(2\frac{\partial u}{\partial X_j}\frac{\partial v}{\partial X_j} + \frac{\partial^2 u}{\partial X_j^2}v\right),$$ which determine the rate of transitions

between different electronic levels.

APPENDIX 19

THE VISCOUS RELAXATION TIME

We wish to demonstrate Eq. (13.2.7), stating that the relaxation time τ for a sphere of radius a in a medium of viscosity η, at temperature T, is proportional to $\eta a^3 / kT$. We shall do this by dimensional analysis, a method very often useful in establishing the general form of physical laws. We assume first that we have analyzed the problem enough to conclude that τ should depend on the quantities η, a, and kT (since it is a problem of statistical nature, it is clear that the temperature can enter only in the combination kT). We assume then that we can set up an equation of the form

$$\tau = \eta^p a^q (kT)^r,$$

where p, q, r, are exponents to be determined. Then we have only to find the dimensions of each quantity entering the equation and to choose the exponents so that the equation will be dimensionally correct.

The time τ is, of course, of the dimensions of a time, which we indicate dimensionally by T. The coefficient of viscosity η is defined by the equation that it is the stress per unit velocity gradient in a fluid. A stress is a force per unit area, so that, since a force has the same dimensions as mass times acceleration, we have

$$\eta = \frac{\text{Force}}{\text{Area}} \frac{\text{Length}}{\text{Velocity}} = \frac{MLT^{-2}}{L^2} \frac{L}{LT^{-1}} = ML^{-1}T^{-1}.$$

The radius a of the sphere is, of course, a length, and kT is an energy, or ML^2T^{-2}, dimensionally. Then we have the dimensional equation

$$T = (ML^{-1}T^{-1})^p (L)^q (ML^2T^{-2})^r.$$

For this to be dimensionally correct, the dimensions of the right side must be T, or $M^0 L^0 T^1$. That is, we must have

$$0 = p + r$$
$$0 = -p + q + 2r$$
$$1 = -p - 2r.$$

The solutions of these equations are found at once to be $p = 1$, $q = 3$, $r = -1$, leading to the result we wished to prove.

APPENDIX 20

THE SUM RULE FOR OSCILLATOR STRENGTHS

We wish to prove that the sum of the oscillator strengths f_k, given in (13.3.8), equals unity. Here $f_k = (4\pi m/e^2 h)\omega_k M_{k1}^2$, where ω_k is the angular frequency of the transition from the ground state (denoted by 1) to the kth excited state, and M_{k1} is the matrix component of electric moment between these states, given by

$-\sum_i \int u_k^{0*} ex_i u_m^0 \, dv.$ We shall carry out the proof only for a one-electron atom,

but it is very simple to extend it to the case of many electrons.

The proof results from the commutation rule (3.7.1), $p_x x - x p_x = h/2\pi i$. Let us consider this as a matrix equation and write the diagonal component corresponding to the ground state. We use the formula for the matrix product and have

$$\sum_k [p_x(1,k)x(k,1) - x(1,k)p_x(k,1)] = \frac{h}{2\pi i}, \tag{1}$$

where we indicate by $p_x(1,k)$ the matrix component of p_x between the states 1 and k, and so on. But now we remember from (3.8.1) that the time rate of change of the average value of x equals the average value of the momentum, divided by m. Using (3.7.3) and (3.7.4), this results in

$$p_x(1,k) = m\left(\frac{2\pi i}{h}\right)(E_1 - E_k)x(1,k)$$
$$= -im\omega_k x(1,k).$$

This result, plus the fact that the matrices are Hermitian, allows us to rewrite (1) in the form

$$\sum_k m\omega_k[x(1,k)]^2 = \frac{h}{4\pi}.$$

We recall that M_{k1} is simply $ex(1,k)$. When we make this substitution, our result follows at once.

APPENDIX 21

EFFECT OF MAGNETIC FIELDS ON SUPERCONDUCTORS

We wish to explain why a magnetic field can destroy the superconducting effect, and why this magnetic field depends on temperature. The experimental situation is shown in Fig. 1, where we show a typical curve of the magnetic threshold field as a function of temperature. Often such a diagram is regarded as a phase diagram, similar to a pressure-temperature diagram in ordinary thermodynamics. In the region of the H-T plane below the curve, the superconducting phase is stable; above the curve, the normal phase is stable. As in any thermodynamic problem of the equilibrium of two phases, we can handle this problem by finding

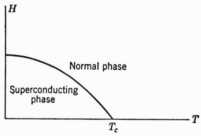

FIG. 1. Magnetic threshold curve for a superconductor.

a suitable free energy for each phase. The stable phase will be that with the lower free energy, and the condition for equilibrium of phases, or for the magnetic threshold curve, is that the free energies of the two phases be equal. By differentiating this relation, we can get an equation equivalent to the Clapeyron-Clausius equation, giving the slope of the threshold curve in terms of measurable quantities.

In the absence of a magnetic field, the normal state will have a free energy which we may denote by F_n, and the superconducting state will have a free energy F_s, both functions of temperature (we neglect changes of pressure, so that the Helmholtz and Gibbs free energies are identical). F_s is less than F_n at temperatures below T_c, the transition temperature for zero magnetic field, and F_n is less than F_s above T_c. These free energies satisfy the condition $\partial F/\partial T = -S$, where S is the entropy. There is good evidence that the entropy of the normal state is proportional to the temperature, in the range of temperatures concerned; this is what the conventional theory of metallic electrons would suggest. If it is AT, we have $F_n = -\frac{1}{2}AT^2$. The entropy of the superconducting state seems to be something like proportional to the third power of the temperature. If this is correct (and, unlike the entropy of the normal state, there is no good theory to predict this value), so that the entropy of the superconducting state is BT^3, we would have $F_s = \text{constant} - \frac{1}{4}BT^4$. If we choose the constant so that $F_n = F_s$ when

504

$T = T_c$, we have

$$F_s = -\tfrac{1}{2}AT_c^2 - \tfrac{1}{4}B(T^4 - T_c^4).$$

A further fact is observed: in the absence of a magnetic field, there is no latent heat at the transition. Thus the entropies of normal and superconducting states must be equal there, or $AT_c = BT_c^3$. This allows us to rewrite F_s in the form

$$F_s = -\frac{1}{4}AT_c^2\left[\left(\frac{T}{T_c}\right)^4 + 1\right].$$

This formula, which, of course, is only an empirical one, only holds below T_c, for it is only there that the superconducting state exists and that we have information about it.

We may now plot F_n and F_s as functions of T, as in Fig. 2. We see, as we have described the situation earlier, that F_s lies below F_n at temperatures below T_c.

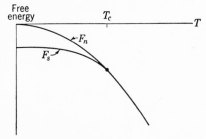

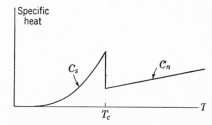

FIG. 2. Free energy of normal and superconducting states, as function of temperature.

FIG. 3. Specific heat of normal and superconducting states.

At that temperature the two curves touch; on account of the equality of entropy, they touch with a common tangent. Such a transition is called a phase change of the second order. If we compute the specific heat, by the relation $C = T \, \partial S/\partial T$, we find for the normal state $C_n = AT$, and for the superconducting state $C_s = 3AT_c(T/T_c)^3$. Thus the specific heat would have the form shown in Fig. 3. This curve, showing a break in the specific heat at T_c, resembles the Greek letter lambda, and for that reason a transition of this type is often called a lambda point.

Now we ask what change a magnetic field produces. Let us think of our sample as an infinitely long cylinder, inside an infinitely long solenoid, so that a magnetic field H is produced along the axis of the cylinder by the solenoid. This is the most convenient shape of sample to use in an idealized magnetic experiment, for it avoids the demagnetizing effects. If the sample is superconducting, there will then be a surface current induced in a thin surface layer, the superconducting penetration depth, such that the interior of the sample will be shielded from the field. We may then adopt various possible conventions about the vectors H and B inside the superconductor. We shall use the convention introduced by Gorter and Casimir in their original treatment of the problem. Certainly $B = 0$ inside the superconductor; but Gorter and Casimir interpreted this as arising from a diamagnetic effect, so that the surface current is to be interpreted as a magnetization current M, associated with a magnetization within the superconductor. In the general equation $B = \mu_0(H + M)$, then, we assume that H is continuous inside and outside the superconductor, but that there is a magnetization vector $M = -H$ inside the superconductor, resulting in $B = 0$. Since this magnetization is opposite to the magnetizing field, we see that we can give this a diamagnetic interpretation.

The contribution of the magnetic field to the change of internal energy is well known from electromagnetic theory to be $H\,dB$ per unit volume. That is, if dU is the change of internal energy, we have $dU = H\,dB$, provided the change is at constant temperature. Since in general $B = \mu_0(H + M)$, we may rewrite this $dU = \mu_0 H(dH + dM)$. Now we wish to find the condition of equilibrium of the two phases, normal and superconducting, in a constant field H. Thus we should like to set up a sort of free energy such that the change of this free energy, at constant temperature, is expressed in terms of dH. To do this, we must set up the combination $U - \mu_0 MH$ per unit volume. For then we have

$$d(U - \mu_0 MH) = \mu_0 H(dH + dM) - \mu_0(M\,dH + H\,dM)$$
$$= \mu_0 H\,dH - \mu_0 M\,dH.$$

We may then convert the quantity $U - \mu_0 MH$ into a free energy by adding the term $-TS$. If we let this resulting free energy or thermodynamic potential be denoted by Z, we have $dZ_s = -S_s\,dT + \mu_0(H - M)dH$. Since for the superconductor $M = -H$, we see that we can integrate this equation and have

$$Z_s = F_s + \mu_0 H^2.$$

Similarly, for the normal state we can set up a Z_n, but the normal state has no magnetization M. Thus we have $dZ_n = -S_n\,dT + \mu_0 H\,dH$, and

$$Z_n = F_n + \tfrac{1}{2}\mu_0 H^2.$$

On account of the general equation $dZ = -S\,dT + \mu_0(H - M)dH$, which holds for either phase, we see that for a change at constant temperature and magnetic field the quantity Z does not change, which is the justification for the statement that this free energy must be equal for the two phases in equilibrium.

We may then equate Z_n and Z_s to get the general condition for equilibrium at an arbitrary magnetic field. This gives us the equation

$$F_n = F_s + \tfrac{1}{2}\mu_0 H^2. \tag{1}$$

This is the general equation of thermodynamic equilibrium for superconductors. We may differentiate this expression along the equilibrium curve, to get the equivalent to the Clapeyron-Clausius equation. When we remember that F_n and F_s are functions of temperature only, independent of H, we see that we have

$$S_s - S_n = \mu_0 H \frac{dH}{dT}. \tag{2}$$

This equation allows us to deduce the difference of entropy between normal and superconducting states from the equilibrium curve of Fig. 1. It is actually in such ways that the best measurements of entropy difference of the two phases are found experimentally; this is more accurate than separate determinations of the specific heat, and hence the entropy, of the two phases. We note one consequence of (2). From the observed curves like Fig. 1, we know that the slope dH/dT is in fact finite at the temperature T_c at which the critical field H is zero. Thus, since

H is zero on the right of Eq. (2), the entropy difference of normal and superconducting states must be zero at zero field, or we have the phase change of the second order which we have already discussed. On the other hand, at other points of the threshold curve, where H is greater than zero, (2) will no longer give zero for its right side, and there will be a finite entropy difference between the two states. In other words, except at $H = 0$, there is a phase change of the first order, with a latent heat; but the latent heat vanishes when H goes to zero.

We can understand this situation better by considering the curves of F_n and F_s as functions of T, from Fig. 2. We see from Eq. (1) that in the presence of a magnetic field, the curve for F_s must be shifted upward with respect to that for F_n, by the amount $\frac{1}{2}\mu_0 H^2$; the resulting curves act as free energy curves in the field, and their intersection gives the condition for equilibrium. It is clear from Fig. 2 that the tangency between the curves, which is the condition for equality of entropy and absence of a latent heat, will be lost once we have a magnetic field; though it is gained again when the point of intersection shifts to the absolute zero of temperature. The critical field at the absolute zero is that required to raise the F_s curve by an amount equal to the difference between F_n and F_s at the absolute zero; that is, by the energy difference between the higher, normal energy of the substance at the absolute zero, and the slightly lower energy characteristic of the superconducting state. Since the critical field at the absolute zero can be estimated by extrapolating observed curves like Fig. 1, that means that we have an experimental measurement of this energy difference.

If we adopt our formulas previously worked out for the values of F_n and F_s, as a result of semiempirical information, we can evaluate the magnetic threshold curve completely. Thus we have

$$ -\frac{1}{2} A T^2 = -\frac{1}{4} A T_c^2 \left[\left(\frac{T}{T_c} \right)^4 + 1 \right] + \frac{1}{2} \mu_0 H^2. $$

We can solve this for H, obtaining

$$ H = \sqrt{\frac{A T_c^2}{2\mu_0}} \left[1 - \left(\frac{T}{T_c} \right)^2 \right]. \tag{3} $$

This equation, though without more theoretical justification than we have given it, holds experimentally well enough to be quite useful in the interpretation of experimental data. The quantity $\sqrt{A T_c^2/2\mu_0}$ is clearly the threshold magnetic field at the absolute zero of temperature, so that we can evaluate the constant A if this threshold field and T_c are known, provided we assume the correctness of these simple formulas. We can also differentiate (3) with respect to the temperature and find for dH/dT at T_c the value $-2\sqrt{A T_c^2/2\mu_0}$, if we assume that (3) is correct.

There is one empirical correlation involving these results which may prove to be significant when more complete data are available. The superconductors are found to lie in two distinct regions of the periodic table. One group of superconductors is found among the transition elements, such as the early elements of the iron group; these are called the hard superconductors. The other group, called the soft superconductors, falls in those elements which are almost approaching covalent binding. The reason for the name lies in the fact that the initial slope

$-dH/dT$ of the threshold curve is very large for the hard superconductors, much larger than for the soft superconductors. This suggests a larger value of A for the hard superconductors. But this is just what we should expect from our general knowledge of the structure of metals. The theory of the electronic specific heat of metals, according to the Fermi statistics,[†] shows that the entropy should be proportional to the temperature, as in our formula AT for the normal metal, and furthermore that the constant A should be proportional to dN/dE, the density of energy levels at the top of the Fermi distribution. We know, from Secs. 10.7 and 10.8, that this quantity is very large in the transition group, small in a metal that almost forms covalent bonds. Thus we may conclude, for reasons having nothing to do with superconductors directly, that A will be large for the hard superconductors, small for the soft ones, giving at least a qualitative explanation for the difference between these two classes of superconductors.

† See J. C. Slater, "Introduction to Chemical Physics," McGraw-Hill Book Company, Inc., New York, 1939, p. 79.

APPENDIX 22

THE ELECTRONIC THEORY OF FERROMAGNETISM

In this appendix we shall elaborate on the treatment of the collective electron theory of ferromagnetism described in the text, giving its limiting case of the ferromagnetism of the free-electron gas, and showing the modifications that the theory undergoes for a real ferromagnetic material. We assume the electronic wave functions to be solutions of a periodic potential problem, so that they are orthogonal to each other. Then the essential part of our problem is to compute the exchange integrals which come in between electrons with parallel spins; as we see from Sec. 14.6, we shall have ferromagnetism if the gain in Fermi energy when electrons set themselves with parallel spin, and hence lie higher in the Fermi band, is more than compensated by the decrease of energy on account of having more exchange integrals. We have exchange integrals of the form

$$\int u_i^*(x_1)u_j(x_1) \frac{2}{r_{12}} u_j^*(x_2)u_i(x_2)dx_1 \, dx_2 \tag{1}$$

between all pairs of wave functions corresponding to parallel spin, and these integrals come in with negative sign in the expression for total energy of the crystal. We shall look at the sum of these integrals, summed over all the electrons in a partially filled band of energy levels, first for the case of free electrons, then for electrons in a periodic potential. If we divide this double sum of integrals, summed over all pairs of wave functions, by the number of such pairs, we can get an average exchange integral, which is what is called I in Sec. 14.6.

Now let us consider the evaluation of the exchange integral (1) for free electrons. We shall not carry through the calculation, which is a little tedious but not in principle difficult, but shall describe the method used. Each of the wave functions is a plane wave, represented by a complex exponential function. We have waves associated with all momenta within a sphere in momentum space, determined by the ordinary condition of Fermi statistics, that there are to be enough occupied states to accommodate all the electrons. We then have the problem of summing over i and j, which can be transformed into integrating over the volume of the occupied sphere in momentum space, as well as integrating over dx_1 and dx_2. Either the summations or integrations can be performed first; the calculations can be carried out fairly easily in either order. It is perhaps more informing to carry out the summations first. Then we have a quantity

$$\sum_{i,j} u_i^*(x_1)u_j(x_1)u_j^*(x_2)u_i(x_2), \tag{2}$$

a function of x_1 and x_2. This has a simple physical interpretation. Expression (1) represents the electrostatic energy of interaction of a charge distribution at point x_1 with a charge distribution at x_2. In Sec. 14.5 we have found the interpretation of this interaction: it is the interaction of an electron with the charge removed from the exchange hole surrounding it. We should then expect (2), which is a function of x_1 and x_2, to be proportional to the charge density of charge at x_1, multiplied by the density of exchange charge at x_2, under the assumption that the first charge is at x_1. Since we are dealing with a free-electron gas, the density of charge at x_1 is really a constant, independent of x_1; thus we should expect (2) to depend only on the distance r between points x_1 and x_2 and to represent the density of exchange charge at this distance r from a given charge.

This interpretation is, as a matter of fact, correct. If we have N_1 electrons of one spin in a volume V, the double sum (2) can be worked out and reduces to

$$\frac{1}{2}\left(\frac{N_1}{V}\right)^2 \times 9\,\frac{(\sin Kr - Kr\cos Kr)^2}{(Kr)^6}, \tag{3}$$

where

$$K = \left(6\pi^2\,\frac{N_1}{V}\right)^{\frac{1}{3}}. \tag{4}$$

This quantity K is 2π times the wave number corresponding to the momentum P of the fastest electron in the Fermi distribution; that is, $P = Kh/2\pi$. Expression (3) is of the form which we should expect. The first factor N_1/V arises because

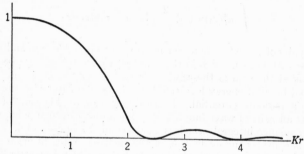

FIG. 1. Function 9 $(\sin Kr - Kr\cos Kr)^2/(Kr)^6$, representing exchange charge density, as function of Kr.

in (1) or (2) we have the interactions of all electrons with their exchange charges; the $\frac{1}{2}$ takes care of the fact that if we wish the interaction of all pairs of electrons, it is only one-half times the interaction of each electron with all others. The remaining quantity, $(N_1/V) \times 9(\sin Kr - Kr\cos Kr)^2/(Kr)^6$, should then represent the density of exchange charge surrounding a given electron. This function is shown in Fig. 1. We see that when $r = 0$, it goes to a limiting value of N_1/V; that is, the exchange charge density at this point is just enough to cancel the total charge density, so that really a given electron finds zero charge density of other electrons of the same spin, at a point infinitely close to it, as we should expect from the exclusion principle. The density of exchange charge rapidly falls off with distance, however, as we see from Fig. 1, the distance at which it reaches a given value being proportional to $1/K$, or to $(N_1/V)^{-\frac{1}{3}}$, as we saw it should be in Sec. 14.5. We can integrate the charge density over all space and show that it does, in fact, integrate to one electron, as it should. Thus in Fig. 1 we have a simple physical picture of the exchange charge density.

To get our exchange energy as given in (1), we can then carry out the additional step of multiplying (3) by $2/r$, and integrating over the coordinates of the two electrons. We carry out this integration first with respect to r; that is, we introduce spherical polar coordinates, introduce an element of volume $4\pi r^2\, dr$, multiply by our potential $2/r$, and integrate with respect to r from zero to infinity. The result is then a constant, and to carry out the integration with respect to the coordinate x_1 of the other electron we must merely multiply by the volume V, removing one of the factors V in the denominator of (3). The resulting value of (1) is then

$$\frac{1}{2}\frac{N_1^2}{V}\times 4\pi \int_0^\infty r^2 \frac{2}{r}\times 9\,\frac{(\sin Kr - Kr\cos Kr)^2}{(Kr)^6}\,dr$$
$$= \frac{1}{2}\frac{N_1^2}{V}\frac{18\pi}{K^2} = \frac{N_1}{2}\frac{3}{\pi}(6\pi^2)^{\frac13}\left(\frac{N_1}{V}\right)^{\frac13}. \quad (5)$$

This gives the interaction energy of each electron with its exchange charge proportional to $(N_1/V)^{\frac13}$, as we saw in Sec. 14.5 that it should be. If, finally, we divide by the volume, to get the exchange interaction energy per unit volume, we find that it can be written $-B(N_1/V)^{\frac43}$, as we saw in the text, where

$$B = 3^{\frac43}2^{-\frac23}\pi^{-\frac13}. \quad (6)$$

The minus sign, we remember, comes because expression (1) is to be subtracted when we compute the total energy.

To complete our discussion of the free-electron gas, we must next compute the Fermi energy. It is easily shown from the Fermi distribution that the mean kinetic energy of the electrons equals three-fifths times the kinetic energy of the fastest electron, and this kinetic energy can be written immediately in terms of our quantity K, or of N_1/V. When we carry out the calculation, finding the total kinetic energy per unit volume, and expressing it in atomic units, as we have expressed the exchange energy, we find that it is $A(N_1/V)^{\frac53}$, where

$$A = 3^{\frac53}2^{\frac23}\pi^{\frac43}5^{-1}. \quad (7)$$

We are then ready to apply the criterion (14.5.2) for the existence of ferromagnetism in a free-electron gas. We see from this that for ferromagnetism we must have the volume per electron, V/N, greater than $\frac12(5A/2B)^3$, or the side of a cube containing an electron greater than $(\frac12)^{\frac13}(5A/2B) = 3^{\frac13}\pi^{\frac53}$ atomic units. This is about 9.7 atomic units, or about 5 A. Since no metal has as large a volume as this per atom, we see that the free-electron picture would not lead to ferromagnetism in any case. The difficulty is that the exchange integral is not nearly great enough.

Now let us consider the modification made in the exchange energy (1), or the charge density (2), when we deal with a real crystal, in which the one-electron wave functions $u_i(x)$ are solutions of a periodic potential problem and, hence, act much like atomic functions when we are inside an atom. For the $3d$ electrons in the iron group, in particular, the overlapping of orbits from neighboring atoms is small enough so that we can say that one of the u_i's is almost exactly like an atomic function within each atom, though modulated in phase from one atom to the next. There is just one reservation to be made in this statement: on account of normalization, the constant factor multiplying the function must be different.

Thus let there be n like atoms in the crystal, and let $w(x)$ be a function which is like an atomic function within one cell, its square integrating to unity over the cell, but which repeats itself in each of the n cells. Then the function $e^{ik \cdot r} w(x)$ will be a representation of the correct wave function, but will not be normalized, since the product of it and its conjugate will integrate to unity over a cell, and hence to n over the whole crystal. On the other hand, the plane wave normalized function is $e^{ik \cdot r}$ divided by $\sqrt{V}$. Hence to modify the plane wave wave functions used in the free-electron calculation, to get the solutions of the periodic potential, we multiply by $\sqrt{V/n}\, w(x)$. The function w really depends on k, for though we can write any solution of the periodic potential problem as a plane wave multiplied by a periodic function, this periodic function is, in general, different for different wave functions. However, in the case of widely separated wave functions, like the $3d$'s in a ferromagnetic crystal, the variation is small enough so that we can neglect it.

We then can modify our plane waves by multiplying them by periodic functions of x; and this means that we can carry out the summation involved in (2), for the real periodic potential problem, just as for free electrons. The only assumption which no longer holds in going from (2) to (3) is that the energy surfaces in the momentum space are spheres; with the periodic potential problem, in general, they are not. It will make only a relatively minor error to replace them by spheres, however, and then we can still use (3) and (4), where now in both equations N_1 is to be replaced by n, the number of unit cells. We must, however, modify by multiplying by the correct factors arising from the periodic parts of the wave functions. These factors are

$$\left(\frac{V}{n}\right)^2 w^2(x_1) w^2(x_2),\tag{8}$$

where the product of (8) and (3) now takes the place of (3), and where the distance r which appears in (3) is the distance between points x_1 and x_2.

We must now substitute this combined expression into (1), multiply by $2/r_{12}$, and integrate over dx_1 and dx_2. The presence of our factor (8) modifies the resulting expression profoundly, when we have the situation really met in the atoms of the iron group. The atomic $3d$ functions are concentrated fairly well toward the middle of the atom. Thus the factor $(V/n)w^2(x_1)$, which averages to unity over a unit cell, becomes much larger than unity when x_1 represents a point near the nucleus of the atom, and much smaller than unity otherwise. Thus in our integral over dx_1 and dx_2, we are going to have very large contributions from the regions where x_1 and x_2 are both simultaneously near the same nucleus; that is, when they are both in the same atom. In such a case, x_1 and x_2 are bound to be near enough to each other so that the quantity r in (3) is small, Kr nearly zero, and in that limit the function $9(\sin Kr - Kr \cos Kr)^2/(Kr)^6$ approaches unity. Since there will be n cells to integrate over, these contributions to the integral will give

$$\frac{n}{2} \int w^2(x_1) w^2(x_2) \frac{2}{r_{12}}\, dx_1\, dx_2,\tag{9}$$

where dx_1 and dx_2 are to range over the interior of the same cell. That is, as far as that integration is concerned, the integral is just as if we were calculating an atomic interaction integral between an atomic wave function and itself. Such an integral is much larger than the exchange integrals we have so far met; it is of the order of magnitude of what we should get from (5) if the volume V/N_1 appearing in that formula did not represent the volume per electron, but the volume in which the $3d$ wave function was large, a very much smaller volume, leading hence to a much greater exchange integral. Clearly we can estimate this contribution to the exchange integral by using the same kind of calculations as are used in working out atomic multiplets. It is these large exchange integrals, of the atomic sort, which we have discussed in Sec. 14.6.

Before leaving our problem with the use of just the terms (9) for the exchange integrals, we should convince ourselves that the other terms in the integral, coming from cases where x_1 and x_2 are on different atoms, can be neglected. If x_1 is at the nucleus of one atom, x_2 at another, factor (8) will be just as large as if the two electrons were on the same atom. On the other hand, two factors make the contribution of this case to the integral much less important. First, the distance r_{12} between electrons, appearing in the denominator of (1), is much greater than before. Second, the factor (3), instead of having a value of unity for the function $9(\sin Kr - Kr \cos Kr)^2/(Kr)^6$, will have a small value for the function, since it decreases rapidly with increase of r. When we examine the magnitudes of these effects, we find that in real cases the contributions of cases where the two electrons are on different atoms are a very small fraction of term (9), which we have already considered. This is another way of saying that the total exchange integral (1) is very much larger for the periodic potential problem than for the free electron problem.

We now have carried out our primary task, to investigate the exchange energy as a function of the number of electrons with a given spin, so as to allow the type of calculation outlined in Sec. 14.6 for the ferromagnetic case, where there are different numbers of electrons with the two spins. There is one respect in which our calculation is not entirely correct. We have computed the diagonal matrix components of energy and have tacitly assumed that these represented the actual energy levels of the problem. This would be correct if the molecular orbital method, which we are using, really gave exactly correct wave functions. This is not the case, however, and a more careful job takes account of the degeneracy problem. We really have a very complicated problem of spin degeneracy. If we have N_1 electrons with positive spin, N_2 with negative spin, we know that the total component of spin along the z axis is determined by the difference $N_1 - N_2$. From our study of atomic multiplets, however, we know that we shall have many states with the same M_z, corresponding to different values of total spin. Thus if we compute the average energy of the states with a given M_z, which is essentially what we have done, the diagonal sum rule tells us only that we have found the average energy of the corresponding perturbed energy levels, and there may well be a considerable spread of energy between levels with different S values, so that our calculation cannot be taken as giving exactly the correct energy. This perturbation problem can be discussed to a certain extent, and though a solution of it modifies our results, it does not make any fundamental or qualitative difference in the general conclusions of Sec. 14.6.

Though the perturbation calculation which we have just been discussing makes no very great difference in the ordinary case of ferromagnetism, still we must not forget that it can be important in some limiting cases. We remember from our discussion of the hydrogen molecule in Chap. 8 that the molecular orbital method without perturbations is quite good for the actual interatomic distances in the molecule, but that as the distances become greater, it becomes more and more inaccurate and gives quite wrong results at infinite separation of the atoms, since it allows large charge fluctuations. A perturbation calculation, combining states of different wave length (in the case of the hydrogen molecule, combining symmetric and antisymmetric molecular orbitals), gives the correct final results. When this perturbation calculation is carried out, the nondiagonal matrix components of energy involve terms like exchange integrals, which do not vanish in the limit of infinite interatomic distance, and which are responsible for the correction in energy resulting from the perturbation calculation. These exchange integrals are like the terms (9) which we have found in our ferromagnetic problem. We might erroneously assume from the calculations of Sec. 14.6, and from the present appendix, that a material should become more ferromagnetic as its lattice spacing increased without limit. We know that to a certain point this is true: it is the metals with their d electrons far apart which are ferromagnetic. But as this trend goes further, quite a different situation arises. We can dilute iron ions with $3d$ electrons, as in going from a metal to a paramagnetic salt, and when we do this, we know that, in fact, the material becomes paramagnetic, as if the ions were independent of each other.

We must then realize that as atoms get further and further apart, and the exchange integrals (9) remain large, while the Fermi energy goes to zero because the energy bands get narrower, our whole method of calculation begins to break down. The large exchange integrals are no longer a sign of ferromagnetism, but simply the integrals whose use in a proper perturbation calculation would remove the charge fluctuations which are characteristic of the molecular orbital method in this limit. Thus we cannot expect to discuss paramagnetic salts by this method, unless we are willing to carry out such perturbation calculations. It should be possible to make such a calculation, though it has not been done. At the interatomic distances met in the actual ferromagnetic materials, however, it seems likely that the molecular orbital method without perturbations is qualitatively correct, though probably far from it, quantitatively.

Let us now go on to the other part of our problem, the temperature dependence of ferromagnetism. To do this, the convenient method is to find the free energy as a function of magnetization. We have already seen that the energy of a ferromagnetic substance has a term in it proportional to the square of the magnetic moment, with a negative coefficient, so that the magnetized state has the lowest energy; if the coefficient of this term is positive, as it would be if the Fermi energy were too large, the nonmagnetized state would have the lowest energy, and we could not expect ferromagnetism. In addition to the internal energy, we must find the entropy in order to get the free energy, which is the internal energy minus the term TS, where T is the temperature, S the entropy. In the model of the ferromagnetic substance which we have been using, we have essentially a mixture of two Fermi gases, one of N_1 electrons with positive spin, the other of N_2 electrons with negative spin. It is a straightforward problem to find the entropy of these two gases, using Fermi statistics. In case there are just enough electrons in all to fill a band, provided they all have the same spin, then it is clear that with the filled band there will be no fluctuations, or no entropy, while with N_1 equal to N_2, or the band half filled, there will be a maximum entropy. The situation is somewhat different if the total number of electrons is different, but the same general situation holds, that the entropy is a maximum when $N_1 = N_2$, or there is no magnetization, and it decreases when the magnetization increases. Since it must be an even function of magnetization, it is obvious that it must be possible to express it as a series $S = -CM^2 - \cdots$, with terms in higher even powers of M. When the calculation is made, it turns out that the next term, $-DM^4$, also has a negative coefficient, as we have indicated. If we write the internal energy as $-FM^2$, we then have $U - TS = (CT - F)M^2 + DTM^4 + \cdots = Z$.

In the presence of an external magnetic field, it can be shown that the derivative of the free energy, as defined in this way, with respect to M, equals the magnetic field H. Thus we have

$$Z = (CT - F)M^2 + DTM^4 + \cdots ,$$

$$H = \left(\frac{\partial Z}{\partial M}\right)_T = 2M(CT - F) + 4DTM^3 + \cdots \qquad (10)$$

We can understand the situation better if we plot the free energy as a function of M, for different temperatures. When we do this, we get results as in Fig. 2. In the absence of a magnetic field, the stable state of the system comes at a minimum

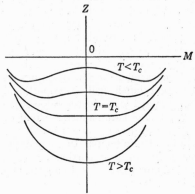

Fig. 2. Free energy of ferromagnetic material as function of magnetization M and temperature T, according to Eq. (10).

of free energy, since there H is zero according to (10); it is easy to show thermodynamically that a maximum of free energy, though it also satisfies (10), is not a stable state. Thus we see from Fig. 2 that at temperatures above a critical temperature given by $CT_c - F = 0$, $T_c = F/C$, the unmagnetized state will be stable in the absence of a field. On the other hand, below this temperature, the stable state will have a magnetic moment, either positive or negative, which increases as the temperature is reduced. This critical temperature is the Curie temperature, which we have discussed in Sec. 14.5. Above the Curie temperature, at ordinary magnetic fields, we need to use only the first term on the right side of (10), and we see, rewriting in terms of T_c, that

$$M = \frac{H}{2C(T - T_c)}, \qquad (11)$$

showing that the magnetic moment is inversely proportional to the difference $T - T_c$, but proportional to the magnetic field. In other words, we have a paramagnetic behavior above the Curie point, but with a susceptibility becoming infinite at the Curie point.

Below the Curie point, the magnetization as a function of temperature, determined from the position of the minimum of the curve of Fig. 2, resembles curves like Fig. 14.5.1, which are observed experimentally. We can get an expression for the part of this curve near the Curie point from (10) by setting $H = 0$ and solving for M. We have

$$ M = \sqrt{\frac{C}{2D} \frac{T - T_c}{T}}, \tag{12} $$

showing that the magnetic moment is proportional to the square root of $T - T_c$, as seen in Fig. 14.5.1, where the magnetic moment approaches the Curie temperature with a vertical tangent.

These general results, as we have seen, can be derived from very general assumptions regarding the behavior of internal energy and entropy with magnetization. Specific assumptions regarding the model lead to detailed values of the various constants concerned, but all the various theories lead to similar qualitative results. Thus we can calculate not only with the molecular orbital model we have discussed but also can start by assuming independent dipoles which can take up various orientations in space and are coupled by some sort of internal field, tending to make them line up in the same direction. This model leads to a simple calculation of entropy, going as before from zero in the completely magnetized state, where all dipoles are parallel, to a maximum when they are randomly oriented. The coupling energy again will be proportional to the square of the magnetization. Thus this model leads to the same sort of results. And it is more easily adapted to the case of paramagnetic salts: to get this limit, we need only omit the coupling term entirely, so that we use only the term $-TS$ in the free energy. This leads then to a Curie temperature equal to the absolute zero and, by (11), to a magnetization inversely proportional to the absolute temperature, as is observed experimentally for these salts, to a good approximation.

SUGGESTED REFERENCES

The student may well wish suggestions regarding books for supplementary reading, both on a more elementary level than the present one for acquiring background, and on a more advanced level for following the subject further. First, some knowledge of elementary atomic and molecular structure is presupposed in the present text. Good outlines of this field, in some cases overlapping the more elementary parts of the present volume, are "Introduction to Atomic Physics," by H. Semat (Rinehart); "Outline of Atomic Physics," by Physics Staff of the University of Pittsburgh (Wiley); "Atomic Physics," by M. Born (Hafner); "Introduction to Atomic Physics," by S. Tolansky (Longmans); and "The Structure of Matter," by F. O. Rice and E. Teller (Wiley). On a slightly more advanced level are "Atoms, Molecules, and Quanta," by A. E. Ruark and H. C. Urey (McGraw-Hill); and "Introduction to Modern Physics," by F. K. Richtmyer and E. H. Kennard (McGraw-Hill).

Some knowledge of mechanics, electromagnetism, and statistical mechanics and thermodynamics is really necessary for studying quantum theory. The present volume, as mentioned in the Preface, is designed to be used with "Mechanics," by J. C. Slater and N. H. Frank (McGraw-Hill); "Electromagnetism," by J. C. Slater and N. H. Frank (McGraw-Hill); and "Introduction to Chemical Physics," by J. C. Slater (McGraw-Hill), which together form a treatment of these fields. For a more advanced treatment of classical mechanics, presented in a way to fit in well with quantum mechanics, we may suggest "Classical Mechanics," by H. C. Corben and P. Stehle (Wiley); and "Classical Mechanics," by H. Goldstein (Addison-Wesley).

A number of other texts cover quantum mechanics on about the same general level of difficulty as the present one, though most of them hardly go as far in treating the applications to the structure of matter. Excellent general texts are "Wave Mechanics and Its Applications," by N. F. Mott and I. N. Sneddon (Oxford); "Quantum Mechanics," by L. I. Schiff (McGraw-Hill); "Introduction to Quantum Mechanics," by L. Pauling and E. B. Wilson, Jr. (McGraw-Hill); "The Elements of Quantum Mechanics," by S. Dushman (Wiley); "Introductory Quantum Mechanics," by V. B. Rojansky (Prentice-Hall); and "Quantum Theory," by D. Bohm (Prentice-Hall). Somewhat older are "Quantum

Mechanics," by E. U. Condon and P. M. Morse (McGraw-Hill); and "Wave Mechanics," by J. Frenkel (two volumes, elementary theory and general theory; Oxford). On a slightly more advanced level, but very useful, is "Fundamental Principles of Quantum Mechanics," by E. C. Kemble (McGraw-Hill). Many detailed applications are presented in "Quantum Chemistry," by H. Eyring, J. Walter, and G. E. Kimball (Wiley). Of great historical interest is "Atomic Structure and Spectral Lines," by A. Sommerfeld (Dutton); the successive German editions of this work formed a developing history of the quantum theory during the 1920's.

A number of the individual topics taken up in the present book have been handled in more detail in numerous publications. The theory of the interaction of matter and radiation is taken up in "The Quantum Theory of Radiation," by W. Heitler (Oxford). In atomic structure, we may mention "Introduction to Atomic Spectra," by H. E. White (McGraw-Hill); "Atomic Spectra and Atomic Structure," by H. Herzberg (Dover); "The Structure of Line Spectra," by L. Pauling and S. A. Goudsmit (McGraw-Hill); and "Atomic Spectra and the Vector Model," by A. C. Candler (Cambridge); as well as the very important but more advanced work "Theory of Atomic Spectra," by E. U. Condon and G. H. Shortley (Cambridge). The data of atomic spectra are presented in "Atomic Energy States," by R. F. Bacher and S. A. Goudsmit (McGraw-Hill); and more recently in "Atomic Energy Levels," prepared and published by the National Bureau of Standards, not yet entirely published. Molecular spectra are treated in "Infrared and Raman Spectra," by G. Herzberg (Van Nostrand); and "Molecular Spectra and Molecular Structure," by G. Herzberg (Van Nostrand).

Chemical problems, from the viewpoint of the electron theory, are handled, among other places, in "The Nature of the Chemical Bond and the Structure of Molecules and Crystals," by L. Pauling (Cornell); "Structural Inorganic Chemistry," by A. F. Wells (Oxford); "Structural Chemistry of Inorganic Compounds," by W. Hückel (Elsevier); and "Electronic Interpretations of Organic Chemistry," by A. E. Remick (Wiley). Crystal structure, and the x-ray methods used to determine it, are closely related to these problems, and treatments of these methods, and the resulting information about crystals, are given in "The Crystalline State," by W. H. and W. L. Bragg (Macmillan); "Introduction to Crystal Chemistry," by R. C. Evans (Cambridge); "The Optical Principles of the Diffraction of X-rays," by R. W. James (Bell); and "X-rays in Theory and Experiment," by A. H. Compton and S. K. Allison (Van Nostrand). The detailed information about crystal structures is contained in "Crystal Structures," by R. W. G. Wyckoff (Interscience; not yet completed).

The theory of solids, and particularly of metals, is treated in a number of excellent texts. We may list "The Modern Theory of Solids," by F. Seitz (McGraw-Hill); "The Physics of Metals," by F. Seitz (McGraw-Hill); "The Theory of the Properties of Metals and Alloys," by N. F. Mott and H. Jones (Oxford); "Theory of Metals," by A. H. Wilson (Cambridge); "The Metallic State, Electrical Properties and Theories," by W. Hume-Rothery (Oxford); "The Structure of Metals and Alloys," by W. Hume-Rothery (The Institute of Metals, London); and "Elektronentheorie der Metalle," by H. Fröhlich (Springer). The theory of semiconductors is taken up in "Electronic Processes in Ionic Crystals," by N. F. Mott and R. W. Gurney (Oxford); and "Electrons and Holes in Semiconductors," by W. Shockley (Van Nostrand). The problem of wave propagation in a periodic lattice, closely related to these questions, is treated in "Wave Propagation in Periodic Structures," by L. Brillouin (McGraw-Hill).

Problems of the rate of chemical reactions, and related questions of properties of liquids, are handled in "The Theory of Rate Processes," by S. Glasstone, K. J. Laidler, and H. Eyring (McGraw-Hill); and "Kinetic Theory of Liquids," by J. Frenkel (Oxford). The behavior of dielectrics is taken up in "Polar Molecules," by P. Debye (Chemical Catalog). Both dielectric and magnetic problems are handled in "The Theory of Electric and Magnetic Susceptibility," by J. H. Van Vleck (Oxford). Additional treatments of magnetism are given in "Introduction to Ferromagnetism," by F. Bitter (McGraw-Hill); and "Magnetism and Matter," by E. C. Stoner (Methuen). Superconductivity is taken up in "Superfluids," by F. London (Wiley).

INDEX